Michael Simmons

Analytical Chemistry
An Introduction

Analytical
Chemistry
An Introduction

Douglas A. Skoog
STANFORD UNIVERSITY

Donald M. West
SAN JOSE STATE COLLEGE

HOLT, RINEHART AND WINSTON
NEW YORK • CHICAGO • SAN FRANCISCO • TORONTO • LONDON

Preface

Quantitative analysis represents an important phase in the training of persons for fields other than chemistry. The demands of such curricula typically limit the time available for the study of analytical chemistry to a single college term; within this short span the amount of material that can be presented is necessarily restricted. Nonetheless, we believe it is possible in this period of time to provide an appreciation for the problems associated with the acquisition and the interpretation of quantitative analytical information and it is toward such a goal that the efforts of student, instructor, and text should all be directed. *Analytical Chemistry: An Introduction* has been conceived as a means toward this end. The subject matter has been selected to supply, it is hoped, a brief but thoughtful exposure to the field of analytical chemistry that will meet the needs of those whose primary interests include medicine, engineering, and the natural sciences. We subscribe to the view that principles take precedence over details and that a clear understanding of the over-all problem will ordinarily provide the guidance needed in meeting the smaller, but no less important, questions encountered in an analysis.

The book may be thought of as consisting of five parts. The initial chapters (1–3) introduce the student to the several aspects of the total analytical process, provide a review of stoichiometry and the quantities associated with it, and consider the problems associated with the evaluation and interpretation of small sets of data. There then follow chapters devoted to gravimetric analysis (4–8) and to volumetric analysis (9–18). Chapter 19 is devoted to electroanalytical chemistry with the limited aim of providing the student with an understanding of potentiometric titration techniques in general, and the operation of the glass electrode in particular. Similarly, the application of electromagnetic radiation to the problem of obtaining analytical information is considered in Chapter 20. A concluding chapter takes a retrospective look at the subject matter of the course and locates this in the context of the analysis of a "real" substance.

Presentation of the material can be varied without difficulty. The chapter devoted to stoichiometry, while needed by many, still represents a review and may be treated as such. Chapters 5 and 10 are concerned with practical aspects and are thus advantageously considered in the laboratory portion of the course. Volumetric analysis may be considered before gravimetric analysis.

Problem sets are to be found at the end of many chapters. Answers are provided for sufficient exercises so that the student can determine the correctness of his approach. We believe that "working for an answer" should not be encouraged, however, and have not given answers to most questions.

Professors J. R. Hayes and A. J. Diefenderfer have read the manuscript critically; to them we extend our thanks for their many valuable suggestions.

D. A. S.
D. M. W.

February, 1965
Stanford, California
San Jose, California

Contents

PREFACE   *v*

1.   **The Scope of Analytical Chemistry**   *1*

2.   **Some Elementary Concepts**
     Important to Quantitative Analysis   *7*

   2.1   The Chemical Composition of Solutions   *7*
   2.2   Some Weight and Concentration Units   *11*
   2.3   Stoichiometric Relationships   *15*
   2.4   Chemical Equilibrium   *18*

3.   **The Evaluation of Analytical Data**   *34*

   3.1   Definition of Terms   *35*
   3.2   Determinate Errors   *38*
   3.3   Indeterminate Error   *40*
   3.4   The Statistical Treatment of Small Sets of Data   *45*
   3.5   The Outlying Result   *50*
   3.6   Significant Figures   *52*

4.   **An Introduction to Gravimetric Methods**   *61*

   4.1   Classification of Gravimetric Methods   *61*
   4.2   Calculation of Results from Gravimetric Analyses   *63*

5.   **The Techniques and Tools of Gravimetric Analysis**   *69*

   5.1   The Measurement of Mass   *69*
   5.2   The Tools of Gravimetric Analysis   *82*
   5.3   Chemical Reagents   *86*
   5.4   Techniques and Operations   *87*

6.   **The Solubility of Precipitates**   *103*

   6.1   The Application of Solubility Product Constants   *103*
   6.2   Additional Variables that Affect the Solubility of
        Precipitates   *118*

7.   **The Particle Size and Purity of Precipitates**   *124*

   7.1   Mechanism of Precipitate Formation   *125*

7.2   Colloidal Suspensions   *129*
7.3   Crystalline Precipitates   *136*
7.4   Contamination of Precipitates   *138*
7.5   Precipitation from Homogeneous Solution   *146*

8.   The Scope and Applications of Gravimetric Analysis   *149*

8.1   Inorganic Precipitating Agents   *149*
8.2   Organic Precipitating Agents   *151*
8.3   Selected Methods of Analysis   *155*

9.   An Introduction to Volumetric Methods of Analysis   *165*

9.1   Definition of Some Terms   *165*
9.2   Reactions and Reagents Used in Volumetric Analysis   *166*
9.3   End Points in Volumetric Analysis, Titration Curves   *168*
9.4   Volumetric Calculations   *172*

10.   The Techniques and Tools of Volumetric Analysis   *190*

10.1   General Considerations   *190*
10.2   Apparatus for Volumetric Measurements   *192*
10.3   The Measurement of Volume—Techniques and
        Operations   *193*
10.4   Calibration of Volumetric Ware   *199*

11.   Precipitation Titrations   *204*

11.1   Titration Curves for Precipitation Reactions   *204*
11.2   End-point Detection   *209*
11.3   Applications of Precipitation-titration Analysis   *215*
11.4   Precipitation Analysis with Silver Ion   *215*

**12.   Volumetric Methods Based on Complex-formation
        Reactions**   *223*

12.1   Titration Curves for Complex-formation Reactions   *224*
12.2   Methods of End-point Detection   *228*
12.3   Application of Organic Chelating Reagents to Volumetric
        Analysis   *230*

13.   Theory of Neutralization Titrations of Simple Systems   *239*

13.1   Acid-base Equilibria—*p*H Calculations   *239*
13.2   Buffer Solutions   *255*
13.3   Acid-base Indicators   *258*
13.4   Titration   Curves for Simple Neutralization Reactions   *264*

14. **Theory of Neutralization Titrations in Complex Systems** **280**

14.1 Calculation of the pH of Solutions of Acid Salts *280*
14.2 Titration Curves for Complex Systems *283*

15. **Applications of Neutralization Titrations** **295**

15.1 Reagents for Neutralization Titrations *295*
15.2 Some Applications of Neutralization Titrations *302*

16. **Equilibrium in Oxidation-reduction Systems** **318**

16.1 Fundamentals of Electrochemistry *321*
16.2 Chemical Equilibrium in Cells; Equilibrium Constants from Standard Electrode Potentials *338*

17. **Theory of Oxidation-reduction Titrations** **345**

17.1 Titration Curves *345*
17.2 Oxidation-reduction Indicators *354*

18. **Applications of Oxidation-reduction Titrations** **361**

18.1 Standard Solutions and Primary Standards *361*
18.2 Auxiliary Reagents *363*
18.3 Volumetric Oxidizing Agents—Potassium Permanganate *370*
18.4 Quadrivalent Cerium *384*
18.5 Potassium Dichromate *388*
18.6 Iodine—Direct Iodimetric Methods *390*
18.7 Iodometric Methods *396*

19. **Potentiometric Methods** **412**

19.1 Methodology *413*
19.2 Potential Measurements *413*
19.3 Precipitation and Complex-formation Titrations *425*
19.4 Neutralization Titrations and the Measurement of pH *431*
19.5 Oxidation-reduction Titrations *440*
19.6 Some Special Techniques *440*
19.7 Laboratory Experiments Involving Potentiometric Titrations *442*

20. **Methods Based on Absorption of Radiation** **447**

20.1 Fundamental Concepts, Definitions, and Laws *447*
20.2 Instruments for the Measurement of Absorption of Radiation *456*

20.3 Photometric and Spectrophotometric Measurement   *470*
20.4 Experiments   *477*

21.   The Analysis of Real Substances   *484*

21.1 Choosing a Method for the Analysis of Complex
     Substances   *486*
21.2 The Literature of Analytical Chemistry   *493*
21.3 Accuracy Obtainable in the Analysis of Complex
     Materials   *497*

Appendices   *501*

A-1   The Quadratic Equation   *501*
A-2   Logarithms   *502*
A-3   Manipulations Involving Exponential Numbers   *506*
A-4   Standard Reduction Potentials   *507*
A-5   Solubility Product Constants   *510*
A-6   Acid Dissociation Constants   *511*
A-7   Ionization Constants for Bases   *512*
A-8   International Atomic Weights   *513*
A-9   Formula Weights   *514*

INDEX   *515*

Analytical Chemistry
An Introduction

(1)

The Scope of Analytical Chemistry

Analytical chemistry is concerned with the methods and techniques employed in determining the composition of matter. Even as "composition" can be described in terms of *what* or in terms of *how much* is present, so also can analytical chemistry be subdivided according to the type of information sought from the analysis. Most readers are familiar with *qualitative analysis*, which deals with discovering the species present in or the structural details of a sample of matter. The question of how much is the province of *quantitative analysis*, the goal here being the determination of the amount of some component in a unit quantity of sample.

Qualitative and quantitative analysis resemble one another in that both make use of such chemical or physical properties the species of interest possesses as will provide the information desired, whether this be a matter of detection or of estimation. Both also require preliminary treatment steps to insure that the analytical observation, when it is made, measures only the component of interest. In contrast to these similarities, however, many problems confronting the analyst are unique only to quantitative analysis. Here, for example, he must work with the aim of keeping losses of the component he seeks to a tolerable minimum during the preliminary phases of the analysis. It is ordinarily a requirement that the reaction on which he bases his analysis proceeds to essential completion with the formation of a single product. Finally, there must be some reproducible relationship between the property or quantity he measures and the amount of the species being determined. These added conditions unquestionably limit the reactions that are suitable for quantitative work.

The ultimate aim of a quantitative analysis is the determination of the amount of a given species present in a sample of matter; whether this is achieved directly or indirectly depends upon the particular method being considered. Under any circumstances, inherent in every determination is some sort of final measurement from which the quantity of species

TABLE 1-1

Classification of Common Analytical Methods

General Classification	Subclassification	Quantity Measured
Gravimetric	direct method	weight of compound containing species
	indirect method	loss of weight due to volatilization of species
Volumetric	titration methods	volume of solution that is chemically equivalent to the wanted species
	gas analysis	volume of a gaseous species produced or consumed
Optical	emission spectroscopy	radiation emitted by species
	absorption spectroscopy including colorimetry	radiation absorbed by a species
	polarimetry	rotation of polarized light by species
	refractometry	refractive index of solution of species
	turbidimetry, nephelometry	scattering of radiation by species
Electro-analytical	potentiometry	potential of an electrode in equilibrium with the species
	conductimetry	conductance of a solution of the species
	coulometry	quantity of current equivalent to the species
	polarography	current associated with reaction at a polarizable electrode
	high-frequency methods	capacitance of solution of species
Miscellaneous	mass spectroscopy	mass to charge ratio of decomposition products of species
	radiochemical methods	radioactive decay of species
	thermal-conductivity methods	thermal conductance of species
	enthalpy titrations	heat of reaction of species

in question can be derived. Quantitative analysis is commonly further subdivided into groupings based upon the nature of this final measurement. Thus, if this process consists of securing the weight of a solid, the method is classified as a *gravimetric analysis;* if the final measurement involves determination of a volume, the method is classed as a *volumetric analysis.* If the absorption of radiant energy is measured, the method is sometimes termed a *colorimetric analysis;* where an electrical property is measured or electric energy is employed the method can be considered to be *electroanalytical.* Reference to Table 1-1 will reveal that the variety of measurements used by the analyst are numerous and diverse.

From a historical standpoint, the majority of early analytical methods were either gravimetric or volumetric procedures; for this reason these are sometimes known as *classical* methods of analysis. Procedures based on the measurement of optical, electrical, thermal, and other properties were developed later, and these as a group are sometimes called *instrumental* methods. In many respects this dual classification is unfortunate, for it implies that classical and instrumental methods are basically different. In reality, fundamental differences between the two categories do not exist; both are based upon the correlation of a physical measurement with concentration; both employ an instrument for this measurement; to the extent that neither is specific, separations often precede both types of analysis. Finally, the treatment of the sample preliminary to the analysis is basically the same for both. The classification of methods as classical or instrumental is thus founded largely on chronological development.

THE IMPORTANCE OF ANALYTICAL CHEMISTRY

To the question "Why should a course in quantitative analysis be included in my training?" the answer will be variable, depending upon the goals of the questioner. There are few exceptions to the statement that every investigator in the experimental sciences has occasion to utilize analytical data in the course of his work. For the prospective chemist it is sufficient to point out that the development of chemistry as a science has always relied heavily upon data provided by quantitative observations and that this situation is as true today as it ever was in the past. To be sure, over the years there have been significant refinements in technique, in sensitivity of measurement, and in our understanding of the principles upon which analyses are based; the fact remains that virtually every chemical investigation involves the acquisition of analytical measurements. Much of the foregoing can be put forth as an argument for those who aspire to careers in medicine. Physicians depend upon the results of clinical tests as aids in diagnosis; many of these tests, performed by persons trained as medical technicians, are based upon quantitative analytical techniques. Applications of chemical analysis are to be found throughout the physical and biological sciences; similar justifications can be presented for each branch.

The role of analytical chemistry in modern industry is difficult to overestimate. Virtually every item of commerce has been subjected to analytical testing at one or more stages in its manufacture. The clothes we wear, the food we eat, the drugs we require, the automobiles we drive— all these and more require the aid of analytical chemistry to assure the production of goods having uniform quality and characteristics.

Finally, above and beyond these practical considerations, the study of quantitative analysis requires development of systematic and orderly work habits as well as intellectually honest observations; these traits are worthy of cultivation regardless of one's ultimate field of endeavor.

STEPS IN A QUANTITATIVE ANALYSIS

While quantitative analytical methods vary greatly in detail, certain common elements can be found in nearly all procedures. It is worthwhile to indicate the nature of these elements at this point.

1. Sampling. To produce meaningful results an analysis must be performed on a sample whose composition faithfully reflects that of the bulk of material from which it was taken. Where the bulk is large and the material inhomogeneous a great deal of effort is required to procure a representative portion for analysis. Consider, for example, a railroad car containing 25 tons of silver ore. Buyer and seller must come to agreement regarding the value of the shipment; this will be based primarily upon its silver content. The ore itself is inherently heterogeneous, consisting of lumps of varying size and of varying silver content. The actual assay of this shipment will be performed upon a sample that weighs perhaps 1 gram; its composition must be representative of the 25 tons— or approximately 22,700,000 grams—of ore in the shipment. It is clear that the selection of a small sample for this analysis cannot be a simple one-step operation; in short, a systematic preliminary manipulation of the bulk of material will be required before it becomes possible to select 1 gram and have any confidence that its composition is typical of the nearly 23,000,000 grams from which it was taken.

Usually the sampling problem is less formidable than that outlined in the previous paragraph. Still the chemist cannot afford to proceed further with an analysis until he has convinced himself that the fraction of the material he plans to work with is truly representative of the whole.

2. Preparation of the Sample for Analysis. Once a sample is selected, it must be converted into a form that is suitable for analysis. With solid materials this may involve grinding to reduce the particle size and then mixing to ensure homogeneity of the solid. The former operation is particularly important with difficultly soluble substances since the rate of solution is increased greatly by reduction in the size of particles; the sampling operation itself frequently includes preliminary crushing and grinding steps.

Another preparatory operation of considerable importance with most solids is that of removal of adsorbed moisture. Any tendency toward adsorption or desorption of water will cause the percentage composition of a substance to be dependent upon the humidity of its surroundings at the time of the analysis. In order to avoid the problems arising from such variations it is common practice to attempt the removal of all such adsorbed moisture and base the analysis on a dry sample. Frequently drying will involve heating of the material to about 100° C, or exposing it to a dry atmosphere for suitable periods of time.

3. Procurement of a Measured Quantity of the Sample. Quantitative analytical results are usually reported in relative terms—that is, in some way that expresses the quantity of the desired component present per unit weight or volume of sample. Percentage composition is probably the most commonly employed of these. In order to express the results in a meaningful manner it is therefore necessary to know the weight of the sample upon which the analysis is performed. The purpose of all subsequent steps is the evaluation of the weight of the desired species present in this weight of sample.

4. Solution of the Sample. Many, but by no means all, methods of analysis are performed upon a solution of the substance being analyzed. In these cases the choice of solvent and method of solution become important preliminaries to the analysis.

The choice of solvent is limited by several considerations. Generally, it is desirable that the solvent be effective in dissolving all of the components of the sample, not just the species being determined. The solution process should take place in a reasonable period of time. The chemical composition of the solvent should be such as to offer no interference in the subsequent steps of the analysis; lacking this quality, such interferences it does produce should be easy to eliminate.

5. Separation of Interfering Substances. There are few, if any, chemical or physical properties of importance in analysis that are entirely unique to a single chemical species; rather, the reactions used and the properties measured are generally characteristic of a number of elements or compounds. This lack of truly specific reactions and properties adds greatly to the difficulties faced by the chemist undertaking an analysis; it means that a scheme must be devised for isolating the species of interest from all others present in the original material that can influence the final measurement. Compounds or elements that prevent the direct measurement of the species being determined are called *interferences*, and their separation prior to the final measurement constitutes an important step in most analyses. No hard and fast rules can be given for the elimination of interferences; this problem is often the most imposing aspect of the analysis.

6. The Completion of the Analysis. All of the preliminary steps in an analysis are undertaken in order to make the final measurement a true gauge of the quantity of the species being determined. An indication of diversity that characterizes final measurements can be gained from inspection of Table 1-1. It is with this aspect that an introductory course in quantitative analysis is chiefly concerned. The student should constantly bear in mind, however, that in most instances the final measurement is the least difficult aspect of the analysis.

7. Calculation and Interpretation of Results. The numerical values of the experimental data comprising the final measurement bear a direct relationship to the quantity of species present in the sample. Since the information desired from the analysis is usually extensive in nature, it is necessary to relate mathematically the value of the final measurement to the weight of the sample employed in its procurement.

Finally, the report of a quantitative analysis is incomplete without some indication being given regarding the reliability of the results. Such an evaluation may be based upon previous experience with the method in question, upon an estimate of the reliability that is likely from the method employed, or from the analytical data themselves.

While the foregoing can be considered to represent the steps common to all quantitative analyses, it must be recognized that no inclusive statement can be made regarding their relative difficulty. Each analysis undertaken is unique to the extent of the importance of the problems arising in the various steps; that which represents the most formidable aspect of one determination may actually be of negligible importance in another.

It should further be pointed out that the mechanical skills necessary to the completion of a successful analysis can readily be taught to persons having little or no scientific background; indeed, a routine analysis may be performed better by the technician than by his more highly trained supervisor. However, an intelligent appraisal of the factors of importance (and those of no import) in the several steps comprising a quantitative analysis requires more chemical knowledge than that possessed by the technician. It is this added knowledge with which this text is concerned.

(2)

Some Elementary Concepts
Important to
Quantitative Analysis

A few fundamental concepts are of particular significance to analytical chemistry. These include the law of chemical equilibrium, weight relationships among reacting substances, the constitution of solutions, and methods for expression of their concentrations.

2.1 The Chemical Composition of Solutions

STRONG AND WEAK ELECTROLYTES

Most of the compounds with which we shall be concerned are electrolytes; that is, in aqueous solutions they are dissociated to a greater or lesser degree into ions. A convenient method of classifying compounds is on the basis of the extent to which they do dissociate. Strong electrolytes are those that are completely or nearly completely dissociated; weak electrolytes are those that are only partially ionized.

It will frequently be important for our purposes to recognize whether we are dealing with solutions of weak or strong electrolytes. Table 2-1 will serve as an aid in making this distinction.

DISSOCIATION OF WATER

Water is an extremely weak electrolyte, being dissociated to the extent of only a few parts per billion. This ionization, minute as it is, assumes

TABLE 2-1

Classification of Electrolytes

Strong Electrolytes	Weak Electrolytes
1. The inorganic acids HNO_3, $HClO_4$, H_2SO_4,[1] HCl, HI, HBr, $HClO_3$, $HBrO_3$	1. Many inorganic acids such as H_2CO_3, H_3BO_3, H_3PO_4, H_2S, H_2SO_3, etc.
2. Alkali and alkaline-earth hydroxides as well as some of the heavy metal hydroxides	2. Most organic acids
	3. Ammonia and most organic bases
3. Most salts	4. Halides, cyanides, and thiocyanates of Hg, Zn, and Cd

[1] H_2SO_4 is completely dissociated into HSO_4^- and H^+ ions and for this reason is called a strong electrolyte. However, it should be noted that the HSO_4^- ion is a weak electrolyte, being only partially dissociated.

considerable importance because of the frequency with which its products influence chemical reactions in aqueous solutions.

The dissociation of water is most accurately represented by the equation

$$2H_2O \rightleftharpoons H_3O^+ + OH^-$$

The positive ion so formed is called the *hydronium ion*, the proton being bonded to the water molecule via a covalent bond involving one of the unshared electron pairs of the oxygen. This hydrate is so remarkably stable that there are essentially no simple protons, as such, in aqueous solution. Higher hydrates of the proton are also undoubtedly present, but these are much less stable than the hydronium ion itself.

In order to emphasize the unique character of the singly hydrated proton, many chemists always use the notation H_3O^+ in writing equations for reactions in which the proton is a participant. For the purpose of describing the stoichiometry of a reaction in aqueous solution, however, the formula H^+ is equally satisfactory, and this notation does possess the distinct advantage of simplifying the process of writing and balancing equations.

ACIDS AND BASES

Historically speaking, the classification of certain substances as acids or bases was founded upon several characteristic properties that these compounds impart to an aqueous solution. Among these were the observations that an acid causes litmus to turn red, gives a sharp taste to water, and reacts with a base to form a salt. A base, on the other hand, gives a bitter

taste and a slippery feel to water, turns litmus blue, and produces a salt
with an acid.

In the late nineteenth century, Arrhenius proposed a more sophisticated basis of classification according to which acids were defined as
hydrogen-containing substances that dissociate into hydrogen ions and
anions when dissolved in water; bases, on the other hand, were defined as
hydroxyl compounds that give hydroxyl ions and cations upon the same
treatment. This fruitful proposal led to a quantitative treatment of the
idea of acidity and basicity. Thus, by measuring the degree of dissociation
of an acid or a base in aqueous solution, it became possible to compare the
relative strengths of these compounds. In addition, the theory provided a
foundation for the mathematical treatment of the equilibria established
when acids and bases react with one another.

A serious limitation to the Arrhenius theory is its failure to recognize
the role played by the solvent in the dissociation process. It remained
for Brønsted and Lowry, in 1923, to propose, independently, a more generalized concept of acids and bases. In their view an acid is any substance
capable of donating a proton; a base is any substance that can accept a
proton. When an acid loses a proton, the entity that remains clearly
becomes a potential proton acceptor, and thus a base; it is called the
conjugate base of the parent acid. The relationship can be represented as

$$\text{acid} \rightleftharpoons \text{base} + \text{proton}$$

It is important to note, however, that a substance can exhibit acidic
behavior only in the presence of a proton acceptor; similarly, basic behavior
requires the presence of a proton donor. Often this acceptor or donor is
the solvent, and the process of dissolving a solute becomes an acid-base
reaction. Consider, for example, the equations

$$\text{acid}_1 + \text{base}_1 \rightleftharpoons \text{acid}_2 + \text{base}_2$$

$$\text{HCl} + \text{H}_2\text{O} \rightleftharpoons \text{H}_3\text{O}^+ + \text{Cl}^-$$

$$\text{HC}_2\text{H}_3\text{O}_2 + \text{H}_2\text{O} \rightleftharpoons \text{H}_3\text{O}^+ + \text{C}_2\text{H}_3\text{O}_2^-$$

$$\text{Al}(\text{H}_2\text{O})_6^{3+} + \text{H}_2\text{O} \rightleftharpoons \text{H}_3\text{O}^+ + \text{Al}(\text{H}_2\text{O})_5\text{OH}^{2+}$$

$$\text{H}_2\text{PO}_4^- + \text{H}_2\text{O} \rightleftharpoons \text{H}_3\text{O}^+ + \text{HPO}_4^{2-}$$

$$\text{NH}_4^+ + \text{H}_2\text{O} \rightleftharpoons \text{H}_3\text{O}^+ + \text{NH}_3$$

$$\text{H}_2\text{O} + \text{NH}_3 \rightleftharpoons \text{NH}_4^+ + \text{OH}^-$$

These equations demonstrate that acids and bases can be anionic, cationic,
or electrically neutral in character. Also noteworthy is the observation

that the solvent, water, acts as a proton acceptor (or base) for the first five solutes and as a proton donor (or acid) for ammonia; the term *amphiprotic* is used to describe solvents that possess this dual capacity.

The extent to which an acid (or base) reacts with a given solvent varies greatly. For example, the reaction between hydrochloric acid and water is essentially complete; thus this substance is classified as a strong acid *in water*. Acetic acid and ammonium ions react to a lesser degree with water and are thus progressively weaker acids.

The position of equilibrium for reactions between an acid or base and a solvent is also greatly dependent upon the ability of the solvent to act as a proton acceptor or donor. Thus, for example, hydrochloric, perchloric, and hydrobromic acids are all completely dissociated in water and are therefore termed strong acids in this solvent. In glacial acetic acid, however, only perchloric acid is completely dissociated and thus a strong acid; hydrobromic and hydrochloric acids are but partially dissociated, and are thus weak acids in this solvent. The solution process in acetic acid is described by equations such as

$$\underset{\text{acid}_1}{\text{HClO}_4} + \underset{\text{base}_1}{\text{HC}_2\text{H}_3\text{O}_2} \rightleftharpoons \underset{\text{acid}_2}{\text{H}_2\text{C}_2\text{H}_3\text{O}_2^+} + \underset{\text{base}_2}{\text{ClO}_4^-}$$

Another important consequence of the Brønsted theory is that the most effective proton donors (strongest acids) give rise to the poorest proton acceptors (weakest conjugate bases). Referring again to the reaction of hydrochloric acid, acetic acid, and ammonium ion with water, it follows that the chloride ion is the weakest base, acetate ion is next, and ammonia is the strongest.

It is also noteworthy that the dissociation of water can be viewed as an acid-base reaction.

$$\underset{\text{acid}_1}{\text{H}_2\text{O}} + \underset{\text{base}_1}{\text{H}_2\text{O}} \rightleftharpoons \underset{\text{acid}_2}{\text{H}_3\text{O}^+} + \underset{\text{base}_2}{\text{OH}^-}$$

A still more general view of acids and bases was put forward by Lewis who defined an acid as an electron-pair acceptor and a base as an electron-pair donor. These definitions free the concept of acid-base behavior from the necessity of involving protons and further increase the number of processes to be considered as acid-base reactions.

In treating acid-base equilibria, we shall adopt the Brønsted view and for emphasis will employ the symbol H_3O^+ in those chapters dealing with equilibrium calculations. On the other hand, where only stoichiometric relationships are of concern, we will employ the more convenient symbol H^+ to represent the hydrated proton.

2.2   Some Weight and Concentration Units

UNITS OF WEIGHT

In the laboratory the chemist generally measures and records the masses of objects in units of grams, milligrams, or micrograms (the microgram is 10^{-6} gram and is sometimes called a *gamma*). In carrying out chemical calculations, however, he finds it more convenient to convert these quantities into units that express the weight relationships among substances in terms of small whole numbers. The gram-formula weight, the gram-molecular weight, and the gram-equivalent weight are such units, and they find wide application in the computations of analytical chemistry; these terms are frequently shortened to the formula weight, the molecular weight, and the equivalent weight, respectively.

Although we must defer a definition of the gram-equivalent weight until a later section it will be worthwhile to consider the other two units here and to differentiate quite carefully between them.

The empirical formula for a substance is the simplest combination of the number and species of atoms present in that substance. It is also the chemical formula unless experimental evidence indicates that the fundamental aggregate of atoms is actually some multiple of the empirical formula. For example, we use H_2 as the chemical formula for hydrogen gas because there is abundant evidence that this substance is encountered, under ordinary conditions, as a diatomic molecule. On the other hand, the symbol Ne serves adequately to describe the composition of neon gas which is monatomic in nature.

The entity expressed by the chemical formula may or may not be real. For example, there is no evidence for the existence of molecules of sodium chloride as such in either the pure solid or in solution. Rather, this substance is made up of sodium ions and chloride ions, no one of which can be said to be in simple combination with any other single ion. Despite this it is convenient to assign the formula NaCl to sodium chloride. It is also noteworthy that the chemical formula of a substance is frequently that of the principal species only. Thus, liquid water contains H_2O, H_4O_2, H_3O^+, OH^-, as well as other entities. The formula assigned to water is that of the predominant species, H_2O, and as such is only an approximation of the actual composition of the real substance.

The *gram-formula weight* (gfw) is the summation of the atomic weights, in grams, of all the atoms appearing in the chemical formula of a substance. Thus, the gram-formula weight of hydrogen is 2.016 grams and that for sodium chloride is 58.45 grams. The definition for the formula weight carries no inference regarding the existence or nonexistence of the substance for which it is calculated.

We shall define the *gram-molecular weight* (gmw) as the gram-formula weight of a single, real chemical species. According to this convention, the molecular weight of H_2 is 2.016 grams; no molecular weight can be assigned to the species NaCl since there is no evidence for its existence. We can, however, properly assign weights to Na^+ (22.99 grams) and Cl^- (35.45 grams) since these are real chemical species; these might more properly be called "ionic weights" rather than "molecular weights".

Since it represents a real, chemical species, 1 gram-molecular weight of any substance has enumerative significance, it being the weight of 6.02×10^{23} particles of that species; this quantity is commonly referred to as the *mol*. Similarly, the gram-formula weight is the weight of 6.02×10^{23} units of the substance, real or not, represented by a chemical formula.

Thus, in 100 grams of H_2 there are

$$\frac{100 \text{ grams}}{2.016 \text{ grams/mol}} = 49.60 \text{ mols } H_2$$

and

$$\frac{100 \text{ grams}}{2.016 \text{ grams/mol}} \times \frac{6.02 \times 10^{23} \text{ molecules}}{\text{mol}} = 2.99 \times 10^{25} \text{ molecules } H_2$$

A like weight of NaCl contains

$$\frac{100 \text{ grams}}{58.44 \text{ grams/gfw}} = 1.711 \text{ gfw NaCl}$$

and

$$1.711 \text{ mols } Na^+$$

$$1.711 \text{ mols } Cl^-$$

Let us further distinguish between the formula and molecular weight by again considering a quantity of water that weighs 18.016 grams. This clearly represents 1 gram-formula weight of water; it contains slightly less than 1 mol of water, however, because some is in the form of H_4O_2, H_3O^+, OH^-, and such other species as may be present.

Some chemists choose to make no distinction between the formula weight and the molecular weight, and employ the terms synonymously. We feel there is merit in differentiating between these quantities in that, by doing so, the possibility for ambiguity in describing the concentration of solutions is eliminated.

The *milliformula weight* and *millimolecular weight* for a substance are simply $\frac{1}{1000}$ of a formula weight and molecular weight, respectively.

Thus, in 100 grams of H_2 there are

$$\frac{100 \text{ grams}}{0.002016 \text{ grams/mmol}} = 49600 \text{ mmol}$$

and in 100 grams of NaCl there are

$$\frac{100 \text{ grams}}{0.05844 \text{ grams/mfw}} = 1711 \text{ mfw}$$

METHODS FOR THE EXPRESSION OF CONCENTRATION

Formality or Formal Concentration. The *formality*, F, of a solution expresses the number of gram-formula weights of solute present in 1 liter of solution. It follows that this term also gives the number of milliformula weights of solute in 1 ml of the solution.

> ★EXAMPLE. Exactly 0.1753 grams of NaCl are dissolved in suffi-
> cient H_2O to give 240 ml of solution. What is the formal concentra-
> tion of NaCl?
>
> The number of milliformula weights of NaCl in 0.1753 gram is
>
> $$\text{no. mfw NaCl} = \frac{0.1753 \text{ gram}}{0.05844 \text{ gram/mfw}} = 3.000$$
>
> $$F = \frac{\text{no. mfw}}{\text{ml}} = \frac{3.00 \text{ mfw}}{240 \text{ ml}} = 0.0125$$

Molarity or Molar Concentration. The *molarity*, M, of a solution defines the number of gram-molecular weights (or mols) of a species in 1 liter of solution, or the number of millimolecular weights in 1 ml of solution.

> The molar concentration and the formal concentration of a
> given solution are frequently different. Thus, the solution that
> results when 1 gram-formula weight of oxalic acid (90.04 grams of
> $H_2C_2O_4$) is dissolved in sufficient water to give 1.00 liter is, by
> definition, 1.00 formal with respect to the *substance* oxalic acid.
> Because this solute undergoes dissociation to the extent of approxi-
> mately 22 percent, however, the molar concentration of the *species*
> $H_2C_2O_4$ will be about 0.78 M only.
>
> Similarly, a solution prepared by dissolving 1.00 gram-formula
> weight of sodium chloride (58.45 grams) in sufficient water to give
> 1.00 liter of solution will be 1.00 formal with respect to NaCl, by
> definition; the concentration of both Na^+ and Cl^- will be 1.00 molar.
> The molar concentration of the species NaCl will be zero. This is the
> general situation for solutions of strong electrolytes.

From these examples we may conclude that quantitative information is needed with regard to the composition of the solute in solution before its molar concentration can be specified. On the other hand, the formal concentration may be calculated from the specifications for preparation of the solution and the formula weight of the solute.

Normality or Normal Concentration. This method of expressing concentration will be defined in Chapter 9.

Percentage Concentration. Chemists frequently denote the concentration of solutions in terms of percentages. This unfortunate practice often leads to ambiguity, inasmuch as the percentage composition of a solution can be expressed in any of several ways. Three of the more common methods are defined as follows:

$$\text{weight percent} = \frac{\text{weight of solute}}{\text{weight of solution}} \times 100$$

$$\text{volume percent} = \frac{\text{volume of solute}}{\text{volume of solution}} \times 100$$

$$\text{weight-volume percent} = \frac{\text{weight of solute, grams}}{\text{volume of solution, ml}} \times 100$$

The reader should note that the denominator in each case refers to the solution and not to the solvent alone. Furthermore the first two expressions are independent of the units of volume or weight used in their definition whereas the third is not. Weight percent has the great advantage of being independent of temperature while the other percentages are not; for this reason it is widely used. The concentrations of commercial aqueous reagents are frequently expressed in terms of weight percent; thus, concentrated nitric acid is stated to be 70 percent HNO_3, which means that the reagent contains 70 grams of HNO_3 per 100 grams of the concentrated solution.

Weight-volume percent is frequently used to indicate the concentration of dilute aqueous solutions of solid reagents; thus, a 5-percent silver nitrate solution is one prepared by dissolving 5 grams of silver nitrate in water and diluting to 100 ml.

To avoid uncertainty, the type of percentage employed must be explicitly stated when using this method to express concentration; when this information is omitted, the reader is forced to decide intuitively which of the several types has been employed by the writer.

Parts per Million. In dealing with concentrations of very dilute solutions, percentage compositions become awkward to use because of the number of zeros needed to place the decimal point. Under these circumstances the concentration is conveniently expressed in parts per million (ppm). This term is defined by the equation

$$\text{ppm} = \frac{\text{weight of solute}}{\text{weight of solution}} \times 1,000,000$$

Thus a solution containing 0.0003-percent nickel by weight contains 3 ppm of nickel.

Titer. This useful, but somewhat specialized, system for expressing concentration is defined on page 177.

2.3   Stoichiometric Relationships

A chemical equation is a statement of the combining ratios of the substances involved, expressed in terms of a chemical system of weights. Thus, the equation[2]

$$2AgNO_3 + K_2CrO_4 = Ag_2CrO_4 + 2KNO_3$$

indicates that 2 formula weights of silver nitrate and 1 of potassium chromate combine to yield 1 formula weight of silver chromate and 2 of potassium nitrate, respectively. Now, experimental measurements are seldom acquired directly in terms of formula weights, but instead have units of grams or milligrams, liters or milliliters. The chemist, interested in relating his raw data to the weight of some other compound, must first convert these data into units of formula weights, take into account the stoichiometry of the process, and then reconvert to ordinary metric units of weight. These transformations are of fundamental importance in analytical chemistry; they are summarized in Tables 2-2 and 2-3. Examples of the application of these transformations follow.

★EXAMPLE. How many grams of $AgNO_3$ (gfw = 170) are needed to prepare 300 ml of a 0.200 F solution?

The number of milliformula weights required is given by

$$\text{no. mfw} = \text{ml solution} \times F$$

$$= 300 \text{ ml} \times 0.200 \frac{\text{mfw}}{\text{ml}} = 60$$

The weight in grams of $AgNO_3$ will be

$$\text{grams } AgNO_3 = \text{no. mfw} \times \frac{\text{gfw}}{1000}$$

$$= 60 \text{ mfw} \times \frac{170 \text{ grams}}{1000 \text{ mfw}}$$

$$= 10.2 \text{ grams}$$

---

[2] For our present purposes it is advantageous to depict this reaction in terms of chemical formulas. Ordinarily it will be more desirable to use the net-ionic representation

$$2Ag^+ + CrO_4^{2-} = Ag_2CrO_4$$

TABLE 2-2

Expression of Weight in Chemical Units

Chemical Unit	Weight of Unit in Grams Given by	Method of Conversion from Metric Units to Chemical Units
formula-weight (fw)	gfw	$\text{no. fw} = \dfrac{\text{grams of substance}}{\text{gfw}}$
milliformula-weight (mfw)	$\dfrac{\text{gfw}}{1000}$	$\text{no. mfw} = \dfrac{\text{grams of substance} \times 1000}{\text{gfw}}$
mol	gmw	$\text{no. mol} = \dfrac{\text{grams of species}}{\text{gmw}}$
millimol	$\dfrac{\text{gmw}}{1000}$	$\text{no. mmol} = \dfrac{\text{grams of species} \times 1000}{\text{gmw}}$
equivalent (eq)	eq wt	$\text{no. eq} = \dfrac{\text{grams of substance}}{\text{eq wt}}$
milliequivalent (meq)	$\dfrac{\text{eq wt}}{1000}$	$\text{no. meq} = \dfrac{\text{grams of substance} \times 1000}{\text{eq wt}}$

TABLE 2-3

Expression of Concentration in Chemical Units

Chemical Term for Concentration	Method of Calculation from Chemical Units of Weight	Method of Calculation from Metric Units of Weight
Formality, F	$F = \dfrac{\text{no. fw}}{\text{liter of soln}}$ $= \dfrac{\text{no. mfw}}{\text{ml of soln}}$	$F = \dfrac{\text{grams solute}}{\text{liter of soln} \times \text{gfw}}$ $= \dfrac{\text{grams solute} \times 1000}{\text{ml of soln} \times \text{gfw}}$
Molarity, M	$M = \dfrac{\text{no. mol}}{\text{liter of soln}}$ $= \dfrac{\text{no. mmol}}{\text{ml of soln}}$	$M = \dfrac{\text{grams solute}}{\text{liter of soln} \times \text{gmw}}$ $= \dfrac{\text{grams solute} \times 1000}{\text{ml of soln} \times \text{gmw}}$
Normality, N	$N = \dfrac{\text{no. eq}}{\text{liter of soln}}$ $= \dfrac{\text{no. meq}}{\text{ml of soln}}$	$N = \dfrac{\text{grams solute}}{\text{liter of soln} \times \text{eq wt}}$ $= \dfrac{\text{grams solute} \times 1000}{\text{ml of soln} \times \text{eq wt}}$

★EXAMPLE. Calculate the weight of Ag_2CrO_4 (gfw = 332) formed from 0.500 gram of $AgNO_3$ (gfw = 170) by reaction with an excess of K_2CrO_4 (gfw = 194).

From the chemical equation for the reaction we know that 2 formula weights of $AgNO_3$ are required to produce 1 formula weight of Ag_2CrO_4. Therefore

$$\text{no. fw } AgNO_3 = 2 \times \text{no. fw } Ag_2CrO_4$$

Substituting equivalent expressions for the number of formula weights yields

$$\frac{\text{grams } AgNO_3}{\text{gfw } AgNO_3} = \frac{2 \times \text{grams } Ag_2CrO_4}{\text{gfw } Ag_2CrO_4}$$

Rearranging

$$\text{grams } Ag_2CrO_4 = \text{grams } AgNO_3 \times \frac{\text{gfw } Ag_2CrO_4}{\text{gfw } AgNO_3 \times 2}$$

and substituting numerical values

$$\text{grams } Ag_2CrO_4 = 0.500 \times \frac{332}{2 \times 170} = 0.488$$

★EXAMPLE. How many milliliters of 0.100 F $AgNO_3$ would be required to precipitate all of the CrO_4^{2-} from 1.40 grams of K_2CrO_4 (gfw = 194)?

Because the answer is desired in milliliters it is convenient to base our calculations on the milliformula weight. As before, the equation for the process indicates that

$$\text{no. mfw } AgNO_3 = 2 \times \text{no. mfw } K_2CrO_4$$

Substituting equivalent expressions for these quantities we obtain

$$ml_{AgNO_3} \times F_{AgNO_3} = \frac{2 \times \text{grams } K_2CrO_4}{\text{mfw } K_2CrO_4}$$

After rearranging and substituting numerical quantities

$$ml_{AgNO_3} = \frac{2 \times 1.40 \text{ grams}}{0.100 \text{ mfw/ml} \times 0.194 \text{ grams/mfw}} = 144 \text{ ml}$$

★EXAMPLE. What volume of H_2 (gfw = 2.016), measured at STP, will be evolved when 1.000 gram of Zn (gfw = 65.4) is treated with 21.5 ml of 0.0930 F HCl?

The equation for the chemical reaction is

$$Zn + 2H^+ \rightleftharpoons H_2 + Zn^{2+}$$

from which we conclude that

$$\text{no. mfw } H^+ \text{ consumed} = 2 \times \text{no. mfw Zn consumed}$$

The number of milliformula weights of the two reactants can be calculated readily

$$\text{no. mfw Zn} = \frac{1.00 \text{ gram}}{0.0654 \text{ grams/mfw}} = 1.53 \text{ mfw}$$

$$\text{no. mfw H}^+ = 21.5 \text{ ml} \times 0.0930 \text{ mfw/ml} = 2.00 \text{ mfw}$$

Since 2.00 mfw of H^+ will consume only 1.00 mfw Zn, there will remain 0.53 mfw Zn after the reaction is complete and the number of mfw H_2 produced is determined by the number of mfw H^+ originally present. Thus we may say

$$\text{no. mfw H}_2 = \tfrac{1}{2} \text{ no. mfw H}^+$$

then

$$\text{no. mfw H}_2 \text{ produced} = \frac{2.00 \text{ mfw}}{2} = 1.00 \text{ mfw} = 0.001 \text{ gfw}$$

and since 1 formula weight of any gas occupies 22.4 liters under standard conditions

$$V_{H_2} = 0.001 \text{ gfw} \times 22.4 \frac{\text{liters}}{\text{gfw}} = 0.224 \text{ liter}$$

Any problem involving stoichiometry can be solved through application of these fundamental definitions. The ability to manipulate them to produce a desired equation must be cultivated.

2.4   Chemical Equilibrium

Most of the reactions with which we shall be concerned do not proceed to completion but tend, instead, toward a condition in which two opposing reactions occur at the same rate. For example, mixture of solutions containing iron (III) and iodide ions gives rise to the reaction

$$2Fe^{3+} + 3I^- \rightleftharpoons 2Fe^{2+} + I_3^-$$

Similarly, iron (II) will, upon addition to a solution of triiodide ion, produce the reverse reaction. Now, the extent of either process can readily be gauged through measurement of the orange-red color imparted to the system by the triiodide ion. Such a measurement would reveal that the quantity of this substance very rapidly reaches a constant level and remains there so long as conditions are not altered. If, however, we were able to examine this reaction on a molecular level, we would find that the two opposing reactions were occurring continuously, and the observed constant concentration of triiodide ion was the result of equality in the reaction rates. Under these circumstances, a state of dynamic equilibrium has been reached.

The relative concentrations of reactants and products at equilibrium (that is, the position of the equilibrium) are greatly dependent upon the inherent nature of the substances involved. Thus if the species on the left side of a chemical equation have a much greater tendency to react than those on the right, the equilibrium will tend to lie to the right.

Reactant concentrations corresponding to equilibrium can be altered by the application of stress to the system; this can take the form of an alteration in temperature, pressure, or concentration of one of the reactants. The effects of these variables can be predicted from the well-known *principle of LeChatelier* which states that a chemical equilibrium will always shift in such a direction as to counteract the effects of an added stress. Thus an increase in temperature will cause a shift in a direction that absorbs heat. Similarly an increase in pressure will result in a shift favoring production of those participants that occupy the smallest volume. The alteration of an equilibrium through the addition of a participating species is of special interest to the analytical chemist. We shall examine the quantitative aspects of this effect in considerable detail in later chapters.

EQUILIBRIUM CONSTANTS

Formulation of Equilibrium Constants. We have thus far considered only the qualitative effects of temperature, pressure, and concentration on a chemical equilibrium; it is also quite possible to describe the influence of the latter two variables in quantitative terms by means of mathematical equations that are called *equilibrium-constant expressions*. These are of great importance in analytical chemistry; large portions of this text will be devoted to their application to chemical problems. The following paragraphs will serve as a brief review of the subject.

We will first consider a generalized equation for a chemical equilibrium

$$lL + mM + \cdots \rightleftharpoons pP + qQ + \cdots \qquad (2\text{-}1)$$

where the capital letters represent the formulas of the chemical species participating in the reaction and the small letters are the integers required to balance the chemical equation. Thus this equation states that l mols of L react with m mols of M, and so on, to yield p mols of P and q mols of Q, and so on. The equilibrium-constant expression for this reaction is

$$K = \frac{[P]^p[Q]^q \cdots}{[L]^l[M]^m \cdots} \qquad (2\text{-}2)$$

where the letters in brackets represent the molar concentrations of dissolved solute species or partial pressures (in atmospheres) if the reacting species are gases.[3] These concentrations are raised to powers that correspond numerically to the molar proportions required in the balanced equation for the process. The letter K represents a quantity called the *equilibrium constant* for the reaction. By convention, the products of the reaction *as written* are always placed in the numerator and the reactants in the denominator.

Equation (2-2) applies to all chemical equilibria and represents a mathematical expression of the *law of chemical equilibrium* or the *mass law*. It has a sound theoretical basis and can be derived from fundamental concepts. Furthermore, the expression has been found experimentally to apply to a wide variety of chemical reactions. It is certainly one of the most important generalizations of chemistry.

Equilibrium constants have been measured for a large number of chemical reactions; their values vary over a range of 10^{100} or more. A large value of K for an equilibrium clearly indicates that the reaction proceeds far to the right, while a value much smaller than unity indicates the position of equilibrium lies to the left. When the concentration of one of the participants in a reaction at equilibrium is changed independently, the concentrations of the other species readjust in such a way as to maintain K constant. When this occurs, the equilibrium is said to have been shifted. For example, the addition of substance L to the equilibrium represented by equation (2-1) would require a decrease in the concentration of M and a corresponding increase in the concentrations of P and Q until equilibrium was again achieved. At this new equilibrium the new concentrations of L, M, P, and Q would be such as to give again the constant K when substituted into equation (2-2).

Effect of Temperature on Equilibrium Constants. The numerical value of an equilibrium constant is independent of concentration and pressure but dependent on temperature. As might be expected from our previous discussion the numerical values of equilibrium constants for some reactions increase with temperature increases, while others decrease and still others change very little at all. For example, the equilibrium constant for the endothermic reaction

$$2H_2O \rightleftharpoons H_3O^+ + OH^-$$

increases by a factor of almost 100 as the temperature is raised from 0 to 100° C. On the other hand the constant for the exothermic reaction

$$H_2 + I_2 \rightleftharpoons 2HI$$

---

[3] The use of molar concentrations and partial pressures in this equation represents an approximation. More accurately the bracketed letters represent quantities called *activities*. This is discussed briefly on page 25.

decreases with increasing temperature and is only 0.6 as great at 400° C as it is at 300° C. Thus a certain amount of care is required in the use of equilibrium constants to be sure that they are applied only at the proper temperature.

SOME COMMON TYPES OF EQUILIBRIUM CONSTANTS

The analytical chemist is vitally concerned with chemical equilibria in aqueous solutions. Five types are commonly encountered. These are listed in Table 2-4. Each will be considered in detail in later chapters.

Role of Water. A concentration term for water does not appear in the equilibrium expressions in Table 2-4, even in those instances where water is a reactant or product. This is because these expressions apply only to relatively dilute systems where the concentration of water is enormous with respect to the other substances involved. As a result, the concentration of water remains essentially constant despite shifts in such equilibria, and the term for this substance can thus be considered to be part of the constant K.

Role of a Solid. The heterogeneous equilibrium between a solute and its saturated solution is of particular importance to the analyst. An unmistakable requirement for equilibrium is the existence of some undissolved solid. It is experimentally demonstrable, however, that *the position of equilibrium is totally unaffected by the quantity of solid as long as some of this second phase is present.* Thus no concentration term for the solid participant of an equilibrium appears in equilibrium constant expressions, it being implicit that the equation applies only when *an excess of solid phase is present.* For example, the equilibrium that results when an excess of silver chloride is shaken with water is

$$AgCl \underset{\text{solid}}{\rightleftharpoons} Ag^+ + Cl^-_{\text{solution}}$$

The corresponding equilibrium-constant expression is

$$K_{sp} = [Ag^+][Cl^-]$$

Stepwise Equilibria. Many weak electrolytes dissociate in a stepwise manner, and equilibrium-constant expressions can be written for each step. For example, oxalic acid dissociates to give both hydrogen oxalate and oxalate ions; thus we may write

$$H_2O + H_2C_2O_4 \rightleftharpoons H_3O^+ + HC_2O_4^- \qquad K_1 = \frac{[H_3O^+][HC_2O_4^-]}{[H_2C_2O_4]}$$

and

$$H_2O + HC_2O_4^- \rightleftharpoons H_3O^+ + C_2O_4^{2-} \qquad K_2 = \frac{[H_3O^+][C_2O_4^{2-}]}{[HC_2O_4^-]}$$

TABLE 2-4

Equilibria and Equilibrium Constants of Importance to Analytical Chemistry

Type of Equilibrium	Name and Symbol of Equilibrium Constant	Typical Example	Equilibrium-constant Expression
Dissociation of water	ion-product constant, K_w	$2H_2O \rightleftharpoons H_3O^+ + OH^-$	$K_w = [H_3O^+][OH^-]$
Heterogeneous equilibrium between a slightly soluble substance and its ions in a saturated solution	solubility product, K_{sp}	$Ag_2CrO_4 \rightleftharpoons 2Ag^+ + CrO_4^{2-}$	$K_{sp} = [Ag^+]^2[CrO_4^{2-}]$
Dissociation of a weak acid or base	dissociation constant, K_d, K_a or K_b	$HCN + H_2O \rightleftharpoons H_3O^+ + CN^-$ $CN^- + H_2O \rightleftharpoons HCN + OH^-$	$K_d = \dfrac{[H_3O^+][CN^-]}{[HCN]}$ $K_b = \dfrac{[HCN][OH^-]}{[CN^-]}$
Dissociation of a complex ion	instability constant, K_{inst}	$Ni(CN)_4^{2-} \rightleftharpoons Ni^{2+} + 4CN^-$	$K_{inst} = \dfrac{[Ni^{2+}][CN^-]^4}{[Ni(CN)_4^{2-}]}$
Oxidation-reduction equilibrium	K	$MnO_4^- + 5Fe^{2+} + 8H^+ \rightleftharpoons Mn^{2+} + 5Fe^{3+} + 4H_2O$	$K = \dfrac{[Mn^{2+}][Fe^{3+}]^5}{[MnO_4^-][Fe^{2+}]^5[H^+]^8}$

The subscripts on the constants are used to indicate the dissociation step to which K refers. The numerical value of K_2 will be less than K_1.

Equilibrium Constants for Conjugate Acids and Bases. Ordinarily, tables of equilibrium constants do not contain data for equilibria involving the conjugate bases of weak acids nor the conjugate acids of weak bases, it being possible to calculate the values for these quantities from the dissociation constants for the weak acid or base. For example, cyanide ion is the conjugate base of the weak acid, HCN. When sodium cyanide is dissolved in water, a basic solution is produced as a consequence of the reaction

$$CN^- + H_2O \rightleftharpoons HCN + OH^- \qquad K_b = \frac{[HCN][OH^-]}{[CN^-]}$$

The numerical value for this basic constant, K_b, is not found in most tables but can be readily calculated from the acid dissociation constant of hydrogen cyanide K_{HCN} as follows:

$$K_b = \frac{K_w}{K_{HCN}}$$

One can readily show that this is so by making the appropriate substitution into the above expression

$$K_b = \frac{[H_3O^+][OH^-]}{[H_3O^+][CN^-]/[HCN]}$$

which rearranges to the expression for the desired constant

$$K_b = \frac{[HCN][OH^-]}{[CN^-]}$$

Similarly the acidic behavior of a solution of an ammonium salt is a consequence of the equilibrium

$$NH_4^+ + H_2O \rightleftharpoons H_3O^+ + NH_3 \qquad K_a = \frac{K_w}{K_{NH_3}} = \frac{[H_3O^+][NH_3]}{[NH_4^+]}$$

where the value for K_b, the basic ionization constant for NH_3, is readily available.

LIMITATIONS OF THE EQUILIBRIUM LAW

The equilibrium law, as we have presented it, is what is called a *limiting law* in the sense that it applies exactly only to dilute solutions in which the electrolyte concentration is vanishingly small. With solutions containing appreciable concentrations of electrolytes, marked departures are observed unless the law is properly modified. The magnitude of these

TABLE 2-5

Dissociation Constants for Acetic Acid in Solutions
of Sodium Chloride at 25° C [4]

Concentration of NaCl, Formality	Apparent K_d
0.00	1.75×10^{-5}
0.02	2.29×10^{-5}
0.11	2.85×10^{-5}
0.51	3.31×10^{-5}
1.01	3.16×10^{-5}

[4] H. S. Harned and B. B. Owen, *The Physical Chemistry of Electrolyte Solutions*, 3d ed., 676. New York: Reinhold Publishing Corporation, 1958.

departures is demonstrated by the data in Table 2-5 which presents experimental values for the relationship

$$K = \frac{[H_3O^+][OAc^-]}{[HOAc]}$$

in solutions containing various concentrations of sodium chloride. In these experiments the molar concentrations of hydronium ion, acetate ion, and acetic acid were measured experimentally. It is clear from this study that the degree of dissociation of acetic acid is appreciably greater in sodium chloride solution than in pure water; similar effects are found when other electrolytes such as potassium nitrate are substituted for sodium chloride. Furthermore, other equilibria display analogous behavior. Thus the solubility of barium sulfate is greater in a solution of potassium nitrate than in water (see p. 119) indicating that the equilibrium

$$BaSO_4 \rightleftharpoons Ba^{2+} + SO_4^{2-}$$

is displaced to the right in the presence of the electrolyte.

A large number of empirical observations on the effects of electrolyte concentration on chemical equilibria have revealed several important facts. One of these is that the magnitude of the effect is very much dependent upon the charges of the participants in the reaction. Where all are neutral particles, little variation in the equilibrium constant is observed; on the other hand, the effect becomes greater as the charges on the reactants or products increase. Thus, for example, of the following equilibria:

$$AgCl \rightleftharpoons Ag^+ + Cl^-$$

$$BaSO_4 \rightleftharpoons Ba^{2+} + SO_4^{2-}$$

the second is shifted further to the right in the presence of moderate amounts of potassium nitrate than is the first.

A second pertinent generality is that the observed effects are essentially independent of the kind of electrolyte and dependent only upon an electrolyte concentration parameter of the solution called the *ionic strength*. This is defined by the equation

$$\text{ionic strength} = \mu = \tfrac{1}{2}(m_1 Z_1^2 + m_2 Z_2^2 + m_3 Z_3^2 + \cdots) \qquad (2\text{-}3)$$

where m_1, m_2, m_3, and so on, are molar concentrations of the various ions in the solution and Z_1, Z_2, Z_3, and so on, are their charges. Thus the degree of dissociation of acetic acid is the same in the presence of sodium chloride, potassium nitrate, barium iodate, or aluminum nitrate provided the concentrations of these species are such that the ionic strength is fixed.

The effects we have just described can be attributed to the influence of a charged environment on the behavior of the anions and cations participating in an equilibrium reaction. At moderate ionic strengths, this environment has the consequence of making an ion less effective in influencing the position of a chemical equilibrium. Thus in a solution of acetic acid containing sodium chloride, the acetate ions and hydronium ions are each surrounded by particles of opposite charge; this charged atmosphere makes less probable the recombination of the two species to form the undissociated acid molecule. The result of this is a greater degree of dissociation.

In order to describe, in quantitative terms, the effect of ionic strength on equilibria, chemists have chosen to invent a concentration parameter called the *activity* of a substance; this is defined as

$$a_A = [A] f_A \qquad (2\text{-}4)$$

where a_A is the activity of the species A, $[A]$ is its molar concentration, and f_A is a dimensionless number called the *activity coefficient*. Now the activity coefficient (and thus the activity) of A varies with ionic strength in such a way that when a_A is employed in equilibrium-constant expressions, the numerical value of the equilibrium constant is independent of the ionic strength. For example, for the dissociation of acetic acid

$$K_a = \frac{a_{H_3O^+} \cdot a_{OAc^-}}{a_{HOAc}} = \frac{[H_3O^+][OAc^-]}{[HOAc]} \times \frac{f_{H_3O^+} \cdot f_{OAc^-}}{f_{HOAc}}$$

where $f_{H_3O^+}$, f_{OAc^-}, and f_{HOAc} vary with ionic strength in such a manner that K_a is constant over a wide range of ionic strengths (in contrast to the *apparent K* shown in Table 2-5).

The relationship between the activity coefficient and the ionic strength is not a straightforward one and is beyond the scope of this text. Tabulations that list values for activity coefficients of a variety of ions as a function of ionic strength have been compiled.[5] Such data make it possible to take into account the effects of the presence of electrolytes when equilibrium calculations are performed.

Throughout this text we shall neglect the effect of ionic strength and employ molar concentrations rather than activities in all equilibrium calculations. In this way the computations are simplified and the amount of data required is reduced. The reader should be aware, however, that the results obtained are, as a consequence, approximations of the true values. In most cases the error introduced will not be great enough to invalidate the general conclusions drawn from these calculations.

MATHEMATICAL OPERATIONS ASSOCIATED WITH EQUILIBRIUM CALCULATIONS

Exponential Numbers. Because the data associated with chemical equilibria frequently consist of very large or very small numbers, exponential notation finds widespread use. The reader must acquire skill in carrying exponential numbers through common mathematical operations; these are summarized in Appendix A-3.

Logarithms. A knowledge of the use of logarithms will be required in this text. A brief discussion of this useful mathematical function is found in Appendix A-2.

The Quadratic Equation. Problems dealing with chemical equilibrium frequently require solution of a quadratic equation. The use of this equation is reviewed in Appendix A-1.

Solutions of Higher-order Equations. Equilibrium calculations involving a single unknown raised to powers greater than two are not at all uncommon. While methods for their rigorous solution exist, it is frequently simpler to find the roots of these equations by a systematic trial-and-error process known as the method of successive approximations.

★EXAMPLE. The solubility, s, of a precipitate is given by the expression

$$s^2(1 \times 10^{-3} + s) = 2 \times 10^{-6}$$

In solving for s, all terms are first collected on one side of the equation

$$s^3 + 1 \times 10^{-3}s^2 - 2 \times 10^{-6} = 0$$

Values for s are then systematically tried; the one that causes the left side of the equation most closely to approach zero represents the desired solution.

---

[5] See for example, J. Kielland, *J. Am. Chem. Soc.*, **59,** 1675 (1937).

Because s represents a solubility we need concern ourselves only with a positive root. If we assume a value of 0.0 for s, the equation becomes

$$-2 \times 10^{-6} = 0$$

Assuming $s = 1.0$, we find that

$$1 + 1 \times 10^{-3} - 2 \times 10^{-6} = 0$$

$$1.001 = 0$$

Clearly, s will have a value between 0 and 1. Using $s = 0.1$

$$1 \times 10^{-3} + 1 \times 10^{-5} - 2 \times 10^{-6} = 0$$

$$0.001008 = 0$$

With $s = 0.01$

$$1 \times 10^{-6} + 1 \times 10^{-7} - 2 \times 10^{-6} = 0$$

$$-0.9 \times 10^{-6} = 0$$

Because this gives a slightly negative number, s must lie between 0.1 and 0.01. Further, it appears that the latter represents the closer estimate of the two.

Setting $s = 0.012$

$$1.73 \times 10^{-6} + 1.44 \times 10^{-7} - 2 \times 10^{-6} = 0$$

$$1.87 \times 10^{-7} - 2 \times 10^{-6} = 0$$

This estimate still gives a slightly negative value for s. Use of a slightly larger value, $s = 0.013$, gives a positive result

$$2.20 \times 10^{-6} - 1.69 \times 10^{-7} - 2 \times 10^{-6} = 0$$

$$2.37 \times 10^{-6} - 2 \times 10^{-6} = 0$$

Thus, s lies between 0.012 and 0.013; if it were desired to define this quantity more closely, values between these limits could be tested in the same way.

With practice this process can be performed quite rapidly.

Neglecting Terms in Equations. Terms that consist of sums or differences can frequently be simplified, without serious error, provided the quantities making up the term differ sufficiently in magnitude. Thus, in the term $(0.001 + x)$ two possibilities for simplification exist

$$(0.001 + x) = x \qquad \text{provided } x \gg 0.001$$

or $\qquad (0.001 + x) = 0.001 \qquad \text{provided } x \ll 0.001$

A knowledge of the physical significance of x will frequently provide the basis for choice between these assumptions. It is clear, however, that the validity of either will ultimately depend upon the numerical value of x and the accuracy with which the answer must be known. *Whenever a simpli-*

fying assumption has been made, the answer obtained must be considered provisional until it is established that the assumption was indeed justified.

★EXAMPLE. Considering again the previous example

$$s^2(1 \times 10^{-3} + s) = 2 \times 10^{-6}$$

If we assume that s is very small with respect to 1×10^{-3}, the equation simplifies to

$$1 \times 10^{-3}s^2 = 2 \times 10^{-6}$$

$$s = 4.5 \times 10^{-2}$$

This yields a value for s that is larger, instead of smaller, than 1×10^{-3}. Clearly the original assumption was not justified.

Assuming that s is large with respect to 1×10^{-3} the equation becomes

$$s^3 = 2 \times 10^{-6}$$

and

$$s = 1.26 \times 10^{-2}$$

This provides a value for s that is about 13 times greater than 1×10^{-3}. Whether this approximation is proper or not will depend upon the magnitude of error we can tolerate in the answer. If an uncertainty of something less than one part in ten (10 percent) is satisfactory for our purposes, we may use this value of s as the solution to the equation. If, on the other hand, a greater accuracy is required, we must proceed with the previously illustrated method of successive approximations. It is noteworthy that the value for s obtained by this method represents an excellent starting point for the more rigorous solution.

Problems

1. How many formula weights and how many milliformula weights are there in
   (a) 14.1 grams $AgNO_3$ ans. 8.3×10^{-2} gfw; 83 mfw
   (b) 137 mg $BaSO_4$ ans. 5.88×10^{-4} fw
   (c) 20.0 ml of $0.100\ F$ KCN   ans. 2.00×10^{-3} fw
   (d) 20.0 liters of $0.200\ F$ Na_2CO_3 ans. 4.00 fw
   (e) 1 liter of pure water at 25° C

2. How many milliformula weights are contained in
   (a) 1.73 grams $K_4Fe(CN)_6$
   (b) 3.10 grams NaCl
   (c) 937 ml of $0.100\ F$ NaCl
   (d) 1.94 liters of $0.200\ F$ KCl

3. Calculate the following weights in grams
   (a) 2.00 mfw NaCl   ans. 0.117 gram
   (b) 0.500 fw KCl   ans. 37.2 grams
   (c) 0.100 mol K$^+$

4. What weight in grams of Na_2SO_4 is present in
   (a) 1.00 liter of 0.100 F Na_2SO_4
   (b) 13.6 ml of 0.200 F Na_2SO_4
   (c) 16.0 mfw Na_2SO_4
   (d) 15.0 ml of a solution which is 3 percent Na_2SO_4 (weight-volume)

5. A solution was prepared by dissolving 1.30 grams $AgNO_3$ in water and diluting
   to 50.0 ml. Calculate
   (a) the weight-volume percent $AgNO_3$ ans. 2.60 percent
   (b) the number of mfw $AgNO_3$ taken
   (c) the formal concentration of the solution
   (d) the number of mfw Ag$^+$ present

6. Calculate the formal concentration of a solution
   (a) prepared by dissolving 1.00 mfw $AgNO_3$ in water and diluting to 1.00 ml
   (b) prepared by dissolving 4.70 mfw Na_2SO_4 in water and diluting to 1327 ml
                                                              ans. 3.54×10^{-3} F
   (c) containing 18.3 mg NaCl in 123 ml of water   ans. 2.55×10^{-3} F
   (d) containing 196 grams KCN in 2.00 liters

7. Calculate the formal concentration of
   (a) a solution containing 63 fw $KMnO_4$ in 100 liters of solution
   (b) a 4.70 percent (weight-volume) $BaCl_2$ solution

8. What is the formal concentration of a solution that is 3 percent KNO_3 by
   weight and has a specific gravity of 1.01?   ans. 0.30 F

9. What is the formal concentration of a solution prepared
   (a) by dissolving 71.7 grams alcohol (C_2H_5OH) in water and diluting to 647 ml
   (b) by dissolving 1.71 mfw alcohol in water and diluting to 10.0 ml

10. What is the formal concentration of
    (a) a mixture of 13.0 ml of 0.131 F $AgNO_3$ and 87 ml of water   ans. 0.0170 F
    (b) 67 ml of 0.100 F NaCl diluted to 450 ml   ans. 0.0149 F
    (c) a mixture prepared by diluting 63 liters of 1.00 F HCl to 1000 liters
                                                                        ans. 0.063 F
    (d) a mixture of 8000 gallons of 1.00 F NaOH and enough water to make
        20,000 gallons

11. Water allowed to equilibrate with the atmosphere is 1.5×10^{-5} F in CO_2.
    (a) What weight of CO_2 is present in 100 ml of water?
    (b) What volume of CO_2 (measured at STP) will dissolve in 100 liters of water?
                                                              ans. 33.6 ml

12. How would you prepare
    (a) 365 ml of 0.170 F $AgNO_3$ from the solid salt
                        ans. Dissolve 10.5 grams $AgNO_3$ and dilute to 365 ml

(b) 2.00 liters of 0.100 F $AgNO_3$ from 0.600 F $AgNO_3$
(c) 10.00 liters of 0.1000 F KSCN from the salt
                    ans. Dissolve 97.2 grams KSCN and dilute to 10.00 liters
(d) 434.0 ml of 0.100 F KSCN from 0.157 F KSCN

13. How would you prepare
    (a) a 5 percent (weight-volume) solution of NaCl
                    ans. Dissolve 5 grams NaCl in water and dilute to 100 ml
    (b) a 5 weight-percent solution of NaCl
                    ans. Dissolve 5 grams NaCl in 95 ml of water

14. Describe a method for the preparation of
    (a) 250 ml of approximately 0.2 F $KMnO_4$ from the solid
    (b) 500 ml of 0.71 F $BaCl_2$ from solid $BaCl_2 \cdot 2H_2O$
    (c) a liter of solution that is 0.100 M in Na^+; starting with NaCl
    (d) a liter of solution that is 0.100 M in Na^+; starting with Na_2CO_3

15. How would you prepare
    (a) 3700 ml of 0.100 F $NaHCO_3$ from a 1.00 F solution
                    ans. Dilute 370 ml of the 1 F solution to 3700 ml
    (b) 220 ml of 0.0050 F NaCl from a 5 percent (weight-volume) solution

16. A bottle of concentrated HCl has the following information on its label:
    specific gravity 1.185; percent HCl 36.5.
    (a) How many grams HCl are contained in each ml?   ans. 0.433 gram/ml
    (b) What is the formal concentration of HCl?   ans. 11.9 F
    (c) How would you prepare 200 ml of 3.0 F HCl from the concentrated
        reagent?   ans. Dilute 50 ml of the concentrated acid to 200 ml

17. How many milliliters (measured at STP) of dry HCl gas has dissolved in
    1 liter of concentrated HCl? See Problem 16 for pertinent data.

18. Concentrated HNO_3 has a specific gravity of 1.42 and is 69 percent HNO_3.
    (a) How would you prepare a liter of 0.5 F HNO_3 from the concentrated
        reagent?
    (b) What volume of the concentrated acid contains 37 grams of HNO_3?
    (c) What is the formal concentration of the concentrated reagent?

19. Lead ion reacts with IO_3^- to form an insoluble precipitate

$$Pb^{2+} + 2IO_3^- \rightleftharpoons Pb(IO_3)_2$$

    (a) What weight of KIO_3 will react with 0.100 fw of Pb^{2+}?   ans. 42.8 grams
    (b) How many grams $Pb(IO_3)_2$ could be formed from 7.00 mfw Pb^{2+}?
                                        ans. 3.90 grams
    (c) How many grams KIO_3 are required to react completely with 2.00 grams
        $Pb(NO_3)_2$?   ans. 2.58 grams
    (d) How many grams $Pb(IO_3)_2$ are formed upon mixing 4.00 grams $Pb(NO_3)_2$
        and 4.00 grams KIO_3?   ans. 5.21 grams
    (e) How many milliliters of 0.300 F KIO_3 are required to precipitate 1.00 mfw
        Pb^{2+}?   ans. 6.67 ml

20. How much of the substance in the second column is needed to react completely with the indicated amount of the substance in the first column?

(a) 13.1 mfw HCl   (a) grams NaOH

(b) 14.7 grams H_2SO_4 (b) grams NaOH

(c) 100 mfw $BaCl_2$ (c) ml of 0.25 F $AgNO_3$

(d) 30 ml of 0.100 F $BaCl_2 \cdot 2H_2O$ (d) ml of 0.25 F $AgNO_3$

(e) 18.1 mg $BaCl_2 \cdot 2H_2O$ (e) ml of 0.25 F $AgNO_3$

(f) 100 grams $AlCl_3$ (f) grams $AgNO_3$

(g) 50 grams NaOH   (g) ml of concentrated HCl

                                       specific gravity 1.18,

                                       36 percent HCl

(h) 500 ml of 0.200 F $AgNO_3$ (h) ml of 0.300 F K_2CrO_4

(i) 1.00 ml of 0.2 F $AgNO_3$ (i) mg K_2CrO_4

(j) 1 liter of 0.050 F $Ba(OH)_2$ (j) ml of HCl of density 1.12 and containing 24.0 percent HCl

21. How many grams of 90.0 percent pure $Fe(NH_4)_2(SO_4)_2 \cdot 6H_2O$ are required to prepare 1.00 liter of 0.200 F solution of Fe^{2+}?

22. How many milliliters of H_2SO_4 (specific gravity 1.84, 98 percent H_2SO_4) should be taken to prepare 5 liters of 0.10 F acid?

23. How many grams of $FeSO_4$ will react with 0.600 gram of $KMnO_4$?

$$5Fe^{2+} + MnO_4^- + 8H^+ \rightarrow 5Fe^{3+} + Mn^{2+} + 4H_2O$$

24. How many grams of $H_2C_2O_4 \cdot 2H_2O$ are required to precipitate 37.0 mg of Ca^{2+} as CaC_2O_4?

25. How many milliliters of 0.100 F $Na_2C_2O_4$ are required to precipitate 37.0 mg of Ca^{2+}?

26. What volume of H_2S gas (measured at STP) would just precipitate 1.00 gram of Zn^{2+}?

27. When $NaHCO_3$ is ignited, the following quantitative reaction occurs

$$2NaHCO_3 \rightarrow Na_2CO_3 + H_2O + CO_2$$

(a) What would be the loss in weight when 1.00 gram of $NaHCO_3$ is ignited?

(b) How many formula weights of CO_2 are formed when 2.00 grams $NaHCO_3$ are ignited?

(c) What volume of CO_2 (measured at STP) would be formed from 2.00 grams $NaHCO_3$?

28. What weight of AgCl would be obtained by decomposing 0.312 gram of an inorganic compound having the formula C_6H_5Cl and precipitating all of the chloride as AgCl?   ans. 0.397 gram

29. Exactly 22.1 ml of an HCl solution were required to react completely with 0.176 gram of pure $CaCO_3$ by the reaction

$$CO_3^{2-} + 2H^+ \rightarrow H_2O + CO_2$$

Calculate the formal concentration of HCl.

30. It was found that 27.6 ml of a $AgNO_3$ solution would just precipitate all Cl^- in 88.1 mg of $BaCl_2 \cdot 2H_2O$. What was the formal concentration of the $AgNO_3$?

31. Use 4-place tables to evaluate the logarithm of
(a) 61.4
(b) 0.00000369
(c) 7.96
(d) 10.05
(e) 3.46×10^7
(f) 3.46×10^{-7}
(g) 0.100
(h) 26.7
(i) 1804
(j) 56.2×10^{-4}

32. Evaluate x, given that
(a) $\log x = 3.1164$
(b) $\log x = 9.1492 - 10$
(c) $\log x = 17.4138 - 20$
(d) $\log x^2 = 1.6944$
(e) $\log x = -4.8806$
(f) $\log x = 0.0000$
(g) $\log x = 2.3164 + 8.0096 - 10$
(h) $\log x = 2.3164 - 8.0096 - 10$
(i) $\log x = 3 \times 9.7844 - 10$
(j) $\log x = 0.9031 + 3$

33. Use 4-place log tables to evaluate x
(a) $x = (3.71 \times 10^{-4})(1.46 \times 10^{-2})$
(b) $x = \dfrac{1}{3.71 \times 10^{-4}}$
(c) $x = \dfrac{0.000048}{0.00729}$
(d) $x = \dfrac{671.4}{16.9}$
(e) $x = \dfrac{21.6 \times 0.083 \times 0.0355}{0.770}$
(f) $x = \dfrac{98}{41.0 \times 0.037}$
(g) $x = (0.012)^4$
(h) $x = \dfrac{(6.6 \times 10^{-3})(2.93)}{16.7}$
(i) $2x^2 = 3.16 \times 10^{-8}$
(j) $4.16x^3 = 19.36 \times 10^2$

34. Compute a value for x in each of the following equations. Consider only positive values for x, and keep the error in the answer smaller than 2 percent of x.

(a) $x(x - 0.0100) = 4.00$ ans. $x = 2.00$

(b) $x(x - 0.100) = 4.00$ ans. $x = 2.05$

(c) $x(2.00 \times 10^{-3} + x) = 1.00 \times 10^{-3}$

(d) $4.00x^2 - 7.00x - 3.00 = 0$

(e) $\dfrac{x(0.0100 + x)}{(0.910)} = 2.00 \times 10^{-3}$

(f) $x(x - 0.200)^2 = 1.7 \times 10^{-5}$

(g) $x^3 - 4.00x = 7.00$

(h) $\dfrac{x(1.00 - 4.00x)^4}{(0.0100 - x)} = 1.00 \times 10^{-12}$

(i) $\dfrac{x^3}{(1.00 \times 10^{-3} + x)} = 1.00 \times 10^{-12}$

(j) $\dfrac{x^3}{(1.00 \times 10^{-3} + x)} = 1.00 \times 10^{-9}$

(3)

The Evaluation of Analytical Data

If a physical measurement is to be of much worth to its user, some idea regarding the reliability of its value is essential. Unfortunately the measurement of any physical quantity is subject to a degree of uncertainty; the experimenter can only strive to achieve an acceptably close approach to the actual value for the quantity. The estimation of the uncertainties affecting measurements, while often difficult, is thus an essential task of the experimental scientist. This chapter is devoted to a consideration of some of the problems associated with these estimations.

The accuracy to be expected from a measurement is directly related to the time and effort expended in its attainment. The addition of another decimal place to the value for a physical quantity often involves days, months, or even years of labor. The experimenter is thus unavoidably faced with the necessity of making a compromise between high accuracy and expenditure of effort; the reader should recognize that this dichotomy exists in all scientific work. As a consequence of the additional time required to improve materially the reliability of a measurement, the experienced scientist will always give serious consideration to the uses to which his data are to be put before he undertakes any laboratory work. A small investment of time at this juncture of an investigation may often result in the saving of significant amounts of time and effort that would otherwise be wasted in obtaining unnecessary accuracies. This point cannot be too strongly stressed; the scientist's time is far too valuable to be wasted in the indiscriminate pursuit of the last possible decimal place where such is not needed.

3.1   Definition of Terms

Each of the measurements in an analysis is subject to uncertainty. For the present we need only recognize that these uncertainties are responsible for the variations observed among measurements of the same quantity. In practice the chemist generally makes replicate measurements, his reasoning being that the confidence in which his results can be held is increased by demonstrating their reproducibility. Having obtained several values for some quantity, he is then confronted with the problem of defining the best value for the measurement. Two quantities, the *mean* and the *median*, are available to him for this purpose.

THE MEAN

The *mean, arithmetic mean,* and *average* are synonymous terms that refer to the numerical value obtained by dividing the sum of a set of replicate measurements by the number of individual results in the set.

THE MEDIAN

The *median* of a set is that value about which all others are equally distributed, half being numerically greater and half being numerically smaller. If the set consists of an odd number of measurements, selection of the median may be made directly; for a set containing an even number of measurements, the average value of the central pair is taken.

★EXAMPLE. Calculate the mean and median for 10.06, 10.20, 10.08, 10.10.

$$\text{mean} = \frac{10.06 + 10.20 + 10.08 + 10.10}{4} = 10.11$$

Since there is an even number of measurements in the set, the median is given by the average of the middle pair of results, which is

$$\frac{10.08 + 10.10}{2} = 10.09$$

Ideally, the mean and median should be numerically identical; more often than not, however, this condition is not realized when the number of measurements in the set is small.

PRECISION

The term *precision* is frequently used to describe the reproducibility of results. It can be defined as the agreement between the numerical values of two or more measurements that have been made *in an identical fashion*. Chemists frequently choose to measure the precision of their results in terms of *deviation*.

Absolute Deviation. The absolute deviation is simply the absolute difference between an experimental value and that which has been selected as the best for the set, be it the mean or the median.

Inspection of a typical set of analytical data will serve to illustrate this concept. Suppose that a series of analyses has revealed the percentage of chloride in a sample to be 24.39, 24.20, and 24.28 percent, respectively. We observe at the outset that there is a *spread* (or range) of 0.19 percent separating the high and low values of the set. It should be noted in passing that this information is, of itself, a measure of the precision of the analysis. In the absence of any qualifying information, we have no way of judging which of the three determinations is the most reliable; by taking the average of 24.29 percent for this, we are inferring that there was an equal likelihood for the individual determinations to be high and low. Having decided upon the most likely value to report, we are able to calculate the deviation of the individual results from this; the average of these deviations is a measure of the precision of the analysis. In calculating the average deviation, the sign of the individual deviation is not taken into account; we are concerned only with its absolute value, not whether it is high or low. In the present instance

Sample	Percent Chloride	Deviation from Average
1	24.39	0.10
2	24.20	0.09
3	24.28	0.01
Average	24.29	0.07

We may thus report the result as 24.29 ± 0.07 percent chloride.

Relative Deviation. Precision may also be expressed in relative terms as *percentage average deviation* or as *average deviation in parts per thousand*. Thus, for the above data the average value is 24.29, and

$$\text{relative deviation} = \frac{0.07 \times 100}{24.29} = 0.29 \cong 0.3 \text{ percent}$$

$$\text{relative deviation} = \frac{0.07 \times 1000}{24.29} = 2.9 \cong 3 \text{ parts per thousand}$$

Chemists frequently express the precision of their results in terms of absolute or relative deviation because these are readily computed quantities. Of greater value is the *standard deviation*, which will be discussed in a later section.

ACCURACY

The term *accuracy* denotes the nearness of a measurement to its accepted value and is expressed in terms of *error*. The reader should note the fundamental difference between this term and precision. Accuracy involves a comparison with respect to a true, or accepted value; in contrast, precision compares a result with the best value of several measurements made in the same way.

Absolute Error. The absolute error can be defined as

$$E = O - A \tag{3-1}$$

where the error E is the difference between the observed value O and the accepted value A. In many instances the accepted value of A is itself subject to considerable uncertainty. As a consequence it is frequently difficult to arrive at a realistic estimate for the error of a measurement.

Returning to the example given above, suppose that the true or accepted value for the percentage of chloride in the sample is 24.34 percent. The absolute error is thus $24.29 - 24.34 = -0.05$ percent; here we ordinarily retain the sign of the error to indicate whether the result is high or low.

Relative Error. Equation (3-1) defines error in absolute terms; a more useful quantity is the *relative error*. As before, this is commonly expressed as a percentage or in parts per thousand. The calculation is also analogous; however, the accepted value is used as the basis for comparison in this case. For example, we find

$$\text{relative error} = -\frac{0.05 \times 100}{24.34} = -0.21 \cong -0.2 \text{ percent}$$

$$\text{relative error} = -\frac{0.05 \times 1000}{24.34} = -2.1 \cong 2 \text{ parts per thousand } \textit{low}$$

In summary, then, the accuracy of a measurement can be ascertained only if the true, or accepted, value of that measurement is available; given a set of replicate measurements, the precision can always be expressed. In the absence of further information, the attainment of good precision is the only indication of a successful analysis; we shall see, however, that this is not necessarily a valid criterion. Judgments based upon precision alone must always be considered guardedly.

TYPES OF ERROR IN ANALYTICAL RESULTS

The errors that accompany the performance of an analysis may be classified into two broad categories depending upon their origin. *Determi-*

nate errors are those for which we can account, in principle if not in actuality. *Indeterminate errors* are due to random errors that arise from extending a system of measurement to its maximum; the effect of indeterminate error upon a set of results can often be reduced to acceptable limits but can never be entirely avoided.

3.2 Determinate Errors

SOURCES

A complete listing of conceivable determinate errors is a patent impossibility; we can, however, recognize that they may be traced to the *personal* errors of the experimenter, the *instrumental* errors of his measuring devices, the errors that repose in the *method* of analysis he employs, or a combination of these.

Personal Errors. In a preponderance of cases where a gross error exists in the results obtained by an established method of analysis, the cause lies with the experimenter. He may have failed to take down the correct value for a weighing, having either misread his weights or transposed the correct numbers. He may have erred in the reading of a volume. The beginning student in quantitative analysis may incur errors of a manipulative nature, failing to transfer materials completely from one container to another or allowing a sample to become contaminated in some way. Failure to introduce the proper amount of a reagent in the course of an analysis must also be classed as a personal error.

One personal error that should always be guarded against is *prejudice*. Where an estimation is involved, there is a natural tendency for the experimenter to choose that value which is most favorable to him. Intellectual honesty is the keystone of all science; it is essential for the attainment of significant analytical results.

Instrumental Errors. Instrumental errors are those that are attributable to imperfections in the tools with which the analyst works. The tolerances of the chemist's weights may be the potential source of an instrumental error; mishandling of analytical weights will often cause them to differ significantly from their nominal values. Volumetric equipment—burets, pipets, and volumetric flasks—frequently deliver or contain volumes slightly different from those indicated by their graduations; for analytical work of the highest order, these variations must be measured by calibration and taken into account; otherwise they become a source of instrumental error.

Method Errors. Analytical procedures are also subject to limitations; these give rise to errors that can be traced to the method. For example, even the least soluble of substances has a finite solubility. In gravimetric analysis the chemist is confronted with the problem of isolating the element to be determined in the form of a precipitate of the greatest possible purity. If he fails to wash it sufficiently, the precipitate will be contaminated with foreign substances and have a spuriously high weight. On the other hand, excessive washing may lead to the loss of weighable quantities of the precipitate; this will have the opposite effect upon the results. It should be clear that an error will result in either case, and that there is a limit of accuracy that can be attained by such an analysis.

THE DETECTION OF DETERMINATE ERRORS

From the standpoint of magnitude, determinate errors are the more important in an analysis, and in some instances are difficult to detect. They can affect a single result, a series of results, or an entire method of analysis depending upon their nature and the phase of the analysis in which they occur. A personal error, such as the misreading of a weight while weighing a sample, would result in a spurious value for that sample alone; the same error incurred during the preparation of a reagent might cause its propagation throughout all analyses undertaken with that solution. In the first instance the divergence of the result from the others in the set would possibly provide a clue that the error had been incurred. If the approximate value to be expected were unknown, the error in the latter case could well pass undetected. An error of this sort would be revealed by repetition of the analysis with another reagent or by a check analysis with the original solution against a sample of established purity.

Instrumental errors attributable to the discrepancies from the nominal values of analytical weights and the volumes contained by volumetric flasks or delivered by pipets and burets can be eliminated by the periodic calibration of such equipment.

Errors of method are the most serious, since they affect all results obtained by that method. Detection of the errors inherent in an analytical scheme may take any of several courses. Among these is the analysis of a standard sample of known composition. Preparation of a standard sample resembling a complex natural substance is often difficult or impossible; as a result the application of this technique is frequently impractical.

The parallel analysis of a sample by an independent method of established reliability is frequently useful in uncovering errors in a method under investigation.

Account can be taken of certain types of determinate errors through performance of a blank determination; here all steps of the analysis are carried out in the absence of sample. The result is then applied as a correction to the actual measurement.

Finally, determinate errors that are constant and independent of sample size can be detected by performing several analyses of a single material employing samples that differ considerably in size. The presence of a constant error is indicated by an increase or a decrease in the results with increasing quantity of material taken.

3.3   Indeterminate Error

SOURCES

The necessity for making estimations is inherent in the process of collecting data for the measurement of any quantity. Common among these in quantitative analysis are the interpolations involved in the observation of balance swings and in judging the liquid level in volumetric apparatus. It follows that the final value of any measurement will be uncertain in an amount that depends upon the relative magnitude of the estimations involved in its evaluation. Appropriate design of an experiment will serve to reduce this uncertainty to a tolerable limit, but there is no way in which it can be entirely eliminated. It must be accepted that all physical measurements are subject to a degree of uncertainty, or indeterminate error.

EFFECT OF INDETERMINATE ERROR ON RESULTS

Let us consider the effect of indeterminate error upon the results of the relatively simple process of calibrating a pipet. The details for this and other calibrations are given in Chapter 10; here it is sufficient to recognize that the procedure is based upon determining the weight of liquid of known density (commonly water) that the pipet is found to deliver. A set of data pertaining to a 10-ml volumetric pipet is given in Table 3-1. Even though these measurements were performed with great care, a spread of 0.022 ml

TABLE 3-1

Calibration of a 10-ml Volumetric Pipet

Trial	Volume of Water Delivered, ml	Trial	Volume of Water Delivered, ml	Trial	Volume of Water Delivered, ml
1	9.975	5	9.980	9	9.973
2	9.981	6	9.967	10	9.972
3	9.982	7	9.971	11	9.989
4	9.977	8	9.968	12	9.975
				Average	9.976

is seen to separate the high and low values; we attribute this dispersion to the operation of indeterminate error.

Sources of these errors reside with each estimation required in the calibration process as well as with a variety of uncontrolled variables that affect the outcome. Thus, the level of the liquid must be judged with respect to the etch mark on the pipet, the time allowed for drainage must be kept uniform, and the swings of the balance pointer must be estimated in evaluating the mass of liquid that was delivered. Each of these factors (and undoubtedly many others) will contribute to the uncertainty affecting the ultimate result.

Now, although we can define some of the principal sources for uncertainty in this process, we can predict neither the manner nor the magnitude of their effect upon the final result. Insofar as they are independent of one another, however, we can expect that they tend to cancel each other out in some trials, and to reinforce one another in others. Considered in this light it is not surprising that only one pair of duplicate results appears in the set.

THE NORMAL-ERROR CURVE

Two very important assumptions form the basis for the application of statistics to the problem of indeterminate error; experimental evidence indicates that we are justified in making them. First, results will be high or low with equal probability owing to the effect of indeterminate error. The reader will notice that this behavior is altogether different from that of determinate error. Second, indeterminate error will cause small deviations to occur more often than large deviations.

The consequences of these assumptions may be envisioned by considering a very large number of measurements of some quantity that have been made in the same manner. If we plot the deviations of the individual measurements from the arithmetic mean against the number of times each such deviation occurs, we obtain curves having the shape of those in Figures 3.1 and 3.2. These are called *normal-error curves;* they are of great importance because they describe graphically the distribution of indeterminate error in a typical physical measurement.

In Figure 3.1 the solid line is the normal-error curve for a measurement that is entirely free of determinate error. We see that the deviations from the average distribute themselves symmetrically about zero, measurements possessing zero deviation occurring with the highest frequency. Under these circumstances the mean or average value for the measurement is the true value; furthermore the median value corresponds numerically to the average since positive and negative deviations occur with equal frequency.

The effect of an undetected, uniform *determinate* error on the normal-error curve is illustrated by the dotted curve in Figure 3.1. While the shape is unaltered by the presence of such an error, the curve is displaced so that the arithmetic average of the measurements is no longer equal to the true value. The extent to which the curve is displaced is indicative of the size of the determinate error.

It cannot be too strongly emphasized that the preceding paragraphs describe the operation of *indeterminate* error for any physical measurement.

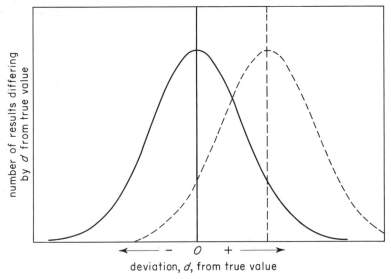

Fig. 3.1 A Normal-error Curve. The effect of determinate error upon a normal distribution is illustrated by the broken line.

This is why the distribution of replicate measurements caused by indeterminate error is predictable to a degree; we can, in short, make statements concerning the *probability* of occurrence of an indeterminate error of a given magnitude.

The properties of the normal-error curve must now be examined in greater detail. If we measure some quantity by two entirely different methods, there is no reason to expect the normal-error curves for the two processes to be identical; the magnitude of the indeterminate error, after all, depends upon the method rather than the nature of the measurement. Suppose, for example, we wish to measure the diameter of a piece of glass tubing. We perform this first with a ruler and then with a micrometer caliper, taking a very large number of data with each device. Each set of measurements will be affected by indeterminate error; the magnitude of this error, however, will certainly be numerically smaller for the micrometer caliper data because of the greater reproducibility afforded by this method of measurement. The effect of this difference will be reflected in the appearance of the normal-error curves for the two measurements. If sufficiently large sets of data were taken, graphs such as those in Figure 3.2 would result. The more refined measurement would give a taller and narrower curve as a

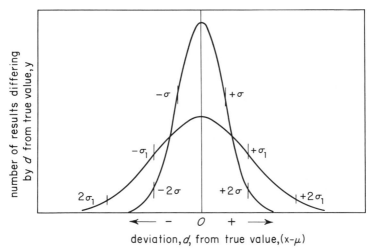

Fig. 3.2 Normal-error Curves. Determination of the same quantity by two methods of inherently different reliability.

result of the smaller indeterminate error, whereas the curve for the more crude measurement would be broad and flat. Notwithstanding this difference in shape, both curves are similar in that they are symmetrical about the true value for the measurement and that large deviations are less frequently observed than small ones. The difference in magnitude of the indeterminate error is reflected in the breadth of the curve.

Curves in Figure 3.2 as well as all normal-error curves, are described by the following expression:

$$y = \frac{e^{-(x-\mu)^2/2\sigma^2}}{\sigma\sqrt{2\pi}} \tag{3-2}$$

In this equation, x is the value of an individual measurement and μ is the arithmetic mean of a very large number of values for this measurement.

The quantity $(x - \mu)$ is thus the deviation of x from the mean; this is the quantity that is plotted as the abscissa of the normal-error curve. The term y is the frequency with which any particular deviation occurs and is the ordinate of the normal-error curve. The symbol π has its usual meaning; e represents the base for Naperian logarithms, $2.718 \cdots$. The term σ is called the *standard deviation* and is a constant having a unique value for any set consisting of a very large number of measurements. The breadth of the normal-error curve is fixed by the numerical value of σ; σ is thus a very useful measure of the dispersion to be expected owing to the operation of indeterminate error.

THE STANDARD DEVIATION

Inspection of equation (3-2) has shown that a unique curve exists for each value of the standard deviation. This constant, then, provides the means of relating the magnitude of a given indeterminate error to its probability of occurrence. Thus, it may be shown mathematically that in a normally distributed population 68.3 percent of the results will differ from the average by less than one standard deviation $(\pm 1 \times \sigma)$, 95.5 percent by less than $(\pm 2 \times \sigma)$, 99.7 percent by less than $(\pm 3 \times \sigma)$, and so forth (see Figure 3.2). In practice, if an individual result deviates by, say, 3σ from the mean, we are able to conclude that the likelihood is very remote that this deviation is due to the operation of indeterminate error.

It is possible to calculate an approximate value for the standard deviation of a limited set of data by means of the equation

$$s = \sqrt{\frac{d_1^2 + d_2^2 + d_3^2 + \cdots d_n^2}{N - 1}} \tag{3-3}$$

where s is the approximate standard deviation for a set consisting of N measurements. Here $d_1, d_2, d_3, \cdots d_n$ are the deviations of the individual results $x_1, x_2, x_3, \cdots x_n$ from the mean of the set, m; that is,

$$d_1 = (x_1 - m)$$

$$d_2 = (x_2 - m)$$

$$d_n = (x_n - m)$$

As N becomes larger the calculated value for s improves as an approximation of the true standard deviation, σ, appearing in equation (3-2).

★EXAMPLE. Estimate the standard deviation s for the following series of data:

4.28, 4.21, 4.30, 4.36, 4.26, 4.33

The arithmetic mean (m) for this set is 4.29. The individual deviations may then be computed and squared.

	d	d^2
4.28	0.01	0.0001
4.21	0.08	0.0064
4.30	0.01	0.0001
4.36	0.07	0.0049
4.26	0.03	0.0009
4.33	0.04	0.0016
		0.0140 $= \Sigma(x_i - m)^2$

The denominator ($N - 1$) is equal to 5.
Substituting these into equation (3-3) we find

$$s = \sqrt{\frac{0.0140}{5}}$$

$$= \sqrt{0.0028} = 0.053$$

In summary, when reference is made to the standard deviation of some experimental quantity, it is to be understood that this is a prediction of the interval about the mean within which 68 percent of an infinite number of replicate measurements of this quantity would be expected to lie.

3.4   The Statistical Treatment of Small Sets of Data

When confronted with a set of data comprising a small number of measurements, we are dealing with a situation that is far removed from the infinite set of the previous section; analytical results are most commonly encountered in sets that contain from two to perhaps six measurements only. Furthermore, one value in a set often diverges considerably from the rest. In any actual situation we do not know whether this outlying result is due to an undetected gross error or to an infrequently occurring indeterminate error of large magnitude; in the former instance the result clearly should be rejected while in the latter it represents a statistically significant part of the data. We are justified in arbitrarily discarding a result *only* when it is known to have been affected by a gross determinate error; this is an excellent argument for maintaining a careful record of all observations in a laboratory notebook. When, as is frequently the case, we have no reason to suspect the validity of an outlying result, the application of statistics can aid in the decision of retention or rejection by indicating the *probability* that the suspected value is or is not a legitimate member of the set.

Statistical tests may be applied phenomenologically to provide an estimate of the precision based upon the experimental data that have been collected. The average or median is taken as the best value for the set, the average deviation, standard deviation, or the spread being employed to express the precision. In addition, statistics may be used to estimate the probable limit of precision inherent to a given process. This, in turn, provides an estimate of the indeterminate error to be expected in an analysis.

THE EVALUATION OF EXPERIMENTAL DATA

Table 3-2 gives the results of a series of replicate analyses for the percentage of calcium oxide in a sample of calcite ($CaCO_3$). They are arranged in order of increasing magnitude rather than the order in which they were obtained; this is an aid in selecting the median. The reproducibility of these data can be expressed in any of several ways.

TABLE 3-2

Analysis for the Percentage of Calcium Oxide in a Sample of Calcite

Trial	CaO Found, percent	Deviation from Average (56.06 percent) d	d^2	Deviation from Median (56.04 percent) d_m
3	55.95	0.11	0.0121	0.09
4	56.00	0.06	0.0036	0.04
2	56.04 (median)	0.02	0.0004	0.00
1	56.08	0.02	0.0004	0.04
5	56.23	0.17	0.0289	0.19
Average	56.06	0.08		0.07

Average Deviation. As described previously, the average deviation is obtained by summing the deviations of the individual measurements from the average value (56.06 percent) and dividing this sum (0.38 percent) by the number of trials (5) in the set. We could thus report these results as 56.06 ± 0.08 percent CaO; alternatively, the precision could be expressed in the relative terms of percentage deviation or parts per thousand.

Note that the result from the fifth trial deviates rather considerably from the others; intuitively we question its validity. By arbitrarily discarding this measurement, however, we are adjusting the data to conform with a subjective notion of how they should appear; statisticians refer to this as the introduction of *bias*. Retention of the measurement has its disadvantages also; a widely diverging result has a disproportionate effect upon the average value of a set of measurements. We can avoid the necessity of making this choice by selecting the median, 56.04 percent, as being the most reliable estimate available for the true value. The average deviation is calculated as before; the results would now be reported as 56.04 $\pm$ 0.07 percent CaO.

It is advantageous to select the median, rather than the average, as the best value for a small set of measurements. We have seen that its employment makes possible the inclusion of all the data in a set without undue influence from an outlying value. In addition, the average deviation from the median will never exceed that calculated from the average; in the present instance, a slight improvement was achieved. Finally, for a set consisting of three measurements free from gross error, it has been shown that the median value of the three is more reliable than the average of the two closest measurements.[1]

Use of the average deviation as a criterion for precision suffers from the disadvantage of lacking reproducibility; more often than not the average deviation of a large set will be greater than that found for subsets made up from the same data.[2] Since most of the data in quantitative analysis are obtained in small sets, the average deviation of these will supply a misleading and optimistic indication of the attainable precision of the method employed in procuring them.

The Standard Deviation. The data of Table 3-2 can be considered as being five of an infinite number of values we might have obtained; as such they should fit under a normal-error curve in some fashion. The standard deviation s calculated for the set should thus be indicative of the distribution to be expected from this method of measurement; it has the further advantage of showing less variation with changes in the size of the set than does the average deviation. Computation may be accomplished by use of equation (3-3). The mean is used exclusively since the smallest standard deviation results from its employment. Taking the values for d^2 from Table 3-2, we calculate the standard deviation to be

$$s = \sqrt{\frac{0.0121 + 0.0036 + 0.0004 + 0.0004 + 0.0289}{5 - 1}}$$

$$= 0.106 \text{ or } 0.11 \text{ percent}$$

[1] National Bureau of Standards, *Technical News Bulletin*, July, 1949; *J. Chem. Ed.*, **26**, 673 (1949).

[2] W. J. Youden, *Statistical Methods for Chemists*, 8. New York: John Wiley and Sons, Inc., 1951.

Accordingly we should expect approximately two thirds of the results of subsequent analyses to fall in the range of plus or minus one standard deviation (0.11 percent) about the average value of 56.06 percent, and nineteen out of twenty within twice this range (2 × 0.11 percent). These estimates are, of course, provisional upon the reliability of *s*. It is fortunate that a very rapid increase in reliability attends an increase in the number of individuals in the set.

CONFIDENCE LIMITS

Calculation of the standard deviation for a set of data is valuable in that it provides an indication of the precision inherent to the particular method of measurement. It does not, however, of itself allow us to predict how closely the true mean μ has been approached by an experimentally derived mean m because it is practical to secure analytical data in relatively small sets only. Unfortunately the average (m) of such a small number of measurements may deviate considerably from the true mean (μ). The probability of such a difference being large becomes less as the number of measurements (N) in the set increases and if the precision is high.

The true mean value (μ) of a measurement is a constant that must always remain unknown. With the aid of statistical theory, however, limits may be set about the experimentally determined mean (m) within which we might expect to find the true mean with some given degree of probability. The limits obtained in this manner are called *confidence limits;* the range defined by these limits is known as the *confidence interval.*

It is worthwhile to consider qualitatively some of the properties of the confidence interval. For a given set of data the size of the interval depends in part upon the odds for correctness desired. Clearly, if a prediction is to be absolutely correct, we will have to choose an interval about the mean that is large enough to include all conceivable values (μ) might take; this, of course, is of no value as a prediction. On the other hand, the interval does not need to be this large if we are willing to accept the probability of being correct 99 times in 100; it will be even smaller if 95 percent correctness is acceptable. In short, as the probability for making a correct prediction becomes less favorable, the interval included by the confidence limits becomes smaller. These limits can be brought so close together that predictions based upon them stand to be incorrect a prohibitively large portion of the time; this condition, too, is of marginal utility.

The confidence limit may be calculated from the following expression:

$$\text{confidence limit} = \pm \frac{ts}{\sqrt{N}} \tag{3-4}$$

where s is the estimated standard deviation determined as described previously, and N is the number of measurements included in the set. The term t is dependent upon the number of measurements as well as the degree of probability for correctness that is desired. Statisticians have compiled tables for numerical values of t for various confidence levels. Representative values are given in Table 3-3.

TABLE 3-3

Values of *t* for Various Levels of Probability

Number of Observations (N)	Factor for Confidence Interval of			
	80%	90%	95%	99%
2	3.08	6.31	12.7	63.7
3	1.89	2.92	4.30	9.92
4	1.64	2.35	3.18	5.84
5	1.53	2.13	2.78	4.60
6	1.48	2.02	2.57	4.03
7	1.44	1.94	2.45	3.71
8	1.42	1.90	2.36	3.50
9	1.40	1.86	2.31	3.36
10	1.38	1.83	2.26	3.25
11	1.37	1.81	2.23	3.17
12	1.36	1.80	2.20	3.11
13	1.36	1.78	2.18	3.06
14	1.35	1.77	2.16	3.01
15	1.34	1.76	2.14	2.98

Let us calculate the 95-percent confidence interval for the calcium oxide data. The standard deviation has been estimated to be 0.11 (p. 47). The value of t for the 95-percent confidence level and five measurements is 2.8. Thus

$$95\text{-percent confidence limit} = \pm \frac{(2.8)(0.11)}{\sqrt{5}} = \pm 0.14 \text{ percent}$$

We may therefore state that there are 95 chances out of 100 that the true average for this analysis lies within ± 0.14 percent of 56.06—that is, that μ is included in the interval between 55.92 and 56.20 percent. An analogous calculation indicates that the limits at the 99-percent confidence level are ± 0.23 percent.

3.5   The Outlying Result

When a set of data contains an outlying result that appears to deviate excessively from the average or median, the decision must be made to retain or disregard it. The choice of criteria for the rejection of a suspected result has its perils. If we demand overwhelming odds in favor of rejecting a questionable measurement and thereby render this difficult, we run the risk of retaining results that are spurious and that have an inordinate effect on the average of the data. On the other hand, if we set lenient limits on precision and make easy the rejection of a result, we stand to discard measurements that rightfully belong to the set. It is an unfortunate fact that there is no universal rule that can be invoked to settle this question.

Three statistical tests widely employed as guides in making this decision are presented for consideration and discussion; each is applied to the calcium oxide data from Table 3-2.

THE $4d$ RULE

Scope. Requires four or more results in the set.

Method. Disregarding the questionable result, compute the average deviation for the remaining members of the set from the new average.

Criterion. If the questionable result differs from the new average by more than four times the average deviation of the remaining members, it is to be rejected.

Applying the $4d$ rule to the calcium oxide data
Average of trials 3, 4, 2, 1 = 56.02 percent
Average deviation of trials 3, 4, 2, 1 from 56.02 percent = 0.04 percent
Deviation of outlying result from 56.02 percent = 56.23 − 56.02 = 0.21 percent
Since 0.21 > (4 × 0.04), reject trial 5

THE $2.5d$ RULE

Scope and **Method** are the same as for the $4d$ rule.

Criterion. If the questionable result differs from the new average by an amount greater than 2.5 times the average deviation of the remaining members, it is to be rejected.

Again, using the calcium oxide data for illustration

Since 0.21 > (2.5 × 0.04), reject trial 5

THE Q TEST

Scope. Requires three or more measurements.

TABLE 3-4[3]

Critical Values for Rejection Quotient Q

Number of Observations	$Q_{critical}$ (90 % confidence)
2	—
3	0.94
4	0.76
5	0.64
6	0.56
7	0.51
8	0.47
9	0.44
10	0.41

[3] Reproduced from R. B. Dean and W. J. Dixon, *Anal. Chem.*, **23**, 636 (1951), by permission.

Method. Compute the spread separating the highest and lowest result in the set. Divide this into the spread between the questionable result and its nearest neighbor to obtain the quotient Q. Compare the value of Q with the appropriate figure in Table 3-4.

Criterion. The questionable result may be rejected with 90 percent confidence if Q exceeds that in the table.

In the case of the calcium oxide analysis:

Spread between the highest and lowest values = 0.28 percent
Spread is 56.23 − 56.08 = 0.15 percent between questionable result and nearest neighbor
Therefore Q is equal to 0.15/0.28 = 0.54
Tabulated value for Q (5 measurements) = 0.64; hence retain trial 5

Application of these tests to the same set of data reveals that they do not necessarily yield consistent answers regarding the fate of a questionable result. The difficulty lies, for the most part, in the fact that the $4d$ and $2.5d$ tests require larger sets of data for validity; employment for the evaluation of small sets is open to serious objections. For example, provided the set is sufficiently large, the probability that an outlying value rejected by the $4d$ test is indeed spurious is on the order of 99 to 1; with a small set, however, this criterion is strict to the point that erroneous measurements are likely to be retained. This is why the $2.5d$ test, which will correctly recommend rejection 19 times out of 20, was proposed. It has been found, however, that in sets consisting of only four normally distributed values, the outlying measurement will differ by $4d$ or more from the average of the other three nearly 60 percent of the time;[4] this frequency of occurrence is, of course, even greater if $2.5d$ is chosen as the criterion. That the rejection of a statistically significant observation from a small set is justified on the grounds of its disproportionate effect upon the average is, of course, open to argument. An objection to employment of the Q test[5] is that for small sets of data the rejection quotient is so large that erroneous data are likely to be retained. Its employment, nonetheless, is to be preferred to the other two.

In light of the foregoing, a number of recommendations suggest themselves for the treatment of a set of results that contains a suspect value.

(1) Estimate the precision that can reasonably be expected from the method as it was employed. Be certain, in short, that the outlying result actually is questionable.

(2) Re-examine carefully all data relating to the questionable result to see if a gross error has affected its value. Remember that the certain knowledge of a gross error is the only sure justification for disregarding a doubtful measurement.

(3) Repeat the analysis, if sufficient sample and time are available. Agreement of the newly acquired data with those that appear to be valid will lend weight to the notion that the outlying result should be rejected.

(4) If further data cannot be secured, apply the Q test to the existing set to see if the doubtful result can be rejected on these grounds.

(5) In the event that retention is necessary from the standpoint of the Q test, give consideration to the reporting of the median, rather than the average value of the set; as pointed out previously, this will tend to minimize the influence of the outlying value.

3.6 Significant Figures

The report of a set of results should include not only the "best" value for the set, be it average or median, but also give an indication of the precision observed between the individual members; we have seen that the

[4] W. J. Blaedel, V. W. Meloche, and J. A. Ramsay, *J. Chem. Ed.*, **28**, 643 (1951).

[5] R. B. Dean and W. J. Dixon, *Anal. Chem.*, **23**, 636 (1951).

latter may be expressed in terms of the average deviation or the standard deviation. Either of these serves to reveal the number of digits that we are entitled to include in an answer; common practice dictates that all numbers known with certainty shall be reported, and that in addition the first uncertain one shall also be included.

For example, the average of 61.64, 61.41, 61.55, and 61.62 is 61.555. The average deviation of the individuals from the mean is ± 0.075. Clearly, the number in the second decimal place is subject to uncertainty; such being the case, all numbers in succeeding decimal places are without meaning and we are forced to round the average value accordingly. The question of taking 61.55 or 61.56 must next be considered, 61.555 being equally spaced between them. A good guide here is always to round to the nearest even number; in this way any tendency to round in a set direction is eliminated, there being an equal likelihood that the nearest even number will be the higher or the lower in any given instance. Thus, we report the foregoing results as 61.56 $\pm$ 0.08.

In the absence of qualifying information of this sort, it is assumed that the last and uncertain digit is known to within plus or minus one unit. Thus the ratio of the circumference of a circle to its diameter (π) has been calculated to many decimal places. When using 3.1416 for π, we are inferring that this is the best value for the constant to four decimal places, but that its true value lies somewhere between 3.1415 and 3.1417. A further complication arises when we wish to express very large numbers whose values are subject to considerable uncertainty; a case in point is Avogadro's number. We know with certainty that the first three digits are 6, 0, and 2, and that the next is uncertain but probably is 3. Since the digits that follow are not known, and since it is necessary to indicate the position of the decimal point relative to 6023, we use zeros in place of the unknown digits. Here, the zeros indicate the order of magnitude of the number only, and have no other meaning. It is clear that we must make a distinction between those figures that have physical significance—that is, significant figures—and those that are either unknown or meaningless owing to the inadequacies of measurement. The following rules will be found useful in this regard.

1. *The significant figures in a number comprise all those digits whose values are known with certainty plus the first digit whose value is uncertain.* The position of the decimal point is irrelevant. Thus, 0.12345, 1.2345, 123.45, and 12,345 all contain five significant figures.

2. *Zeros are significant when part of the number; they are not significant when employed to indicate order of magnitude.* Zeros bounded left and right by digits other than zero are always significant. Thus 21.03 contains four significant figures; so does 20.03.

Zeros bounded only on the right by digits are never significant, for here they are being used to indicate the position of the decimal point. Thus 0.123, 0.000123, and 0.000000123 all contain three significant figures.

Zeros bounded by digits only on the left present a problem in that they may or may not be significant. If the zeros are a part of the number, as well they may be, they are significant. Thus, the mass of a 20-mg weight that carries no correction (to a tenth of a milligram) is known to three significant figures, 20.0 mg. When this is expressed as 0.0200 gram, the number of significant figures does not change. If, on the other hand, we wish to express the volume of a 2-liter beaker as 2000 ml, the latter number contains but one significant figure; the zeros simply indicate the order of magnitude. It can, of course, happen that the beaker in question has been found by experiment to contain 2.0 liters; here the zero following the decimal point infers that the volume is known to plus or minus 0.1 liter and hence is significant. When this volume is expressed in milliliters, the zero following the 2 is still significant but the other two zeros are not. The confusion that inevitably attends this dual employment of zeros is easily eliminated by the use of exponential notation; that is, in the present instance we could indicate the volume as 2.0×10^3 ml.

SIGNIFICANT FIGURES IN A DERIVED RESULT

The calculations of analytical chemistry often involve the manipulation of numerical quantities that contain widely varying numbers of significant figures. It is thus necessary to consider how many significant figures there are in a derived result.

The manner in which the uncertainty of an individual quantity is propagated into the final result depends upon the nature of the mathematical operation. By way of example, consider the processes of addition, subtraction, multiplication, and division with the numbers 142.7 and 0.081. That the last digit in each number is uncertain to the extent of one unit must be assumed, since no amplifying information in this regard has been supplied. Thus

Number	Uncertainty	
	Absolute	Relative, parts per thousand
142.7	0.1	0.7
0.081	0.001	12

Addition. Upon adding these numbers, we obtain the sum

$$\begin{array}{r} 142.7 \\ 0.081 \\ \hline 142.781 \end{array}$$

Recalling that the significant figures in a number include all those that are known with certainty plus the first uncertain one, we see that this sum will have to be rounded off to 142.8 since there is an uncertainty in the first decimal place. We are thus entitled to report the answer to four significant figures. An entirely too pessimistic estimate [142.7 ± (0.012 × 142.7) = 142 ± 2] would have resulted had we employed the relative, rather than the absolute uncertainties of the two numbers.

Subtraction. The arguments advanced for addition may be applied with equal force when taking the difference between two numbers.

Multiplication. Upon multiplying 142.7 by 0.081, we find that the product is equal to 11.5587. Here the number of significant figures that we are entitled to report is governed by the relative uncertainties in the two numbers. This may be roughly demonstrated by considering the range of answers that could result from the assumed uncertainties in these numbers —that is, in multiplying 0.081 ± 0.001 by 142.7 ± 0.1, the maximum estimated value is given by

$$0.082 \times 142.8 = 11.7096$$

and the minimum by

$$0.080 \times 142.6 = 11.4080$$

The difference between these is (11.7096 − 11.4080) = 0.3016. Thus, the answer is uncertain by about

$$\pm \frac{0.1508 \times 1000}{11.5587} = \pm 13 \text{ parts per thousand}$$

This closely approximates the relative uncertainty inherent in 0.081; thus the uncertainty in a product may be estimated from the relative deviation of the least certain quantity involved.

In the present instance

$$0.012 \times 11.5587 = 0.138$$

Hence, uncertainty appears in the first decimal place; the answer must be rounded to 11.6.

Division. The same considerations hold true in the case of a division as in a multiplication; again it is the relative uncertainty of the least certain quantity that dictates the number of significant figures in the quotient.

$$\frac{142.7}{0.081} = 1761.728 \cdots$$

The relative uncertainty in this quotient will be about twelve parts per thousand; in absolute terms the uncertainty will be

$$0.012 \times 1761.728 = 21$$

and the answer must be rounded off. To report it as 1760 involves ambiguity since this notation is incapable of indicating that the zero is not significant. It is preferable to employ the exponential notation of 1.76×10^3.

These examples illustrate three important rules with regard to the number of significant figures in a derived result:

(1) Where the mathematical operation is an addition or subtraction, it is the *absolute* uncertainty of the component quantities that determines the number of significant figures in the sum or difference.

(2) Where the mathematical operation is a multiplication or division, it is the *relative* uncertainty of the component quantities that governs the number of significant figures in the product or quotient.

(3) Where the quantities being manipulated have widely differing degrees of uncertainty, the number of significant figures in the derived result will be limited by the least certain of the component quantities; whether the absolute or relative uncertainty should be considered depends upon the nature of the calculation.

Evaluation of the number of significant figures to be shown in the result of a multistep calculation is accomplished by first considering any sums or differences, and then the products or quotients. This is best illustrated by an example; suppose we wish to know the number of significant figures that should appear in the answer to

$$\frac{(41.27 - 0.414)(0.0521)(7.090)}{(0.5135 + 0.0009)} = 29.3385 \cdot \cdot \cdot$$

Since no further information is given, each quantity in this expression is considered to be uncertain to the extent of one unit in the last decimal place.

We first consider the sums and differences, recalling that the absolute uncertainty is important for these. The difference in the numerator turns out to be 40.856; since an uncertainty exists in the second decimal place, however, this should be rounded to 40.86. Notwithstanding the fact that 0.0009 contains but one significant figure, the sum in the denominator will still contain the four figures of the larger number since the uncertainty in its value continues to reside in the fourth decimal place; it is thus taken as 0.5144.

We may now compute the relative uncertainty of the individual quantities in the simplified equation

$$\frac{(40.86)(0.0521)(7.090)}{(0.5144)} = 29.3414 \cdot \cdot \cdot$$

Number	Relative Uncertainty, Parts per Thousand
40.86 ± 0.01	0.2
0.0521 ± 0.0001	1.9
7.090 ± 0.001	0.1
0.5144 ± 0.0001	0.2

The uncertainty in 0.0521 is approximately ten times that of any of the other three quantities; we are justified in stating that this figure will govern the number of significant figures in the answer. Thus

$$29.3414 \cdots \times 0.0019 = 0.0557 \cdots = 0.06$$

Uncertainty will appear in the second decimal place in the answer; it should therefore be rounded off to 29.34.

Much time can be saved in the performance of calculations if an estimate of uncertainty is made before the actual computation is begun; with practice this may be done by inspection. It is generally advisable, in computation, to carry one figure in excess of the number estimated, and then round off the answer. The numerical value may otherwise suffer somewhat owing to the rounding-off process. Had the components of the foregoing example been rounded before calculation, an answer of 29.36 would have resulted.

Caution must be exercised in evaluating the number of significant figures in a derived result that is numerically close to some power of ten. For example, the relative error in 999 (three significant figures) is substantially identical to that in 1001 (four significant figures). Thus a result that is somewhat less than some power of ten possesses a smaller relative error than the number of significant figures indicate; this must be taken into account when rounding of such an answer.

THE ESTIMATED UNCERTAINTY IN A DERIVED RESULT

The foregoing procedures serve only to indicate the number of significant figures in the derived result; they do not, however, give a realistic numerical estimate of the probable uncertainty in this quantity when all of the components in a calculation possess the same order of uncertainty. This is best illustrated by an example. In the ratio

$$\frac{0.210}{0.197} = 1.06598 \cdots$$

both divisor and dividend have essentially the same uncertainty (0.5 percent). This will cause the quotient to be uncertain in the third decimal place (1.06 $\cdots \times$ 0.005). According to our convention, however, expression of this quotient as 1.066 infers a reliability of one part per thousand that simply is not justified in this case. We are thus forced to round off to 1.07, this being a better representation for the quotient.

If we wish to retain four figures in this result, an estimate of the probable uncertainty must be made and included as part of the report. The relative uncertainty could possibly be as great as 1 percent; this may be seen, as before, by evaluating the quotients (0.211/0.196) and (0.209/0.198) which approximate the extremes to which the result is uncertain. It is equally possible that the two component uncertainties could exactly cancel one another. Neither of these is likely, however. More probably the individual uncertainties will affect the quotient to some intermediate extent. An evaluation of this, based upon the square root of the sum of the squares of the component uncertainties will yield a more realistic estimate of the uncertainty to be expected in the final answer. In the present instance this is found to be 0.7 percent. With this information we would be entitled to report the quotient as 1.066 ± 0.007. If we do not wish to include the numerical estimate of uncertainty, it would be necessary to round the answer to 1.07, in agreement with the treatment based upon significant figures.

In summary, then, there are two methods available for ascertaining the proper number of figures to which a derived result should be reported. Whenever there is an individual uncertainty that is much greater than the others in the computation, it may safely be used as the basis for decision. In the event of doubt regarding the propriety of this approach, the analyst should resort to the more laborious estimation of probable error and base his decision upon the result of this calculation.

Problems

1. Replicate analyses of a sample of blood meal has produced the following percentages for nitrogen content: 4.16, 4.21, 4.18, 4.12.
   For these data, calculate
   (a) the average value for percent nitrogen
   (b) the median value for percent nitrogen   ans. 4.17 percent
   (c) the average deviation of these results in absolute terms
   (d) the average deviation of these results in parts per thousand

                                            ans. ±7 parts per thousand

2. Calculate the average deviations for each of the following sets of data in absolute and in relative terms.

A	B
93.6 percent	10.02 percent
93.7	10.01
93.5	10.09

   (a) Which set possesses the larger absolute deviation?   ans. *A*
   (b) Which set possesses the larger relative deviation?   ans. *B*

3. How many significant figures are there in the following:
   (a) 0.062005   (g) 60.025   (m) 0.0003014   (s) 6.111
   (b) 31.4   (h) 3.14 × 10⁻²   (n) 35.458   (t) 0.002605
   (c) 0.00625   (i) 4.2   (o) 91.22   (u) 2.6528
   (d) 2.81   (j) 620.1   (p) 0.0011   (v) 0.0314
   (e) 0.60025   (k) 96.494   (q) 0.014334   (w) 0.0101
   (f) 41.3798   (l) 44.21   (r) 1.008   (x) 0.01922

4. Express each of the numbers in Problem 3 to three significant figures.

5. Calculate the standard deviation for the calibration data in Table 3-1.

   ans. 0.006 ml

6. Divide the data of Table 3-1 into two sets, the one consisting of trials 1–6, the other trials 7–12. For each of these subsets calculate and compare
   (a) the average
   (b) the median
   (c) the average deviation, calculated from the medians
   (d) the standard deviation
   (e) the 95-percent confidence interval

7. Express the result of each of the following calculations to the proper number of significant figures:
   (a) $4.1374 + 2.81 + 0.0603 = 7.0077$
   (b) $4.1374 - 0.0603 = 4.0771$
   (c) $4.1374 - 2.81 = 1.3274$
   (d) $2.81 - 0.0603 = 2.7497$
   (e) $4.1374 - (2.81 + 0.0603) = 1.2671$

8. Express the result of each of the following calculations to the proper number of significant figures:
   (a) $14.37 \times 6.44 = 92.5428$
   (b) $0.0613 \times 0.4044 = 0.02478972$
   (c) $0.0613 \div 0.4044 = 0.151582$
   (d) $0.841 \div 297.2 = 0.00282974$
   (e) $4.1374 \times \dfrac{0.841}{297.2} = 0.0117077$

9. Express the result of each of the following calculations to the proper number of significant figures:
   (a) $\dfrac{4.178 + 0.0037}{60.4} = 0.0692334 \cdot \cdot \cdot$ ans. 0.0692
   (b) $\dfrac{4.178 \times 0.0037}{60.4} = 0.000255937 \cdot \cdot \cdot$
   (c) $\dfrac{4.178 - 4.032}{1.217} = 0.119967 \cdot \cdot \cdot$
   (d) $\dfrac{4.178 + 4.032}{1.217} = 6.74609 \cdot \cdot \cdot$
   (e) $\dfrac{(6.3194 - 4.1387)(204.2)}{0.2148} = 2{,}073.08 \cdot \cdot \cdot$

10. Evaluate the probable uncertainty in the result for each of the calculations in Problem 9.

11. For each of the following sets of data:

7.031	31.41	63.74	90.91
7.039	30.64	63.62	90.42
7.126	31.52	63.93	90.31
7.027	31.18	63.68	90.24

(a) Apply the Q test to see if rejection of the outlying result is justified.
(b) Report the best value for each set and defend your choice.
(c) Calculate the 95-percent confidence interval for each set.

12. The accompanying data were obtained when a new method for the analysis of iron was evaluated against a sample known to assay 21.68 percent Fe.

Sample	Weight of sample taken, grams	Weight of iron found, grams	Percent of iron found
1	0.7044	0.1524	21.64
2	0.7118	0.1552	21.80
3	0.7293	0.1588	21.77
4	0.7344	0.1572	21.40
5	0.7263	0.1579	21.74

(a) Evaluate the mean and median percentages of Fe for these data; explain in one or two sentences which of these you consider to be the more reliable measure for this method of analysis.
(b) Use the value selected in (a) to calculate the absolute average deviation for the analysis, the relative deviation (in parts per thousand), and the relative error (in percentage terms).
(c) Evaluate the absolute range and the relative range (in parts per thousand) for the data.
(d) Compute the standard deviation for the results, and compare its value with the absolute deviation calculated in (a).
(e) Apply the Q test to the outlying result to determine the advisability of its retention in the set.

$$\left(\, 4 \, \right)$$

An Introduction to Gravimetric Methods

4.1 Classification of Gravimetric Methods

The term *gravimetric* pertains to a weight measurement, and a gravimetric method is one in which the analysis is completed by a weighing operation. Two types of gravimetric analyses may be distinguished. In the first of these the substance to be determined is isolated from the other constituents in the sample by formation of an insoluble precipitate; the analysis is completed by determining the weight of this precipitate, or of some substance formed from it, by suitable treatment. The second general type takes advantage of the property of volatility; here the substance to be determined is isolated by distillation. The product may either be collected and weighed, or the weight loss in the sample as a result of the distillation may be measured. Of the two, precipitation methods are the more widely used.

PRECIPITATION METHODS

Not all insoluble precipitates are suitable for gravimetric analysis. Several that are of importance in the qualitative analysis scheme, for example, are not used for various reasons. It is worthwhile here to consider what properties are required in order that a precipitate be applicable for a quantitative precipitation method.

Solubility. Clearly a precipitate for gravimetric work must be sufficiently insoluble so that the amount lost does not seriously affect the outcome of the analysis. Where the quantity of substance being determined is low and where the demands for accuracy are high, solubility losses may be of real concern.

Purity. A gravimetric precipitate should be such that it can be readily freed from normally soluble contaminants by fairly simple treatment. During formation, all precipitates carry down some soluble constituents from the solution. The applicability of a precipitate to gravimetric analysis will depend upon the quantity of these contaminants and the ease with which they can be removed.

Filterability. It must be possible to isolate quantitatively the solid precipitate from the liquid phase by reasonably simple and rapid filtration methods. Whether or not a precipitate meets this requirement will depend upon its particle size. If this is too small, filtration may become difficult indeed.

Chemical Composition. A gravimetric precipitate must either be of known chemical composition or be readily converted to a compound of known composition. Only under these conditions can the precipitate weight be used for the calculation of the percent composition of the original sample.

VOLATILIZATION METHODS

Gravimetric methods based on the volatilization of a compound containing the element to be determined fall into two categories. The evolved substance is either collected and weighed, or the determination is based upon the loss of weight suffered by the original material. The former method is to be preferred, being a good deal more specific and less subject to uncertainty.

Perhaps the two most common examples of the first method concern the determination of water and the analysis of carbonates. Water can be separated from most inorganic compounds by ignition; the evolved water can then be absorbed on any of several solid desiccants. The weight of water evolved may be calculated from the gain in weight of the absorbent.

Carbonates are readily decomposed by acids, the evolved carbon dioxide being removed from solution by distillation. As in the case of water there are solid absorbents that will remove carbon dioxide from a gas stream; from the increase in weight of such an absorbent the chemist can calculate the weight of carbon dioxide evolved from the sample.

Water is also frequently determined by the indirect method. Here the weighed sample containing the water is simply ignited and then reweighed. Any loss in weight is assumed to be due to the distillation of the moisture from the sample. Unfortunately this assumption is frequently unjustified; ignition of many compounds results in their decomposition and consequent change in weight irrespective of the presence of water.

4.2   Calculation of Results from Gravimetric Analyses

A gravimetric analysis is based upon the experimental measurement of two quantities, the weight of sample taken and the weight of a compound of known composition derived from that sample. The conversion of these data to a number expressing the concentration of the substance sought is a relatively simple process.

Generally, we wish to express our results in terms of percentage composition

$$\text{percent } A = \frac{\text{weight of } A}{\text{weight of sample}} \times 100$$

In the usual case, however, the experimental data will not include the weight of A directly, but rather the weight of some compound that contains A or is chemically equivalent to A. To convert this to the desired quantity involves multiplication of the experimental datum by a constant called the *chemical factor* or the *gravimetric factor*. The nature of this constant can be readily seen by considering a few examples.

★EXAMPLE. A precipitate of AgCl was found to weigh 0.204 gram.
(a) To what weight of Cl would this correspond? From the formula for AgCl, we conclude that

$$\text{no. fw Cl} = \text{no. fw AgCl}$$

Since

$$\text{no. fw AgCl} = \frac{0.204}{\text{gfw AgCl}}$$

and

$$\text{wt Cl} = \text{no. fw Cl} \times \text{gfw Cl}$$

Then

$$\text{wt Cl} = \frac{0.204 \times \text{gfw Cl}}{\text{gfw AgCl}}$$

$$= 0.204 \times \frac{35.5}{143.3} = 0.0505$$

(b) To what weight of AlCl$_3$ would this correspond? We know that one AlCl$_3$ would yield three AgCl. Therefore

$$\text{no. fw AlCl}_3 = \tfrac{1}{3} \text{ no. fw AgCl}$$

By the above arguments

$$\text{wt AlCl}_3 = 0.204 \times \frac{\text{gfw AlCl}_3}{3 \times \text{gfw AgCl}}$$

$$= 0.204 \times \frac{133.3}{3 \times 143.3} = 0.0633$$

Both of these calculations are similar in that we multiply the known weight of the substance by a ratio of gram-formula weights. This ratio is the gravimetric factor and in the previous examples it is

$$\text{(a)} \quad \frac{\text{gfw Cl}}{\text{gfw AgCl}} \qquad\qquad \text{(b)} \quad \frac{\text{gfw AlCl}_3}{3 \times \text{gfw AgCl}}$$

In the latter case, it was necessary to multiply the formula weight of AgCl by three in order to balance the number of chlorides in the numerator and denominator.

★EXAMPLE. What weight of Fe_2O_3 can be obtained from 1.00 gram of Fe_3O_4? What is the gravimetric factor for this conversion?

Here it is necessary to assume that all of the Fe in the Fe_3O_4 is transformed into Fe_2O_3 and that extra oxygen is available to accomplish this change. That is,

$$2Fe_3O_4 + [O] = 3Fe_2O_3$$

We see from this equation that $\frac{3}{2}$ formula weights of Fe_2O_3 are obtained from 1 formula weight of Fe_3O_4. Thus the number of formula weights of Fe_2O_3 is greater than the number of formula weights of Fe_3O_4 by a factor of $\frac{3}{2}$ or

$$\text{no. fw } Fe_2O_3 = \frac{3}{2} \times \text{no. fw } Fe_3O_4$$

$$= \frac{3}{2} \times \frac{\text{wt } Fe_3O_4}{\text{gfw } Fe_3O_4}$$

and

$$\text{wt } Fe_2O_3 = \frac{3}{2} \times \frac{\text{wt } Fe_3O_4}{\text{gfw } Fe_3O_4} \times \text{gfw } Fe_2O_3$$

or rearranging

$$\text{wt } Fe_2O_3 = \text{wt } Fe_3O_4 \times \frac{3 \times \text{gfw } Fe_2O_3}{2 \times \text{gfw } Fe_3O_4}$$

and substituting numerical values

$$\text{wt } Fe_2O_3 = 1.00 \times \frac{3 \times 160}{2 \times 232} = 1.03 \text{ grams}$$

$$\text{gravimetric factor} = \frac{3 \times \text{gfw } Fe_2O_3}{2 \times \text{gfw } Fe_3O_4}$$

We can generalize by defining the gravimetric factor as follows:

$$\text{gravimetric factor} = \frac{\text{gfw of the substance sought}}{\text{gfw of the substance weighed}} \times \frac{a}{b}$$

where *a* and *b* are small integers that take such values as are necessary to make the formula weights in the numerator and denominator *chemically equivalent.*

We have shown, further, that

$$\begin{matrix}\text{weight of substance} \\ \text{sought, grams}\end{matrix} = \begin{matrix}\text{weight of substance} \\ \text{weighed, grams}\end{matrix} \times \begin{matrix}\text{gravimetric} \\ \text{factor}\end{matrix}$$

Tables of gravimetric factors and their logarithms are to be found in chemical handbooks. A few are listed in Table 4-1.

TABLE 4-1

Typical Gravimetric Factors

Substance Sought	Substance Weighed	Gravimetric Factor
$BiCl_3$	Bi_2O_3	$\frac{2 \text{ gfw } BiCl_3}{\text{gfw } Bi_2O_3}$
KNO_3	K_2PtCl_6	$\frac{2 \text{ gfw } KNO_3}{\text{gfw } K_2PtCl_6}$
K_3PO_4	K_2PtCl_6	$\frac{2 \text{ gfw } K_3PO_4}{3 \text{ gfw } K_2PtCl_6}$
P_2O_5	$Mg_2P_2O_7$	$\frac{\text{gfw } P_2O_5}{\text{gfw } Mg_2P_2O_7}$

In all the gravimetric factors considered so far, the establishment of chemical equivalence between the numerator and denominator could be accomplished merely by balancing the number of atoms of the element other than oxygen that was common to both. There are, however, instances where this procedure is not feasible. For example, suppose the sulfate in iron (III) sulfate were precipitated and weighed as barium sulfate and we wished to know the weight of iron in the original compound. Each iron (III) sulfate is equivalent to three barium sulfates; two irons, then, are equivalent to three barium sulfates. Therefore the gravimetric factor for calculation of the weight of iron would be

$$\frac{2 \times \text{gfw Fe}}{3 \times \text{gfw } BaSO_4}$$

Here, although the substances in the gravimetric factor are not directly related by a common element, we can determine their equivalence through knowledge of the stoichiometry that exists between them.

The example given below demonstrates the use of the gravimetric factor in the calculation of results from an analysis.

★EXAMPLE. The phosphate in a 0.680-gram mineral sample was precipitated as $MgNH_4PO_4$. This yielded 0.435 gram of $Mg_2P_2O_7$ upon ignition. Calculate the percentage of phosphorous in the original sample.

$$\text{percent P} = \frac{0.435 \times \dfrac{2 \text{ gfw P}}{\text{gfw } Mg_2P_2O_7} \times 100}{0.680}$$

$$= \frac{0.435 \times 0.278 \times 100}{0.680} = 17.8$$

Problems

1. Write gravimetric factors for each of the following:

Substance Sought	Substance Weighed
Mn_3O_4	MnO_2
$K_2Cr_2O_7$	$PbCrO_4$
$FeSO_4(NH_4)_2SO_4 \cdot 6H_2O$	Fe_2O_3
CCl_4	$AgCl$
$2K_2CO_3 \cdot UO_2CO_3$	CO_2

2. A 0.396-gram sample containing $BaCl_2 \cdot 2H_2O$ was analyzed by precipitation of the Cl^- with $AgNO_3$. This yielded 0.328 gram of $AgCl$.
   (a) Calculate the percent $BaCl_2 \cdot 2H_2O$ in the sample.   ans. 70.6 percent
   (b) What weight of H_2O is associated with the $BaCl_2$ in the sample?
   ans. 0.0412 gram

3. The aluminum in a 0.600-gram sample was precipitated as the basic oxide, $Al_2O_3 \cdot xH_2O$. Upon ignition this gave a 0.163-gram residue of Al_2O_3. Calculate the percent $Al_2(SO_4)_3$ in the sample.

4. How many pounds of cobalt can be obtained from 30.0 lb of Co_3S_4?

5. A 0.886-gram sample containing CaC_2O_4 was ignited at high temperature. After ignition the weight was 0.614 gram. Calculate the percent CaC_2O_4. (Assume loss in weight due to $CaC_2O_4 \rightarrow CaO + CO_2 + CO$.)   ans. 54.6 percent

6. How many tons of H_2SO_4 can theoretically be produced from 1 ton of pyrite, FeS_2?

7. How many grams of $Pb(NO_3)_2$ are required to precipitate all of the chromium in 1.50 grams $K_2Cr_2O_7$ if the precipitate composition is $PbCrO_4$?
   ans. 3.38 grams

8. Consecutive determinations of a 0.843-gram brass sample yielded 0.0162 gram of SnO_2, 0.0228 gram of $PbSO_4$, 1.295 grams of $CuSCN$, and 0.316 gram of $Zn_2P_2O_7$. Calculate the percentage of each element in the alloy.

9. The carbon in a 0.710-gram sample of steel was ignited to CO_2 in a stream of air, collected on Ascarite, and found to weigh 0.0175 gram. What is the percentage of carbon in the steel?

10. A 0.8000-gram sample containing chloride and iodide gave a silver halide precipitate weighing 0.5941 gram. The precipitate was then ignited in a stream of Cl_2 gas that converted the AgI in the mixture to AgCl. The weight of this precipitate was 0.4592 gram. Calculate the percentage of chloride and iodine in the sample.   ans. 23.4 percent I and 7.67 percent Cl

11. A 0.510-gram sample containing $Ca(ClO_3)_2$ was dissolved, the ClO_3^- was reduced to Cl^- and then precipitated as AgCl. The precipitate weighed 0.330 gram. Calculate the percentage of calcium in the sample.

12. What sample weight must be taken so that each milligram of ignited $Mg_2P_2O_7$ will represent 0.05 percent MgO?   ans. 0.7243 gram

13. A 0.500-gram sample containing 5.0 percent Fe, 6.2 percent Al, and 1.8 percent Ti was dissolved and the metals precipitated as the basic oxides. What was the weight of the mixture of Fe_2O_3, Al_2O_3, and TiO_2?

14. A 0.179-gram sample of an organic compound was burned completely to carbon dioxide and water. The CO_2 was collected in a solution of barium hydroxide

$$Ba(OH)_2 + CO_2 \rightarrow H_2O + BaCO_3$$

The precipitated barium carbonate was filtered, washed, and dried by ignition. What was the percentage of carbon in the sample if 0.561 gram of $BaCO_3$ was recovered?

15. Ammonical nitrogen can be determined by treatment of the sample with chloroplatinic acid, the slightly soluble ammonium chloroplatinate being produced

$$H_2PtCl_6 + 2NH_4^+ \rightarrow (NH_4)_2PtCl_6 + 2H^+$$

The precipitate decomposes upon ignition, yielding metallic platinum and gaseous products

$$(NH_4)_2PtCl_6 \rightarrow Pt + 2Cl_2 + 2NH_3 + 2HCl$$

The accompanying data refer to such an analysis

wt. bottle + sample, grams 24.3617   wt. crucible + Pt, grams 18.5330
wt. bottle less sample   24.1938   wt. crucible, empty   17.9466

Calculate the percentage of ammonia in the sample.

16. A series of sulfate samples is to be analyzed by precipitation as $BaSO_4$. If it is known that the sulfate in these samples ranges between 20 and 55 percent, what minimum sample weight should be taken to ensure a precipitate weight

no smaller than 0.300 gram? What will be the maximum precipitate weight to be expected if this quantity of sample is taken?

17. A 0.6440-gram quantity of manganese dioxide was added to an acidic solution of a 1.140-gram sample containing chloride ion. After evolution of chlorine according to the equation

$$MnO_2 + 2Cl^- + 4H^+ \rightarrow 2H_2O + Mn^{2+} + Cl_2$$

the excess MnO_2 was collected by filtration, washed, and weighed, 0.3520 gram being recovered. Calculate the result of this analysis in terms of percentage ammonium chloride in the sample.

18. The hydrogen sulfide in crude petroleum may be removed by distillation and collection in a solution of cadmium chloride. The precipitated CdS is then filtered, washed, and ignited to cadmium sulfate. Calculate the percentage of H_2S if a 50.0-gram sample of petroleum yielded 0.108 gram of $CdSO_4$.

19. The aluminum in a sample of impure ammonium aluminum sulfate was precipitated as the hydrous oxide, $Al_2O_3 \cdot xH_2O$, with aqueous ammonia. After filtration and washing, the precipitate was ignited to Al_2O_3. A 1.200-gram sample was found to yield 0.180 gram of Al_2O_3. Calculate the results of this analysis in terms of percentage
    (a) $NH_4Al(SO_4)_2$
    (b) Al_2O_3
    (c) Al

20. The following data pertain to the gravimetric determination of chloride in a soluble sample:

wt. bottle + sample, grams	26.0750	25.7549
wt. bottle, less sample	25.7549	25.4003
wt. crucible + AgCl, grams	23.7552	22.2789
wt. crucible, empty	23.3564	21.8368

Calculate the percentage of chloride in these samples; the use of logarithms is recommended.

(5)

The Techniques and Tools
of Gravimetric Analysis

A gravimetric analysis involves determination of the weight of a substance produced from a given weight of sample. The common operations of gravimetric analysis thus include weighing, filtration, and drying or ignition of the substance isolated. We must now consider the various implements employed by the analytical chemist in the performance of these operations.

5.1   The Measurement of Mass

Accurate weighing data are a requisite for virtually all chemical methods of analysis. In addition, the approximate weight of substances is frequently required in analytical work. We therefore need to consider the various types of weighing instruments and the techniques employed in their use.

THE DISTINCTION BETWEEN MASS AND WEIGHT

The reader should clearly recognize that there is a difference between the concepts of mass and weight. The more fundamental of these is *mass*—an invariant measure of the quantity of matter in an object. The *weight* of an object, on the other hand, is the force of attraction exerted between it and its surroundings, principally the earth. Since this gravitational attraction is subject to slight geographical variation with altitude and latitude, the weight of an object is likewise a somewhat variable quantity. For example, the weight of a crucible would be less in Denver than in Atlantic City since the attractive force between it and the earth is less at the greater altitude. Similarly, it would weigh more in Seattle than in Panama; since the earth is somewhat flattened at the poles, the force of attraction increases appreciably with latitude. The mass of this crucible, on the other hand, remains constant regardless of the location in which it is measured.

Weight and mass are simply related to one another through the familiar expression

$$W = Mg$$

where the weight W is given by the product of the mass M of the object and the acceleration due to gravity g.

In chemical analysis we are invariably interested in the determination of mass, since we do not wish our results to be dependent upon the locality in which the experiment was performed. This is readily accomplished by comparing the mass of an unknown to that of objects of known mass through the use of a balance; since the quantity g affects both known and unknown to exactly the same extent, a fair measure of masses will result.

The distinction between weight and mass is not always observed; in common usage the operation of comparing masses is called *weighing*, and the objects of known mass as well as the results of the process are called *weights*. While the two terms are hereafter used synonymously, strictly speaking it is *mass* to which we refer.

EQUAL-ARM ANALYTICAL BALANCES

Construction. The principal moving part of a balance is the *beam*. In an equal-arm design the point of pivot is a central agate knife edge that bears upon an agate surface mounted at the top of a fixed pillar. Two outer knife edges are located equidistant from the fulcrum; these support the *stirrups* which serve as the links through which the balance pans are connected to the beam. Movement of the beam is gauged by observing the motion of a vertical pointer with respect to a deflection scale at the base of the pillar.

The beam of the typical equal-arm balance is calibrated at intervals to accommodate a small metal *rider*. Movement of the rider along the beam has the effect of altering the loading on the balance; its position is adjusted with a rodlike control that extends through the balance case. The use of a rider eliminates the necessity for handling large numbers of small weights.

Analytical balances are adjusted with their riders in place over the zero marking on the beam; the rider should be so placed when determining the no-load equilibrium point.

The three knife edges of a balance are precision ground to reduce to a minimum the area of contact with the bearing surface. As a consequence, loading at the point of contact between knife edge and bearing is severe; for the central knife edge this is on the order of hundreds or thousands of kilograms per square centimeter. Sudden shocks can result in extensive damage to either of these parts. In order to prevent this, an analytical balance is equipped with a *beam support* system which isolates the knife edges from their bearing surfaces by lifting the beam slightly and supporting its weight. This safeguard, unfortunately, is effective only when properly used; the beam support must always be engaged when the balance is not in use and when a change is being made in the loading on the pans. The beam support is operated by a knob on the front of the balance case, usually in the center. *Pan arrests*, also actuated by a control on the front of the case, tend to minimize the independent oscillation of the pans owing to poor arrangement of loads and also provide a means of releasing the beam in a reproducible manner; these too should always be engaged when the loading of the balance is changed.

Theory of Operation. In essence, an equal-arm analytical balance acts as a first-class lever. The addition of weight to one side of such a lever at rest will cause it to seek a new rest position. The force moment tending to change its position is given by the product of the mass added and the horizontal distance from the fulcrum through which it is acting. When the lever again achieves a position of equilibrium, the force moment tending to give it motion in one direction is exactly balanced by that which tends to impart motion in the opposite sense. Thus, we may write for the equilibrium state that

$$F_1 = F_2$$

where F_1 and F_2 represent these opposing forces. We may also express this relationship as

$$M_1 L_1 = M_2 L_2 \tag{5-1}$$

where M_1 is the mass located a distance L_1 to the left of the fulcrum, and M_2 and L_2 stand for the analogous mass and lever arm to the right of the fulcrum. An equal-arm lever will assume an equilibrium position that is horizontal when the force moment is identical on its left and right sides; provided the two arms have equal masses and lengths, the loads they carry will also be identical. The weighing operation thus consists of duplicating, under load, the equilibrium position of the unloaded balance.

Stability of a Balance. When set in motion, the beam of an analytical balance oscillates slowly about some equilibrium point at which it will eventually come to rest. In order for this to occur it is necessary that the center of gravity of the beam and pans be *below* the central knife edge. Under these conditions, the weight of the beam tends to act as a restoring force that will return the deflected beam to a stable equilibrium position.

Sensitivity of the Analytical Balance. The *sensitivity* of a balance describes the magnitude of the change in equilibrium position of the beam resulting from the addition of a given weight to one of the pans. This change is observed as an alteration in position of the pointer with respect to the scale at the base of the pillar supporting the beam. The sensitivity is conveniently expressed in terms of deflection of the pointer in scale divisions per milligram of added weight; that is,

$$\text{sensitivity} = \frac{\text{divisions of deflection}}{\text{milligram}}$$

The sensitivity of a balance is directly proportional to the length of the beam as well as the length of the pointer; it is inversely proportional to the weight of the beam and the distance between the central knife edge and the center of gravity of the beam and pans.

AUXILIARY DEVICES

The weighing operation can be performed more rapidly on a balance equipped with any of several supplementary devices; these function either to expedite achievement of the equilibrium position of the beam or to reduce the number of weights that must be manipulated by hand.

Dampers. Dampers act to shorten the time required for the beam to come to rest. This is accomplished by either of two methods. An *air damper* consists of a piston that moves within a concentric cylinder. The former is attached to the beam while the latter is firmly mounted to the balance case. When the beam is set in motion, the enclosed air suffers slight expansions and contractions because of the close spacing between piston and cylinder. The beam comes rapidly to equilibrium as a consequence of this opposition to its movement. Air dampers suffer from being somewhat bulky; considerable attention must also be paid to positioning of the loads on the pans to ensure that piston and cylinder do not touch. These are not serious limitations for single pan (unequal-arm) balances; it is on these that air dampers are most widely employed. Of more common use is the *magnetic damper*. A metal (generally aluminum) plate secured to the end of the beam is positioned between the poles of a fixed permanent magnet. When the beam is set in motion and the plate moves through the field of the magnet, the currents induced tend to oppose oscillation and to bring the beam rapidly to its equilibrium position.

Chain Balances. As illustrated in Figure 5.1, a balance of this type is fitted with a small gold chain that is attached some distance to the right of the fulcrum and also to an externally operated crank. The amount of weight supported by the beam can be varied by lengthening or shortening the chain. A scale arrangement and vernier makes possible the direct reading of weight so introduced. Since the chain generally allows introduction of any weight within the range of 0 to 100 mg, the beam of such a

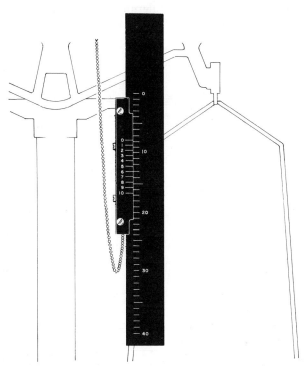

Fig. 5.1 The Chain Balance. Note arrangement of chain and vernier. Loading indicated is 7.6 mg.

balance will be notched for a rider that allows addition of 100-mg increments from 0 to 1 gram. Thus no weight smaller than 1 gram need be manually introduced.

A chain balance fitted with magnetic damping will yield accurate results for a minimum expenditure of time.

Keyboard Balances. Keyboard balances represent a further refinement with respect to the expeditious handling of weights. Knobs or keys on the case of the balance allow the rapid addition of weights up to several grams in size. Balances of this type are often arranged so that any weight smaller than 100 mg is read directly from a projected image. Both single- and double-pan balances are available which incorporate these features.

UNEQUAL-ARM BALANCES

Figure 5.2 shows the essential features of an unequal-arm balance. It is seen to consist of a single pan (1) suspended from the end of the shorter arm of the beam. Also on this side of the fulcrum is a full complement of weights

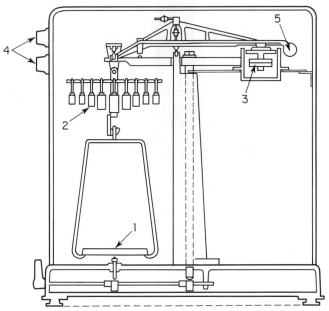

Fig. 5.2 Schematic Diagram, Unequal-arm Balance. (Diagram courtesy of Mettler Instrument Corporation, Hightstown, New Jersey.)

(2). At the longer end of the beam is a counterweighted damper (3) designed to impart equilibrium to the system. Placement of an object on the pan results in an imbalance that is corrected by *removal* of weights from the beam; reattainment of balance requires that the mass of the weights removed be equal to the mass of the object that replaced them. An unequal-arm balance thus operates under conditions of constant load and has the advantage of possessing a truly constant sensitivity.

Speed of operation is provided by the damper, the mechanical handling of weights greater than 100 mg (4), and an optical system (5) that projects a direct reading of weights smaller than this amount on a frosted glass window. Weighing with an unequal-arm balance reduces simply to manipulation of several dials and reading of the fractional weight projected upon the window.

OTHER TYPES OF BALANCES

In a ranking with respect either to sensitivity or permissible loading the ordinary analytical balance occupies an intermediate position. Typically, the maximum allowable load on each pan is 200 grams; the sensitivity commonly runs between 1.5 and 4 divisions per milligram. By way of contrast, *semimicrobalances* usually have capacities no greater than 100 grams and reciprocal sensitivities on the order of 0.05 mg per division. *Microbalances* accommodate only 20 to 50 grams on each pan but have reciprocal sensitivities in the range 0.01 to 0.001 mg per division. Yet another order of diminution is possible through the use of quartz fibers, either in the form of beams or helices. Such weighing devices have very low capacities but are sensitive to as little as 0.005 microgram (1 microgram = 1×10^{-6} gram).

Since approximate weights are frequently needed in the analytical laboratory, balances that are less sensitive but more rugged than the analytical balance are also required.

WEIGHTS

For each balance there should be a set of weights. These will be of such number and denomination as to allow, in conjunction with the riders and chains built into the balance, addition of any weight within the capacity of the balance. Weights are manufactured from materials that render them resistant to changes in mass. Brass plated with platinum, gold, or rhodium is preferred for denominations larger than 1 gram, although highly polished, nonmagnetic stainless steel and lacquered brass weights also give good service. These integral weights are either carefully machined from a single piece of metal or are built in two pieces; with the latter, final adjustment of mass has been accomplished by inserting small compensating weights in the space between the two parts. Fractional weights—that is, those smaller than 1 gram—are fabricated from sheets of platinum, tantalum, or aluminum.

WEIGHING WITH AN EQUAL-ARM BALANCE

A number of techniques exist for determining the weight of an object with an equal-arm analytical balance. Regardless of the method, the pointer on the beam and the deflection scale at the base of the central pillar are used to determine the state of equality of loading between the pans. In this connection two terms must be defined. The *zero point* refers to the equilibrium position of the pointer for the empty balance. A *rest point* is the equilibrium position assumed by the pointer when a load has been imposed on the balance. In these terms, then, the weighing operation consists of determining the weight necessary to produce a rest point that corresponds with the zero point. Owing to the prohibitive length of time necessary for an undamped beam to come to rest, its equilibrium position is estimated from an observation of the magnitude of the swings of its pointer.

The Deflection Scale. The deflection scale of the typical analytical balance does not have numerical values assigned to the division lines. All

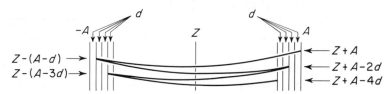

Fig. 5.3 Schematic Diagram Illustrating the Damping of the Pointer of an Analytical Balance.

that is required is a consistent numbering system, and this is left to the discretion of the operator. We shall employ the notation that assigns a value of 10 to the midline of the scale. The lines to the left, then, represent integers less than 10 while those to the right have values greater than this number.

We shall restrict discussion to the method of long swings and to that of short swings. The former is included because of its established reliability for the most exacting work; the latter, being the quicker method, is recommended for all routine weighing. The principal difference between these schemes is the number of observations made upon the pointer; the long swing method involves an odd number of these observations (either 5 or 3), while the short swing method uses but two observations under somewhat restricted conditions.

Figure 5.3 illustrates why an odd number of observations is preferred. This indicates the position the pointer takes in making two and one-half full cycles, or five "swings." In actuality these would all be superimposed on a single arc. Each swing is less than the previous one by an amount d, owing to the operation of damping and frictional forces. This is an essentially constant decrement for any small set of swings (*d* in Fig. 5.3 is somewhat exaggerated for the purposes of clarity). Now, if the maximum position reached by the pointer on the first swing we choose to observe is a distance *A* from the as yet unknown rest point *Z*, our observed reading for this swing will be $(Z + A)$. On the return swing, the pointer will fail to reach $-A$ by the amount of the decrement *d*. Similarly, the following swing will be short of $(Z + A)$ by the amount of 2*d*. The course of subsequent swings can be predicted in the same manner. Using the data of Figure 5.3, we see that the average of the two swings observed to the left is $Z - (A - 2d)$, while that for those to the right is $Z + A - 2d$. Clearly, the average of these two will yield the value of the rest point. As long as an odd number of consecutive swings are observed, the average of the mean swing yields an estimate of the rest point; on the other hand, if an even number of consecutive readings is averaged, values other than *Z* are consistently obtained.

The Method of Long Swings. To obtain an estimate of the zero point of the balance, lower the beam support gently, and then release by disengaging the pan arrests (this is the order always followed in freeing the beam; the opposite order is used when arresting the beam); allow the beam to swing freely through several cycles. Motion can be imparted to the beam, if necessary, by temporarily displacing the rider (or chain) from its zero position. The balance case is kept closed throughout this process. Next observe and record the maximum position attained by the pointer during a right-hand swing, estimating this to the nearest tenth of a division. Continue until observations of three or five consecutive maxima have been made. Calculate the average value for the swings in each direction; take the mean of these two quantities as the zero point of the balance. Since uncertainty resides in the first decimal place, the calculations should not be carried further than this.

★EXAMPLE. Calculate the zero point for a balance if the following consecutive readings were observed: 12.4, 6.9, 12.2, 7.1, 11.9.

readings	6.9	12.4
	7.1	12.2
	14.0	11.9
		36.5
averages	7.0	12.2

$$\text{-zero point} = \frac{7.0 + 12.2}{2} = 9.6$$

It should be noted parenthetically that the zero point will undergo slight changes in position with time owing to changes in temperature and humidity; as a consequence, its value should be determined for each series of weighings. Pronounced shifts in the zero point are indicative of trouble; in such event the instructor should be consulted.

After ascertaining that the pan arrests and beam supports have been re-engaged, place the object to be weighed on the left pan of the balance. Make a rough estimate of its mass and, using forceps, place on the right pan the single weight that is believed to have a slightly greater mass. Gently and partially disengage the beam support, and note the behavior of the pointer; it will swing away from the pan that has the heavier load. If no oscillation occurs, the loadings are within 1 to 2 grams of each other; under such circumstances, cautious disengagement of the pan arrests will allow determination of which pan has the heavier load. Continue a systematic trial-and-error loading of weights until the closest approach to balance has been achieved where the object is still heavy. Then use the rider in a similar manner; the balance case should be closed henceforth. When balance has apparently been obtained, take a rest point in the manner described for determining the zero point and compare this with the zero point. Subsequent corrections with the rider can be checked in the same fashion until balance is achieved.

A significant saving in time can be made by employing the balance sensitivity to calculate the number in the final decimal place. Here, the weight of the object is determined to the nearest whole milligram and a rest point (RP_1) is obtained. Then 1 mg is either added or subtracted from the load on the balance and another rest point (RP_2) is taken. The difference between these yields the sensitivity of the balance for the particular loading involved. With this the correction needed to shift either rest point into coincidence with the zero point can be readily calculated.

★EXAMPLE. Zero point (ZP)   10.2
          Rest point with 10.422 grams (RP_1) 11.1
          Rest point with 10.423 grams (RP_2) 8.7
          Sensitivity (11.1 − 8.7)   2.4 divisions
                                                                        per mg
          Difference between RP_1 and ZP   0.9 division

Since

$$\frac{1 \text{ mg}}{2.4 \text{ div}} = \frac{x \text{ mg}}{0.9 \text{ div}}$$

then

$$x = 0.4 \text{ mg}$$

This correction should be *added* to 10.422 grams, because the rest point corresponding to this loading lies to the *right* of the zero point. Thus the weight of the object is 10.422 + 0.0004 = 10.4224 grams. Note that the same result is obtained from RP_2 data

Difference between ZP and RP$_2$ 1.5 divisions

Since

$$\frac{1 \text{ mg}}{2.4 \text{ div}} = \frac{x \text{ mg}}{1.5 \text{ div}}$$

then

$$x = 0.6 \text{ mg}$$

This correction should be *subtracted* from 10.423 grams, because the rest point corresponding to this loading lies to the *left* of the zero point. Thus, the weight is again 10.423 − 0.0006 = 10.4224 grams.

The Method of Short Swings. The decrement d becomes vanishingly small when the amplitude of the swings is small (from 1 to 3 divisions on either side of the mean); under these circumstances the arithmetic mean of a consecutive left and right swing of the pointer gives a sufficiently close approximation of the equilibrium point. Thus, only two observations are made and the average is taken for use; this represents a considerable saving of time. Whether the weight is determined to a tenth of a milligram directly or is calculated from the sensitivity is a matter of personal preference; with a knowledge of the approximate sensitivity of the balance, the direct method is quite rapid.

Weighing with a Damped Balance. A damped balance, particularly if also equipped with a chain, is well adapted for the direct determination of the weight of an object. Here the zero point is determined by releasing the beam support and pan arrest and allowing time for the pointer to cease moving. Weighing is accomplished by placing the object on the left pan and weights on the right until a rest point equal to the zero point is obtained. It is preferable to adjust the rider and chain to exact balance.

WEIGHING WITH A SINGLE-PAN BALANCE

Obtaining the weight of an object with a modern single-pan balance is a very simple operation.

To adjust the empty balance, rotate the arrest knob. Then manipulate the zero adjusting control until the illuminated scale indicates a reading of zero. Next, arrest the balance and place the object to be weighed on the pan. Again turn the arrest knob, this time to its clockwise position. Rotate the dial controlling the heaviest likely weight for the object until the illuminated scale changes position or the notation "remove weight" appears; then turn back the knob one step. Repeat this procedure with the other dials, working successively through the lighter weights. Then turn the arrest knob to its counterclockwise position and allow the balance to achieve equilibrium. The weight of the object is found by taking the sum of the weights that have been introduced with the dials and that which appears on the illuminated scale. The vernier is helpful in reading this scale to the nearest tenth of a milligram.

NOTE:

Directions for operation of some one-pan balances will differ somewhat from the foregoing. Consult with the instructor for any modifications as may be required.

BUOYANCY CORRECTION

Ordinarily, weighing is the most reliable step in a chemical analysis. Errors can arise from changes in the weights that result from their heavy use. Periodic calibration against a standard set of weights will eliminate this source of error.

When an object having a density considerably different from that of the weights is weighed, a *buoyancy* error is observed. This discrepancy arises from the difference in the buoyant force of the medium (air) as it acts on the object and on the weights. A correction for this effect is seldom needed when solid objects are weighed since the density of most solids approaches that of the weights. When liquids, gases, or low-density solids are weighed, however, a correction must be applied. It is easily shown that the correct weight can be obtained by means of the equation

$$W_1 = W_2 + W_2 \left(\frac{d_{air}}{d_1} - \frac{d_{air}}{d_2} \right) \tag{5-2}$$

where W_1 is the corrected weight of the object and W_2 is the mass of the weights. The terms d_1 and d_2 represent the densities of the object and the weights, respectively, and d_{air} is the density of the air displaced; the density of air can be taken as 0.0012 gram per ml. Table 5-1 gives the density d_2 of the various metals used in the construction of weights.

TABLE 5-1

Density of Metals Used in the Manufacture of Weights

Metal	Density, grams/ml
Aluminum	2.7
Brass	8.0
Gold	19.3
Platinum	21.4
Stainless steel	7.8
Tantalum	16.6

★EXAMPLE. A sample of an organic liquid having a density of 0.92 gram/ml was weighed into a glass bottle. The weight of the empty bottle was 8.6500 grams against stainless steel weights. After addition of the sample, it was 9.8600 grams. Correct the weight of sample for buoyancy.

The apparent weight of the liquid is (9.8600 − 8.6500) or 1.2100 grams. Inasmuch as the buoyant force acted on the glass container for both weighings we need only consider the buoyant force acting on the 1.2100 grams liquid. Applying equation (5-2), using the density of stainless steel from Table 5-1, and the value 0.0012 gram/ml for the density of air we obtain

$$W_1 = 1.2100 + 1.2100 \left(\frac{0.0012}{0.92} - \frac{0.0012}{7.8} \right)$$

$$= 1.2100 + 1.2100(0.0013 - 0.00016)$$

$$= 1.2114 \text{ grams}$$

SUMMARY OF RULES GOVERNING THE USE OF AN ANALYTICAL BALANCE

Continued good performance from an analytical balance is highly dependent upon the treatment accorded it. Similarly, reliable data are obtained only when careful attention is paid to the details of the weighing operation. Since weighing data are required for virtually every quantitative analysis, it is worthwhile to summarize the rules and precautions that relate to their acquisition.

To Avoid Damage or Minimize Wear to the Balance and Weights:

1. Be certain that the beam support and pan arrests are engaged whenever the loading on the balance is being changed and when the balance is not in use.

2. Insofar as possible, center the loads on the pans.

3. When freeing the beam, first release the beam support slowly and then the pan arrests. When arresting the beam, the opposite order should be followed; the pan arrests should be engaged as the pointer passes through the center of the deflection scale.

4. Protect the balance from corrosion. Only vitreous materials and nonreactive metal or plastic objects should be placed directly on the pans. Weighing of volatile materials requires special precautions.

5. Do not attempt to adjust the balance without the prior consent of the instructor.

6. Handle weights gently and with special forceps only. Weights should never be touched, as perspiration from one's hands can initiate corrosion. Keep weights in their closed box except during use.

7. If possible, avoid bringing weights into the laboratory.

8. Balance and case should be kept scrupulously clean. A camel's hair brush is useful for removal of spilled material or dust.

To Obtain Reliable Weighing Data:

9. Place the object on the left pan, the weights on the right.

10. Do not attempt to weigh an object until it has returned to room temperature.

11. Do not touch a dried object with bare hands; handle it with tongs or use finger pads to protect against the uptake of moisture.

12. If a weight is accidentally mishandled, it should be recalibrated before being used again.

13. At the completion of the weighing, sum the weights at least twice to avoid numerical and reading errors. Some analysts do this by counting first the weights on the pan and then the empty spots in the weight box.

5.2   The Tools of Gravimetric Analysis

EQUIPMENT ASSOCIATED WITH THE WEIGHING OPERATION

Many solid substances absorb atmospheric moisture and as a consequence change in composition. This effect assumes appreciable proportions when a large surface area is exposed, as in the case of a sample that has been finely ground. Thus, wherever possible, analyses are based upon dried samples in order to free the results from dependence upon the humidity of the surrounding atmosphere.

Weighing Bottles. Samples are conveniently dried and stored in weighing bottles, two common varieties of which are illustrated in Figure 5.4. Ground glass contacting surfaces ensure a snug fit between container and lid. In the newer design, the lid acts as a cap; with this style of weighing bottle there is less possibility of the sample being entrained on and subsequently lost from a ground-glass surface. Weighing bottles usually have numbers from 1 to 100 etched on their sides for purposes of identification.

Polyethylene weighing bottles are commercially available; ruggedness is the principal advantage possessed by these over their glass counterparts.

Desiccators, Desiccants. Oven drying is by all odds the most convenient method for the evolution of adsorbed moisture from a sample. The technique cannot, of course, be employed where the sample undergoes decomposition at the ambient temperature of the oven. Furthermore, with some types of solids, the temperatures attainable in ordinary drying ovens are insufficient to effect complete removal of the bound water.

While they cool, dried materials are stored in desiccators; these provide a measure of protection from the uptake of moisture. As illustrated in Figure 5.5, the base section of a desiccator contains a quantity of chemical drying agent. Samples are placed on a perforated plate that is supported by a constriction in the wall. Lightly greased ground-glass surfaces ensure a tight seal between lid and base.

Fig. 5.4 (Above) Typical Weighing Bottles.

Fig. 5.5 (Right) A Typical Desiccator.

Several substances find use as drying agents in desiccators. Among these are anhydrous calcium chloride, calcium sulfate (Drierite[1]), anhydrous magnesium perchlorate (Anhydrone[2] or Dehydrite[3]), and phosphorous pentoxide. These are listed in an increasing order of effectiveness in removing moisture from a gas stream.

CRUCIBLES

Simple Crucibles. Simple crucibles serve as containers only. Of the two varieties available the more common comprises those whose weight remains constant within the limits of experimental error while in use. They

---

[1] (R) W. A. Hammond Drierite Co.

[2] (R) J. T. Baker Chemical Company.

[3] (R) Arthur H. Thomas Company.

are generally made of porcelain, aluminum oxide, silica, or platinum, and are employed to convert precipitates into suitable weighing forms. Crucibles made of nickel, iron, silver, or gold serve as containers for the high-temperature fusion of difficulty soluble samples. These are appreciably attacked by their contents; the fused mass will thus hold contaminants derived from the crucible. For this type of use the analyst chooses the crucible whose components will offer the least interference in subsequent phases of the analysis.

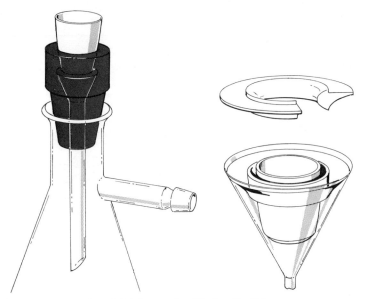

Fig. 5.6 Adapters for Filtering Crucibles.

Filtering Crucibles. Filtering crucibles may also be subdivided into two groups. There are those in which the filtering medium is an integral part of the crucible. In addition, there is the *Gooch crucible*, in which a filter mat (usually, but not always, asbestos) is supported upon a perforated bottom. A description of these is given in the next section.

The great saving in time often afforded by filtering crucibles is due to the use of a partial vacuum to speed the process. Heavy walled filter flasks equipped with adapters to accommodate the crucibles are employed for this purpose. Adapters for filter crucibles are encountered in considerable variety, two of which are illustrated in Figure 5.6; a diagram of a complete suction filtration train is shown in Figure 5.14.

EQUIPMENT EMPLOYED IN THE FILTRATION
PROCESS

An extremely common unit operation of gravimetric analysis involves the separation of a solid phase from the liquid in which it was formed; this requires the use of filtering media that will retain all of the former while offering little or no resistance to the flow of the latter.

Filtering Media. Asbestos is commonly used as the filtering medium in a Gooch crucible, being formed as a mat by suction of an aqueous suspension of the material through the small holes in the bottom of the crucible. Asbestos is a mineral of somewhat variable composition and structure. Since some forms are appreciably water soluble, use should be limited to material that has been especially selected and prepared for filtration purposes.

When using asbestos, care must be taken to bring the crucible and mat to constant weight under the same conditions as will be employed in the analysis; since the material is appreciably hygroscopic, uniform treatment is a necessity for satisfactory performance.

Small circles of glass matting are available commercially, and these can be employed in the bottom of a Gooch crucible in place of the asbestos mat; these are used in pairs to protect against accidental disintegration while adding liquid. They can tolerate temperatures in excess of 500° C and are a good deal less hygroscopic than asbestos.

Glass also finds application as a filtering medium in the form of fritted disks sealed permanently into filtering crucibles. These are known as sintered glass crucibles and are available in a variety of porosities. With extreme care, their use can be extended to temperatures as high as 500° C; normally, however, 150° to 200° C represents the upper practical temperature limit.

Filtering crucibles made entirely of fused quartz are also available; these may be taken to high temperatures and can be cooled rapidly without damage.

Unglazed porcelain can serve as a filtering medium. Crucibles of this type have the versatility of temperature range possessed by the Gooch crucible and are not as costly as fused quartz. They require no preparation comparable to the Gooch crucible and are not appreciably hygroscopic. Crucibles made of aluminum oxide offer similar advantages.

Paper is an important filtering medium for analysis; this material, however, is noticeably hygroscopic, and it is quite impractical to weigh a solid on a large disk of paper because the weight of the paper cannot be reproduced. Thus it is necessary to remove the paper before weighing is attempted; this is done by ignition in air.

Ashless filter paper, so-called because of the extremely small inorganic residue that remains after its ignition, is an important filtering medium for analysis. The fibers that go into the manufacture of this paper have been washed with hydrochloric and hydrofluoric acids; this ultimately results in a paper that is virtually free of inorganic matter. Thus, typically, 9- or 11-cm circles of such paper will leave an ash weighing less than 0.1 mg, an amount that is ordinarily negligible. Ashless paper is manufactured in various grades of porosity.

Gelatinous precipitates, such as hydrous iron (III) oxide, present special problems owing to their tendency to clog the pores of the paper upon which they are being retained. This problem can be minimized by mixing a dispersion of ashless filter paper pulp with the precipitate prior to filtration. The pulp may be prepared by briefly treating a piece of ashless paper with concentrated hydrochloric acid and washing the disintegrated mass free of acid; tablets of pulp are also commercially available.

5.3   Chemical Reagents

CLASSIFICATIONS OF REAGENTS

Technical or Commercial Grade. Chemicals labeled technical or commercial grade are of indeterminate quality and should only be used where high purity is not of paramount importance. Thus, the potassium dichromate and the sulfuric acid used in the preparation of cleaning solution can be of this grade. In general, however, technical or commercial grade chemicals are not used in analytical work.

Chemically Pure, or C.P. Grade. The term, *Chemically Pure*, has little definite meaning. Reagents so labeled are usually more refined than the technical grades, but no specifications define what is meant by the term. Thus, it is prudent to avoid the use of C.P. reagents in analytical work; if this is not possible, testing the reagent for contaminants of importance and also the running of frequent reagent blanks may be necessary.

U.S.P. Grade. U.S.P. chemicals have been found to conform to tolerances specified in the United States Pharmacopoeia.[4] The specifications are designed to control the presence of contaminants dangerous to health; thus, chemicals passing U.S.P. tests may still be quite heavily contaminated with impurities that are not physiological hazards.

Reagent Grade. For the most part the analytical chemist employs reagent grade chemicals in his work. These have been tested and found to conform to the minimum specifications set down by the Reagent Chemicals

[4] U.S. Pharmacopoeial Convention, *Pharmacopoeia of the United States of America,* 16th rev. Easton, Pa.: Mack Publishing Co., 1960.

Committee of the American Chemical Society.[5] In addition to meeting these requirements the results of the analysis are, in some instances, printed on the label. Thus reagent grade chemicals fall into two categories: namely, those that simply pass the tests and those for which the actual results of the tests are additionally supplied.

Primary Standard Grade. A discussion of the full implications of the term *primary standard* is to be found in Chapter 9; we shall merely state here that in addition to possessing desirable chemical properties, these are substances that are obtainable in extraordinarily pure form. Primary standard grade reagents are available commercially; these have been carefully analyzed and the assay value is printed on the label. An excellent source for primary standard chemicals is the National Bureau of Standards. The current edition of *Circular 552* lists these as well as *reference standards* —complex mixtures that have been exhaustively analyzed.[6]

5.4 Techniques and Operations

HANDLING REAGENTS AND SOLUTIONS

For successful analytical work the availability of reagents and solutions of established purity is of prime importance. A freshly opened bottle of a reagent grade chemical can be used with confidence in most applications; whether the same confidence is justified when this bottle is half full depends entirely upon the care with which it was handled after being opened. The rules that are given here will be successful in preventing contamination of reagents only if they are conscientiously followed.

1. Select the best available grade of chemical for analytical work. If there is a choice, pick the smallest bottle that will supply the desired quantity of substance.

2. Replace the top of every container immediately after removal of reagent; do not rely on having this done by someone else.

3. Stoppers should be held between the fingers and should never be set on the desk top.

4. Unless specifically directed to the contrary, never return any excess reagent or solution to a bottle; the minor saving represented by the return

---

[5] American Chemical Society, Committee on Analytical Reagents, *Reagent Chemicals, American Chemical Society Specifications.* Washington D.C.: American Chemical Society, 1955.

[6] United States Department of Commerce, *Standard Materials Issued by the National Bureau of Standards, Circular 552*, 3d ed. Washington D.C.: Government Printing Office, 1959.

of an excess is indeed a false economy compared to the risk of contaminating the entire bottle.

5. Again, unless specifically instructed otherwise, do not insert spoons, spatulas, or knives into a bottle containing a reagent chemical. Instead, shake the bottle vigorously with the cap in place to dislodge the contents; then pour out the desired quantity.

6. Keep the reagent shelf and the laboratory balances clean. Immediately clean up any spilled chemicals, even though others may be making the same transfer of reagent in the same area.

PRELIMINARY OPERATIONS

Cleaning of Equipment. Care must be taken that all glass and porcelain ware are thoroughly clean. The use of detergents is recommended for this purpose. After thorough cleaning, an extensive rinse with tap water followed by a rinse with several small portions of distilled water should yield an object that shows uniform and unbroken wetting on its inner surfaces. Glassware seldom needs drying before use; this practice should, in fact, be discouraged on the grounds of being wasteful of time and potentially the source of contamination.

If a grease film should remain after thorough cleaning with detergent, a cleaning solution consisting of sodium or potassium dichromate in strong sulfuric acid may be employed. For best results it is warmed to about 70° C. After cleaning with this reagent it is important to rinse the glassware numerous times to remove the last traces of dichromate ion which adhere strongly to glass or porcelain surfaces. Hot cleaning solution will rapidly attack plant and animal matter and is thus a potentially dangerous preparation. Any spillages should be promptly diluted with copious volumes of water.

> **Preparation of Cleaning Solution.** In a 500-ml heat-resistant conical flask mix 10 to 15 grams of potassium dichromate with about 15 ml of water. Add concentrated sulfuric acid slowly and with thorough swirling between increments. The contents of the flask will become a semisolid red mass; add just enough sulfuric acid to bring the mass into solution. Allow to cool somewhat before attempting to transfer to a soft glass bottle. The solution may be reused until it acquires the green color of chromium (III) ion, at which time it must be discarded.

Marking of Equipment. Most chemical analyses are run in duplicate; it is therefore necessary to mark all beakers and crucibles to indicate the location of each sample. The identification of beakers is simple—the etched area on each beaker can be semipermanently marked with a pencil. Special marking inks are available for porcelain surfaces; after the marking is made, it is baked permanently into the glaze. A saturated solution of iron (III) chloride can be used in the same fashion although it is not as satisfactory as the commercial preparations.

Preparation of a Desiccator for Service. The filling of a desiccator is readily accomplished by employing a crude paper funnel to direct the flow of desiccant to the bottom section. Any dust adhering to the upper walls should be scrupulously wiped off before putting the desiccator into service. The ground-glass surfaces should be sufficiently greased to allow a tight seal; this is indicated when the contacting surfaces appear transparent when viewed from above. An excess of grease is a nuisance and should be avoided. It is good practice to label the desiccator, indicating the date of filling and the drying agent employed.

MANIPULATIONS ASSOCIATED WITH THE WEIGHING OPERATION

Use of the Desiccator. Whether it is being replaced or removed, the lid of the desiccator is properly moved by a sliding, rather than a lifting, motion. An air-tight seal is achieved by slight rotation and direct downward pressure upon the positioned lid.

When a heated object is placed in a desiccator, the increased pressure of the enclosed air is often sufficient to break the seal between lid and base; if heating has caused the grease on the ground-glass surfaces to soften, there is the further danger that the lid may slide off and break. Upon cooling, the opposite effect is likely to occur, the interior of the desiccator being under a partial vacuum. Both of these conditions are undesirable because of the danger of disrupting or contaminating the sample being stored. While it in part defeats the purpose of the desiccator, it is wise to allow some cooling to occur before finally sealing the lid, and also to break the seal several times during cooling in order to relieve any vacuum that may have developed. It is also prudent to lock the lid in place with one's thumbs while moving the desiccator to ensure against accidental breakage.

Very hygroscopic materials should be stored in containers equipped with snugly fitting covers, the covers remaining in place during storage in the desiccator. Other substances may be stored with container covers removed.

Manipulation of Weighing Bottles. Heating of many solid materials at 105° to 110° C for about an hour is sufficient to remove moisture bound to the surface of the particles. Figure 5.7 depicts the arrangement recommended for the drying of a sample in a weighing bottle. Note that the bottle is contained in a labeled beaker, which in turn is covered by a watch glass supported on glass hooks. In this manner the sample is protected from accidental contamination while the free access of air is maintained.

This arrangement also satisfactorily accommodates crucibles containing precipitates that can be freed of moisture by simple drying.

Weighing data will often be significantly affected by the moisture picked up as a consequence of handling a dried weighing bottle with one's fingers. In such cases the bottle should be manipulated with tongs or with strips of clean paper. The latter technique is illustrated in Figure 5.8, which shows the sequence followed in weighing a sample by difference. The sample is transferred from the bottle to the container, the utmost care being taken to avoid losses during transfer; gentle tapping of the weighing bottle with its top provides adequate control over the process.

Fig. 5.7 Arrangement for the Drying of Samples.

Tared Watch Glasses. When weighing out a precisely known quantity of solid, use may be made of a pair of tared watch glasses. These have been carefully matched according to weight; a rest point that corresponds closely to the zero point will be observed with one of these glasses on each pan of the balance. In practice, this rest point is determined, the desired weight is introduced to the right pan watch glass, and the required amount of solid is then added to the left pan watch glass by means of a spatula, care being taken to avoid spillage. When balance has been achieved, the solid is transferred from the watch glass to the desired container, a camel's hair brush or a stream of water being employed to assure quantitative transfer. This technique is suitable only for the weighing of substantially non-hygroscopic materials.

The Weighing of Hygroscopic Substances. Many substances are hygroscopic to a relatively limited extent. These often equilibrate very rapidly, taking up moisture almost to capacity in a short space of time. Where this effect is pronounced, individual weighing bottles should be used, the approximate weight of a sample being introduced to each. After drying and cooling, the exact weight is determined by difference, care being taken to remove the sample and replace the top of the weighing bottle as rapidly as possible.

The Weighing of Liquids. The weight of a liquid is always obtained by difference. Samples that are noncorrosive and relatively nonvolatile can be weighed into a tared container fitted with a snugly fitting cover, such as a weighing bottle. If the sample is extremely volatile or corrosive, it should be sealed in a tared glass ampoule before weighing. The bulb of the ampoule is first heated. Then the neck is immersed in the sample; as cool-

Fig. 5.8 The Weighing Operation. A convenient method for transfer of a solid for weighing by difference.

ing occurs the liquid is drawn into the bulb. The neck is then sealed off with a small flame. After cooling, the bulb and contents are weighed, any glass removed during the sealing being also included in this weighing. The ampoule is then broken in the vessel where the sample is desired; for very precise work, the preparation of dilute solutions in volumetric flasks by this method requires a small correction for the volume of the glass in the ampoule.

MANIPULATIONS ASSOCIATED WITH SOLUTIONS

An arrangement such as that illustrated in Figure 5.9 is satisfactory for most evaporations. The process is sometimes difficult to control owing to the tendency of some solutions to superheat locally. The bumping that results, if sufficiently violent, can lead to the physical loss of part of the sample. This danger is minimized by careful and gentle heating; the introduction of glass beads, where permissible, is also helpful.

Fig. 5.9 Arrangement for the Evaporation of Liquids.

MANIPULATIONS ASSOCIATED WITH THE
FILTRATION AND IGNITION PROCESSES

Preparation of Crucibles. Irrespective of type, a crucible employed in converting a precipitate into a form suitable for weighing must maintain a substantially constant weight throughout the drying or ignition process; it is thus necessary to demonstrate that this condition applies at the outset.

As a first step, each crucible should be inspected for defects; this is of particular importance where the crucible has previously been subjected to high temperatures. A porcelain crucible should be placed upright on a hard surface and gently tapped with a pencil. A clear, ringing tone indicates an intact crucible while a dull sound is characteristic of one that is cracked and should be discarded.

The crucible is then cleaned thoroughly. Filtering crucibles are conveniently cleaned by backwashing with suction.

Finally, the crucible should be brought to constant weight using the same heating cycle as will be required for the precipitate. For most purposes, agreement within 0.2 mg between consecutive weighings can be considered as constant weight.

Decantation. The actual filtration process may be considered to consist of the three operations of decantation, washing, and transfer. Decan-

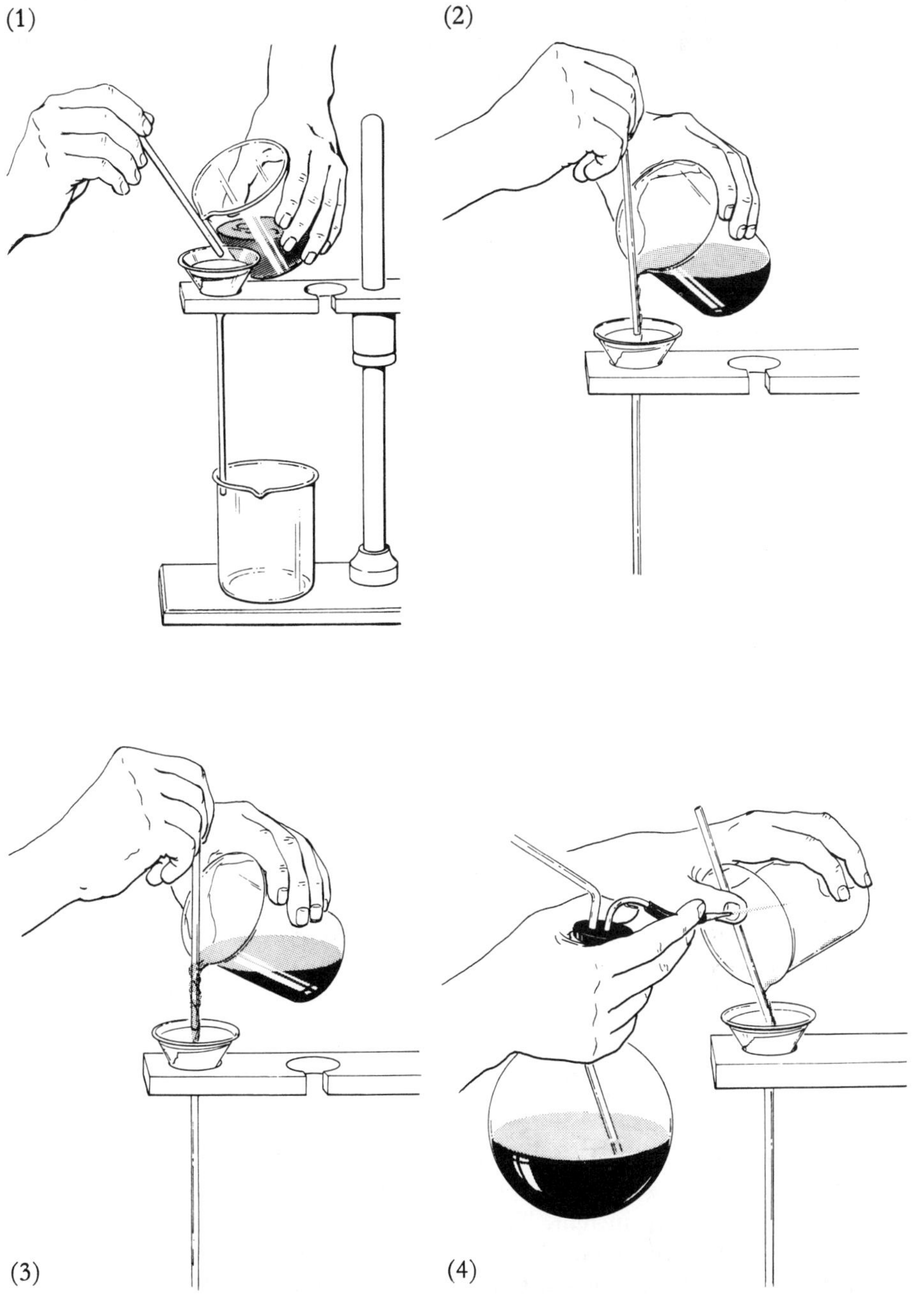

(1)

(2)

(3)

(4)

Fig. 5.10 The Filtering Operation. Techniques for decantation and transfer of precipitates are illustrated.

tation is the process of gently pouring off the liquid phase while leaving the precipitated solid essentially undisturbed. The pores of any filtering medium will become clogged with precipitate; the longer the transfer of solid can be delayed, the more rapid will be the over-all process. To this end, the liquid phase is decanted through the filter, a stirring rod being employed to direct the flow (see Figure 5.10). Wash liquid is then added to the beaker and is thoroughly mixed with the precipitate; after allowing the solid to settle, this too is decanted through the filter. It can be seen that the principal washing of the precipitate is carried out *before* the solid is transferred, a procedure to be highly recommended since it results in a more thoroughly washed precipitate and a more rapid filtration.

Many precipitates have the exasperating property of spreading over wetted surfaces against the force of gravity; this is known as *creeping*. It is because of this phenomenon that the cone of a paper filter is never filled more than three quarters full at any time. Similar precautions must be observed with filter crucibles.

Washing. Several washings with small volumes of liquid are more effective in removing soluble contaminants than the same total volume used in one washing.

Transfer of the Precipitate. Figure 5.10 shows the method whereby the decantation and transfer operations are performed. With respect to the latter, the bulk of the precipitate is moved from beaker to filter by means of suitably directed streams of wash liquid; as always, a stirring rod is used to provide direction to the flow of liquid to the filtering medium.

Removal of the last traces of precipitate is accomplished with a *rubber policeman*. This is a small section of tubing, one end of which is crimped shut; it is fitted on the end of a stirring rod and is used to scrub those surfaces to which precipitate may cling. It should be wetted with wash liquid before use. Any solid collected is added to the main portion on the filter. An alternate procedure which is preferable where appropriate is to use small pieces of ashless paper to collect the last traces of solid; this is most conveniently accomplished with the aid of clean forceps.

SPECIFIC DIRECTIONS FOR THE USE OF ASHLESS FILTER PAPER

Preparation of a Filter Paper. Figure 5.11 illustrates the sequence followed in folding a filter paper and seating it in a funnel. The paper is first folded exactly in half. The second fold is made so that the corners fail to coincide by about $\frac{1}{8}$ inch in each dimension. A small triangular section is torn from the short corner; this permits a better seating of the filter in the funnel. The paper is next opened out so that a cone is formed; it is then gently seated in the funnel with the aid of water from a wash bottle. When properly seated, there will be no leakage of air between paper and funnel; as a result, the stem of the funnel will be filled with an unbroken column of liquid, a condition that markedly increases the rate of filtration.

A gelatinous precipitate should not be allowed to dry out before the washing cycle is complete because the mass shrinks and develops cracks on

(1)   (2)

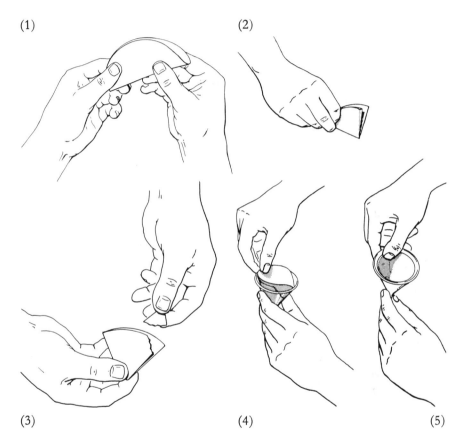

(3)   (4)   (5)

Fig. 5.11 Technique for Folding and Seating of a Filter Paper.

drying; any liquid subsequently added merely passes through these cracks and accomplishes little or no washing.

Transfer of Paper and Precipitate to Crucible. Upon completion of the filtration and washing steps, the filter paper and its contents must be transferred from the funnel to a tared crucible. Because ashless paper has very low wet strength, considerable care must be exercised in performing this operation. The danger of tearing can be reduced considerably if the paper is allowed to dry partially prior to transfer from the funnel.

Figure 5.12 illustrates the preferred method of transfer. First, the cone is gently flattened along its upper edge and the corners are folded inward. Next, the top is folded over. Finally, the paper and contents are eased into the crucible so that the bulk of the precipitate is near the bottom.

Ashing of a Filter Paper. If a heat lamp is available, the crucible is placed on a clean, nonreactive surface; an asbestos pad covered with a

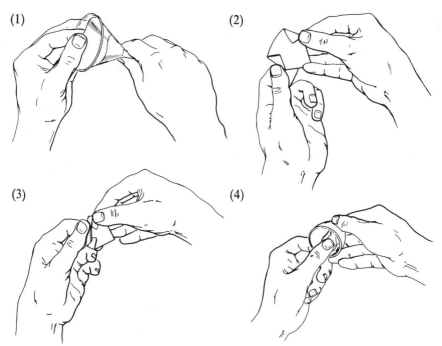

Fig. 5.12 Method for Transfer of a Filter Paper and Precipitate to a Crucible.

layer of aluminum foil is very satisfactory. The lamp is then positioned about $\frac{1}{2}$ inch from the top of the crucible and is turned on. Charring of the paper will take place without further intervention; the process is considerably accelerated if the paper can be moistened with no more than one drop of strong ammonium nitrate solution. Removal of the remaining carbon is accomplished with a burner as described in the following paragraphs.

Considerably more attention must be paid the process when a burner is employed to ash a filter paper. Since the burner can produce much higher temperatures, there exists the danger of expelling moisture so rapidly in the initial stages of heating that mechanical loss of the precipitate occurs. A similar possibility arises if the paper is allowed to flame. Finally, as long as there is carbon present there is also the possibility of chemical reduction of the precipitate; this is a serious problem where reoxidation following ashing of the paper is not convenient.

In order to minimize these difficulties the crucible is placed as illustrated in Figure 5.13. The tilted position of the crucible allows for the ready access of air. A clean crucible cover should be located nearby, ready for use if

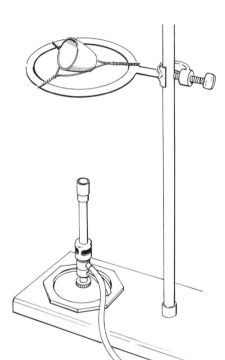

Fig. 5.13 Ignition of the Precipitate. Arrangement of the crucible for the preliminary charring of the paper is illustrated.

necessary. Heating is then commenced with a small burner flame. This is gradually increased as moisture is evolved and the paper begins to char. The smoke that is given off serves as a guide with respect to the intensity of heating that can be safely tolerated. Normally this will appear to come off in thin wisps. If the volume of smoke emitted rapidly increases, the burner should be temporarily removed; this condition indicates that the paper is about to flash. If, despite precautions, a flame does appear, it should be immediately snuffed out with the crucible cover. (The cover may become discolored owing to the condensation of carbonaceous products; these must ultimately be removed by ignition so that the absence of entrained particles of precipitate can be confirmed.) Finally, when no further smoking can be detected, the residual carbon is removed by gradually lowering the crucible into the full flame of the burner. Strong heating, as necessary, can then be undertaken. Care must be exercised to avoid heating the crucible in the reducing portion of the flame.

The foregoing procedure must precede final ignition of the sample in a muffle furnace, a reducing atmosphere being equally undesirable here.

SPECIFIC DIRECTIONS FOR THE USE OF FILTERING CRUCIBLES

Preparation of a Gooch Crucible. A white, silky grade of long-fibered asbestos is required for use in Gooch crucibles. There should be few, if any, inclusions of iron in the material. In preparing it for use, asbestos should be cut into 0.5-cm lengths; any large clumps of fibers should be manually broken apart. It should then be digested overnight in $4\ F$ hydrochloric acid. Following this, the fibers should be collected, washed free of acid, and stored as an aqueous slurry.

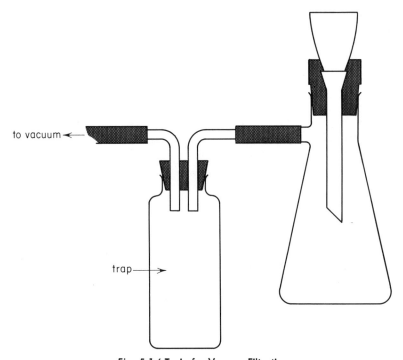

to vacuum

trap

Fig. 5.14 Train for Vacuum Filtration.

An asbestos mat is prepared by arranging the Gooch crucible in a vacuum filtration train similar to that illustrated in Figure 5.14. A few milliliters of the well-mixed and diluted suspension are poured into the crucible and allowed to stand for about a minute. In this interval the heavier filaments tend to settle and form the basis for supporting the finer fibers; most of the liquid also drains off. Next suction is applied to set the mat. The mat is then washed until no further loss of asbestos can be detected in the washings; several hundred milliliters may be required. Finally, the crucible is dried and ignited to constant weight.

A proper mat is one through which the pattern of holes in the crucible can barely be discerned when viewed against a strong light. Once set, a vacuum must always be applied when introducing material to the crucible. Care must be taken to avoid destroying the mat through the direct pouring of liquids. The flow is always directed with a stirring rod down the wall of the crucible; the mat can be further protected through introduction of a small perforated disk called a *Witt plate*.

Ignitions with a Filtering Crucible. In general, the use of a filtering crucible tends to shorten the time necessary for the ignition of a precipitate. The porous bottom of such a crucible, however, greatly increases the danger of reducing the precipitate with the burner flame. This difficulty is readily circumvented by placing the filtering crucible inside an ordinary crucible and igniting both.

The reader is again cautioned against subjecting crucibles to unnecessarily abrupt changes in temperature.

RULES FOR THE MANIPULATION OF HEATED OBJECTS

1. A crucible that has been subjected to the full flame of a burner should be allowed to cool in place momentarily before being moved to the desiccator.

2. Hot objects should not be placed directly on the desk top but should be set on an asbestos pad or a clean wire gauze.

3. Manipulations should be practiced first to demonstrate that adequate control can be maintained with the implements employed.

4. The tongs and forceps employed in handling heated objects should be kept scrupulously clean. The tips, particularly, should not be allowed to come in contact with the desk top.

RULES FOR KEEPING THE LABORATORY NOTEBOOK

1. The notebook should be permanently bound with consecutively numbered pages.

2. Entries should be legible and well spaced from one another. Most notebooks have more than ample room; crowding of data is unnecessary.

3. The first few pages of the notebook should be reserved for a table of contents, which should be conscientiously kept up to date.

4. All data should be entered directly into the notebook, and in ink.

(a) Entries should be liberally identified with labels. If a series of weights refers to a set of empty crucibles, they should be labeled "Empty Crucible Weights," or some such. The significance of an entry is obvious when it is recorded, but rapidly loses this quality with the passage of time.

(b) It is good practice to date each notebook page as it is used.

(c) Erroneous entries should not be erased, nor should they be obliterated. If some entry has been erroneously made, it should be crossed out with a single horizontal line; the corrected entry should then be entered as nearby as possible. Numbers should never be written over; in time it may be difficult to recall which was written over which.

(d) Pages should not be removed from the notebook. Rather, a single line drawn diagonally across the page to be disregarded is sufficient. It is proper to make a brief notation of the reason for striking out the page.

Suggested Form. A satisfactory format involves the consecutive use of all pages for the recording of data. Upon completion of the analysis, the next pair of facing pages is used to summarize the results. The right-hand page should contain:

(1) The title of the experiment—for example, *The Gravimetric Determination of Chloride.*

(2) A brief statement of the principles upon which the analysis is based.

(3) A summary of the data collected, and the result calculated for each sample in the set.

(4) A report of the best value (mean or median, whichever is adjudged the better) for the set and a statement of the precision attained in the analysis.

A sample summary is shown in Table 5-2.

The left-hand page should show:

(1) Equations for the principal reactions in the analysis.

(2) An equation that shows the calculation employed in computing the results.

(3) The calculations themselves.

TABLE 5-2

Gravimetric Determination of Chloride

The chloride in a soluble sample was precipitated as AgCl and weighed as such

	1.	2.	3.
Weight of bottle + sample, grams	27.1911	26.7874	26.4065
Weight of bottle	26.7874	26.4065	25.9873
Weight of sample taken, gram	0.4037	0.3809	0.4192
Weight of crucible + AgCl, grams	21.8309	21.4140	21.5743
Weight of crucible	21.3406	20.9527	21.0683
Weight of AgCl found, gram	0.4903	0.4613	0.5060
Percent Cl^-	30.04	29.96	29.86
Average		29.95	
Deviation	0.09	0.01	0.09
Average deviation		0.06	
(or) Range		0.18	

Problems

1. Determine the weight of the following to the nearest 0.1 mg from the accompanying long swing data:
- (a) Swings for empty balance   6.7, 13.8, 6.9, 13.6, 7.1
  - Weights on pan and rider   20 grams, 1 gram, 400 mg
    - Swings with chain at 67 mg   9.3, 17.6, 9.5, 17.4, 9.6
    - Swings with chain at 68 mg   7.5, 12.4, 7.7, 12.2, 8.0
      - ans. 21.4679 grams
- (b) Swings for empty balance   6.8, 12.6, 7.1, 12.4, 7.3
  - Weights on pan and rider   5 grams
    - Swings with chain at 21 mg   12.4, 19.3, 12.6, 18.9, 12.9
    - Swings with chain at 22 mg   10.0, 15.5, 10.2, 15.3, 10.4
- (c) Swings for empty balance   5.8, 14.6, 6.1, 14.4, 6.3
  - Weights on pan and rider   10 grams, 700 mg
    - Swings with chain at 2 mg   9.1, 17.3, 9.3, 17.0, 9.5
    - Swings with chain at 3 mg   6.5, 13.4, 6.7, 13.2, 6.9

2. Determine the weight of the following to the nearest 0.1 mg from the accompanying short swing data:
- (a) Swings for empty balance   7.8, 12.4
  - Weights on pan and rider   5 grams, 2 grams, 300 mg
    - Swings with chain at 37 mg   9.4, 16.0
    - Swings with chain at 38 mg   7.3, 11.5
      - ans. 7.3379 grams

(b) Swings for empty balance   7.0, 12.2
     Weights on pan and rider   10 grams, 600 mg
       Swings with chain at 47 mg   7.7, 11.9
       Swings with chain at 48 mg   4.2, 9.0
(c) Swings for empty balance   7.7, 12.5
     Weights on pan and rider   20 grams
       Swings with rider at 7 mg   10.5, 14.3
       Swings with rider at 8 mg   7.6, 11.0

3. Estimate the relative error (in parts per thousand) attributable to the weighing operation when
   (a) a 5-gram sample is weighed directly to the nearest 0.1 mg
   (b) a 0.1-gram sample is weighed directly to the nearest mg
   (c) the weight of a 0.5-gram sample is obtained as the difference between two weighings carried to the nearest 0.1 mg
   (d) the weight of a 40-mg sample is obtained as the difference between two weighings carried to the nearest 0.1 mg

4. Brass weights were used to determine the mass of the accompanying samples. Correct each for the effect of buoyancy.
   (a) 0.4800 gram of diethyl ether ($d = 0.714$)
   (b) 0.2540 gram of hexachloroethane ($d = 2.09$)
   (c) 0.8440 gram of vanadium ($d = 5.87$)
   (d) 1.110 grams of nickel ($d = 8.90$)
   (e) 2.104 grams of mercury ($d = 13.55$)

$$\left(\mathbf{6} \right)$$

The Solubility of Precipitates

The ultimate accuracy of a gravimetric analysis is limited in part by the loss of precipitate owing to its solubility in the reaction medium and in the wash liquid employed for purification. These losses often assume serious proportions, particularly where extensive washing is necessary to assure a pure precipitate or where an overly soluble precipitate is involved. Although he is powerless to eliminate solubility losses completely, the chemist does have a degree of control over the factors that influence the solubility of precipitates; by the judicious regulation of these and the employment of a sample of suitable size, he is usually able to reduce solubility losses to the point where their effect upon the result of the analysis is a tolerable minimum.

This chapter is devoted to a discussion of the common variables that influence the solubility of precipitates—that is, temperature, pH, reagent concentration, salt concentration, and solvent composition. Some of these are readily treated in quantitative terms by means of the equilibrium law; we shall examine in considerable detail the techniques used for this purpose.

6.1 The Application of Solubility Product Constants

THE SOLUBILITY PRODUCT CONSTANT

In Chapter 2 we presented an expression for the solubility product. Thus for the equilibrium

$$A_x B_y \rightleftharpoons x A^{y+} + y B^{x-}$$

the solubility product constant is given by

$$K_{sp} = [A^{y+}]^x[B^{x-}]^y$$

This constant is generally applicable in defining equilibrium conditions for saturated solutions of slightly soluble strong electrolytes.

Solubility product constants have been determined for a large number of inorganic compounds; numerical values for many of these will be found in Table A-5 of the Appendix. The examples that follow demonstrate the uses to which such data can be put.

★EXAMPLE. How many milligrams of $Ba(IO_3)_2$ can be dissolved in 150 ml of water at 25° C?

$$Ba(IO_3)_2 \rightleftharpoons Ba^{2+} + 2IO_3^- \qquad K_{sp} = 1.57 \times 10^{-9}$$

Setting x equal to the solubility of $Ba(IO_3)_2$ in formula weights per liter it follows that

$$[Ba^{2+}] = x \text{ mol/liter}$$

$$[IO_3^-] = 2x \text{ mol/liter}^1$$

Substituting these values into the expression for K_{sp}

$$[Ba^{2+}][IO_3^-]^2 = 1.57 \times 10^{-9}$$

$$x(2x)^2 = 4x^3 = 1.57 \times 10^{-9}$$

$$x = 7.3 \times 10^{-4} \text{ gfw/liter}$$

Multiplication of this result by the formula weight of $Ba(IO_3)_2$ in milligrams (487×1000) yields the solubility in milligrams per liter.

$$\text{solubility} = 7.3 \times 10^{-4} \text{ gfw/liter} \times 4.87 \times 10^5 \text{ mg/gfw}$$

The solubility in mg/150 ml is thus

$$\text{solubility} = 7.3 \times 10^{-4} \times 4.87 \times 10^5 \times \tfrac{150}{1000}$$

$$= 53 \text{ mg/150 ml}$$

The solubility product constant can be used to predict whether or not a precipitate will form under a given set of conditions.

★EXAMPLE. Will a precipitate of $AgBrO_3$ form when equal volumes of a 0.001 F $AgNO_3$ solution and 0.02 F $KBrO_3$ solution are mixed?

The precipitation reaction will occur only if the solubility product constant is exceeded by the product of the initial Ag^+ and BrO_3^- concentrations. In this problem, the initial concentration of Ag^+ ion will be 0.0005 F and of BrO_3^- will be 0.01 F since dilution

---

[1] The student should understand clearly that the $2x$ used in this equation represents the IO_3^- concentration in the solution and *not two times the IO_3^- concentration*. This is sometimes a point of confusion; it is readily avoided by recalling the quantity for which x stands, it being the formal solubility of $Ba(IO_3)_2$ in this case.

will have occurred in the mixing; the product of these concentrations is given by

$$F_{Ag^+} \times F_{BrO_3^-} = (5 \times 10^{-4})(1 \times 10^{-2})$$

$$= 5 \times 10^{-6} \text{ mol}^2/\text{liter}^2$$

The solubility product for $AgBrO_3$, 6×10^{-5} mol^2/liter^2, is larger than the concentration product obtained above. Therefore we conclude that precipitation will not occur.

★EXAMPLE. What is the minimum silver ion concentration required to initiate the precipitation of $AgBrO_3$ from a 0.01 F solution of $KBrO_3$?

Precipitation will occur when the product of the initial concentrations of Ag^+ and BrO_3^- just exceeds the solubility product. Since we know the BrO_3^- concentration of the solution, we can calculate the equilibrium concentration of Ag^+ that corresponds to this value. This will be the maximum Ag^+ concentration that can exist in solutions with that BrO_3^- concentration. It will also represent the minimum Ag^+ concentration needed for the precipitation of $AgBrO_3$ from such solutions.

$$[Ag^+][BrO_3^-] = 6 \times 10^{-5}$$

$$[Ag^+](0.01) = 6 \times 10^{-5}$$

$$[Ag^+] = 6 \times 10^{-3} \text{ mol/liter}$$

THE COMMON ION EFFECT

From a knowledge of the LeChatelier principle we would predict that the solubility of an electrolyte should be lowered by the presence in solution of an excess of one of the ions common to the compound. This has been amply verified experimentally. The chemist performing gravimetric analyses takes advantage of this fact by using an excess of precipitating agent to reduce solubility losses. The quantitative aspects of the common ion effect can be treated with the aid of the mass law. Some examples are given below.

★EXAMPLE. What is the solubility of $Ba(IO_3)_2$ in formula weights per liter in a 0.020 F solution of KIO_3? The K_{sp} for $Ba(IO_3)_2$ is 1.57×10^{-9}.

$$Ba(IO_3)_2 \rightleftharpoons Ba^{2+} + 2IO_3^-$$

$$[Ba^{2+}][IO_3^-]^2 = 1.57 \times 10^{-9}$$

If we represent the solubility of $Ba(IO_3)_2$ in formula weights per liter by x, it follows that

$$[Ba^{2+}] = x \text{ mol/liter}$$

Iodate ions arise from two sources—namely, the KIO_3 and the $Ba(IO_3)_2$. The contribution from the former is 0.02 F and the latter

$2x$. The total iodate concentration is the sum of these

$$[IO_3^-] = (0.02 + 2x) \text{ mol/liter}$$

Substituting these quantities into the solubility product expression we get

$$x(0.02 + 2x)^2 = 1.57 \times 10^{-9}$$

Since the exact solution for x will involve a cubic equation, it is worthwhile to make some approximations in order to simplify the algebra. The solubility of $Ba(IO_3)_2$ is not very great, as indicated by the small numerical value of K_{sp}; therefore, it is reasonable to suppose that the concentration of IO_3^- due to solution of the $Ba(IO_3)_2$ is small relative to the iodate concentration from the KIO_3. If we assume that $2x$ is negligible relative to 0.02, that is,

$$(0.02 + 2x) \cong 0.02$$

the expression then becomes much simpler

$$x(0.02)^2 = 1.57 \times 10^{-9}$$

$$x = \frac{1.57 \times 10^{-9}}{4 \times 10^{-4}} = 3.9 \times 10^{-6} \text{ fw/liter}$$

We must now check our assumption; that is, that

$$(0.02 + 2 \times 3.9 \times 10^{-6}) \cong 0.02$$

We see that it was quite reasonable and can conclude that the approximate solution is valid.

It is interesting to compare the solubility of barium iodate in 0.02 F potassium iodate with the solubility in pure water, calculated previously to be 7.3×10^{-4}. The amount dissolved in water is nearly two hundred times greater, which illustrates the rather large effect the presence of a common ion can have upon solubility.

★EXAMPLE. Calculate the solubility of $Ba(IO_3)_2$ in the solution that results when 100 ml of 0.014 F $BaCl_2$ are mixed with 100 ml of 0.030 F KIO_3.

As a first step, we must evaluate the number of milliformula weights of reactants to determine whether an excess of one will remain after reaction has occurred.

$$\text{no. mfw } BaCl_2 = 100 \times 0.014 = 1.4$$

$$\text{no. mfw } KIO_3 = 100 \times 0.030 = 3.0$$

If the formation of $Ba(IO_3)_2$ is complete

$$\text{no. mfw } KIO_3 \text{ remaining} = 3.0 - 2 \times 1.4 = 0.2$$

Since the volume of the mixture is 200 ml, the formal concentration of KIO_3 will be

$$F_{KIO_3} = \frac{0.200}{200} = 1 \times 10^{-3} F$$

The problem now consists of determining the solubility of $Ba(IO_3)_2$ in a $1.00 \times 10^{-3} F$ solution of KIO_3. If we let x be the solubility in formula weights per liter, then

$$[Ba^{2+}] = x \text{ mol/liter}$$

and as before

$$[IO_3^-] = (1 \times 10^{-3} + 2x) \text{ mol/liter}$$

$$(x)(1 \times 10^{-3} + 2x)^2 = 1.57 \times 10^{-9}$$

Let us again assume that x is small; then

$$x(1 \times 10^{-3})^2 = 1.57 \times 10^{-9}$$

$$x = 1.57 \times 10^{-3}$$

If we examine the original assumption, however, that

$$(1 \times 10^{-3} + 2 \times 1.57 \times 10^{-3}) \cong 1 \times 10^{-3}$$

we see that it is not satisfactory. A more exact solution for the equation must be found. Rearranging the original equation to collect all terms on one side, we find that

$$x(2x + 1 \times 10^{-3})^2 - 1.57 \times 10^{-9} = 0$$

The solution is then obtained by successive approximation. If $x = 0$, the left side of the equation is negative and if $x = 1 \times 10^{-3}$, it is positive; that is,

$$9 \times 10^{-9} - 1.57 \times 10^{-9} = 7.4 \times 10^{-9}$$

Therefore the correct solution is somewhat smaller than 1×10^{-3}. Letting $x = 0.5 \times 10^{-3}$, gives

$$2 \times 10^{-9} - 1.57 \times 10^{-9} = 0.4 \times 10^{-9}$$

and while this is closer to a true solution, the correct value of x is still smaller than 0.5×10^{-3}. Assuming $x = 0.4 \times 10^{-3}$, we find

$$1.3 \times 10^{-9} - 1.57 \times 10^{-9} = -0.3 \times 10^{-9}$$

Since the algebraic sum is now negative, x must lie between 0.4×10^{-3} and 0.5×10^{-3}. By substituting further values for x between these limits, we find that

$$x = 0.44 \times 10^{-3} \text{ fw/liter}$$

Calculations of this type suggest that the solubility of a precipitate theoretically decreases rapidly and approaches zero at high concentrations of the common ion. Thus it might be concluded that use of the largest possible excess of precipitating agent would be desirable in order to reduce solubility losses in the analysis to the very minimum. Actually, however, this is not the case; with high concentrations of the common ion other factors start to operate which result in marked departures from the theoretical behavior. As a consequence, actual *increases* in solubility are often observed. These factors include complex formation and effects due to increased electrolyte concentrations.

We may summarize by stating that a moderate excess of the precipitating reagent is commonly used to reduce solubility losses in gravimetric analysis, but large excesses generally have a deleterious effect and are avoided.

EFFECT OF pH ON SOLUBILITY

Types of Compounds Affected by pH. The solubilities of most of the precipitates of importance in quantitative analysis are affected by the hydronium or hydroxyl ion concentration of the solvent. Two types of pH dependence can be distinguished. The first of these is a simple common ion effect in which either the hydroxyl ion or the hydronium ion is one of the constituents of the precipitate. With magnesium hydroxide, for example,

$$Mg(OH)_2 \rightleftharpoons Mg^{2+} + 2OH^-$$

the solubility decreases with increasing hydroxyl ion concentrations. The techniques described in the previous section can be used to calculate its solubility for any particular hydronium-ion concentration.

The second type of dependence is more complicated and is encountered when the anions or cations of the precipitate are capable of reacting with hydronium or hydroxyl ions of the aqueous solvent. As an example of this class of compounds consider calcium fluoride, a salt of the weak acid, hydrogen fluoride. The solubility of this compound increases with increasing acidity as a result of the following sequence:

$$CaF_2 \rightleftharpoons Ca^{2+} + 2F^-$$
$$+$$
$$2H_3O^+$$
$$\updownarrow$$
$$2HF + 2H_2O$$

By the LeChatelier principle, we predict that increases in the hydronium ion concentration of the solution will result in an increase in the hydrogen fluoride concentration and a decrease in the fluoride ion concentration. The latter change, however, is partially offset by a shift to the right in the solubility equilibrium; the net effect is an increase in the solubility of the precipitate.

Most of the compounds in which we will be interested are salts of weak acids and will behave in a manner similar to calcium fluoride. Exceptions are the hydroxides of several of the metallic ions and the salts of strong acids—notably some of the halides and oxyhalides.

Quantitative Treatment of Multiple Equilibria. We shall frequently be faced with the problem of calculating the concentration of constituents in a solution in which several competing equilibrium reactions are occurring simultaneously. The dissolution of calcium fluoride in an aqueous solution, cited above, is an example. As a more general case consider the hypothetical precipitate AB which dissolves to give A and B ions

$$AB \rightleftharpoons A + B$$
$$+ \quad +$$
$$C \quad D$$
$$\Updownarrow \quad \Updownarrow$$
$$AC \quad BD$$

If A and B are capable of reacting with species C and D to form the soluble substances AC and BD, the introduction of either C or D into the solution will cause a shift in the solubility equilibrium in such a direction as to increase the solubility of AB.

The calculation of the solubility of AB in a case such as this requires knowledge of the formal concentrations of C and D as well as equilibrium constants for all three of the equilibria. Generally several algebraic expressions are needed to describe completely the concentration relationships in such a case; not infrequently the chemist finds the solving of these algebraic equations more formidable than the task of setting them up.

One point that should be constantly borne in mind by the student when dealing with multiple equilibria is that the validity and form of a given equilibrium-constant expression is in no way affected by the existence of additional competing equilibria in the solution. Thus, in the present case the solubility product expression for AB describes the relationship between the concentrations of A and B in the solution regardless of whether or not C and D are present; that is, the product $[A][B]$ is a constant under any conditions as long as any solid AB is present. The *amount* of AB that dissolves is greater in the presence of C or D, but this is not because the product of the concentrations of A and B has changed but rather because some of the precipitate has been converted to AC and BD.

In the following paragraphs we shall present a systematic approach by which any equilibrium problem involving several equilibria can be attacked. The several general steps to be followed will then be applied to some solubility problems.

Method for the Solution of Problems Involving Several Equilibria

1. Write down chemical equations for all the reactions that appear to have any bearing on the problem.

2. State in terms of equilibrium concentrations what is being sought in the problem.

3. Write equilibrium-constant expressions for all of the equilibria shown in (1).

4. Write mass-balance equations for the system. These are algebraic expressions relating the equilibrium concentrations of the various species in the solution to one another and to the formal concentrations of the substances present in the solution.

5. Write a charge-balance equation. In any solution the concentrations of the cations and anions must be related to one another in such a way that the solution is electrically neutral. The charge-balance equation expresses this relationship.[2]

6. Count the number of unknown quantities in the equations from steps (3), (4), and (5) and compare with the number of independent equations. If the number of equations is equal to the number of unknown concentrations, the problem can be solved exactly by suitable algebraic manipulations. If there are fewer equations than unknowns, try to see if additional equations can be derived. If this is not possible, it must be concluded that an exact solution to the problem is not possible; it may, however, be possible to arrive at an approximate solution.

7. Make suitable approximations to simplify the algebra or to reduce the number of unknowns so that the problem can be solved.

8. Solve the algebraic equations for these equilibrium concentrations that are necessary to the solution of the problem as given in step (2).

9. With the equilibrium concentrations obtained in (8), check the approximations made in (7) to be sure of their validity.

---

[2] As a simple example of a charge-balance equation consider a solution prepared by dissolving NaCl in water. Such a solution has a net charge of zero although it contains both positive and negative ions. In this case we can express the neutrality by the following equation:

$$[Na^+] + [H^+] = [Cl^-] + [OH^-]$$

Thus the solution is neutral by virtue of the fact that the sum of the concentrations of the singly charge positive species is equal to the sum of the concentrations of the negative species. Now consider an aqueous solution of $BaCl_2$ dissolved. Here we must write

$$2[Ba^{2+}] + [H_3O^+] = [Cl^-] + [OH^-]$$

Electrical neutrality is preserved because there are two chloride ions for each barium ion; that is, charge balance requires that the chloride ion concentration be *twice* the barium ion concentration. Were there a triply charged species, the concentration of this ion would have to be multiplied by three. Thus for a solution made up of $Al_2(SO_4)_3$, $BaCl_2$, and water we could write

$$3[Al^{3+}] + 2[Ba^{2+}] + [H_3O^+] = 2[SO_4^{2-}] + [Cl^-] + [OH^-]$$

Step (6) in the above scheme is particularly significant because it indicates whether an exact solution for the problem is theoretically feasible. If the number of equations is as great as the number of unknowns, then the problem becomes the purely mechanical one of obtaining an algebraic solution to several simultaneous equations. On the other hand, if the number of equations is less than the number of unknowns, a search for further equations or an approximation that will reduce the number of unknowns is essential. The student should never undertake the algebraic solution of a complex equilibrium problem without first assuring himself that he has sufficient data; otherwise he may waste a great deal of time to no avail.

CALCULATION OF THE SOLUBILITY OF A SALT OF A WEAK ACID IN A SOLUTION OF KNOWN HYDRONIUM-ION CONCENTRATION

★EXAMPLE. Calculate the solubility of CaC_2O_4 in formula weights per liter in a solution maintained at a hydronium ion concentration of 1.0×10^{-4}.

Step 1. Chemical equations.

$$CaC_2O_4 \rightleftharpoons Ca^{2+} + C_2O_4^{2-} \qquad (6\text{-}1)$$

Since oxalic acid is a weak acid, the oxalate ions will react in part with the hydronium ions added to maintain the specified hydronium-ion concentration.

$$C_2O_4^{2-} + H_3O^+ \rightleftharpoons HC_2O_4^- + H_2O \qquad (6\text{-}2)$$

$$HC_2O_4^- + H_3O^+ \rightleftharpoons H_2C_2O_4 + H_2O \qquad (6\text{-}3)$$

Step 2. Definition of the unknown. What is sought? We wish to know the solubility of CaC_2O_4 in formula weights per liter. Since CaC_2O_4 is ionic, its formal solubility will be equal to the molar concentration of calcium ion; it will also be equal to the sum of the equilibrium concentrations of the oxalate species; that is,

$$\text{solubility} = [Ca^{2+}]$$

$$= [C_2O_4^{2-}] + [HC_2O_4^-] + [H_2C_2O_4]$$

Thus if we can calculate either of these quantities, we will have obtained a solution to the problem.

Step 3. Equilibrium-constant expressions.

$$K_{sp} = [Ca^{2+}][C_2O_4^{2-}] = 1.9 \times 10^{-9} \qquad (6\text{-}4)$$

Equation (6-2) above is simply the reverse of the dissociation reaction for $HC_2O_4^-$; we can thus use the value of K_2 for oxalic acid.

$$K_2 = \frac{[H_3O^+][C_2O_4^{2-}]}{[HC_2O_4^-]} = 6.1 \times 10^{-5} \qquad (6\text{-}5)$$

Similarly for (6-3)

$$K_1 = \frac{[H_3O^+][HC_2O_4^-]}{[H_2C_2O_4]} = 6.2 \times 10^{-2} \qquad (6-6)$$

Step 4. *Mass-balance equations.* Since the only source of Ca^{2+} and the various oxalate species is the dissolved CaC_2O_4, it follows that

$$[Ca^{2+}] = [C_2O_4^{2-}] + [HC_2O_4^-] + [H_2C_2O_4] \qquad (6-7)$$

Furthermore it is given that at equilibrium

$$[H_3O^+] = 1.0 \times 10^{-4} \qquad (6-8)$$

Step 5. *Charge-balance equations.* A useful charge-balance equation cannot be written in this case because there has been added to this solution some unknown acid HX to maintain the H_3O^+ concentration at 1.0×10^{-4} mol per liter. In order to write an equation based on the electrical neutrality of the solution, it would be necessary to include the concentration of the anions of the unknown acid $[X^-]$. An equation containing this additional unknown term would be of no help to us.

Step 6. *Comparison of equations and unknowns.* We have four unknowns—namely, $[Ca^{2+}]$, $[C_2O_4^{2-}]$, $[HC_2O_4^-]$, and $[H_2C_2O_4]$. We also have four independent equations: (6-4), (6-5), (6-6), and (6-7) above. Therefore an exact solution is possible and the problem has now become one of algebra.

Step 7. *Approximations.* We are not forced to make any approximations since we have enough data available; we shall attempt an exact solution to the problem.

Step 8. *Solution of the equations.* A convenient way to effect a solution is to make suitable substitutions into equation (6-7) thereby establishing a relationship between $[Ca^{2+}]$ and $[C_2O_4^{2-}]$. We must first derive an expression for $[HC_2O_4^-]$ and $[H_2C_2O_4]$ in terms of $[C_2O_4^{2-}]$. This is done as follows. Substituting the value of 1.0×10^{-4} for $[H_3O^+]$ in equation (6-5), we get

$$\frac{(1.0 \times 10^{-4})[C_2O_4^{2-}]}{[HC_2O_4^-]} = 6.1 \times 10^{-5}$$

and

$$[HC_2O_4^-] = \frac{1.0 \times 10^{-4}}{6.1 \times 10^{-5}} [C_2O_4^{2-}] = 1.64[C_2O_4^{2-}]$$

Substituting this into equation (6-6)

$$\frac{(1.0 \times 10^{-4})(1.64[C_2O_4^{2-}])}{[H_2C_2O_4]} = 6.2 \times 10^{-2}$$

Thus

$$[H_2C_2O_4] = \frac{1.0 \times 10^{-4} \times 1.64[C_2O_4^{2-}]}{6.2 \times 10^{-2}} = 0.0026[C_2O_4^{2-}]$$

Substituting these values for $[H_2C_2O_4]$ and $[HC_2O_4^-]$ into equation (6-7)

$$[Ca^{2+}] = [C_2O_4^{2-}] + 1.64[C_2O_4^{2-}] + 0.0026[C_2O_4^{2-}]$$
$$= 2.64[C_2O_4^{2-}]$$

or

$$[C_2O_4^{2-}] = \frac{[Ca^{2+}]}{2.64}$$

Substituting into equation (6-4) gives

$$[Ca^{2+}]\frac{[Ca^{2+}]}{2.64} = 1.9 \times 10^{-9}$$

$$[Ca^{2+}]^2 = 5.02 \times 10^{-9}$$

$$[Ca^{2+}] = 7.1 \times 10^{-5} \text{ mol/liter}$$

and from step (2) we conclude

solubility of $CaC_2O_4 = 7.1 \times 10^{-5}$ fw/liter

COMPLEX ION FORMATION AND SOLUBILITY

The solubility of a precipitate may be greatly altered by the presence in solution of an ion that will react with the anion or cation of the precipitate to form a soluble complex. For example, the precipitation of aluminum with base is never complete in the presence of fluoride ion although the aluminum hydroxide precipitate formed is an extremely insoluble substance. The explanation for this is found in the fact that the aluminum ion forms sufficiently stable fluoride complexes to prevent quantitative removal of the cation from solution. The equilibrium involved can be represented by

$$Al(OH)_3 \rightleftharpoons Al^{3+} + 3OH^-$$
$$+$$
$$6F^-$$
$$\updownarrow$$
$$AlF_6^{3-}$$

Fluoride ions compete with hydroxyl ions for aluminum ion; as the fluoride concentration becomes larger, more and more of the precipitate is dissolved and converted to fluoroaluminate ions.

Quantitative Treatment of the Effect of Complex Formation on the Solubility of Precipitates. The solubility of a precipitate in the presence of various concentrations of a complexing reagent can be calculated provided the equilibrium constant for the complex-formation reaction is known. The techniques used are similar to those discussed in the previous section.

★EXAMPLE. Find the solubility of AgCl in a solution that is 0.10 F in NH_3.

Equilibria

$$AgCl \rightleftharpoons Ag^+ + Cl^-$$

$$Ag^+ + 2NH_3 \rightleftharpoons Ag(NH_3)_2^+$$

$$NH_3 + H_2O \rightleftharpoons NH_4^+ + OH^-$$

solubility of AgCl = $[Cl^-]$

$$= [Ag^+] + [Ag(NH_3)_2^+]$$

Equilibrium constants

$$[Ag^+][Cl^-] = K_{sp} = 1.82 \times 10^{-10} \qquad (6\text{-}9)$$

$$\frac{[Ag^+][NH_3]^2}{[Ag(NH_3)_2^+]} = K_{inst.} = 6.3 \times 10^{-8} \qquad (6\text{-}10)$$

$$\frac{[NH_4^+][OH^-]}{[NH_3]} = K_d = 1.86 \times 10^{-5} \qquad (6\text{-}11)$$

Mass-balance expressions

$$[Cl^-] = [Ag^+] + [Ag(NH_3)_2^+] \qquad (6\text{-}12)$$

Since the NH_3 concentration was initially 0.10, we may write

$$0.10 = [NH_3] + 2[Ag(NH_3)_2^+] + [NH_4^+] \qquad (6\text{-}13)$$

Furthermore

$$[NH_4^+] \cong [OH^-] \qquad (6\text{-}14)$$

Charge-balance equation

$$[NH_4^+] + [Ag^+] + [Ag(NH_3)_2^+] = [Cl^-] + [OH^-] \qquad (6\text{-}15)[3]$$

A close examination of these seven equations indicates that there are only six independent expressions since (6-15) is the sum of (6-14) and (6-12). There are only six unknowns, however, so a solution is possible.

Approximations

(a) $[NH_4^+]$ is much smaller than the other terms in equation (6-13). This seems reasonable in light of the rather small numerical value of (6-11).

(b) $[Ag(NH_3)_2^+] \rangle \rangle [Ag^+]$. An examination of the constant for equation (6-10) shows that this is a good assumption except for very dilute solutions of NH_3.

Application of these approximations lead to the simplified equations

$$[Cl^-] = [Ag(NH_3)_2^+] \qquad (6\text{-}16)$$

$$[NH_3] = 0.1 - 2[Ag(NH_3)_2^+] \qquad (6\text{-}17)$$

---

[3] We have neglected the $[H_3O^+]$ since its concentration will certainly be negligible in a 0.1 F solution of NH_3.

and substituting (6-16) into (6-17)

$$[NH_3] = 0.1 - 2[Cl^-] \qquad (6\text{-}18)$$

Introducing (6-18) and (6-16) into (6-10)

$$\frac{[Ag^+](0.1 - 2[Cl^-])^2}{[Cl^-]} = 6.3 \times 10^{-8}$$

Now replacing the $[Ag^+]$ in this equation by the equivalent quantity from (6-9) we have

$$\frac{\left(\dfrac{1.82 \times 10^{-10}}{[Cl^-]}\right)(0.1 - 2[Cl^-])^2}{[Cl^-]} = 6.3 \times 10^{-8}$$

$$\frac{(0.1 - 2[Cl^-])^2}{[Cl^-]^2} = 3.5 \times 10^2$$

$$350[Cl^-]^2 = 0.01 - 0.4[Cl^-] + 4[Cl^-]^2$$

This can be rearranged to the following:

$$[Cl^-]^2 + 1.16 \times 10^{-3}[Cl^-] - 2.89 \times 10^{-5} = 0$$

Solving this quadratic equation we obtain

$$[Cl^-] = 4.8 \times 10^{-3} \text{ mol/liter}$$

$$\text{solubility} = 4.8 \times 10^{-3} \text{ fw AgCl/liter}$$

A check on the assumptions will indicate that they were valid.

Complex Formation Involving a Common Ion of the Precipitate.
Many precipitates have a tendency to react with one of their constituent ions to form soluble complexes. For example, silver chloride is capable of reacting with chloride ions to form complexes believed to be of the composition $AgCl_2^-$, $AgCl_3^{2-}$, and so on. These reactions tend to counteract the common ion effect and to give rise to increases in solubility at high concentrations of the common ion. This effect is illustrated by Figure 6.1 where the experimentally determined solubility of silver chloride is plotted against the log of the potassium chloride concentration of the solution. At chloride concentrations less than 10^{-3} F, the data found by experiment do not differ greatly from solubilities calculated from the solubility product for silver chloride. At higher concentrations of the salt, however, the calculated solubilities approach zero, while the measured values rise very rapidly. At about 0.3 F potassium chloride, the solubility of silver chloride is the same as in pure water, and in 1 F solution it is approximately eight times this figure. If complete information were available regarding the composition of the complexes and their stability constants, a quantitative description of these effects should be possible.

Solubility increases in the presence of large excesses of a common ion are by no means rare. A case of particular interest is that of the amphoteric hydroxides such as those of aluminum and zinc which form insoluble precipitates upon treatment with base; these redissolve in the presence of

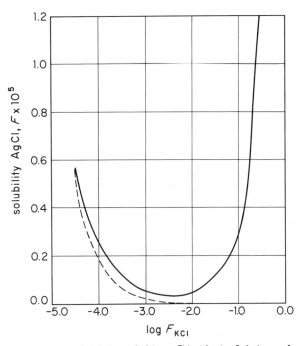

Fig. 6.1 The Solubility of Silver Chloride in Solutions of Potassium Chloride. The dotted line is based on calculation; the solid line represents experimental values of A. Pinkus and A. M. Timmermans, *Bull. Soc. Chim. Belg.*, 46, 46-73 (1937).

excess hydroxyl ions to give the complex aluminate and zincate ions. For aluminum the equilibria can be represented as

$$Al^{3+} + 3OH^- \rightleftharpoons Al(OH)_3$$

$$Al(OH)_3 + OH^- \rightleftharpoons Al(OH)_4^-$$

As with silver chloride, the solubilities of aluminum hydroxide and zinc hydroxide pass through minima and then increase rapidly with increasing concentrations of the common ion. The hydroxyl ion concentration corresponding to the minimum solubility can be calculated readily if the equilibrium constants for the reactions are known.

In general an excess of a precipitating agent is to be recommended in most gravimetric methods of analysis in order to minimize solubility losses. On the other hand, because of the possibility of complex formation between the precipitate and the common ion, large concentrations should be avoided.

SEPARATION OF IONS BY CONTROL OF THE CONCENTRATION OF THE PRECIPITATING REAGENT

When two ions form precipitates of different solubilities with a reagent, the less soluble of these will form at a lower concentration of the precipitating reagent. If the solubilities are sufficiently different, the quantitative removal of the first ion from solution may be achieved without the precipitation of the second. Such separations require careful control of the concentration of the precipitating reagent at some suitable, predetermined level. A number of important analytical procedures, notably those involving metallic sulfides and hydroxides, are based on this method.

Calculation of the Feasibility of Separations. An important application of solubility product calculations involves determining the feasibility and the optimum condition for separations based on the control of reagent concentration. The following problem illustrates such an application.

★EXAMPLE. Is it theoretically possible to separate Fe^{3+} and Mg^{2+} quantitatively from one another in a solution which is $0.1 F$ in each ion by differential precipitation with OH^-? Assuming that separation is possible, what range of OH^- concentrations should be used? Solubility product constants for the two hydroxides are

$$[Fe^{3+}][OH^-]^3 = 1.5 \times 10^{-36}$$

$$[Mg^{2+}][OH^-]^2 = 5.9 \times 10^{-12}$$

The fact that the K_{sp} for $Fe(OH)_3$ is so much smaller than that for $Mg(OH)_2$ suggests that the former will precipitate at a much lower OH^- concentration.

We can answer these questions (1) by calculating the OH^- concentration required to effect the quantitative precipitation of Fe^{3+} from this solution, and (2) by determining the OH^- concentration at which $Mg(OH)_2$ will just begin to precipitate. If (1) is smaller than (2), a separation is feasible and the range of OH^- concentrations to be used will be defined by the values obtained in (1) and (2).

In order to determine (1), we must first decide what constitutes a quantitative removal of Fe^{3+} from the solution. Under no conditions will we be able to precipitate every iron (III) ion; we must arbitrarily set some limit below which we can, for all practical purposes, neglect the further presence of this ion. When the Fe^{3+} concentration has been reduced to 10^{-6} F, only 1/100,000 of the original quantity of iron will remain in the solution and for most purposes this is certainly a quantitative separation.

We can readily calculate the OH^- concentration in equilibrium with 1.0×10^{-6} F Fe^{3+} by substituting directly into the solubility product expression.

$$(1.0 \times 10^{-6})[OH^-]^3 = 1.5 \times 10^{-36}$$

$$[OH^-] = 1.1 \times 10^{-10} \text{ mol/liter}$$

Thus, if we maintain the OH^- concentration at 1.1×10^{-10} mol/liter, the Fe^{3+} concentration will be 1.0×10^{-6} mol/liter. It is of interest to note that quantitative precipitation of $Fe(OH)_3$ is achieved in a distinctly acidic solution.

We must now consider question (2)—that is, the determination of the maximum OH^- concentration that can exist in solution without causing formation of $Mg(OH)_2$. Precipitation will occur when the Mg^{2+} concentration multiplied by the square of the OH^- concentration exceeds the solubility product, 5.9×10^{-12}. On the other hand no precipitate formation will take place if the product of these quantities is equal to or less than this number. By substituting 0.1, the molar Mg^{2+} concentration of the solution, into the solubility product expression we can calculate the *maximum* OH^- concentration that can be attained without formation of $Mg(OH)_2$.

$$0.1[OH^-]^2 = 5.9 \times 10^{-12}$$

$$[OH^-] = 7.7 \times 10^{-6} \text{ mol/liter}$$

When the OH^- concentration exceeds this amount, the solution will be supersaturated with respect to $Mg(OH)_2$ and precipitation will begin.

From these calculations we conclude that quantitative separation of $Fe(OH)_3$ can be expected if the OH^- concentration is greater than 1.1×10^{-10} mol/liter, and that $Mg(OH)_2$ will not precipitate until a concentration of 7.7×10^{-6} mol/liter is reached. Therefore it should be possible to separate Fe^{3+} from Mg^{2+} by maintaining the OH^- concentration between these figures.

6.2   Additional Variables that Affect the Solubility of Precipitates

TEMPERATURE

During the process of solution of most solids, heat is absorbed. Therefore, the solubility of precipitates generally increases with rising temperatures; that is, the solubility products for most insoluble compounds become larger numerically at higher temperatures.

Generally, it is desirable to form and wash precipitates for gravimetric analyses at elevated temperatures since this tends to enhance their purity. Where the compounds are sufficiently insoluble, the increased losses attending such a procedure do not result in serious errors. A few precipitates of analytical importance are so soluble, however, that treatment in this manner is not possible; with these, the filtering and washing operations must be carried on at room temperature or even ice temperature if serious losses are to be avoided. Examples of such compounds are lead sulfate and magnesium ammonium phosphate.

ELECTROLYTE CONCENTRATION

The solubility of most compounds is greater in solutions of an electrolyte than in pure water. This is shown in Figure 6.2 where the solubilities of three substances are plotted as a function of the potassium nitrate concentration of the solution. In the case of barium sulfate the effect is the largest, the solubility increasing by a factor of about two between 0.0 F and 0.02 F potassium nitrate. In the same range the solubility of barium iodate

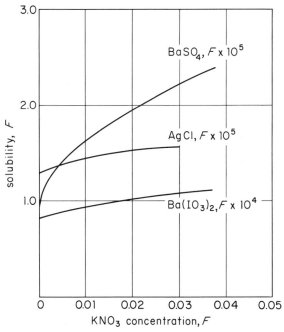

Fig. 6.2 Effect of Electrolyte Concentration on the Solubility of Some Salts.

increases by a factor of only 1.25 while that of silver chloride changes by 1.20.

These effects arise from an increased attraction for the ions of the solute by the dissolved electrolyte in the solvent. As pointed out in Chapter 2 (pp. 23–26), this phenomenon is not unique with solubility equilibria, but can be observed in the behavior of other types of reversible reactions. For example, the degree of dissociation of weak acids is appreciably greater in the presence of electrolytes than in their absence (see Table 2-5).

The application of solubility product constants to the calculation of the solubility of a precipitate in a strong electrolyte solution may result in fairly large errors unless suitable corrections are made for the attractive forces exerted on the solute ions by the electrolyte. The calculation of such corrections is beyond the scope of this text.

In all of the calculations made thus far we have assumed that the solubility of a precipitate is not affected by the presence of electrolytes. We shall continue to do this for the sake of simplicity. The student should realize, however, that this assumption can only lead to approximate results in cases where the electrolyte concentration of the solution is high. He should note, also, that decreases in the solubility of precipitates resulting from the presence of a common ion are in part counteracted by the larger electrolyte concentration associated with the presence of the salt containing the common ion. This gives added reason for avoiding large excesses of precipitating reagent in an analytical precipitation.

SOLVENT COMPOSITION

The solubility of most inorganic compounds is markedly less in aqueous solutions of organic solvents than in pure water. Occasionally the chemist finds it necessary to take advantage of this effect to minimize losses. Examples include methods based on the precipitation forms of the alkali metals. Indiscriminate use of organic solvents is avoided in gravimetric analysis, however; their use may also result in the reduction of the solubility of normally soluble compounds to the point where contamination of the precipitate results.

Problems

1. The solubility of TlI was found to be 0.52 mg/100 ml. Calculate the solubility product.   ans. 2.5×10^{-10}

2. The compound M_2SO_4 (gfw = 320) was found to have a solubility of 1.7×10^{-3} gram/liter. What is the solubility product of the compound?

3. A saturated solution of $Mn(OH)_2$ was found to have a OH^- concentration of 2.1×10^{-5} mol/liter. What is the solubility product for the compound?

4. Calculate the solubility of the following compounds in mg/100 ml.
   (a) $Pb(OH)_2$ ans. 0.096 mg/100 ml
   (b) $PbCl_2$
   (c) $La(IO_3)_3$

5. Will precipitates be produced in the following solutions? Explain your answer.
   (a) A mixture of 100 ml of $1 \times 10^{-5} F$ $AgNO_3$ and 100 ml of $1 \times 10^{-5} F$ $NaCl$
   ans. No; in this mixture $[Ag^+][Cl^-] = 2.5 \times 10^{-11}$.
   This is smaller than the K_{sp} for AgCl.
   Therefore, no precipitation will occur.
   (b) A mixture of 100 ml of $0.2 F$ $Pb(NO_3)_2$ and 100 ml of $0.1 F$ $NaCl$
   (c) A $0.01 F$ solution of Mn^{2+} brought to a hydronium concentration of 1×10^{-8} mol/liter (Possible precipitate of $Mn(OH)_2$)

6. Will $Al(OH)_3$ form from a solution which is $0.1 F$ in $AlCl_3$ and which is at all acidic?

7. Calculate the equilibrium solubility of the following (in fw/liter) in a solution which is $0.0050 F$ in $NaCl$.
   (a) AgCl
   (b) TlCl   ans. 1.2×10^{-2} fw/liter
   (c) $PbCl_2$

8. How much water is required to dissolve 0.10 mg of
   (a) $PbCl_2$ ans. 0.012 ml
   (b) $Fe(OH)_3$

9. Calculate the equilibrium concentration of each ion in the solution that results when 34.0 ml of $0.162 F$ $AgNO_3$ are mixed with 16.0 ml of
   (a) distilled H_2O
   (b) $0.0450 F$ KNO_3
   (c) $0.0450 F$ KI
   (d) $0.0450 F$ MgI_2

10. Calculate the equilibrium concentration of each ion in the solution that results when 19.8 ml of $0.0439 F$ $Ba(OH)_2$ are mixed with 16.1 ml of
    (a) $0.0820 F$ MgI_2
    (b) $0.0820 F$ $MgSO_4$
    (c) $0.0540 F$ $MgSO_4$
    (d) $0.0346 F$ $MgSO_4$

11. Calculate the equilibrium concentration of each ion in the solution that results when 0.1740 gram of $Mg(OH)_2$ is added to
    (a) 40.0 ml of distilled H_2O
    (b) 40.0 ml of $0.105 F$ HCl
    (c) 40.0 ml of $0.150 F$ HCl
    (d) 40.0 ml of $0.205 F$ HCl

12. Iodate ion was precipitated from solution by the addition of $AgNO_3$. When the precipitation was complete the supernatant liquid was 0.003 F in $AgNO_3$ and had a volume of 200 ml. After filtration the precipitate was washed with 200 ml of water.
    (a) Calculate the milligrams of precipitate lost by solubility in the original solution.   ans. 0.58 mg
    (b) Calculate the milligrams of precipitate lost in the wash liquid. Assume that equilibrium is achieved and that the wash water contains no $AgNO_3$.
                                                                                                                        ans. 10 mg
    (c) If the precipitate weighed 0.502 gram, what percentage error would result from these solubility losses?   ans. 2.1 percent

13. What weight of $Ba(IO_3)_2$ remains unprecipitated when 100 ml of 0.10 F $BaCl_2$ are mixed with 300 ml of 0.10 F KIO_3?   ans. 0.49 mg

14. How many mfw of $Mg(OH)_2$ will dissolve in 100 ml of 0.20 F NaOH?

15. Silver chromate was precipitated from a solution that had a total volume of 250 ml. Sufficient $AgNO_3$ was present to make the solution 0.0020 F in Ag^+. The precipitate was filtered and washed with 200 ml of water. Neglect any reaction of CrO_4^{2-} with H_3O^+.
    (a) Calculate the solubility loss in the original solvent.
    (b) What was the solubility loss in the wash water, assuming equilibrium and negligible $AgNO_3$ concentration?

16. The solubility product for the compound AB_2 is 2.00×10^{-6}. Calculate the solubility of AB_2 (in fw/liter) in the following solutions:
    (a) pure water
    (b) a 0.00100 F solution of A^{2+}
    (c) a 0.00100 F solution of B^-

17. What is the maximum volume of wash water that may be used for a $BaSO_4$ precipitate if losses during washing are to be kept below 0.2 mg of precipitate?

18. A solution of Na_2SO_4 is added to a solution which is 0.100 F in Ba^{2+} and 0.100 F in Ca^{2+}.
    (a) Which sulfate will precipitate first?
    (b) At what SO_4^{2-} concentration will $CaSO_4$ begin to form?
    (c) What will be the concentration of the less soluble compound when the more soluble precipitate begins to form?

19. To 1 liter of a solution that is initially 0.010 F in IO_3^- and 0.010 F in Br^- is added 0.015 gfw of $AgNO_3$. What is the concentration of Ag^+, Br^-, and IO_3^- in the resulting mixture?   ans. $[Ag^+] = 6.2 \times 10^{-6}$ mol/liter
                                                                                      $[IO_3^-] = 5.0 \times 10^{-3}$ mol/liter
                                                                                      $[Br^-] = 1.2 \times 10^{-7}$ mol/liter

20. What would be the percentage relative error in a lead determination due to solubility losses if the following conditions prevailed?
      wt Pb^{2+} in solution: 0.125 gram
      wt Na_2SO_4 added: 0.342 gram

final volume of solution after precipitation: 150 ml

volume of wash water: 75 ml   ans. 1.7 percent

21. Would it be theoretically possible to separate quantitatively Cu^{2+} and Mn^{2+} by precipitation of the more insoluble hydroxide from a solution that is $0.10\ F$ in each ion? If a separation is feasible what range of OH^- concentrations should be employed?

22. Calculate the solubility of $BaSO_4$ in (a) $0.10\ F$ HCl and (b) a solution of H_3O^+ concentration of 10^{-7} mol/liter.   ans. (a) 3.1×10^{-5} fw/liter

          (b) 1.0×10^{-5} fw/liter

23. Calculate the formal solubility of $Ag_2C_2O_4$ in a solution whose H_3O^+ concentration is (a) 1.0×10^{-5} mol/liter and (b) 1.0×10^{-8} mol/liter.

24. What is the formal solubility of Ag_3AsO_4 in a solution that is maintained at $[H_3O^+] = 1.0 \times 10^{-3}$ mol/liter?

25. What is the solubility of CaC_2O_4 in a solution that is $0.01\ F$ in $Na_2C_2O_4$ and has an equilibrium $[H_3O^+]$ of 1.0×10^{-5} mol/liter?

26. The dissociation constant for the complex, $Ag(S_2O_3)_2^{3-}$ is 6.0×10^{-14}. How many grams of AgI will dissolve in a liter of $1.0\ F\ Na_2S_2O_3$?   ans. 8.1

27. The dissociation constant for the copper (I) complex $Cu(NH_3)^+$ is 6.6×10^{-7}. A solution was prepared that contained 0.01 formula weight of a copper (I) compound per liter of $1.0\ F\ NH_3$. To a 1-liter portion of this solution was added 0.10 formula weight of NaCl. To a second 1-liter portion was added 0.10 formula weight of NaBr and to a third 0.10 formula weight of NaI. From which, if any, of these solutions would copper (I) halide precipitate form? Show how you arrived at your answer.

28. The approximate dissociation constant for

$$AgCl_2^- \text{ is } 1.0 \times 10^{+5}\ (AgCl_2^- \rightleftharpoons AgCl + Cl^-)$$

Calculate the approximate solubility of AgCl in a $1.0\ F$ solution of NaCl.

29. How many grams of AgBr will dissolve in 1 liter of $6.0\ F\ NH_3$?

(7)

The Particle Size and Purity
of Precipitates

The size of the particles making up a precipitate profoundly affects the ease and the completeness of the filtering operation. A solid made up of large particles or particle aggregates is quantitatively retained by a coarse filter through which the liquid can be passed at a relatively high speed. On the other hand, a finely divided solid requires the use of a dense medium and results in a slow filtration rate.

Precipitates formed as the result of mixing two solutions show enormous variations in particle size. In some instances the individual particles are so small as to be invisible to the naked eye; these tend to remain suspended indefinitely and cannot be separated by any of the common filtering devices. A solid-liquid system of this kind is termed a *colloidal suspension*. By way of contrast other precipitates form as discrete particles that may have dimensions as large as several tenths of a millimeter; these particles rapidly settle out of solution and are readily separated by ordinary filtering media. The temporary dispersion of such particles in the liquid medium is called a *crystalline suspension*.

The physical properties of a solid-liquid mixture change continuously as the particle size of the solid phase increases. No sharp discontinuities are discernible; instead there is a gradual and continuous change in behavior of the mixture as it is transformed from a colloidal suspension to a crystalline one. As a result there exists a range of particle sizes displaying properties intermediate between the defined extremes. Despite this, the classification is a useful one for our purposes. Most of the precipitates

encountered in analytical chemistry are readily identified as being pre-
dominately in either one or the other category; the way in which the two
types of precipitates are treated is entirely different.

7.1   Mechanism of Precipitate Formation

The particle size of a precipitate is determined to some extent by the
experimental conditions prevailing at the time of its formation. The
temperature, rate of mixing of reagents, concentration of reagents, and
the solubility of the precipitate at the time of precipitation are variables
affecting particle size over which the chemist possesses some control. All
of these can be related to a single property, the *relative supersaturation*
of the system.

SUPERSATURATION AND PARTICLE SIZE

A solution is said to be supersaturated when it contains a concentration
of solute in excess of that found in a saturated solution. Supersaturation
may be defined as

$$\text{supersaturation} = Q - S$$

where Q is the concentration of solute in solution at any instant and S
is its equilibrium concentration in a saturated solution. A supersaturated
solution is unstable and eventually reverts to a saturated state by formation of a solid phase. In some instances relief of supersaturation by precipitation occurs rapidly and the supersaturated condition exists only momentarily. In other cases, however, supersaturation may last for hours, days, or
even months before formation of a solid phase occurs.

Relative supersaturation is another term that is useful in describing
the state of supersaturation. It is defined as

$$\text{relative supersaturation} = \frac{Q - S}{S}$$

Numerous experimental observations have shown that the particle
size of a precipitate is intimately related to the degree of relative supersaturation at the instant before precipitation begins. For example, relative
supersaturations of the order of 175,000 can be achieved momentarily by
rapidly mixing 3.5 F solutions of manganese (II) sulfate and barium thiocyanate. The barium sulfate precipitate that results is gelatinous in form,
the individual particles of the solid being so small as to be invisible even at
high magnification with a microscope. When, on the other hand, dilute
solutions of the same two reagents are mixed so that the relative super-

saturation is about 25, the precipitate is crystalline and the individual particles, which are about 0.02 mm in length, can be readily seen with the naked eye. Many other examples of this sort make it clear that there is an inverse relationship between particle size of a solid and the relative supersaturation at the instant of formation of the particles. Thus, when the relative supersaturation is high, the particles are microscopic or submicroscopic in size; when this quantity is small, the particles are large.

STEPS IN PRECIPITATE FORMATION

The formation of a solid phase from a solution involves two processes. One of these is called *nucleation* or *nucleus formation*, the second *particle growth*. The size of the particles of a solid is dependent upon the relative rates at which these two competing processes take place.

Nucleation. For any precipitate there is some minimum number of ions or molecules required to produce a stable second phase in contact with a solution. That is, until this number of ions or molecules collects together in some ordered arrangement, a solid phase having a finite lifetime will not exist in the solution. We shall call this minimum-sized stable particle a *nucleus;* the first step in the formation of a precipitate involves the generation of many such nuclei. For an insoluble ionic compound AB, nucleus formation involves a reaction that can be written

$$nA^+ + nB^- \rightleftharpoons (AB)_n$$

where n is the minimum number of A^+ and B^- ions that must combine in order to yield the stable particle $(AB)_n$.

The rate at which nuclei form in a solution is dependent upon the degree of supersaturation. If this is low, the rate may be very low—indeed it may approach zero. On the other hand, in a highly supersaturated solution the velocity of nucleation must be very great.

There have been numerous attempts to determine quantitatively how the rate of nucleation varies as a function of supersaturation in typical cases. The experimental difficulties associated with such measurements have proved to be great; no unequivocal answers have as yet been obtained. The bulk of the evidence suggests, however, that the rate increases exponentially with the supersaturation. That is,

$$\text{rate of nucleation} = k(Q - S)^x$$

where k and x are constants, x being greater than one.[1]

---

[1] For example, S. H. Bransom, W. J. Dunning, and B. Willard, *Discussions Faraday Society*, **5**, 83 (1949), suggest that $x = 3$ in the system they studied.

A plot of a function such as the foregoing is given in Figure 7.1; this shows that there is a range of low supersaturation wherein the nucleation rate is essentially zero. Supersaturation corresponding to the rapidly rising portion of the nucleation curve indicates a region of very rapid nucleus formation.

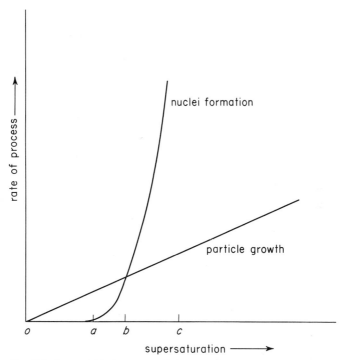

Fig. 7.1 Rate of Nucleation and Particle Growth as a Function of Supersaturation.

Particle Growth. The second process that can occur during precipitation is the growth of particles already present in the solution. This growth can only begin when nuclei or other seed particles are present. With an ionic solid the process involves deposition of cations and anions on appropriate sites

$$(AB)_n + A^+ + B^- \rightleftharpoons (AB)_{n+1}$$
$$(AB)_{n+1} + A^+ + B^- \rightleftharpoons (AB)_{n+2}, \text{ etc.}$$

Since particle growth can be followed readily in the laboratory, considerably more is known about this process than about nucleation. The rate of growth is found to be directly proportional to the supersaturation and can be expressed by the equation

$$\text{rate of growth} = k'A(Q - S)$$

where A is the surface area of the exposed solid and k' is a constant that is characteristic of the particular precipitate. A plot of the rate of growth as a function of supersaturation, as shown in Figure 7.1, is approximately linear.

THE PRECIPITATION PROCESS

With information regarding the relative rates of the two precipitation processes we can construct a fairly satisfactory picture of a precipitate formation and adequately explain the experimental observation relating particle size to supersaturation.

Initially, reagent added to the solution causes supersaturation. When this becomes great enough (greater than a in Figure 7.1), nucleation occurs at an appreciable rate. If the supersaturation caused by the initial addition of reagent is not large, the number of nuclei formed in a given time will be relatively small. On the other hand, if a high degree of supersaturation is attained, the nucleation rate will be very rapid and a large number of nuclei will result. Further addition of the reagent will again cause at least momentary supersaturation that will be relieved either by further nucleus formation or by particle growth. Which of these processes predominates will depend upon the degree of supersaturation. If this is low (for example, between o and a on Figure 7.1), the rate of nucleation will be negligible and growth of the nuclei already present will be the more important. We see from Figure 7.1, however, that the rate of nucleus formation increases far more rapidly with supersaturation than does the rate of growth; thus if the supersaturation becomes appreciably greater than b, much of the new precipitate formed will appear as nuclei and only a small part as growth.

This mechanism adequately accounts for the experimental observations relative to the effects of supersaturation on particle size. If the supersaturation is maintained at a low level throughout a precipitation, the relatively few nuclei formed will grow to give a small number of large particles. On the other hand, with high supersaturation many more nuclei are formed initially and nucleation may occur throughout the entire precipitation process. As a result there are many more centers upon which the growth process can take place; none of the particles can become very large. The net effect is a solid phase consisting of a very large number of small particles—in, other words, a colloidal suspension. If this interpretation is correct, it should be possible to form a given precipitate with particles of any desired size, ranging from colloidal to crystalline dimensions, provided the supersaturation of the solution can be varied over a sufficient range during precipitation. With some precipitates—for example, barium sulfate—this is experimentally demonstrable.

The supersaturation of a solution can be varied by changing either the solubility of the precipitate S or its concentration Q in solution at any instant. Temperature changes or changes in the composition of the solvent (see Chap. 6) will alter the former. Variations in reagent concentrations and the rate at which these are mixed will affect Q. Theoretically, then, it should be possible to form all precipitates as easily filtered crystalline solids simply by keeping the supersaturation sufficiently low. In practice, however, this is not always feasible. With very insoluble precipitates, S is so very small relative to Q that the difference $(Q - S)$ remains large despite all efforts to reduce it. Attempts to decrease Q sufficiently to give low supersaturations result in the use of such extremely dilute solutions and inordinately slow rates of reagent addition as to be impractical. Nor can S be increased sufficiently by heat or variation in solvent composition to have much effect. As a result, all of the very insoluble precipitates, such as the hydrous oxides and sulfides, occur as colloidal suspensions when formed under conditions that are practical for analysis. Only with the more soluble precipitates, such as the oxalates, sulfates, and carbonates, can the supersaturation be kept sufficiently low to yield crystalline precipitates under practical conditions.

Both colloidal and crystalline precipitates are encountered in gravimetric analysis. However, the treatment of the two types of solids varies considerably; we must consider the properties and behavior of each in the following sections.

7.2 Colloidal Suspensions

PROPERTIES OF COLLOIDAL SUSPENSIONS

The colloidal suspensions with which we shall be concerned consist of dispersions of finely divided solid particles in a liquid phase. Typically, these particles will have diameters of 0.001 to 0.1 micron,[2] and will be invisible to the naked eye or the ordinary light microscope. As a result, colloidal suspensions or, as they are sometimes called, colloidal solutions, will often appear to be clear and completely homogeneous despite the fact that they may contain several grams of dispersed solid in a few hundred milliliters of the liquid.

The properties of a colloidal solution are quite different from those of a true solution. In the former, the solid is dispersed in the form of aggregates

---

[2] The micron, μ, is equal to 0.001 mm.

of the ions or molecules making up the precipitate while in the latter, the dissolved solid is homogeneously dispersed as individual ions or molecules. In contrast to the true solution, the solid present in a colloidal suspension has a negligible effect on such properties as freezing point, boiling point, and osmotic pressure. Furthermore, the particles of a colloid are of such dimensions as to scatter visible radiation. Thus when a light beam passes through a colloidal solution, its path can be readily seen. This is the well-known *Tyndall effect.* True solutions do not exhibit this effect because the individual particles present are too small to reflect visible radiation.

Colloidal particles are so small that they pass through the ordinary filtering media used by the chemist. They can, to be sure, be retained by certain ultrafilters whose pore sizes are much smaller. Unfortunately, the rate at which liquids pass through these ultrafilters is very slow, and for this reason they are not ordinarily used for the filtration of analytical precipitates.

The individual particles of a colloid are so small they will not settle out as such under the influence of gravity but will remain indefinitely suspended in the liquid in which they are formed. Under some circumstances, however, they can be caused to come together and adhere to one another, the result being a mass of material that will settle out rapidly from solution. The resulting solid is called a *colloidal precipitate* and the process by which it is formed is termed *coagulation* or *agglomeration.* Coagulated colloidal precipitates are quite different in appearance from typical crystalline precipitates. Some are slimy and gel-like; others are curdy. They have no regularity in structure and appear as large amorphous masses.

SPECIFIC SURFACE AREA OF COLLOIDS

Many of the unique properties of colloidal suspensions arise from the very large surface area exhibited by a solid in this state of subdivision. The *specific surface* of a solid is defined as the exposed surface area per unit weight of the solid, and is often expressed in units of square centimeters per gram. As the particle size is reduced, the specific surface increases, becoming enormous when dimensions of a typical colloid are reached. For example, for a cube of a solid 1 cm on a side and weighing 3 grams, the surface area is 6 cm^2 and the specific surface 2 cm^2/gram. This cube could be divided into 1000 cubes, 0.1 cm on a side, or into 1,000,000 cubes, 0.01 cm on a side, and so forth. It is interesting to calculate the specific surface in each of these cases in order to see how the surface area increases with subdivision. Table 7-1 gives such data.

The last figures in this table are for particles having the dimensions of a typical colloid; we see that 1 gram of the solid in this state of subdivision has a surface area of 2,000,000 cm^2, or somewhat more than 2000 ft^2.

TABLE 7-1

Specific Surface Area of 3 Grams of a Solid
in Various States of Subdivision

Number of Particles	Dimensions of Cube, cm	Specific Surface cm²/gram
1	1	2
10^3	0.1	20
10^6	0.01	200
10^{12}	0.0001	20,000
10^{18}	0.000001	2,000,000

A colloidal suspension of only 1 gram of this solid, then, would present a surface that is equivalent to the floor area of a good-sized house. One might expect that any properties of a solid-liquid system that are related to the interface between the solid and liquid would be tremendously amplified in a colloidal suspension where the specific surface area is great. Actually there are such properties, and we shall discuss these in later sections.

ADSORPTION OF IONS BY COLLOIDS

Any solid surface exposed to an aqueous solution of an electrolyte is found to be charged either positively or negatively with respect to the solution. This charge results from the tendency of the ions of the solution to attach themselves to the solid surfaces. With solids of ordinary dimensions, the magnitude of the charge is quite small, and its existence goes undetected unless sensitive means are used to observe it. However, with colloidal suspensions, where the surface to weight ratio—that is, the specific surface—is very high, the phenomenon becomes one of primary importance in determining the properties and behavior of the particles.

The process by which ions, or in some cases molecules, are held on the surface of a solid is called *adsorption*. The solid itself is called the *adsorbent* and the substance that is adsorbed is the *adsorbate*.

Absorption of Ions on Solid Surfaces. Consider a colloidal suspension that is in contact with a solution containing an excess of one of the ions making up the lattice structure of the solid. Figure 7.2 is a schematic diagram of one particle in such a medium. Here silver ions are shown as being absorbed on the surface of a silver chloride particle and, as a result, the particle is positively charged. The adsorbed ions are seen to be held in positions adjacent to some of the chloride ions in the lattice of the solid itself. The forces holding the ions on the surface are the normal chemical forces that bind the ions together in the solid lattice. Undoubtedly a silver chloride particle in such an environment as that shown in the diagram adsorbs other ions from the solution also; these might include hydrogen, sodium, nitrate, etc. The lattice ion, however, would normally predominate.

By no means are all of the possible sites occupied by adsorbed silver ions at any given time; indeed, as the number of cations on the surface increases, the accumulation of positive charges tends to prevent further adsorption. Thus a balance is struck in which the bonding forces are just matched

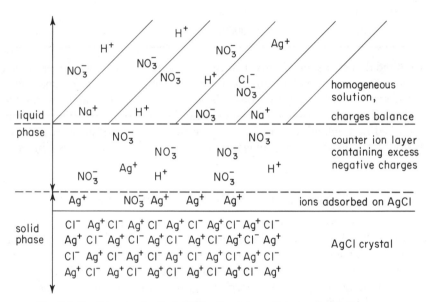

Fig. 7.2 Conditions at the Surface of a Precipitate. Cross-sectional diagram of a silver chloride particle suspended in a solution containing an excess of silver ions.

by the electrostatic repulsive forces. It should be understood that the resulting state is a dynamic one in which silver ions are constantly being adsorbed and desorbed at a rapid rate.

The ions adsorbed on a solid are firmly attached and should be considered a part of the solid. This is shown by the fact that the charge resulting from adsorption will cause a colloidal particle to migrate in an electric field; thus the silver chloride particle in Figure 7.2 would move toward a negative electrode and away from a positive one.

Chemical Composition of the Adsorbed Layer. Some ions are much more strongly adsorbed by a given solid than others. Thus, when a colloid is exposed to a solution containing several ions, the adsorption of one of these will ordinarily predominate. Where the solution contains an excess of one of the ions making up the precipitate, that ion is so strongly held that it will nearly always be adsorbed in preference to any others in the solution. For example, the colloidal particles of a silver chloride precipitate formed in the presence of an excess of silver ions are positively charged owing to the adsorption of silver ions; if sufficient chloride ions are then added to the system so that they are in excess, the charge on the particles will change from positive to negative as the adsorbed ions change from silver to chloride. Most of the precipitates with which we deal in analytical chemistry are formed in the presence of an excess of a common ion. Thus it is easy to decide what the composition of the adsorbed layer will be.

Counter-ion Layer. The existence of a surface charge will lead to an inhomogeneity in the solution immediately surrounding the particle. Thus the positively charged silver chloride particle illustrated in Figure 7.2 will tend to attract anions and repulse cations. As a result there will be a layer of solution in which the concentration of negatively charged ions exceeds that of positively charged ions. This region is called the *counter-ion layer*.

A sufficient excess of ions of opposite charge will be found within the counter-ion layer to balance that carried by the colloidal particle. The thickness of the layer of solution required to contain this number of ions will be variable and will depend upon the concentration and the nature of the electrolyte. Thus if the solution is dilute, the thickness of the layer having an equivalent number of counter ions will be relatively great. On the other hand, if the solvent has a large concentration of ions, this layer will be thin. In either case, we conceive of the counter-ion layer as being somewhat diffuse and a part of the solution, not the solid.

COAGULATION OF COLLOIDS

From the viewpoint of the analytical chemist, one of the most important properties of a colloid is its tendency to coagulate into a larger, more readily filtered mass. Generally, this can be brought about by heat or by the addition of an electrolyte. Coagulation makes possible the use of colloidal suspensions in gravimetric analysis.

Attractive Forces between Particles. We would expect the particles of a colloid to have a considerable tendency to adhere to one another if brought into close contact, since the same bonding forces that cause adsorption would certainly operate between two like particles and tend to hold them together. Thus, if perfectly plane surfaces of two particles made contact, as pictured in Figure 7.3, the positive ions of one could line up opposite the negative ions of the second and vice versa. A strong bond between the two particles would result. Actually the situation pictured in Figure 7.3 is highly idealized in that the particle surfaces are pictured as being perfectly flat and regular. It seems more probable, however, that the colloidal particles formed by chemical reaction are irregular in shape so that only a limited area of contact between any two particles is possible. This is illustrated by Figure 7.4 which shows how several coagulated particles might appear if they could be sufficiently magnified to be seen. Only at areas of contact would there be bonding between the particles.

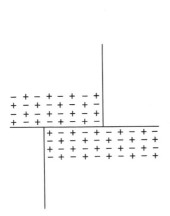

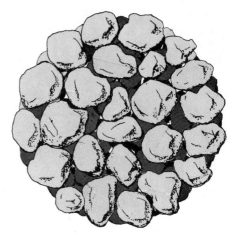

Fig. 7.3 Adhesion of Two Similar Particles to One Another.

Fig. 7.4 Coagulated Colloidal Particles.

A solid made of thousands or millions of colloidal particles agglomerated as in Figure 7.4 would be expected to have quite different properties from a crystalline solid. Since the particles are arranged irregularly, the solid phase should be amorphous in appearance; in addition, the apparent density of such a solid should be less than that of a crystalline solid where the ions are tightly packed in a regular arrangement. Finally, this solid should be porous in nature and be capable of containing large volumes of the solvent internally. As a result, a coagulated colloid might be expected to have a considerably larger surface area than would be surmised from the external dimensions of the solid.

Stability of Colloidal Suspensions. The individual particles making up a colloidal suspension are surrounded by a double layer of ions bearing opposite charges. The innermost of these layers is made up of adsorbed ions tightly held on the surface of the particles. The outer layer (or counterion layer) is composed of ions of the solution having charge opposite to the adsorbed ions. The stability of colloidal suspensions is a direct consequence of the repulsive forces set up among the double layers of the individual particles. These layers prevent the close approach necessary for the cohesive forces between the particles to be effective in bringing about agglomeration. The charged double layer, then, acts as a sort of buffer, causing the particles to sheer away from one another as they travel through the solution.

Mechanism of Coagulation. The coagulation process involves a reduction in the forces of repulsion exerted among the colloidal particles by the charged double layers. One way to accomplish this is to reduce the total charge of the layers by reducing the number of ions adsorbed on the particles. This can be done by raising the temperature of the system; experimentally we find that many colloidal solutions are coagulated by heating for short periods of time.

A more effective way of causing a colloidal suspension to agglomerate is to add an electrolyte to the solution. This tends to minimize the effective charge of the double layer; with sufficiently high electrolyte concentrations the layer shrinks to the point where the particles come in contact with one another and adhere.

Experimental data indicate a considerable variation in the efficiency of different electrolytes in causing coagulation of a given colloidal suspension. Effectiveness is dependent upon the nature of the ion *opposite* in charge to that possessed by the colloidal particles. There is little difference in behavior among the ions having the same charge. In addition the coagulating power of the ion of opposite charge increases greatly with increasing ionic charge.

PEPTIZATION OF COLLOIDAL PRECIPITATES

The process of coagulation of a colloid is at least partially reversible with many, but not all, colloidal precipitates; that is, a coagulated colloid can often be reconverted into its original finely divided state by suitable treatment. This process is called *peptization*. A most effective method of bringing about peptization is by washing with water. For example, if a coagulated colloidal silver chloride precipitate is transferred to a filter paper and washed with a few hundred milliliters of water, the washings are first clear but later become opalescent as the precipitate peptizes and is converted back into particles of such dimensions that can pass through the pores of the paper.

In order to understand how peptization occurs, we must inquire further into the nature of a coagulated colloid, such as silver chloride. A precipitate of this sort consists of a very large number of minute particles adhering together in a random orientation. The solid still has a relatively large surface area exposed to the solution because the particles are irregularly shaped and are not fitted together in any regular fashion. This leaves internal surfaces in the solid exposed to the solvent. Figure 7.4 shows several such inner surfaces interspersed among the particles. On these surfaces are the adsorbed ions that gave the original particles their charge; while the total number of adsorbed ions on the solid has been reduced as a result of agglomeration, the number remains large.

The counter-ion layer also exists on the coagulated colloid in the film of liquid immediately adjacent to the exposed surfaces. Thus when a colloid is coagulated, it carries down with it appreciable concentrations of compounds consisting of the primary adsorbed ions and an equivalent number of oppositely charged counterparts in the counter-ion layer. The solution wetting the surfaces of the coagulated colloid contains, in addition to the counter ions, an appreciable concentration of the electrolyte that was used to coagulate the particles. As a result, a typical coagulated colloidal precipitate is heavily contaminated by foreign ions when filtered from solution.

When a precipitate such as silver chloride is washed with water, the wash liquid is not very effective in removing the primarily adsorbed ions from the surface of the solid; the bond between them and the surface is too strong. Nor can the wash liquid remove the counter ions since these are attracted to the primarily adsorbed ions by strong electrostatic forces. However, the wash water will dilute and remove the electrolyte that was used for the coagulation of the colloid. When this occurs, the counter-ion layer tends to occupy a larger volume; as a result, the repulsive force between the double layers of the particles again acquires appreciable magnitude. If enough of the electrolyte is removed, this force may become sufficient to cause particles to break away from the coagulated mass and bring about peptization.

In handling a colloidal precipitate, the chemist is thus faced with a dilemma. If he chooses to wash it with water to reduce the amount of foreign contaminants, he runs a good chance of losing a part of his precipitate by peptization. On the other hand, while he can prevent this loss by washing with an electrolyte, he will inevitably obtain a solid badly contaminated with that electrolyte. The one answer to this problem is to wash with an electrolyte that can subsequently be removed by volatilization. As an example, a silver chloride precipitate can conveniently be washed with dilute nitric acid which will remove at least part of the nonvolatile contaminants without causing peptization; the nitric acid can later be volatilized by heating the filtered precipitate at about 100° C.

7.3   Crystalline Precipitates

A number of the more soluble precipitates used in analysis form as crystalline compounds. With these, filtering characteristics can be improved by increasing the size of the individual crystals or by cementing the single crystals together into larger agglomerates of several such crystals.

METHODS FOR INCREASING THE SIZE OF CRYSTALS

The reader will recall from earlier discussions that the particle size of a precipitate is increased by reduction of the relative supersaturation of the solution from which it is formed. Experimentally, there are several ways of accomplishing this.

Concentration and Rate of Mixing of Reagents. One method of reducing supersaturation entails the use of dilute solutions so that the solubility product of the compound is only slightly exceeded with the addition of each increment of reagent. Slow addition of the precipitating reagent is also helpful because time is allowed for the precipitate to form; the build-up of a large supersaturation is thereby prevented.

Variation of Solubility of Precipitates. The relative supersaturation can often be reduced by increasing the solubility of a precipitate during the period of its formation; this leads to increased particle size. One common way of doing this is to carry out the precipitation at elevated temperatures. Before filtration, the mixture is usually cooled to room temperature, or below, to minimize solubility losses.

With some compounds, large particles are conveniently obtained by precipitating the substance from an environment in which the solubility is relatively high and the supersaturation correspondingly low. After the reagent has been added, the precipitation is completed by altering the solvent composition to lower the solubility to a tolerable level. Solids whose solubilities are affected by pH are particularly susceptible to this treatment. For example, very large crystals of calcium oxalate can be obtained by forming the bulk of the precipitate in a somewhat acid solution. The precipitation can then be completed by the slow addition of ammonia until the pH is great enough for quantitative removal of the compound; the additional precipitate thus produced forms on the solid already present.

While these techniques are quite useful for the more soluble compounds, they are of little importance in handling the very insoluble substances that normally separate as colloids. The variations in relative supersaturation that can be attained by these alterations are simply insufficient to convert such solids to crystalline precipitates, nor do they make handling the colloids any easier.

DIGESTION OF CRYSTALLINE PRECIPITATES

It has been found experimentally that a crystalline precipitate is more easily filtered if allowed to stand quietly in contact with the solution from which it was precipitated (that is, the so-called *mother liquor*). This improvement in filterability is hastened by heating; it is common practice to treat crystalline precipitates in this manner prior to filtration. The process is called *digestion.*

Considerable experimental evidence indicates that the digestion process consists of a cementing together of crystals. The resulting aggregates are appreciably larger than the individual crystals and are therefore more easily retained on filtering media less dense than that required for the freshly formed solid. We can easily understand how such agglomeration might occur when we recall that the ions making up a precipitate are in dynamic equilibrium with their counterparts in the solution. As a result, solution and reprecipitation of the solid take place constantly. The latter process can occur in such a way as to form bridges between adjacent solid particles and give rise to crystalline aggregates. At elevated temperatures, where the solubility is greater, the process would be expected to take place at an accelerated rate; this is in keeping with the experimental observation that the effectiveness of digestion is greater at higher temperatures.

7.4   Contamination of Precipitates

A precipitate formed in solution by the combination of suitable reagents is invariably contaminated to a greater or lesser extent by the other ions present during the precipitation process. For a gravimetric analysis, the level of such contamination must be kept low in order to avoid any appreciable alteration in the weight of the solid. This is not always possible; many precipitates are not very suitable for analytical purposes for this reason.

Contamination of precipitates can occur by several mechanisms. The most obvious of these is encountered when the solubility product of some compound other than the one desired is also exceeded during addition of the precipitating reagent. Under these circumstances the impurity is simply codeposited as a second precipitate. This will occur, for example, when silver chloride is formed from a solution containing bromide ion. Ordinarily, simultaneous precipitation of this sort is not of great concern to the analytical chemist because he can readily predict its occurrence provided he has some knowledge of the composition of his solutions. In avoiding such precipitation, he is frequently forced to resort to preliminary separations of one sort or another.

A much more insidious source of error in gravimetric analyses results from the carrying down of normally soluble substances by the insoluble phase. Such contamination occurs to some extent any time a precipitate is formed. The amount of impurity so introduced is often small and has little effect on the weight of the precipitate. Under some conditions, however, surprisingly large quantities of normally soluble compounds are removed from solution in conjunction with the insoluble solid. In fact, complete removal is occasionally observed.

The phenomenon by which normally soluble substances are carried out of solution by an insoluble precipitate is called coprecipitation. The student should note that this term refers only to the contamination of precipitates by substances that would otherwise remain in solution under the conditions imposed on the solution. The term does not include contamination resulting from precipitation of another insoluble compound.

TYPES OF COPRECIPITATION

The particle size of the solid as well as the chemical composition of both solid and solution will determine the type of coprecipitation that will predominate in any given situation. Because the measures that are effective in reducing analytical errors from this source depend in turn upon the various types, it is highly desirable that the chemist attempt to recognize in advance the coprecipitation problem he is most likely to encounter in a particular analysis.

At least four types of coprecipitation can be discerned.

(1) *Surface adsorption,* in which the contaminant is a compound made up of the ions adsorbed on the surface of the solid and the counter ions of opposite charge in the liquid film immediately adjacent to the particle.

(2) *Isomorphic inclusion* (or mixed crystal formation), in which the coprecipitated compound has dimensions and chemical composition such that it can fit into the crystal structure of the precipitate without causing appreciable strains or distortions.

(3) *Nonisomorphic inclusion* (or solid solution formation), in which small quantities of the impurity appear to be dissolved in the precipitate.

(4) *Occlusion,* where the impurities are entrapped as imperfections within the crystals of the precipitate.

The reader should be cautioned that the type of coprecipitation responsible for the contamination of a given precipitate may not always be readily apparent.

SURFACE ADSORPTION BY COLLOIDAL PRECIPITATES

All precipitates carry down soluble impurities by adsorption on their surfaces. However, only where the specific surface areas are great does coprecipitation of this type have an appreciable effect on the weight of the solid. Therefore we need be concerned with contamination by surface adsorption only when dealing with colloidal precipitates.

Chemical Composition of Adsorbed Contaminants. We have seen that colloidal particles formed under analytical conditions will always have one of the constituent ions of the precipitate adsorbed on their surfaces. This will, of course, be the one in excess when the precipitation has been completed. Ordinarily, a part of these adsorbed ions remain attached to the solid surface even after coagulation has occurred and are carried down with the solid. Owing to electrostatic forces, an equivalent number of oppositely charged ions from the counter-ion layer are also carried down in the liquid film surrounding the coagulated solid. *Thus a soluble chemical compound consisting of one of the ionic species making up the precipitate and a corresponding number of oppositely charged counter ions is coprecipitated.*

While the nature of one of the adsorbed ions is always fixed in an analytical precipitation by its presence in excess at the end of the precipitation process, the constitution of the counter-ion layer is subject to variation. Experimental studies with a wide variety of precipitates have revealed great differences in the tendency of various ions to be carried down as counter ions. Numerous attempts have been made to relate these differences in adsorbability to various properties of the ions in question; however, no simple, quantitative correlations have been found.

One of the properties that appears to have a bearing on adsorbability is the magnitude of the charge on the ion. In general ions with multiple charge are more strongly held in the counter-ion layer than are singly charged species. This relationship is far from perfect, however, and many notable exceptions can be cited.

Another important effect is related to the solubility of the salt composed of the counter ion and the primarily adsorbed common ion. Where this solubility is low, the tendency for the ion in question to appear as a counter ion is enhanced. Experiments have shown, however, that this relationship is not always observed.

Other factors—such as ionic size, deformability, and degree of hydration—also appear to influence the relative amounts of various ions that are adsorbed as counter ions. These are difficult to evaluate in quantitative terms.

Amounts of Adsorption. The amount of contaminant adsorbed by colloidal precipitates varies tremendously. For example, soluble metal hydroxides tend to be strongly adsorbed by the hydrous oxides of the heavy metals. Similarly, the sulfides of most of the heavy metals are often found to be seriously contaminated by normally soluble sulfides. By way of contrast, adsorption by the colloidal silver halide precipitates is seldom sufficient to lead to serious errors. Undoubtedly, part of these differences in the adsorptive capacity of various precipitates is related to differences in the surface development—that is, the specific surface areas. Other specific factors also appear to play a part.

For any given precipitate, the quantity of a compound adsorbed is related to its concentration in solution in a manner shown in Figure 7.5.

Reduction of Errors Caused by Adsorption. Several paths are open to the chemist seeking to reduce the magnitude of error arising from adsorption of contaminants on a colloidal precipitate. Among these are the use of elevated temperatures and dilute solutions, digestion, washing, and reprecipitation.

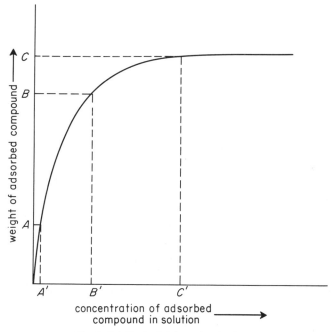

Fig. 7.5 A Typical Adsorption Isotherm.

The amount of adsorption by a colloid decreases with increases in temperature. As a consequence, a purer analytical precipitate is produced by the use of elevated temperatures during the formation, filtration, and washing operations. Fortunately, the solubilities of most precipitates that form as colloids are small enough so that such treatment does not result in significant solubility losses.

The quantity of a compound adsorbed by a colloid is directly related to its concentration in the solution as shown in Figure 7.5. As a result it is advantageous from the standpoint of purity to form a colloidal precipitate from as dilute a solution as possible. There are practical limitations to this technique, however, since filtering and handling large volumes of solutions is tedious and time-consuming.

The purity of some colloidal precipitates is increased by digestion for short periods of time. Silver halide precipitates, for example, benefit from this treatment. Purification in such instances probably results from a decrease in the specific surface area of the coagulated solid and perfection of the particles by the process of solution and reprecipitation. With gelatinous colloids such as the hydrous oxides, digestion is of little or no help.

The adsorbed compound on a colloidal particle is in a state of dynamic equilibrium with the ions of that compound in solution. As a result, the washing of a coagulated colloid can be effective in reducing the amount of adsorbed contaminants. A study of a typical adsorption isotherm such as shown in Figure 7.5 reveals, however, that the washing process becomes less and less effective as the quantity of adsorbed impurity decreases—that is, as the washing proceeds. For example, if we assume that the first wash of a precipitate results in a concentration C' of contaminant in the wash liquid, the corresponding quantity, C is thus left on the precipitate. Further washing would reduce the amount adsorbed to some smaller value B; the equilibrium concentration in the wash liquid B' is now considerably smaller relative to the weight of contaminant remaining on the precipitate. By the time the amount of impurity on the precipitate has been reduced to A, the equilibrium concentration A' in the wash liquid is negligible, and washing is no longer effective in removing the remaining contaminant from the precipitate. It must constantly be borne in mind that one runs the risk of peptization of the solid if pure water is used to wash a coagulated colloid.

There is little the chemist can do to influence the nature of the ion directly adsorbed on the surface of an analytical precipitate; this is fixed through the necessity of having an excess of the precipitating ion in the solution and the strong tendency of the solid to adsorb that ion in preference to all others. The constitution of the counter-ion layer can be varied, however, and in some instances advantage can be taken of this to produce adsorbed compounds that are volatile; for this reason the choice of electrolyte in the wash liquid may be of prime importance. Thus, when silver is determined by precipitation as the chloride, the primary adsorption of chloride ions is inevitable; the counter-ion layer will clearly be cationic in nature. The chemical species in this layer will be determined in part by the relative concentrations of the various cations present in the solution; if the precipitation is made from a nitric acid solution and the solid washed with a dilute solution of this same acid, a fair portion of the counter ions will be hydrogen ions. As a consequence, the coprecipitated compound will be hydrochloric acid; this will have no effect on the final weight of the precipitate since it is volatilized when the solid is dried. By contrast, when the silver chloride precipitate is employed for the determination of chloride ion, the primarily adsorbed ion will necessarily be silver. Since no common volatile silver salts exist, no improvement in the purity of the precipitate can be expected through exchange of the anions of the wash liquid with those present initially in the counter-ion layer. The dilute nitric acid solution commonly employed serves only to prevent peptization. Thus the analysis of silver by precipitation as silver chloride is inherently more accurate than the determination of chloride using the same precipitate.

Another example of improving the purity of a precipitate through the judicious choice of wash liquid arises when iron is precipitated as the hydrous iron (III) oxide; here, hydroxyl ions are adsorbed on the surface of the solid. By precipitating from and washing with solutions of ammonium nitrate, the counter-ion layer can often be made to consist largely of ammonium ions. A compound is thus produced that can be volatilized during subsequent ignition steps. Unfortunately, this treatment is not always successful in producing a pure oxide residue. Several of the metal hydroxides exhibit extraordinary tendencies to adsorb on hydrous iron (III) oxide; these metal ions will predominate even when high concentrations of ammonium ion are maintained in the surrounding solution. Severe coprecipitation errors can result. In these cases the adsorption errors are minimized by filtration and washing, followed by solution and reprecipitation of the solid. Only a small fraction of the total contaminant present in the solvent is carried down with the precipitate. When the solid is redissolved, the new solution will contain a much lower concentration of the contaminant than the original solvent. Consequently, the precipitate formed from this environment will contain much less of the impurity.

Reprecipitation obviously is not feasible where good solvents for the precipitate do not exist. Furthermore, the time required for the process and the possible mechanical losses of precipitate make this method undesirable, particularly where several reprecipitations are necessary.

COPRECIPITATION WITH CRYSTALLINE PRECIPITATES

Adsorption does not play an important role in the contamination of crystalline precipitates because the specific surface area is relatively small. Coprecipitation by mixed crystal formation, nonisomorphic inclusion, and occlusion can, however, occur to an extent that will appreciably affect the weight of crystalline solids.

Mixed Crystal Formation. Mixed crystal formation or isomorphic inclusion is encountered when a precipitate is formed in the presence of some other ion that can fit into the crystal lattice without causing appreciable distortion of the crystal. The included ion then replaces one of the ions making up the lattice. For this to be possible it is necessary that the included ion be of about the same size and have the same crystal habit as the ion it replaces.

Coprecipitation resulting from mixed crystal formation presents major difficulties to the analytical chemist. There is really little he can do to prevent its occurrence short of removing the offending ion before precipitation.

Nonisomorphic Inclusion. It has been found experimentally that small quantities of *nonisomorphic* substances are sometimes carried out of solution by precipitates in a form that in many respects, resembles isomorphic inclusions. Such impurities appear to be more or less homogeneously distributed throughout the crystal; they do not cause sufficient distortion of the host crystal to form large imperfections; further, the amount of such coprecipitation appears to be essentially independent of the conditions existing at the time of precipitation and of the manner in which the precipitate is digested and washed. The problems in handling this type of coprecipitation are essentially the same as those for isomorphic inclusion.

Solid-solution formation has been demonstrated to be the cause of coprecipitation of several compounds with barium sulfate.[3] For example, barium nitrate, ammonium bisulfate, sodium bisulfate, and potassium bisulfate all coprecipitate at least in part in this form.

Occlusion. *Occlusion* is a type of coprecipitation in which the soluble impurity is enclosed or entrapped within the crystal structure of the solid. As such it acts as a seat of imperfection within the crystal. Occlusion differs from the two previous types of coprecipitation in several respects. Generally, occluded substances are distributed in a nonhomogeneous fashion throughout the crystal.

It is not difficult to see how the process of occlusion might occur during the formation of crystalline precipitates. Consider, for example, the precipitation of barium ion as the sulfate. During the early stages, the solution will contain an excess of barium ions, and the solid will have a large number of these ions adsorbed on its surface. With further additions of reagent, the sulfate ions find their way to the surface of the particles, displace the anions in the counter-ion layer, and combine with the adsorbed barium ions. This process undoubtedly takes place very rapidly; the possibility thus exists that some of the foreign counter ions may not be displaced in time to avoid being completely surrounded by the growing solid. When this occurs, there will be an imperfection within the crystal that will contain internally adsorbed barium ions and counter ions.

⁴ G. H. Walden and M. V. Cohen, *J. Am. Chem. Soc.*, **57**, 2591 (1935); G. Walton and G. H. Walden, *J. Am. Chem. Soc.*, **68**, 1742 (1946).

If, indeed, adsorption plays an intermediate part in the occlusion process, we might expect that reversal of the order of mixing would lead to coprecipitation of a different compound. In this case we would anticipate coprecipitation of sulfate salts, for under these conditions it would be sulfate ions that were primarily adsorbed; cationic counter ions such as sodium would be entrapped by the rapid growth of the solid. Experiments tend to confirm this hypothesis.

It has been found that the quantity of a substance occluded in a precipitate is reduced—often greatly—during digestion. The effectiveness of the digestion process undoubtedly arises from the rapid recrystallization and resultant perfection of the lattice that takes place while the solid stands in contact with its mother liquor. During this time, continuous solution and reprecipitation takes place; this opens up the crystal and exposes at least part of the sites containing the trapped impurities. These can then be replaced by the lattice ion present in excess in the mother liquor to give a more perfect crystal structure.

Two somewhat different approaches have been suggested to decrease the amounts of occluded impurities accompanying analytical precipitates. The classical method has been to form the precipitate slowly—that is, under conditions of low supersaturation—and then to digest for a short period at elevated temperatures. If, as we have postulated, occlusion results from entrapping of the ions of the counter-ion layer by the rapidly growing solid, then we might expect a reduction in amount if the rate of growth of the crystal were reduced. The methods for achieving this would be the same as those for growing large crystals—namely, the slow addition of reagent, the use of dilute solutions, and precipitation from hot solutions. That such measures do improve the purity of precipitates has been amply demonstrated by many investigations; quite often, however, the digestion process is more effective than these measures in producing a pure solid.

An alternative method, proposed by Kolthoff and Sandell,[4] involves rapid formation of the precipitate from cold concentrated solutions followed by dilution of the resulting mixture and digestion overnight at elevated temperatures. The initial particle size of the solid formed under these conditions is smaller than that produced by the classical method; the amount of occlusion would be expected to be greater initially. On the other hand, digestion of such precipitates is more effective because more recrystallization occurs as a result of the larger specific surface area of the finely divided solid. Furthermore, with the smaller particles, the impurities can never be trapped as far from the surface; therefore, the likelihood that these will be exposed to the solution during digestion is appreciably

---

[4] I. M. Kolthoff and E. B. Sandell, *Textbook of Quantitative Inorganic Analysis*, 3d ed., 136. New York: The Macmillan Company, 1952.

greater. With some precipitates, at least, this increased effectiveness of digestion more than outweighs the deleterious effects of rapid formation of the solid. Unfortunately, it is not possible to decide which of these procedures will be the more satisfactory for a given precipitate; this can only be learned by experiment.

The washing of crystalline precipitates is not very effective for removing occluded impurities since these are retained within the crystal structure and therefore do not come in contact with the wash liquid.

Reprecipitation will generally improve the purity of precipitates suffering from contamination by occlusion. During the second precipitation, the amount of contaminant adsorbed is likely to be lower since its concentration in the solution is less. As a result, less will be enclosed within the crystalline structure of the solid when it is again formed. Crystalline calcium oxalate precipitates are often purified by this procedure.

DIRECTION OF COPRECIPITATION ERRORS

Coprecipitated impurities may lead either to high or low values for an analysis. If the contaminant is not a compound of the ion being determined, positive errors will always result. Thus a positive error results when colloidal silver chloride adsorbs silver nitrate during a chloride analysis. On the other hand, where the coprecipitant is a compound of the ion being determined, either positive or negative errors may be observed. In the determination of barium ions by precipitation as barium sulfate, for example, occlusion of barium salts occurs. If the occluded compound is barium nitrate (gfw 261), a positive error will result since this compound has a greater formula weight than the barium sulfate (gfw 233) that would have formed had no coprecipitation occurred. If barium chloride (gfw 208) were the contaminant, however, a negative error would arise since its formula weight is less than that of the sulfate salt.

7.5   Precipitation from Homogeneous Solution[5]

The chemist ordinarily seeks to form an analytical precipitate from solutions in which the supersaturation is as low as possible since, in general, this leads to a product that is more easily filtered and is less contaminated by coprecipitation. The degree of supersaturation can be kept low by the slow, dropwise addition of the reagent and by the use of dilute solutions

---

[5] For an interesting review article on this subject see L. Gordon, *Anal. Chem.*, **24,** 459 (1952). See also L. Gordon, M. L. Salutsky, and H. H. Willard, *Precipitation from Homogeneous Solution*. New York: John Wiley and Sons, Inc., 1959.

of both the ion to be precipitated and the reagent. The obvious practical limits to these expedients are the increased solubility losses in the more dilute solutions and the tedium of the slow addition process. Furthermore, these techniques do not entirely eliminate high supersaturation and rapid precipitation. At the point where a new drop of reagent first makes contact with the solution there is, at least momentarily, a relative high concentration of reagent. Until stirring disperses the drop, there exists a high degree of local supersaturation and a consequent rapid formation of the solid. Even with the most efficient stirring, this local effect cannot be entirely eliminated.

Precipitation from homogeneous solution is an ingenious method for introducing a precipitating reagent in such a way as to avoid the local excesses that accompany mechanical addition of the reagent. Here precipitation is caused by slowly generating the reagent throughout the entire solution by means of a suitable chemical reaction. During the process the solvent remains homogeneous with respect to the concentration of the ion being precipitated and the reagent; if the generating reaction is slow, high supersaturation is avoided and gradual formation of the solid takes place throughout the entire solution.

An important example of this type of precipitation involves the use of urea as a source of hydroxyl ions for the precipitation of aluminum, iron (III), thorium, and other heavy metal ions. The precipitating reagent is formed by the reaction

$$(NH_2)_2CO + 3H_2O \rightarrow CO_2 + 2NH_4^+ + 2OH^-$$

At temperatures just below the boiling point of water this reaction proceeds slowly; one to two hours are required to complete the precipitation in a typical case. The physical appearance of a hydrous oxide so formed is dramatically different from that produced by the slow addition of ammonia. Colloids are obtained by either method, but the densities of the coagulated solids in the first case are much greater than in the second. Generally, the homogeneously formed solids occupy from one tenth to one twentieth the volume of those formed by the classical procedure; as a result they are much easier to filter and wash. In addition the amount of coprecipitation associated with such precipitates is generally appreciably smaller. For example, Gordon[6] reports that hydrous aluminum oxide prepared by the slow addition of ammonia to a solution containing 0.1 gram of the element and 1 gram of manganese was contaminated by a sufficient quantity of manganese salts to increase the weight of the ignited precipitate by 1.2 mg. When the aluminum was precipitated by means of urea, the weight of contaminant was only 0.2 mg. Similar data for other compounds

---

[6] L. Gordon, *Anal. Chem.*, **24,** 459 (1952).

can be found in the literature. It seems probable that the improvement in purity is a direct result of the decreased surface area associated with the denser precipitates and the consequent reduction in surface adsorption.

Many crystalline precipitates can also be formed from homogeneous solution to give solids of greater particle size. The urea method, for example, can be applied to the precipitation of calcium oxalate. Here the calcium and oxalate ions are brought together in a solution that is sufficiently acid to prevent formation of the solid. Precipitation is then induced through homogeneous neutralization of the acid by heating with urea. Large coarse crystals result.

Methods have been developed for the homogeneous generation of a number of other precipitating reagents.

(8)

The Scope and Applications of
Gravimetric Analysis

In previous chapters we have dealt with the principles underlying gravimetric analysis. A consideration of the more practical aspects of this important topic may now be undertaken.

It was pointed out in Chapter 4 that specificity of behavior is a most desirable property in a precipitating agent. Were a substance to exhibit true specificity, the need for preliminary separations would be entirely eliminated and the analysis would consist simply of isolating the compound formed between the component sought and the reagent. Such specificity is rarely, if ever, encountered. Instead, precipitating agents are ordinarily selective in behavior, forming slightly soluble substances with more than one species. Specificity is achieved only after preliminary separation has isolated the desired species from interfering substances. The need for pretreatment of the sample to eliminate potential interferences is more often the rule than the exception.

8.1 Inorganic Precipitating Agents

The lack of specificity on the part of most reagents is amply illustrated in Table 8-1, which indicates the scope of applications to which a number of inorganic precipitating agents have been put. Where a given reagent offers a method for the analysis of several ions, each ion represents a potential source of interference with respect to determination of the others.

TABLE 8-1

Some Applications of Inorganic Precipitating Agents[1,2]

Precipitating Agent	Element Precipitated (weighing form is indicated in parentheses)
NH$_3$ (aq)	Be (BeO), Al (Al$_2$O$_3$), Sc (Sc$_2$O$_3$), Cr (Cr$_2$O$_3$)*, Fe (Fe$_2$O$_3$), Ga (Ga$_2$O$_3$), Zr (ZrO$_2$), In (In$_2$O$_3$), Sn (SnO$_2$), U (U$_3$O$_8$)
H$_2$S	Cu (CuO)*, Zn (ZnO, or ZnSO$_4$), Ge (GeO$_2$), As (As$_2$O$_3$, or (As$_2$O$_5$), Mo (MoO$_3$), Sn (SnO$_2$)*, Sb (Sb$_2$O$_3$, or Sb$_2$O$_5$), Bi (Bi$_2$S$_3$)
(NH$_4$)$_2$S	Hg (HgS), Co (Co$_3$O$_4$)
(NH$_4$)$_2$HPO$_4$	Mg (Mg$_2$P$_2$O$_7$), Al (AlPO$_4$), Mn (Mn$_2$P$_2$O$_7$), Zn (Zn$_2$P$_2$O$_7$), Zr (Zr$_2$P$_2$O$_7$), Cd (Cd$_2$P$_2$O$_7$), Bi (BiPO$_4$)
H$_2$SO$_4$	Li, Mn, Sr, Cd, Pb, Ba (all as sulfates)
H$_2$PtCl$_6$	K (K$_2$PtCl$_6$, or Pt), Rb (Rb$_2$PtCl$_6$), Cs (Cs$_2$PtCl$_6$)
H$_2$C$_2$O$_4$	Ca (CaO), Sr (SrO), Th (ThO$_2$)
(NH$_4$)$_2$MoO$_4$	Cd (CdMoO$_4$)*, Pb (PbMoO$_4$)
HCl	Ag (AgCl), Hg (Hg$_2$Cl$_2$), Na (as NaCl from butyl alcohol), Si (SiO$_2$)
AgNO$_3$	Cl (AgCl), Br (AgBr), I (AgI)
(NH$_4$)$_2$CO$_3$	Bi (Bi$_2$O$_3$)
NH$_4$SCN	Cu (Cu$_2$(SCN)$_2$)
NaHCO$_3$	Ru, Os, Ir (pp'ted as hydrous oxides, reduced with H$_2$ to metallic state)
HNO$_3$	Sn (SnO$_2$)
H$_5$IO$_6$	Hg (Hg$_5$(IO$_6$)$_2$)
NaCl, Pb(NO$_3$)$_2$	F (PbClF)
BaCl$_2$	SO$_4^{2-}$ (BaSO$_4$)
MgCl$_2$, NH$_4$Cl	PO$_4^{3-}$ (Mg$_2$P$_2$O$_7$)

[1] Double underline indicates preferred method of analysis; single underline indicates most reliable gravimetric method; asterisk indicates that method is seldom used.

[2] Source: W. F. Hillebrand, G. E. F. Lundell, H. A. Bright, and J. I. Hoffman, *Applied Inorganic Analysis*. New York: John Wiley and Sons, Inc., 1953.

The majority of inorganic precipitating agents function by forming slightly soluble salts or hydrous oxides with the species being determined. In addition, however, several metal ions can be isolated in elemental form either by electrochemical reduction or by treatment with a suitable chemical reducing agent. Table 8-2 summarizes these applications; organic as well as inorganic reducing agents have been employed for this purpose.

TABLE 8-2

Gravimetric Methods Based upon Reduction to the Elemental State

Reducing Agent	Analysis
SO_2	Se, Au
$SO_2 + H_2NOH$	Te
H_2NOH	Se
$H_2C_2O_4$	Au
H_2	Re, Ir
HCOOH	Pt
$NaNO_2$	Au
$TiCl_2$	Rh
$SnCl_2$	Hg
Electrolytic reduction	Co, Ni, Cu, Zn, Ag, In, Sn, Sb, Cd, Re, Bi

8.2 Organic Precipitating Agents

Many organic compounds are used as precipitating agents. Of the several ways in which they react, the most important involve either the formation of slightly soluble non-ionic complexes—known also as *coordination compounds*—or the formation of slightly soluble salts.

REAGENTS THAT PRODUCE SLIGHTLY SOLUBLE COORDINATION COMPOUNDS

A slightly soluble coordination compound is typically the result of bonding between an organic molecule and a metal ion that gives rise to an uncharged five- or six-membered ring. This requires the presence of two functional groups, properly oriented within the organic molecule, that have the ability to bond with the metal ion. Insofar as the products are nonpolar, they will have low solubility in water and high solubility in organic liquids. In general, these precipitates are low-density solids; they often possess intense and characteristic colors. Because they are not wetted by water, they are readily freed of moisture at low temperatures. At the same time, the hydrophobic nature of these precipitates endows them with the annoying tendency to creep during the washing and transferring operations.

Two examples of this type of reagent are 8-hydroxyquinoline and dimethylglyoxime.

8-Hydroxyquinoline. This compound, known also as *oxine*, has the structure

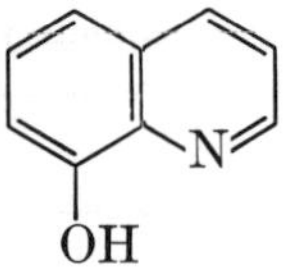

8-hydroxyquinoline

A metal ion is bonded to this molecule through the oxygen and nitrogen atoms. By way of specific example, the product with magnesium can be represented as

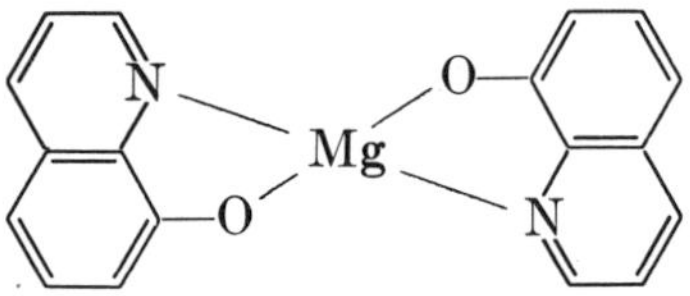

Approximately two dozen cations form precipitates with 8-hydroxyquinoline. The solubilities of these vary considerably from cation to cation. Furthermore the solubilities of all are influenced by pH, inasmuch as hydrogen ions are evolved in the formation of the metal oxines. In general the precipitates become more soluble as the hydrogen-ion concentration increases. In addition, some of the precipitates are soluble in strongly alkaline media. These differences in solubility, particularly with respect to pH, enhance somewhat the selectivity of the reagent.

Notwithstanding its rather low selectivity, a large number of methods have been developed that make use of 8-hydroxyquinoline in conjunction with other reagents. In most of these the coordination compound itself serves as the weighing form with which the determination is completed. The most widespread applications of the reagent are concerned with the analysis for magnesium and aluminum.[3]

Dimethylglyoxime. Oxine shows a marked lack of specificity. By way of contrast, dimethylglyoxime is virtually without peer with respect

---

[3] For a definitive reference with respect to the applications of 8-hydroxyquinoline, see R. G. W. Hollingshead, *Oxine and its Derivatives*, in 4 volumes. London: Butterworth's Scientific Publications, 1954.

to this property. It will precipitate only palladium quantitatively from acid media, and only nickel from weakly basic solutions.

There are three possible geometric isomers of the reagent.

$$H_3C-C\text{————}C-CH_3$$

(structures labeled *amphi-* and *anti-*)

(structure labeled *syn-*)

Of these, only the anti form has analytical uses. Owing to its rather low solubility in water, alcoholic solutions of the reagent are ordinarily employed.

Dimethylglyoxime gives a compound with nickel having the structure

(nickel dimethylglyoxime complex structure)

This forms as an intense red precipitate that is so bulky only small quantities of nickel can be conveniently handled. The solid is readily dried at 110° C and is of definite composition.

Experimental directions for the gravimetric determination of nickel with this reagent are given in a later section.

REAGENTS THAT PRODUCE SALTLIKE PRECIPITATES

A number of important organic precipitating agents produce slightly soluble compounds in which the bond with the species precipitated is primarily ionic in character.

Sodium Tetraphenylboron. Sodium tetraphenylboron has the formula $(C_6H_5)_4B^-Na^+$, and in cold mineral acid solution is a specific precipitating agent for potassium and ammonium ions. Under these conditions, only mercury (II), rubidium, and cesium interfere and must be removed by prior treatment. The precipitates are stoichiometric, corresponding to the potassium or ammonium salt, as the case may be. Analysis for potassium by this reagent is an improvement over the perchlorate method, where magnesium, calcium, aluminum, iron, cobalt, nickel, manganese, sulfate, and phosphate ions interfere.

Benzidine. Another salt-forming reagent is benzidine

$$H_2N-\langle\ \rangle-\langle\ \rangle-NH_2$$

benzidine

which precipitates sulfate from a slightly acid medium as $C_{12}H_{12}N_2 \cdot H_2SO_4$. The solubility of the precipitate increases rapidly with temperature and also with the acidity of the environment; both of these variables must be carefully controlled. Instead of weighing as a gravimetric precipitate, benzidine sulfate may be titrated with a standard solution of sodium hydroxide. The method succeeds in the presence of copper, cobalt, nickel, zinc, manganese (II), iron (II), chromium (III), and aluminum ions. Yet another method for completion of the analysis calls for titration of the benzidine with a standard solution of permanganate. Benzidine is well suited to the rapid analysis of sulfate on a routine basis.

Substituted Arsonic Acids. Substituted arsonic acids have the structure

$$R-As{\overset{\displaystyle OH}{\underset{\displaystyle OH}{=}}}O$$

where R represents an organic radical, such as phenyl or propyl.

A large number of arsonic acids have been found to yield saltlike precipitates with such quadrivalent metal ions as tin, zirconium, titanium, and thorium. The composition of the precipitates generally involves approximately 2 mols of arsonic acid per mol of quadrivalent cation. The nature of the organic portion of the molecule (R) determines, to some extent, the cations that form precipitates as well as the conditions under which they are formed. Whether or not iron (III) will precipitate, for example, depends upon the particular arsonic acid employed.

Because they are difficult to dry without decomposition, metallic arsonates are ignited to their respective oxides.

The reagents discussed in this section represent but a few of literally hundreds that have been investigated as organic precipitating agents.[4]

8.3   Selected Methods of Analysis

DETERMINATION OF WATER IN BARIUM CHLORIDE DIHYDRATE

The water of hydration in a crystalline hydrate such as $BaCl_2 \cdot 2H_2O$ is present in stoichiometric proportions. Thus the determination of the water content of a sample containing such a compound provides a basis for the estimation of that substance. The analysis may be performed either by collecting and weighing the water evolved from a measured quantity of sample or by weighing the residue and determining the weight of water by difference.

★PROCEDURE. Throughout this experiment perform all weighings to the nearest 0.1 mg.

Carefully clean two weighing bottles. Dry them for 1 hour at 105° to 110° C, using the beaker and watch-glass arrangement described in Chapter 5 to prevent accidental contamination. After they have cooled to room temperature in a desiccator, determine the weight of each bottle. Repeat this operation until a constant weight has been attained. Next introduce a quantity of unknown into each bottle and determine its weight. Heat the samples for about 2 hours at 105° to 110° C, then cool and weigh as before. Repeat the heating cycle until constant weights for the bottles and their contents have been achieved. Report the percentage of water in the sample.

NOTES:

1. If the unknown consists of the pure dihydrate, $BaCl_2 \cdot 2H_2O$, take samples weighing approximately 1 gram. If the unknown is a mixture of the dihydrate and some anhydrous diluent, obtain the proper sample size from the instructor.

2. Barium chloride can be heated to elevated temperatures without danger of decomposition. If desired, the analysis can be performed in crucibles with a Bunsen flame as the source of heat.

---

[4] For further information regarding these and other organic precipitating agents see J. F. Flagg, *Organic Reagents Used in Gravimetric and Volumetric Analysis.* New York: Interscience Publishers, Inc., 1948.

DETERMINATION OF CHLORIDE IN A SOLUBLE SAMPLE

The chloride content of a soluble salt can be determined by precipitation of that ion as its silver salt

$$Ag^+ + Cl^- \rightarrow AgCl$$

The precipitate is collected in a filtering crucible, washed, and brought to constant weight by drying at 105° to 110° C. Precipitation is carried out in acid solution to eliminate potential interference from anions of weak acids (for example, CO_3^{2-}) which form precipitates with silver in neutral media. A moderate excess of silver ion is required to diminish the solubility of the precipitate, but large excesses are undesirable because they will lead to serious coprecipitation.

Silver chloride first precipitates as a colloid; it is coagulated with heat and a relatively high electrolyte concentration. A small quantity of nitric acid is added to the wash liquid to maintain the electrolyte concentration and prevent peptization during washing; the acid is volatilized during the subsequent heat treatment.

In common with other silver halides, silver chloride is susceptible to photodecomposition, the reaction being

$$AgCl \rightarrow Ag + \tfrac{1}{2}Cl_2$$

The precipitate acquires a violet color due to the accumulation of finely divided silver. If photochemical decomposition occurs in the presence of excess silver ion, the following reaction takes place:

$$3Cl_2 + 3H_2O + 5Ag^+ \rightarrow 5AgCl + ClO_3^- + 6H^+$$

This will cause the analytical results to be high. In the absence of silver ion, the results will be low. Dry silver chloride is virtually unaffected by exposure to light.

Unless elaborate precautions are taken, some photochemical decomposition of silver chloride is unavoidable but, with reasonable care, this effect will not induce an appreciable error in the analysis.

Iodide, bromide, and thiocyanate, if present in the sample, will be precipitated along with silver chloride and cause high results. In addition the chlorides of tin and antimony are likely to hydrolyze and precipitate under the conditions of the analysis.

★PROCEDURE. Clean and dry three fritted glass or porcelain filtering crucibles; bring these to constant weight during periods of waiting in the analysis.

Dry the sample at 105° to 110° C for 1 to 2 hours in a weighing bottle (p. 90). Store in a desiccator while cooling. Weigh (to the nearest 0.1 mg) individual 0.4-gram samples into 400-ml beakers, and to each add about 200 ml of distilled water and 1 to 2 ml of concentrated nitric acid. Slowly, and with good stirring, add 5-percent silver nitrate to the cold solution until the precipitate is observed to coagulate, and then add an additional 3 to 5 ml. Heat the solution almost to boiling, and digest the precipitate at this temperature for about 10 minutes; check for completeness of precipitation by adding a few drops of silver nitrate to the supernatant liquid; should additional silver chloride appear, continue the addition of silver nitrate until precipitation is complete. Store in a dark place for at least 1 to 2 hours, preferably overnight. Then decant the supernatant through a weighed filtering crucible. Wash the precipitate several times while it is still in the beaker with a cold solution consisting of 1 to 3 ml of concentrated nitric acid per liter of distilled water; decant these washings through the filter also. Finally, transfer the bulk of the precipitate to the crucible, using a rubber policeman to dislodge any particles that adhere to the walls of the beaker. Continue washing until the filtrate is found to be substantially free of silver ion. Dry the precipitates to constant weight at 105° to 110° C. Report the percentage of chloride in the sample.

NOTES:

1. To determine the approximate amount of silver nitrate needed, calculate the volume required on the assumption that the sample is 100 percent sodium chloride.

2. Washings are readily tested for their silver content by collecting a few milliliters in a test tube and treating with a few drops of hydrochloric acid. Washing is judged complete when little or no turbidity is observed with this test.

ANALYSIS OF A SOLUBLE SULFATE

The analysis of a soluble sulfate is based upon precipitation with barium ion

$$Ba^{2+} + SO_4^{2-} \rightarrow BaSO_4$$

The barium sulfate is collected on a suitable filter, washed with water, and strongly ignited.

Superficially, this method appears straightforward. In fact, however, it is subject to a multiplicity of interferences, due chiefly to the tendency of barium sulfate to occlude anions as well as cations. Table 8-3 summarizes many of the more common interferences affecting this analysis. Purification by reprecipitation is not feasible because there is no practical solvent for barium sulfate. It is therefore necessary to eliminate the principal interferences by preliminary treatment of the sample, and then to precipitate the barium sulfate from hot, dilute solutions. Even then the excellent

TABLE 8-3

Interferences Attending the Gravimetric Determination
of Sulfate as $BaSO_4$

Effect upon Analysis	Nature of the Interference
Low Results	Excessive amounts of mineral acid present. (Solubility of $BaSO_4$ is appreciably greater in strongly acid media.)
	Coprecipitation of sulfuric acid. (Note that this is not a source of error in a gravimetric determination of barium, since this H_2SO_4 is driven off during ignition.)
	Coprecipitation of alkali metal and calcium ions. (Sulfates of these ions weigh less than the equivalent amount of $BaSO_4$ which should have formed.)
	Coprecipitation of ammonium ion. (Ammonium sulfate is volatilized upon ignition of the precipitate.)
	Coprecipitation of iron as a basic iron (III) sulfate.
	Partial reduction of $BaSO_4$ to BaS if filter paper is charred too rapidly.
	Presence of trivalent chromium. (May not achieve complete precipitation of $BaSO_4$ due to formation of soluble complex chromium (III) sulfates.)
High Results	Absence of mineral acid. (The slightly soluble carbonate or phosphate of barium can precipitate under these conditions.)
	Coprecipitation of barium chloride.
	Coprecipitation of anions, particularly nitrate and chlorate as barium salts.

agreement often observed between theoretical and experimental results is due in considerable measure to a cancellation of errors.

★PROCEDURE. Dry the unknown for 1 hour at 105° to 110° C. Weigh (to the nearest 0.1 mg) individual 0.5 to 0.7-gram samples into 400-ml beakers and dissolve each in 200 ml of distilled water to which 2 ml of concentrated hydrochloric acid have been added.

For each sample dissolve 1.3 grams of barium chloride dihydrate in 100 ml of distilled water, and filter if necessary. Heat nearly to boiling before quickly adding, with vigorous stirring, to the samples that have also been heated.

Digest the precipitated barium sulfate for 1 to 2 hours. Decant the supernatant through a fine ashless paper (Note). Wash the precipitate three times with hot water, decanting the washings through the filter. Finally, transfer the precipitate to the paper.

Place papers and contents in porcelain crucibles that have been ignited to constant weight; gently char off the papers. Ignite to constant weight at 900° C. Report the percentage of sulfate in the sample.

NOTE:

Use of Schleicher and Schuell No. 589 White Ribbon, or Whatman No. 42 paper is recommended. If desired, the precipitate can be collected in a Gooch crucible or a porcelain filtering crucible.

ANALYSIS OF IRON IN A SOLUBLE SAMPLE

The analysis of iron in a soluble sample is based upon the precipitation of iron (III) as a hydrous oxide, followed by ignition to Fe_2O_3

$$2Fe^{3+} + 6NH_3 + (x + 3)H_2O \rightarrow Fe_2O_3 \cdot xH_2O + 6NH_4^+$$

$$Fe_2O_3 \cdot xH_2O \rightarrow Fe_2O_3 + xH_2O$$

The hydrous oxide forms as a gelatinous mass that rapidly clogs the pores of most filtering media, and thus a very coarse grade of ashless paper is employed. Even here, however, it is best to delay transfer of the precipitate as long as possible and to wash by decantation.

The ultimate employment of Fe_2O_3 as a weighing form requires that all of the iron present be in the $+3$ state; this is readily achieved by treating the sample with nitric acid before precipitating the hydrous oxide

$$3Fe^{2+} + NO_3^- + 4H^+ \rightarrow 3Fe^{3+} + NO + 2H_2O$$

The complex $FeSO_4 \cdot NO$ sometimes imparts a very dark color to the solution; it decomposes upon further heating.

Owing to its negligible solubility, the precipitate can be safely washed with a hot solution of ammonium nitrate.

★PROCEDURE

Double-precipitation Method. Unless directed otherwise, do not dry the sample. Consult the instructor for the proper sample size; weigh these into 600-ml beakers. Dissolve in 20 to 30 ml of distilled water to which about 5 ml of concentrated hydrochloric acid have been added. Then add 1 to 2 ml of concentrated nitric acid; heat to complete the oxidation and to remove any oxides of nitrogen. Dilute to 350 or 400 ml and slowly add, with good stirring, freshly filtered aqueous ammonia until precipitation is complete (Notes 1 and 2). Digest briefly, and then check for completeness of precipitation with a few additional drops of ammonia. While still warm, decant the clear supernatant through ashless filter paper (Note 3), and wash the precipitate in the beaker with two 30-ml portions of hot 1-percent ammonium nitrate solution.

Return the filter papers to their appropriate beakers. Add about 5 ml of concentrated hydrochloric acid to each and macerate the paper thoroughly with a stirring rod. Dilute to about 300 ml with distilled water and reprecipitate the hydrous iron (III) oxide as before. Again decant the filtrate through ashless filter paper, and wash the precipitate repeatedly with hot 1-percent ammonium nitrate. When the filtered decantate gives little or no test for chloride ion (Note 4), transfer the precipitate quantitatively to the filter cone. Remove the last traces of precipitate adhering to the walls of the beaker by scrubbing with a small piece of ashless paper. Allow the precipitate to drain overnight, if possible. Then transfer the paper and contents to a porcelain crucible that has previously been ignited to constant weight. Char the paper at low temperature, taking care to allow free access of air (Note 5). Gradually increase the temperature until all of the carbon has been burned away. Then ignite to constant weight at 900° to 1000° C.

NOTES:

1. Upon prolonged contact, aqueous ammonia solutions attack the glass of their containers and thereby become contaminated with particles of silica. It is a wise precaution to filter the ammonia prior to use.

2. Aqueous ammonia should be added until its odor is unmistakeable over the solution. The precipitate should appear reddish brown. If it is black (or nearly so), the presence of iron (II) is indicated; the sample is best discarded.

3. A porous grade of ashless paper is required for this gelatinous precipitate. Schleicher and Schuell No. 589 Black Ribbon or Whatman No. 41 are satisfactory papers for this. The time required for filtration is shortened by performing the principal washing of the precipitate while it is still in the beaker. After it has been transferred to the paper, the rate of filtration is markedly slowed.

4. Before making a test for chloride in the washings, the sample of filtrate taken must first be acidified with dilute nitric acid.

5. Heat lamps are convenient for the initial charring of the filter papers.

★PROCEDURE

Single-precipitation Method. Proceed as directed in the first paragraph of the double-precipitation method, making the following changes:

1. Instead of washing with but two 30-ml portions of 1-percent ammonium nitrate, wash repeatedly until the decantate is essentially free of chloride.

2. Then transfer the precipitate quantitatively to the filter and complete the analysis as before.

PRECIPITATION OF IRON FROM HOMOGENEOUS SOLUTION

Iron may also be precipitated from homogeneous solution. The precipitant, hydroxyl ion, is uniformly and gradually generated throughout the solution as a consequence of the slow decomposition of urea

$$H_2N\!-\!\overset{\overset{\displaystyle O}{\|}}{C}\!-\!NH_2 + 3H_2O \rightarrow 2NH_4^+ + CO_2 + 2OH^-$$

Ultimately iron (III) is deposited in the form of its hydrous oxide or as a basic salt; in either event, it is filtered, washed, and ignited to Fe_2O_3. The homogeneous generation of hydroxyl ions yields a rather dense precipitate that is less subject to contamination than that formed by conventional means.

The procedure given here represents a modification of the method reported by Willard and Sheldon[5] and involves precipitation of the iron as a basic formate. The sample is first dissolved in hydrochloric acid and treated with nitric acid to oxidize the iron. A requirement for production of a dense precipitate is that the solution be appreciably acidic at the outset. A large excess of hydrogen ions, on the other hand, is undesirable because of the large quantity of urea needed and the extended time required for neutralization. The acidity of the sample is therefore adjusted by the successive addition of ammonia and hydrochloric acid. Then formic acid and ammonium chloride are introduced, the former to yield the desired basic formate precipitate, and the latter to help maintain the solution at the desired pH. Urea is then introduced and heating is commenced. The time required will depend upon the initial acidity and the temperature; ideally precipitation should begin within about 1 hour. Toward the end of the heating period, hydrogen peroxide is added to oxidize any iron (II) that may have resulted from reaction with formic acid. After filtration the precipitate is ignited to Fe_2O_3.

★PROCEDURE. Carefully weigh samples into individual 600-ml beakers; the weight taken should be such as will contain approximately 100 mg of iron. Dissolve in about 50 ml of water to which 5 ml of concentrated hydrochloric acid have been added. Then introduce 1 to 2 ml of concentrated nitric acid to each sample and boil gently to remove the oxides of nitrogen.

Dilute to approximately 400 ml with distilled water and add concentrated ammonia slowly until the first permanent appearance of the hydrous oxide is observed. Add dilute hydrochloric acid slowly until the precipitate has definitely been discharged and the

[5] H. H. Willard and J. L. Sheldon, *Anal. Chem.*, **22**, 1162 (1950).

solution is again clear (Note 3). Next introduce about 2 ml of concentrated formic acid, 15 grams of ammonium chloride, and 4 to 5 grams of urea. Heat the samples carefully, maintaining a gentle boil (Note 2). Continue heating until precipitation is complete (Note 4). Toward the end of the heating period introduce about 5 ml of 3-percent hydrogen peroxide.

For filtration use ashless paper suitable for the collection of fine, crystalline precipitates (Note 5). Decant most of the supernatant through the filter, taking care to avoid the undue transfer of precipitate. Wash the precipitate three times with 20- to 30-ml portions of hot 1-percent ammonium nitrate solution and decant the washings through the filter. Then quantitatively transfer the bulk of the precipitate. Shred a half circle of ashless paper into each beaker and pour about 5 ml of concentrated hydrochloric acid slowly down the stirring rod. Scrape the stained surfaces of the beaker with the macerated paper, using the stirring rod to provide direction. Dilute with 75 to 100 ml of distilled water, heat nearly to boiling, and slowly add aqueous ammonia until the solution is definitely alkaline. As before, wash the residue in the beaker by decantation before transferring to the filter paper containing the bulk of the precipitate.

Ignition of the residues is carried out in the manner previously described.

NOTES:

1. These instructions are suitable for samples that contain approximately 0.100 gram of iron. With 5 grams of urea, as much as 0.200 gram of iron can be tolerated.

2. Each beaker should be supplied with a special stirring rod to aid in the prevention of bumping. The end of an ordinary stirring rod is heated to the softening point and then firmly pressed into the point of an ordinary thumbtack. The indentation significantly reduces the danger of loss due to local overheating.

3. A pH meter, if available, may be used to adjust the initial pH to about 1.8.

4. Completion of the heating period can be ascertained by measuring the pH of the supernatant. Alternatively, heating may safely be discontinued when it is observed that the supernatant is clear. It is desirable to allow the precipitate to stand overnight prior to filtration.

5. Schleicher and Schuell No. 589 White label, or Whatman No. 42 ashless paper is recommended; 9- or 11-cm circles are convenient.

DETERMINATION OF NICKEL IN STEEL

The nickel content in a steel sample can be determined by precipitation of nickel from a slightly alkaline solution with an alcoholic solution of dimethylglyoxime. Tartaric acid is introduced to prevent interference from iron. The organic-nickel compound serves as a convenient weighing form.

Owing to the bulky character of the precipitate there is a maximum quantity of nickel that can be conveniently handled. The sample weight taken is governed by this consideration. The excess of precipitating agent must be controlled, not only because its solubility in water is low, but also because the nickel compound becomes appreciably more soluble in the presence of alcohol.

★PROCEDURE. Weigh individual samples containing between 30 and 35 mg of nickel into 400-ml beakers and dissolve by warming with about 50 ml of 1:1 hydrochloric acid. Carefully introduce about 10 ml of 1:1 nitric acid and boil gently to expel the oxides of nitrogen. Dilute the resulting solution to 200 ml and heat nearly to boiling. Introduce 5 to 6 grams of tartaric acid (Note 1), and neutralize with aqueous ammonia until a faint odor of ammonia can be detected after blowing away the vapors over the solution; add 1 to 2 ml in excess. If the solution is not clear at this stage, proceed as directed in Note 2. Make the solution slightly acid with hydrochloric acid, heat to 60° to 80° C, and add 20 ml of a 1-percent alcoholic solution of dimethylglyoxime. Then, with good stirring, introduce sufficient dilute ammonia until a slight excess is present as indicated by the odor, plus an additional 1 to 2 ml. Digest for 30 to 60 minutes at about 60° C, cool for at least 1 hour, and filter through weighed filtering crucibles. Wash with water until free of chloride. Finally, bring crucibles and contents to constant weight by drying at 110 to 120° C. Report the percentage of nickel in the sample. The precipitate, $NiC_8H_{14}O_4N_4$, contains 20.31 percent nickel.

NOTES:

1. Tartaric acid is conveniently introduced as a strong solution (25 grams diluted to 100 ml). If necessary, this should be filtered prior to use.

2. If a residue is formed upon the addition of base, the solution should be acidified, treated with additional tartaric acid, and again made alkaline. Alternatively, the residue can be removed by filtration. If this is done, thorough washing with a hot, dilute NH_3/NH_4Cl solution is required; the washings should be combined with the rest of the sample.

3. Gooch crucibles, or filtering crucibles of porcelain or fritted glass, may be used for collection of the precipitate.

Problems

1. Calculate the minimum volume of 0.080-F silver nitrate solution needed to precipitate the chloride from

(a) 0.224 gram of NaCl

(b) 0.104 gram of $BaCl_2$

(c) a 0.640-gram sample that assays 12.8 percent Cl

(d) a 0.640-gram sample that assays 21.3 percent $SnCl_2$

2. The chloride in a 1.34-gram sample of molybdenum (III) chloride is to be precipitated as AgCl. Calculate the volume of $AgNO_3$ required if the solution used
   (a) is 0.120 F
   (b) contains 5.0 percent $AgNO_3$ by weight
   (c) consists of 24.5 grams of $AgNO_3$ dissolved in 400 ml of solution

3. Crude magnesium chloride is to be employed in a manufacturing process. As received, shipments assay between 48 percent and 64 percent $MgCl_2 \cdot 6H_2O$. Directions for the routine gravimetric analysis of the material are required.
   (a) What sample weight should be taken to insure a precipitate of AgCl that weighs at least 0.500 gram?
   (b) If this sample size is taken, what maximum precipitate weight can be expected?
   (c) What volume of 5-percent $AgNO_3$ solution should be specified in order to assure a 10-percent excess of precipitating agent?
   (d) What should be the formal concentration of an $AgNO_3$ solution if 50 ml will constitute, at a minimum, a 5-percent excess over that required for precipitation of the chloride from a 0.250-gram sample?
   (e) What sample weight should be taken in order to have the percentage of $MgCl_2 \cdot 6H_2O$ exceed the weight of AgCl produced by a factor of 100?

4. Estimate the maximum weight of $BaSO_4$ lost as a result of solubility if the supernatant liquid is 8×10^{-3} F with respect to Ba^{2+} and occupies a volume of 300 ml after precipitation is complete, and 120 ml of water are subsequently used to wash the precipitate.

5. Calculate the weight of urea needed to precipitate 0.100 gram of iron (III) as $Fe(OH)_3$.

6. Determine whether differences in the solubility of their hydrous oxides can be used to achieve a separation of iron (III) and aluminum (III) in a solution that is 5×10^{-2} with respect to each cation. Use K_{sp} data in Appendix A-5 for the hydroxides of these cations, and consider that separation is feasible if the concentration of the less soluble precipitate is 1×10^{-6} F (or less) under the conditions needed to initiate precipitation of the more soluble component.

$$\left(\, 9 \, \right)$$

An Introduction to Volumetric
Methods of Analysis

A volumetric method is one in which the analysis is completed by measuring the volume of a solution of established concentration needed to react completely with the substance being determined. Volumetric methods are frequently equivalent in accuracy to gravimetric procedures and are more rapid and convenient; their use is widespread.

9.1 Definition of Some Terms

The process of measuring quantitatively the combining capacity of a substance with a reagent is called a *titration*. Ordinarily a titration is accomplished by the controlled addition of a reagent of known concentration to a solution of the substance until reaction between the two is judged to be complete; the volume of reagent is then measured. Occasionally it is convenient or necessary to perform the analysis by adding an excess of the reagent and then determining the excess by back-titration with a second reagent of known concentration.

The reagent of exactly known composition used in a titration is called a *standard solution*. The accuracy with which its concentration is known sets a definite limit upon the accuracy of the method; for this reason, much care is taken in the preparation of standard solutions. Commonly the concentration of a standard solution is arrived at in either of two ways: (1) a carefully measured quantity of a pure compound is titrated with the reagent and the concentration is calculated from the weight and volume measurements; or (2) the standard solution is prepared by diluting a carefully weighed quantity of the pure reagent itself to an exactly known volume. In either method, a highly purified chemical compound—called a *primary standard*—is required as the reference material. The process whereby the concentration of a standard solution is determined by titration of a primary standard is called a *standardization.*

The goal of every titration is the addition of standard solution in such amount as to be chemically equivalent to the substance with which it reacts. This condition is achieved at the *equivalence point.* For example, the equivalence point in the titration of sodium chloride with silver nitrate is attained when exactly one formula weight of silver ion has been introduced for each formula weight of chloride ion present in the sample. In the titration of sulfuric acid with sodium hydroxide, the equivalence point occurs when two formula weights of the latter have been introduced for each formula weight of the former.

The equivalence point in a titration is a theoretical concept. In actual fact we can only estimate its position by observing physical changes associated with it in the solution. These changes manifest themselves at the *end point* of the titration. It is to be hoped that the volume difference between the end point and equivalence point will be small. Differences do arise, however, owing to inadequacies in the physical changes and our ability to observe them. This results in an analytical error called a *titration error.*

One of the common methods of end-point detection in volumetric analysis involves the use of supplementary chemical compounds that exhibit changes in color as a result of concentration changes occurring near the equivalence point. Such substances are called *indicators.*

9.2 Reactions and Reagents Used in Volumetric Analysis

DESIRABLE CHARACTERISTICS OF A VOLUMETRIC REACTION

In order to be suitable for a volumetric analysis, a chemical reaction should meet certain requirements. (1) The reaction ought to be rapid. Normally, a titration involves addition of the reagent in small increments and observation of the solution for the end point. If the chemical reaction is slow, a period of waiting must follow each addition and the whole process becomes prohibitively time-consuming and tedious. (2) The reaction should proceed reasonably far towards completion. As we shall presently show, satisfactory end points for most titrations are based upon this second condition. (3) The reaction must be such that it can be described by a balanced chemical equation; otherwise the weight of the sought-for substance cannot be calculated directly from the volumetric data. This requirement implies the absence of side reactions between the reagent and the unknown or other constituents of the solution. (4) There must be available a method for detecting the equivalence point in the reaction; that is, a satisfactory end point is required.

Not all volumetric reactions currently in use meet these requirements perfectly; the most widely accepted procedures, however, are all founded on reactions that closely approach them.

REACTION TYPES

Volumetric methods may be divided conveniently into four categories based upon reaction type. These include (1) precipitation reactions, (2) complex-formation reactions, (3) neutralization or acid-base reactions, and (4) oxidation-reduction reactions. These categories differ in such things as types of equilibria, kinds of indicators, nature of reagents, kinds of primary standards, and definitions of equivalent weight.

STANDARD SOLUTIONS AND PRIMARY STANDARDS

A standard solution is generally used to make several analyses; since the quality of these analyses is directly related to the accuracy with which the concentration of the reagent is known, the chemist ordinarily expends considerable effort to assure himself that the materials and methods used for preparation and standardization will lead to a solution of accurately known concentration.

Requirements of a Primary Standard. Certain properties of a compound are required if the substance is to serve as a primary standard. (1) It must be of the highest purity; in order to be assured of this, established methods should be available for the testing of its purity. (2) A primary standard substance should be stable. It should not be attacked by constituents of the atmosphere. (3) The compound should not be hygroscopic, nor should it be efflorescent; otherwise drying and weighing would be difficult. (4) A primary standard should be readily available and not too expensive. (5) Finally, it should have a reasonably high equivalent weight. We shall see that the number of grams of a compound required to standardize or prepare a solution of a given concentration increases with equivalent weight; since the relative error in weighing decreases with increasing weight, a high equivalent weight will tend to minimize weighing errors.

Few substances meet or even approach these requirements. As a result, the number of good primary standard substances available to the chemist is relatively limited.

Stability of Standard Solutions. The concentration of the ideal standard solution should remain constant for months or years after preparation. A few of the reagents used in volumetric analysis are this stable. Many, however, require frequent restandardization and are used only out of necessity.

9.3   End Points in Volumetric Analyses; Titration Curves

The detection of an end point involves observation of some property of the solution that changes in a characteristic way at or near the equivalence point. The properties that have been employed for this purpose are numerous and varied. Some of these include:

(1) Color due to the reagent, the substance being determined, or an indicator substance;

(2) Turbidity resulting from the formation or disappearance of an insoluble phase;

(3) Electric conductivity of the solution;

(4) Electric potential between a pair of electrodes immersed in the solution;

(5) Refractive index of the solution;

(6) Temperature of the solution;

(7) Electric current passing through the solution.

TABLE 9-1

Concentration Changes During Titration
(50.0 ml of 0.1 F NaCl titrated with 0.1 F $AgNO_3$)

Volume $AgNO_3$ added, ml	Concentration of Cl^-, mol per liter	Concentration of Ag^+, mol per liter	$- \log [Cl^-]$ (pCl)	$- \log [Ag^+]$ (pAg)
0	1.0×10^{-1}	0	1.0	—
40.9	1.0×10^{-2}	1.7×10^{-8}	2.0	7.8
49.0	1.0×10^{-3}	1.7×10^{-7}	3.0	6.8
49.9	1.0×10^{-4}	1.7×10^{-6}	4.0	5.8
50.0	1.3×10^{-5}	1.3×10^{-5}	4.89	4.89
50.2	1.0×10^{-6}	1.7×10^{-4}	6.0	3.8
51.7	1.0×10^{-7}	1.7×10^{-3}	7.0	2.8
70.5	1.0×10^{-8}	1.7×10^{-2}	8.0	1.8

Physical changes such as these arise from alterations in reactant concentrations in the vicinity of the equivalence point. To illustrate, the second and third columns in Table 9-1 consist of the chloride- and silver-ion concentrations existing in solution at various stages during titration with

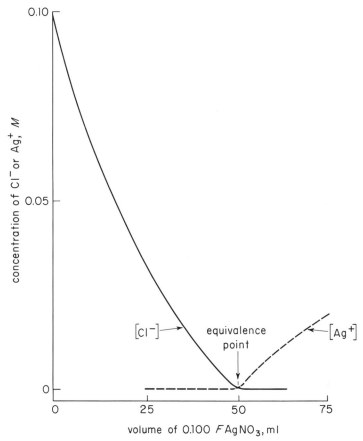

Fig. 9.1 Changes in Reactant Concentrations During a Titration. Plots of $[Ag^+]$ and $[Cl^-]$ as a function of the volume of 0.100 F $AgNO_3$ added to 50.0 ml of 0.100 F NaCl.

50 ml of 0.1 F silver nitrate. To emphasize the *relative* changes that are occurring, the volumes selected for tabulation correspond to the increments needed to cause a tenfold alteration in concentration of the reacting species. Thus, we see that 40.9 ml of reagent are needed to decrease the chloride-ion concentration from its original value of 0.1 molar to 0.01 molar. An

additional 8.1 ml are required to lower the concentration from 0.01 to 0.001 molar, and 0.9 ml are used for yet another tenfold decrease. For a given volume of reagent then, the reactive species clearly undergo the greatest changes in concentration in the region immediately surrounding the equivalence point.

Figure 9.1 consists of a plot of these data. It is seen that the chloride-ion concentration becomes extremely small as the equivalence point is passed; the silver-ion concentration, on the other hand, remains low until the equivalence point has been attained, whereupon it begins to rise rapidly.

The plotting scale for Figure 9.1 must perforce be large to encompass the enormous changes in concentration experienced by the reactants. As a result, changes in the vicinity of the end point tend largely to be obscured. This is the region of greatest interest; it is more effectively depicted when the concentrations are expressed in logarithmic terms. Further, since it is most likely that such concentrations will be smaller than one, it is advantageous to use negative logarithms for this purpose. Such notation allows expression of most concentrations as small positive numbers. These have come to be known as *p functions;* for our purposes *we will define the p values for a solution as the negative logarithms to the base* 10 *of the molar concentrations of the ions in that solution.* Values for pAg and pCl are given in Table 9-1.

★EXAMPLE. Calculate p functions for a solution that is 0.02 F in NaCl and 0.10 F in HCl.

1. $[H^+] = 0.10$

    $$pH = - \log [H^+] = - \log 0.10$$

    $$= 1.0$$

2. $[Na^+] = 0.020 = 2 \times 10^{-2}$

    $$pNa = - \log [Na^+] = - \log (2 \times 10^{-2})$$

    $$= - \log 2 - \log 10^{-2}$$

    $$= -0.3 + 2.0$$

    $$= 1.7$$

3. $[Cl^-] = 0.02 + 0.10 = 0.12$

    $$= 1.2 \times 10^{-1}$$

    $$pCl = - \log 1.2 \times 10^{-1}$$

    $$= - \log 1.2 - \log 10^{-1}$$

    $$= -0.08 + 1$$

    $$= +0.92$$

The p function of an ion will be a negative number if its concentration is greater than 1 molar. For example, in a 2.0 F solution of AgNO$_3$

$$[Ag^+] = 2.0$$

$$pAg = -\log [Ag^+] = -\log 2.0$$

$$= -0.3$$

If we plot the values of pAg and pCl given in Table 9-1 against the volume of reagent added, we obtain curves that give a much clearer picture of the changes in the solution near the equivalence point. Figure 9.2

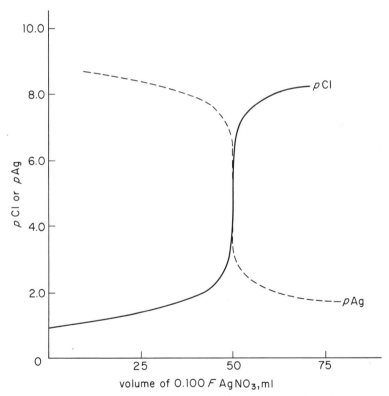

Fig. 9.2 Titration Curve. Plots of pAg and pCl as a function of the volume of 0.100 F AgNO$_3$ added in the titration of 50.0 milliliters of 0.10 F NaCl.

indicates that the pCl shows little change except in the equivalence-point region where it increases rapidly. A sharp decrease in pAg occurs in the same vicinity.

Graphs such as either of those in Figure 9.2 are called *titration curves.* Plots of analogous data for titrations involving neutralization, oxidation-reduction, or complex-formation reactions have the same general appearance. However, the magnitude of the change in p function in the equivalence point region varies considerably, larger changes being associated with reactions that are more complete and with titrations involving relatively concentrated solutions.

The shape of the titration curve and especially the magnitude of the change in the region of the equivalence point are of great interest to the analytical chemist because these determine how easily and how accurately the equivalence point can be located. The extent of the physical change used to signal an end point is usually directly related to the magnitude of change of p values. In general, then, the most satisfactory end points are to be expected where changes in p functions are large.

It is difficult to overstate the importance of titration curves in providing a rational approach to many of the problems confronting the analytical chemist; we shall have frequent occasion to refer to them and to their derivation in future chapters.

9.4   Volumetric Calculations

EQUIVALENT WEIGHT AND MILLIEQUIVALENT WEIGHT

The most commonly used units of weight in volumetric computations are the *milliequivalent weight* and the *equivalent weight*. The manner in which we shall define these will depend upon whether we are dealing with a participant in a neutralization titration, an oxidation-reduction titration, or a precipitation or complex-formation titration. Furthermore, these definitions are such that we need to know the behavior of the compound in its reaction before we can unequivocally decide upon its equivalent weight. As a matter of fact, the equivalent weight of a given compound may assume two or more values if the reactions of the compound are different. *Thus the definition of the equivalent weight for a chemical compound always refers to a specific chemical reaction; evaluation of this quantity is impossible without some knowledge of the nature of this reaction.*

Neutralization Titrations. The *equivalent weight* (eq wt) of a substance participating in a neutralization reaction is that weight which either contributes or reacts with 1 gfw of hydrogen ion in that reaction. The *milliequivalent weight* (meq wt) is $\frac{1}{1000}$ of the equivalent weight.

For acids or bases containing but a single reactive hydrogen or hydroxyl ion and for strong acids or bases, the relationship between equivalent weight and formula weight can be readily determined. For example, the equivalent weight of potassium hydroxide and of hydrochloric acid must be equal to their formula weights since each has only a single reactive hydrogen or hydroxyl ion. Similarly, we know that only one hydrogen in acetic acid, $HC_2H_3O_2$, is acidic; therefore, the formula weight and equivalent weight for this acid must also be the same. Barium hydroxide, $Ba(OH)_2$, is a strong base in which the two hydroxyl ions are identical. Therefore, in any acid-base reaction this compound will necessarily react with two hydrogen ions; by our definition its equivalent weight will be one half its formula weight. In the case of sulfuric acid, the dissociation of the second hydrogen ion is not complete; the bisulfate ion, however, is sufficiently strong so that both hydrogens participate in all neutralization reactions. The equivalent weight of H_2SO_4 as an acid is, therefore, always one half its formula weight.

The situation is not as simple when two or more hydrogen ions or hydroxyl ions of different strengths exist in a given chemical compound. Phosphoric acid provides a good example of this. If a dilute solution of this acid is titrated with base, certain indicators change color when only one of the protons has been neutralized; that is,

$$H_3PO_4 + OH^- \rightarrow H_2PO_4^- + H_2O$$

On the other hand, other indicators change color after two hydrogen ions have reacted.

$$H_3PO_4 + 2OH^- \rightarrow HPO_4^{2-} + 2H_2O$$

In the first instance, the equivalent weight of phosphoric acid is equal to its formula weight, and in the second to one half its formula weight. Without knowing which of these reactions is involved, an unambiguous definition of an equivalent weight for this acid is impossible.

Oxidation-reduction Reactions. The equivalent weight of a participant in an oxidation-reduction reaction is that weight which, directly or indirectly, consumes or produces 1 mol of electrons. In this case the numerical value of the equivalent weight can be conveniently found by dividing the formula weight by the change in oxidation number of the substance or the compound containing the substance. As an example, consider the oxidation of oxalate ion by permanganate

$$5C_2O_4^{2-} + 2MnO_4^- + 16H^+ \rightarrow 10CO_2 + 2Mn^{2+} + 8H_2O$$

In this reaction the change in oxidation number for manganese is five since the element passes from the $+7$ to the $+2$ state. Each carbon atom in the oxalate ion, on the other hand, is oxidized from the $+3$ to the $+4$ state. From a consideration of the number of manganese or carbon atoms contained in any given compound, we can readily calculate the change in oxidation number associated with that component and thus evaluate its equivalent weight with respect to this reaction. This is shown below.

Substance	Equivalent Weight
Mn	$\dfrac{\text{gfw Mn}}{5}$
MnO_4^-	$\dfrac{\text{gfw } MnO_4^-}{5}$
$KMnO_4$	$\dfrac{\text{gfw } KMnO_4}{5}$
$Ca(MnO_4)_2 \cdot 4H_2O$	$\dfrac{\text{gfw } Ca(MnO_4)_2 \cdot 4H_2O}{2 \times 5}$
CO_2	$\dfrac{\text{gfw } CO_2}{1}$
$C_2O_4^{2-}$	$\dfrac{\text{gfw } C_2O_4^{2-}}{2}$

As in neutralization reactions the equivalent weight of a given oxidizing or reducing agent is not an invariant quantity. Potassium permanganate, for example, can react with reducing agents in three different ways depending upon the conditions existing in the solution. The half reactions are

$$MnO_4^- + e \rightarrow MnO_4^{2-}$$

$$MnO_4^- + 3e + 2H_2O \rightarrow MnO_2 + 4OH^-$$

$$MnO_4^- + 5e + 8H^+ \rightarrow Mn^{2+} + 4H_2O$$

The changes in oxidation number for manganese are one, three, and five; the equivalent weight of potassium permanganate would be the formula weight, one third the formula weight, and one fifth the formula weight, respectively.

Precipitation and Complex-formation Reactions. In characterizing the equivalent weight of compounds involved in precipitation or complex-formation reactions, it is difficult to devise a definition that is entirely free of ambiguity. As a result, many chemists prefer to avoid the use of equivalent weights when dealing with reactions of this type and in their place use formula weights exclusively. We are in sympathy with this practice; however, it is highly likely that the student will occasionally encounter situations where equivalent or milliequivalent weights are needed for substances involved in precipitation or complex formation, and he must therefore have knowledge of their definition.

The equivalent weight of a participant in a precipitation or a com-

plex-formation reaction is that weight which reacts with or provides
1 gram-formula weight of the reacting cation if it be univalent, one-half
gram-formula weight if it be divalent, one-third gram-formula weight if
trivalent, and so on. Our earlier definitions of equivalent weight were based
on 1 mol of hydrogen ions or electrons. In the present case the definition
is based on 1 mol of a univalent cation or the equivalent thereof. *The
cation referred to in this definition is always the cation directly involved in the
reaction* and not necessarily the cation contained in the compound whose
equivalent weight is being defined.

To illustrate the application of this definition, consider the reaction

$$Ag^+ + Cl^- \rightarrow AgCl$$

Here the cation referred to in the definition is the univalent silver ion. The
equivalent weights of some compounds that might be associated with this
reaction are given below.

Substance	Equivalent Weight
Ag^+	gfw Ag^+
$AgNO_3$	gfw $AgNO_3$
Ag_2SO_4	$\dfrac{\text{gfw } Ag_2SO_4}{2}$
NaCl	gfw NaCl
$BaCl_2 \cdot 2H_2O$	$\dfrac{\text{gfw } BaCl_2 \cdot 2H_2O}{2}$
BiOCl	gfw BiOCl

The equivalent weight of the barium chloride dihydrate is one half of its
formula weight, *not* because such a weight contains one half a formula
weight of divalent barium ions, but rather because this is the weight that
reacts with 1 formula weight of silver ions. A consideration of the last
example will show why it is important to make this fine distinction. Here
we might be tempted to say that the equivalent weight of the bismuth
oxychloride is one third of its formula weight since this would represent
the weight of this compound that contained one third of a formula weight
of the trivalent bismuth. This would be correct if the bismuth were the
cation involved in the reaction. Here, however, the silver ion is the reacting
cation; therefore, the equivalent weight of the bismuth oxychloride must
be that weight which reacts with 1 formula weight of silver ions; that is,
the formula weight and equivalent weight are identical.

Again, the equivalent weight of a given compound may assume more
than one value. For example, silver ion may be titrated with a solution of

potassium cyanide and the end point established for either of two reactions

$$2CN^- + 2Ag^+ = Ag[Ag(CN)_2]$$

or

$$2CN^- + Ag^+ = Ag(CN)_2^-$$

In the first case the equivalent weight of potassium cyanide would be its formula weight; in the second it would be *twice* the formula weight. This is an example of an equivalent weight that is *greater* than a formula weight.

Equivalent Weights of Compounds not Participating Directly in a Volumetric Reaction. Frequently we need to define the equivalent weight of a compound or element that is only indirectly related to the participants of the titration. In such a case we must know the stoichiometric relationship between that compound and one of the reactants involved in the titration. To illustrate, lead can be determined by an indirect volumetric method in which the cation is first precipitated as the chromate from an acetic acid solution. The precipitate is filtered, washed free of excess precipitant, and then dissolved in dilute hydrochloric acid; this yields a solution of lead and dichromate ions. The latter may then be determined by an oxidation-reduction titration. The reactions are

$$Pb^{2+} + CrO_4^{2-} \xrightarrow[\text{HOAc}]{\text{dil}} PbCrO_4 \text{ (precipitate filtered and washed)}$$

$$2PbCrO_4 + 2H^+ \xrightarrow[\text{HCl}]{\text{dil}} 2Pb^{2+} + Cr_2O_7^{2-} + H_2O \text{ (precipitate redissolved)}$$

$$Cr_2O_7^{2-} + 6I^- + 14H^+ \rightarrow 2Cr^{3+} + 3I_2 + 7H_2O \text{ (titration)}$$

For the purpose of calculations, we must ascribe an equivalent weight to lead; *since the titration is an oxidation-reduction process, the equivalent weight of lead will have to be based on a change of oxidation number.* Clearly the lead exhibits no such change. It is, however, associated in a 1:1 ratio with chromium, and this element changes from the +6 to the +3 oxidation state. Therefore, we can say that the change in oxidation state of three is *associated* with each lead and therefore that its equivalent weight, in this sequence of reactions, is one third of its atomic weight.

It is often helpful to make an inventory of the chemical relationships existing between the substance whose equivalent weight is sought and one of the participants in the titration. In this instance we see from the equations that

$$2Pb^{2+} \equiv 2CrO_4^{2-} \equiv Cr_2O_7^{2-} \equiv 6e$$

Thus the quantity of each substance associated with an electron change of one is

$$\frac{2 \text{ gfw } Pb^{2+}}{6} \equiv \frac{2 \text{ gfw } CrO_4^{2-}}{6} \equiv \frac{1 \text{ gfw } Cr_2O_7^{2-}}{6} \equiv \frac{6 \text{ mols } e}{6}$$

Let us consider one more example. The nitrogen in the organic compound $C_9H_9N_3$ can be determined by quantitative conversion to ammonia followed by titration with a standard solution of acid. The reactions are

$$C_9H_9N_3 + \text{reagent} \rightarrow 3NH_3 + \text{products}$$

$$NH_3 + H^+ \rightarrow NH_4^+ \text{ (titration)}$$

Here titration involves a neutralization process; therefore the sought-for equivalent weight must be based on the consumption or production of hydrogen ions. Since the organic compound forms three ammonia molecules, it can be considered responsible for the consumption of three hydrogen ions; the equivalent weight, then, is the formula weight of $C_9H_9N_3$ divided by three. Using the same reasoning each nitrogen is converted to one ammonia molecule and reacts with one hydrogen ion; the equivalent weight of nitrogen, N, is thus equal to its formula weight in this reaction.

CONCENTRATION UNITS USED IN VOLUMETRIC CALCULATIONS

In Chapter 2 we discussed some of the terms used by chemists to express the concentrations of solutions. These included formal concentration, molar concentration, and various types of percentage composition. We now need to define two additional terms, *titer* and *normality*, that are commonly used for describing solutions used in volumetric analysis.

Titer. *The titer of a solution is the weight of some substance that is chemically equivalent to 1 ml of that solution.* Thus a silver nitrate solution having a titer of 1.00 mg of chloride would contain just enough silver nitrate in each milliliter to react completely with that weight of chloride ion. The titer might also be expressed in terms of milligrams or grams of potassium chloride, barium chloride, sodium iodide, or any other compound that reacts with silver nitrate. The concentration of a reagent to be used for the routine analysis of many samples is advantageously expressed in terms of its titer.

Normality. *The normality, N, of a solution expresses the number of milliequivalents of dissolved solute contained in 1 ml of the solution,* or the number of equivalents contained in 1 liter. Thus a 0.20 N solution of silver nitrate contains 0.20 milliequivalent of this substance in each milliliter of the solution.

SOME IMPORTANT WEIGHT-VOLUME RELATIONSHIPS

The raw data from a volumetric analysis are ordinarily expressed in units of milliliters, grams, and normality. Volumetric calculations involve conversion of such information into units of milliequivalents followed by reconversion again into the weight in grams of some other chemical species. Two relationships, based on the foregoing definitions, are used for these interconversions. The first of these involves converting the weight of a chemical compound from units of grams to those of milliequivalents. This transformation is accomplished by dividing the weight of the substance by its milliequivalent weight; that is,

$$\text{no. meq } A = \frac{\text{wt } A, \text{ grams}}{\text{meq wt } A, \text{ grams}}$$

★EXAMPLE. A quantity of $BaCl_2 \cdot 2H_2O$ is to be titrated with silver nitrate solution. The number of milliequivalents contained in 0.367 gram of pure $BaCl_2 \cdot 2H_2O$ (gfw 244) is sought.

$$\text{no. meq } BaCl_2 \cdot 2H_2O = \frac{\text{grams } BaCl_2 \cdot 2H_2O}{\text{meq wt } BaCl_2 \cdot 2H_2O}$$

$$= \frac{0.367}{244/(2 \times 1000)}$$

$$= \frac{0.367}{0.122} = 3.01 \text{ meq}$$

The second relationship permits calculation of the number of milliequivalents of solute contained in a given volume provided we know the normality of the solution. In this case, by definition, the normality immediately gives the number of milliequivalents in each milliliter; multiplying this by the volume in milliliters gives the number of milliequivalents; that is,

$$\text{no. meq } A = \text{volume } A, \text{ ml} \times N_A$$

★EXAMPLE. The number of milliequivalents involved in a titration that required 27.3 ml of 0.200 N $KMnO_4$ is given by

$$\text{no. meq } KMnO_4 = 27.3 \text{ ml} \times 0.200 \frac{\text{meq}}{\text{ml}}$$

$$= 5.46 \text{ meq}$$

Further applications of these calculations are illustrated in the following examples.

★EXAMPLE. How many grams of primary standard $K_2Cr_2O_7$ (gfw 294) are required to prepare exactly 2 liters of 0.1000 N reagent? Titrations with dichromate involve the half reaction

$$Cr_2O_7^{2-} + 14H^+ + 6e \rightleftharpoons 2Cr^{3+} + 7H_2O$$

The number of milliequivalents of $K_2Cr_2O_7$ required is first calculated

$$\text{no. meq } K_2Cr_2O_7 = ml_{K_2Cr_2O_7} \times N_{K_2Cr_2O_7}$$

$$= 2000 \text{ ml} \times 0.1000 \text{ meq/ml}$$

$$= 200 \text{ meq}$$

To convert this weight in milliequivalents to a weight in grams, we multiply by the milliequivalent weight.

$$\text{grams } K_2Cr_2O_7 = 200 \times \frac{294}{6 \times 1000}$$

$$= 9.80$$

★EXAMPLE. What volume of 0.100 N HCl can be produced by diluting a 150-ml sample of 1.24 N acid?

The number of milliequivalents of HCl must be the same in the two solutions. Therefore we may write

$$\begin{array}{c} \text{no. meq HCl} \\ \text{in diluted solution} \end{array} = \begin{array}{c} \text{no. meq HCl} \\ \text{in concentrated solution} \end{array}$$

$$\text{ml of dilute solution} \times 0.1 \frac{\text{meq}}{\text{ml}} = 150 \text{ ml} \times 1.24 \frac{\text{meq}}{\text{ml}}$$

$$\text{ml of dilute solution} = \frac{150 \times 1.24}{0.1} = 1860$$

Thus a 0.100 N HCl solution would be obtained by diluting 150 ml of 1.24 N acid to exactly 1860 ml.

A Fundamental Relationship between Quantities of Reacting Substances. By definition, 1 equivalent weight of an acid contributes 1 formula weight of hydrogen ions to a reaction; also, 1 equivalent weight of a base consumes 1 formula weight of these ions. As a consequence, at the equivalence point in a neutralization titration the number of equivalents of acid and of base will always be numerically equal. Similarly, the equivalent weights of oxidizing and reducing agents are defined in terms of weights that will produce or consume 1 mol of electrons. Thus, at the equivalence point in such a titration the number of equivalents of oxidizing and reducing agents must also be equal. An identical relationship holds for precipitation and complex-formation titrations. To generalize we may state that *at the equivalence point in any titration the number of milliequivalents of standard is exactly equal to the number of milliequivalents of the substance being determined.* Nearly all volumetric calculations are based on this relationship.

CALCULATION OF NORMALITY OF A SOLUTION

The normality of a standard solution is computed either from the data related to its actual preparation or from standardization titrations.

★EXAMPLE. A standard solution of $AgNO_3$ (gfw 169.9) was prepared by weighing exactly 24.15 grams of the carefully prepared solid, dissolving in water, and diluting in a volumetric flask to exactly 2.000 liters. The normality of the solution is sought.

Since normality is the number of milliequivalents per milliliter, we may write

$$\text{no. meq } AgNO_3 = \frac{24.15}{169.9/1000}$$

$$N = \frac{\text{no. meq}}{\text{ml}} = \frac{24.15/0.1699}{2000} = 0.07107$$

★EXAMPLE. A solution of $Ba(OH)_2$ was standardized by titration against 0.1280 N HCl. Exactly 31.76 ml of the base were required to neutralize 46.25 ml of the acid. What is the normality of the $Ba(OH)_2$ solution?

At the end point in the titration we may say

$$\text{no. meq } Ba(OH)_2 = \text{no. meq } HCl$$

$$ml_{Ba(OH)_2} \times N_{Ba(OH)_2} = ml_{HCl} \times N_{HCl}$$

$$31.76 \times N_{Ba(OH)_2} = 46.25 \times 0.1280$$

$$N_{Ba(OH)_2} = \frac{46.25 \times 0.1280}{31.76} = 0.1864$$

★EXAMPLE. The normality of an iodine solution was established by standardization against As_2O_3 (gfw 197.8), 37.34 ml being required to titrate a 0.2040-gram sample of primary-standard oxide. The reaction is

$$I_2 + H_2AsO_3^- + H_2O \rightarrow 2I^- + H_2AsO_4^- + 2H^+$$

At the end point

$$\text{no. meq } I_2 = \text{no. meq } As_2O_3$$

The number of milliequivalents of I_2 can be related to the volume and normality. For As_2O_3 the number of milliequivalents can be calculated from the grams of the pure compound taken. Thus we may write

$$ml_{I_2} \times N_{I_2} = \frac{\text{grams } As_2O_3}{\text{meq wt } As_2O_3}$$

From the equation for the reaction we see that the oxidation number of each arsenic atom undergoes a change of 2; therefore a total change of 4 is associated with each As_2O_3 molecule making the equivalent weight one fourth of the formula weight. Thus

$$37.34 \times N_{I_2} = \frac{0.2040}{\text{gfw } As_2O_3/4000} = \frac{0.2040}{0.04945}$$

$$N_{I_2} = \frac{0.2040}{37.34 \times 0.04945} = 0.1105$$

CALCULATION OF RESULTS FROM TITRATION DATA

★EXAMPLE. A sample of an iron ore was analyzed by dissolving 0.804 gram of the material in acid, reducing all of the iron to the $+2$ condition, and titrating with a 0.112 N solution of $KMnO_4$. This required 47.2 ml. The results of the analysis are needed in terms of percent Fe (gfw 55.9) as well as percent Fe_2O_3 (gfw 160).

The analytical reaction involves oxidation of Fe^{2+} to Fe^{3+}

$$5Fe^{2+} + MnO_4^- + 8H^+ \rightarrow 5Fe^{3+} + Mn^{2+} + 4H_2O$$

At the end point

$$\text{no. meq Fe} = \text{no. meq } KMnO_4$$

$$= 47.2 \times 0.112$$

The weight of Fe in the sample can be calculated by multiplying the number of milliequivalents of Fe by the milliequivalent weight.

$$\text{grams of Fe} = 47.2 \times 0.112 \times \frac{\text{gfw Fe}}{1000}$$

Therefore

$$\text{percent Fe} = \frac{47.2 \times 0.112 \times 55.9/1000}{0.804} \times 100$$

$$= 36.7$$

The percent Fe_2O_3 can be obtained in essentially the same way. We can state that at the equivalence point

$$\text{no. meq } Fe_2O_3 = \text{no. meq } KMnO_4$$

and by the same arguments

$$\text{percent } Fe_2O_3 = \frac{47.2 \times 0.112 \times 160/2000}{0.804} \times 100$$

$$= 52.6$$

★EXAMPLE. A 0.475-gram sample containing $(NH_4)_2SO_4$ was dissolved in water and made alkaline with KOH. The liberated NH_3 was distilled into exactly 50.0 ml of 0.100 N HCl. The excess HCl was back-titrated with 11.1 ml of 0.121 N NaOH. The percent NH_3 (gfw 17.0), as well as the percent $(NH_4)_2SO_4$ (gfw 132) in the sample are required.

At the equivalence point in this titration we may say that the number of milliequivalents of acid and base are equal. In this case, however, there are two bases involved, NaOH and NH_3. Thus

$$\text{no. meq HCl} = \text{no. meq } NH_3 + \text{no. meq NaOH}$$

After rearranging

$$\text{no. meq } NH_3 = \text{no. meq HCl} - \text{no. meq NaOH}$$

$$= (50.0 \times 0.100 - 11.1 \times 0.121)$$

$$\text{percent } NH_3 = \frac{(50.0 \times 0.100 - 11.1 \times 0.121) \times 17.0/1000}{0.475} \times 100$$

$$= 13.1$$

The number of milliequivalents of $(NH_4)_2SO_4$ is the same as the number of milliequivalents of NH_3; therefore

percent $(NH_4)_2SO_4$

$$= \frac{(50.0 \times 0.100 - 11.1 \times 0.121) \times \frac{132}{2000}}{0.475} \times 100$$

$$= 50.8$$

Here the milliequivalent weight of $(NH_4)_2SO_4$ is one half the milliformula weight because

$$(NH_4)_2SO_4 \equiv 2NH_3 \equiv 2H^+$$

Problems

1. Calculate pH and pCl of
   (a) 0.10 F HCl   ans. $pH = 1.0$ $pCl = 1.0$
   (b) 0.10 F $BaCl_2$ ans. $pH = 7.0$ $pCl = 0.7$
   (c) 3.0 F HCl
   (d) a solution that is 0.010 F in HCl and 0.02 F in $BaCl_2$
   (e) a saturated solution of AgCl

2. Calculate pAg of
   (a) 0.23 F $AgNO_3$
   (b) 0.0070 F Ag_2SO_4
   (c) a 0.100 F solution of NaCl saturated with AgCl   ans. 8.74
   (d) a 0.030 F solution of $BaCl_2$ saturated with AgCl
   (e) a saturated solution of AgI

3. Listed in the first column below are the reactions used for the volumetric analysis of the compounds in the second column. Indicate the type of reaction and the milliequivalent weight of each of these compounds in terms of its formula weight.

Reaction	Compound	
(a) $NH_3 + H_3O^+ \rightarrow$ $NH_4^+ + H_2O$	NH_4Cl	ans. $\dfrac{gfw\ NH_4Cl}{1000}$
	$(NH_4)_2SO_4$	ans. $\dfrac{gfw\ (NH_4)_2SO_4}{2000}$
	$FeSO_4 \cdot (NH_4)_2SO_4 \cdot 6H_2O$	
	$C_6H_8N_2$	ans. $\dfrac{gfw\ C_6H_8N_2}{2000}$
	H_2SO_4	
(b) $Ba^{2+} + CrO_4^{2-} \rightarrow BaCrO_4$	$BaCl_2 \cdot 2H_2O$	
	Ba_3N_2	
	Cr	ans. $\dfrac{gfw\ Cr}{2000}$
	$Na_2Cr_2O_7$	
(c) $MnO_4^- + 5Fe^{2+} + 8H^+ \rightarrow$ $Mn^{2+} + 5Fe^{3+} + 4H_2O$	Mn	
	MnO_2	ans. $\dfrac{gfw\ MnO_2}{5000}$
	Mn_3O_4	
	Fe_2O_3	ans. $\dfrac{gfw\ Fe_2O_3}{2000}$
	Fe_3O_4	

4. Indicate the type of reaction in each of the following and give the equivalent weight of the compounds on the right:

Reaction	Compound	
(a) $Hg^{2+} + 4I^- \rightarrow HgI_4^{2-}$ $2\bar{J}\ Fwt$	$HgSO_4$	ans. $\dfrac{gfw\ HgSO_4}{2}$
	Hg	
	Hg_2Cl_2	
	KI	ans. 2 gfw KI
	BaI_2	
	$Ba(IO_3)_2$	
(b) $B_4O_7^{2-} + 2H^+ + 5H_2O \rightarrow 4H_3BO_3$	$Na_2B_4O_7$	
	B	
	B_2O_3	
	HCl	
(c) $H_2S + I_2 \rightarrow 2I^- + S + 2H^+$	H_2S	
	SO_2	
	$Na_2S_2O_3$	
	KI	
	I_2O_5	

5. Give the type of reaction and the equivalent weight for each of the compounds indicated below

Reaction	Compound
(a) $Al^{3+} + 6F^- \rightarrow AlF_6^{3-}$	Al_2O_3
	SiF_4
	NaF
	C_2F_6
	$AlCl_3$
(b) $Pb^{2+} + SO_4^{2-} \rightarrow PbSO_4$	$KHSO_4$
	$FeOHSO_4$
	$Na_2S_2O_3$
	$Pb(NO_3)_2$
	Pb_3O_4
(c) $2V(OH)_4^+ + H_2C_2O_4 + 2H^+ \rightarrow 2VO^{2+} + 2CO_2 + 6H_2O$	$H_2C_2O_4$
	CO_2
	NH_4VO_3
	V_2O_5

6. Potassium hydrogen iodate, $KH(IO_3)_2$, behaves as a strong acid in aqueous solution and can be used to standardize bases. Solutions of the compound can also be titrated with $AgNO_3$ to give a precipitate of $AgIO_3$. The compound can also participate in an oxidation-reduction reaction in which I_2 is the product. Indicate the equivalent weight of the $KH(IO_3)_2$ in each of these cases.

7. What weight of silver nitrate should be taken to prepare exactly 2 liters of a solution having a titer of 2.00 mg of KI per ml?   ans. 4.09 grams

8. Describe the preparation of 500 ml of a Na_2CO_3 solution having a titer of 0.500 mg of HCl per ml with respect to the reaction

$$Na_2CO_3 + 2HCl \rightarrow H_2CO_3 + 2NaCl$$

9. Describe the preparation of a $K_2Cr_2O_7$ solution having a titer of 3.00 mg of $FeSO_4 \cdot (NH_4)_2SO_4 \cdot 6H_2O$ with respect to the reaction

$$6Fe^{2+} + Cr_2O_7^{2-} + 14H^+ \rightarrow 6Fe^{3+} + 2Cr^{3+} + 7H_2O$$

10. Calculate the total number of milliequivalents in
   (a) 14.2 grams of $AgNO_3$ ($Ag^+ + I^- \rightarrow AgI$)   ans. 83.5
   (b) 30.0 ml of 0.0200 N $Ba(OH)_2$ ans. 0.600
   (c) 13.0 equivalents of KI   ans. 13,000
   (d) 17.0 mg of $FeSO_4 \cdot (NH_4)_2SO_4 \cdot 6H_2O$ ans. 0.0435
       ($Fe^{2+} \rightarrow Fe^{3+} + e$)
   (e) 10.0 liters of 0.200 N $KMnO_4$ ans. 2000
       ($MnO_4^- + 8H^+ + 5e \rightarrow Mn^{2+} + 4H_2O$)
   (f) 375 ml of 0.120 N H_2SO_4 ans. 45.0

11. Calculate the number of milliequivalents in
    (a) 100 grams of pure I_2 ($I_2 + 2e \rightarrow 2I^-$)
    (b) 0.500 equivalent of H_2SO_4
    (c) 5 ml of 0.220 N NaOH
    (d) 48.5 mg of Na_2CO_3 ($CO_3^{2-} + 2H^+ \rightarrow H_2CO_3$)
    (e) 3.25 liters of 0.300 N KSCN ($Ag^+ + SCN^- \rightarrow AgSCN$)
    (f) 1.00 liter of 0.0200 F $Ba(OH)_2$

12. Calculate the number of milliequivalents in
    (a) 4700 ml of 0.200 N $KMnO_4$
    (b) 0.400 gram of As_2O_3 (arsenic oxidized from +3 to +5 state in reaction)
    (c) 10 liters of 0.0012 N $Na_2S_2O_3$
    (d) 40 ml of 0.055 F $KMnO_4$ ($KMnO_4$ reduced to Mn^{2+})
    (e) 0.176 gram of pure $Na_2C_2O_4$ ($C_2O_4^{2-} \rightarrow 2CO_2 + 2e$)

13. How many grams are contained in
    (a) 1.00 meq of $Pb(NO_3)_2$ ans. 0.1656 gram
        ($Pb^{2+} + SO_4^{2-} \rightarrow PbSO_4$)
    (b) 2.000 equivalents of $Ba(OH)_2$ ans. 171.4 grams
    (c) 30.0 ml of 0.100 N $AgNO_3$ ans. 0.510 gram
        ($Ag^+ + Cl^- \rightarrow AgCl$)
    (d) 2.00 liters of 0.330 N $KMnO_4$ ans. 20.8 grams
        ($MnO_4^- + 5e + 8H^+ \rightarrow Mn^{2+} + 4H_2O$)

14. Calculate the number of grams in
    (a) 10.0 meq of H_2SO_4
    (b) 130 ml of 0.150 N Br_2 ($Br_2 + 2e \rightarrow 2Br^-$)
    (c) 6.00 liters of 1.00 $\times$ 10^{-3} N $K_2Cr_2O_7$
        ($Cr_2O_7^{2-} + 14H^+ + 6e \rightarrow 2Cr^{3+} + 7H_2O$)
    (d) 0.520 equivalent of KCN ($Ni^{2+} + 4CN^- \rightarrow Ni(CN)_4^{2-}$)

15. Calculate
    (a) the number of mols of $Ba(OH)_2$ in 1200 ml of a 0.0100 N solution
    (b) the number of milliequivalents of $Ba(OH)_2$ in 2.0 liters of a 0.0300 N solution
    (c) the number of milliequivalents per milliliter of H_2SO_4 in a 2.0 F solution
    (d) the number of grams of $Ba(OH)_2$ in 150 ml of 0.0400 N $Ba(OH)_2$
    (e) the number of milliequivalents per milliliter of $AgNO_3$ in a solution containing 17.0 grams of $AgNO_3$ per liter
    (f) the normality of a $AgNO_3$ solution containing 17.0 grams of $AgNO_3$ per liter

16. Calculate
    (a) the number of milliequivalents of NaOH in a solution that reacts completely with 17.1 ml of 0.200 N H_2SO_4
    (b) the number of grams of NaOH in the solution in part (a)
    (c) the number of milliequivalents of Na_2CO_3 contained in 2.00 grams of the pure compound ($CO_3^{2-} + 2H^+ \rightarrow H_2CO_3$)
    (d) the number of milliliters of 0.100 N HCl that will react completely with 2.00 grams of Na_2CO_3

(e) the number of milliequivalents of $KMnO_4$ that will react completely with 14.9 ml of 3.0 N Fe^{2+}

(f) the weight in grams of $KMnO_4$ in part (e) if the $KMnO_4$ is reduced to Mn^{2+} in the reaction with Fe^{2+}

17. How many grams of solute are required to prepare
(a) 1500 ml of 0.300 N NaCl
(b) 4 liters of 0.0500 N $Ba(OH)_2$
(c) 483 ml of 0.0100 N I_2 $(I_2 + 2e \rightarrow 2I^-)$
(d) 3900 ml of 0.400 N KCN $(Ag^+ + 2CN^- \rightarrow Ag(CN)_2^-)$
(e) 6 liters of 0.700 N acetic acid, $HC_2H_3O_2$

18. How would you prepare 500 ml of approximately 0.20 N HCl from
(a) a solution that was 2.5 N in HCl   ans. dilute 40 ml to 500 ml
(b) a constant boiling HCl solution containing 20.2 grams of HCl per 100 grams of solution   ans. dilute 18.1 grams to 500 ml
(c) concentrated HCl (density 1.18) containing 37 percent HCl
              ans. dilute 8.36 ml of conc HCl to 500 ml

19. Describe the preparation of 2 liters of 0.150 N H_2SO_4 from
(a) a 2.30 N solution of H_2SO_4
(b) a solution containing 15 grams of H_2SO_4 per 100 grams of solution
(c) concentrated H_2SO_4 (density 1.84) containing 96 percent H_2SO_4

20. What is the normality of
(a) a solution containing 1.21 grams of $AgNO_3$ per 750 ml   ans. 0.0095 N
(b) a concentrated $HClO_4$ solution (density 1.66) containing 70 percent $HClO_4$
(c) a solution containing 34.0 grams of Mohr's salt, $FeSO_4 \cdot (NH_4)_2SO_4 \cdot 6H_2O$ in 2400 ml of solution $(Fe^{2+} \rightarrow Fe^{3+} + e)$
(d) a solution containing 1.0 mg of KOH per ml
(e) a solution consisting of 30.0 ml of 1.5 N $KMnO_4$ diluted to 1 liter

21. What is the normality of a KSCN solution if 27.14 ml were required to titrate 25.00 ml of 0.1000 N $AgNO_3$?   ans. 0.0921 N

22. Potassium hydrogen phthalate $(KHC_8H_4O_4)$ contains a single hydrogen available for neutralization, and is widely employed as a primary standard for bases. What is the normality of a $Ba(OH)_2$ solution if 44.1 ml are needed to titrate a 0.271-gram sample of primary-standard potassium hydrogen phthalate?   ans. 0.0301 N

23. A sodium hydroxide solution was standardized against primary standard potassium hydrogen phthalate $(KHC_8H_4O_4)$, the following data being obtained:

weight $KHC_8H_4O_4$ taken, gram	0.6742	0.7966	0.6736
volume NaOH required, ml	30.42	36.08	30.46

Calculate the normality of the NaOH and also the precision of the data.

24. What would be the normality of a solution prepared by dissolving 2.00 grams of oxalic acid, $H_2C_2O_4$, in water and diluting to 250 ml (assume the $H_2C_2O_4$

behaves as a dibasic acid)? How many milliliters of 0.01 *N* NaOH would be required to react with 37.0 ml of this acid?

25. Exactly 1 ml of an I_2 solution was found to be equivalent to 2.32 ml of a 0.176 *N* $Na_2S_2O_3$ solution. What was the normality of the iodine?

26. A solution of iodine was standardized against pure As_2O_3. A 0.441-gram sample required 29.7 ml of the iodine. Calculate the normality of the iodine based on the reaction

$$I_2 + HAsO_3^{2-} + H_2O \rightarrow 2I^- + HAsO_4^{2-} + 2H^+$$

27. A solution of HCl was standardized by treatment of 0.330 gram of pure Na_2CO_3 with exactly 50.0 ml of acid. The solution was boiled to remove all of the CO_2 formed in the reaction, and the excess HCl remaining was back titrated with 2.10 ml of a NaOH solution. Another titration showed that 1.00 ml of the NaOH was equivalent to 1.17 ml of the HCl. Calculate the normality of the acid.   ans. 0.131 *N*

28. Mercury (II) oxide is sometimes employed as a primary standard for acids. Upon being treated with an excess of KI, the following reaction proceeds quantitatively: $HgO + 4I^- + H_2O \rightarrow HgI_4^{2-} + 2OH^-$. The hydroxyl ions so formed can then be titrated with the acid. Exactly 0.483 gram of HgO was treated in this manner and 41.2 ml of HCl were required to neutralize the base. What was the normality of the HCl?

29. A 0.612-gram sample of pure $CaCO_3$ was used to standardize a solution of acid. Exactly 40.0 ml of the acid were added to the solid and the solution boiled until all the CO_2 had been evolved. The unreacted HCl was back-titrated with 7.41 ml of base, 1.00 ml of which was known to be equivalent to 0.936 ml of the acid. Calculate the normality of both the acid and the base.

30. What is the normality of a sodium thiosulfate solution standardized by adding an excess of KI to 25.00 ml of 0.1230 *N* $K_2Cr_2O_7$, the liberated iodine being titrated with 41.40 ml of the thiosulfate solution?

$$Cr_2O_7^{2-} + 6I^- + 14H^+ \rightarrow 3I_2 + 2Cr^{3+} + 7H_2O$$

$$I_2 + 2S_2O_3^{2-} \rightarrow 2I^- + S_4O_6^{2-}$$

ans. 0.0743 N

31. A 25.0-ml aliquot of a potassium hydrogen oxalate (KHC_2O_4) solution was found to require 31.3 ml of 0.125 *N* NaOH to reach an end point. Another 25.00-ml aliquot was used to standardize a $KMnO_4$ solution, 48.5 ml of the latter being required. Calculate the normality of the $KMnO_4$ based upon the reaction

$$2MnO_4^- + 5C_2O_4^{2-} + 16H^+ \rightarrow 10CO_2 + 2Mn^{2+} + 8H_2O$$

32. 0.312 gram of an unknown acid required 40.0 ml of 0.150 *N* NaOH for neutralization.
    (a) What was the equivalent weight of the acid?

(b) If it were known that the acid contained two titratable hydrogens, what would be the formula weight of the acid?

33. What weight of iron wire (99.8 percent pure) would require a 40.0 ml titration with 0.1175 N $K_2Cr_2O_7$?

$$Cr_2O_7^{2-} + 6Fe^{2+} + 14H^+ \rightarrow 2Cr^{3+} + 6Fe^{3+} + 7H_2O$$

34. A solution of HCl was standardized by precipitating all of the Cl^- from a 25.0-ml aliquot with an excess of silver nitrate. The precipitate was filtered, washed, and dried. It was found to weigh 0.0782 gram. What was the normality of the HCl?   ans. 0.0218 N

35. Exactly 75.0 ml of a H_2SO_4 solution produced 0.118 gram of barium sulfate upon precipitation with an excess of $BaCl_2$. What was the normality of the acid?

36. Calculate the milligrams of H_2SO_4 per milliliter of solution if a 25.0-ml aliquot required 37.9 ml of 0.0851 N NaOH for complete neutralization.

ans. 6.32 mg per ml

37. What is the percent $BaCl_2 \cdot 2H_2O$ if a 0.412-gram sample required 26.4 ml of 0.0500 N $AgNO_3$?   ans. 39.1 percent

38. Calculate the percent Fe and the percent Fe_2O_3 in a 0.749-gram sample that consumed 22.2 ml of 0.134 N $KMnO_4$ after suitable treatment.

$$MnO_4^- + 5Fe^{2+} + 8H^+ \rightarrow Mn^{2+} + 5Fe^{3+} + 4H_2O$$

39. A 0.641-gram sample of impure Na_2CO_3 was titrated to a methyl orange end point with 43.0 ml of 0.242 N HCl ($CO_3^{2-} + 2H^+ \rightarrow H_2CO_3$).
    (a) Calculate the percent Na_2CO_3 in the sample.
    (b) How many milligrams of CO_2 would be evolved by boiling the solution during and after the above titration?

40. A sample containing $(NH_4)_2SO_4$ was analyzed by dissolving 1.82 grams in strong base and distilling the liberated NH_3 into 50.0 ml of 0.0804 N HCl. The excess HCl was back-titrated with 9.48 ml of 0.106 N NaOH.
    (a) Calculate the percent $(NH_4)_2SO_4$ in the sample.   ans. 10.9 percent
    (b) Calculate the percent N in the sample.   ans. 2.32 percent

41. A 0.612-gram sample containing $Ca(ClO_3)_2 \cdot 2H_2O$ was analyzed by reduction of the ClO_3^- to Cl^- which was then precipitated by the addition of 25.0 ml of 0.200 N $AgNO_3$. The excess $AgNO_3$ was titrated with 3.10 ml of 0.186 N KSCN ($Ag^+ + SCN^- \rightarrow AgSCN$). Calculate the percent $Ca(ClO_3)_2 \cdot 2H_2O$ in the sample.

42. A 0.500-gram sample of steel was dissolved in acid and the chromium present oxidized to dichromate ($Cr_2O_7^{2-}$) with ammonium persulfate. Exactly 1.242 grams of Mohr's salt, $FeSO_4(NH_4)_2SO_4 \cdot 6H_2O$, was added to the resulting solution, the ferrous ion of which reduced the dichromate ion to Cr^{3+}. The excess iron (II) ion was titrated with 14.1 ml of 0.0463 N $KMnO_4$. Calculate the percent Cr in the steel.

43. A 50.0-ml aliquot of a solution containing uranium in the $+6$ state was passed through a reductor which reduced it to a mixture of the $+3$ and $+4$ states. Bubbling air through the solution converted all of the $+3$ to the $+4$ state which was then oxidized quantitatively back to the $+6$ form with 36.9 ml of 0.0624 N K$_2$Cr$_2$O$_7$.

$$3UO^{2+} + Cr_2O_7^{2-} + 8H^+ \rightarrow 3UO_2^{2+} + 2Cr^{3+} + 4H_2O$$

44. A 2.00-gram sample of chromite (FeO · Cr$_2$O$_3$) was fused with sodium peroxide. The resulting mass was dissolved and the excess peroxide destroyed by boiling. After acidification, 50.0 ml of 0.160 N Fe^{2+} was added which reduced the Cr$_2$O$_7^{2-}$ to Cr^{3+}. A back titration of 3.14 ml of 0.0500 N K$_2$Cr$_2$O$_7$ was required to oxidize the excess Fe^{2+}. Calculate (a) the percent Cr in the sample, and (b) the percent chromite in the sample.

45. The routine analysis for H$_2$SO$_4$ in an electroplating rinse is to be undertaken. A NaOH solution is to be prepared such that the volume used in titration is numerically 10 times as great as the percent H$_2$SO$_4$ in a 20.0-gram sample. What should be the normality of the NaOH solution?

46. The sulfur in an organic compound was determined by burning a 0.471-gram sample in a stream of oxygen and collecting the resulting SO$_2$ in a neutral solution of H$_2$O$_2$, which converted the SO$_2$ to H$_2$SO$_4$

$$SO_2 + H_2O_2 \rightarrow H_2SO_4$$

The sulfuric acid was titrated with 28.2 ml of 0.108 N KOH. Calculate the percent sulfur in the sample.

47. An organic mixture was known to contain the compound, C$_6$H$_4$Cl$_2$. This compound was analyzed by treating a 1.17-gram sample with metallic sodium which converted the chlorine quantitatively to NaCl. After destruction of the excess sodium metal, the chloride was titrated with 30.1 ml of a 0.0884 N solution of Hg(NO$_3$)$_2$ (Hg^{2+} + 2Cl$^-$ → HgCl$_2$). Calculate (a) the percent Cl in the sample and (b) the percent C$_6$H$_4$Cl$_2$.

48. What should be the normality of a AgNO$_3$ solution in order that its titer be 1.00 mg of KCl?

49. The sulfur in a 5.00-gram sample of steel was evolved as H$_2$S which was collected in an ammoniacal solution of CdCl$_2$. The CdS formed was treated with 10 ml of 0.0600 N I$_2$, and the I$_2$ back-titrated with 4.82 ml of 0.0510 N sodium thiosulfate. The reaction of CdS with I$_2$ is

$$CdS + I_2 \rightarrow S + Cd^{2+} + 2I^-$$

Calculate the percent S in the steel.

50. How many grams of AgI are formed when 30.0 ml of 0.100 N AgNO$_3$ are mixed with 20.0 ml of 0.180 N KI?

(10)

The Techniques and Tools of
Volumetric Analysis

In Chapter 5 we considered the common techniques and tools of analytical chemistry, with emphasis on those having particular application to gravimetric methods. We shall now complete the survey by considering three types of apparatus that are indispensible to the performance of a volumetric analysis.

10.1   General Considerations

UNITS OF VOLUME

The fundamental unit of volume is the *liter*, defined as the volume occupied by 1 kilogram of water at the temperature of maximum density (3.98° C) and at 1 atmosphere of pressure.

The *milliliter* is defined as one one-thousandth of a liter and is widely used in the many instances where the liter represents an inconveniently large volume.

Yet another unit of volume is the *cubic centimeter*. While this and the milliliter can be used interchangeably without effect in most situations, these units are not strictly identical, the milliliter being equal to 1.000028 cubic centimeters. It was originally intended that 1 kilogram of water should occupy exactly 1 cubic decimeter; owing to inadequacies of early experimental measurements, however, this relationship was not realized, and this small difference in units was the result. For all volumetric analyses, the liter or the milliliter is used.

EFFECT OF TEMPERATURE UPON VOLUME MEASUREMENTS

The volume of a given mass of liquid varies with temperature. So also does the volume of any device employed to measure this quantity. As a consequence, accurate volumetric measurements may require that the effect of temperature be taken into account.

Most volumetric measuring devices are constructed of glass which fortunately has a small temperature coefficient. Thus, for example, an apparatus of soft glass will change in volume by about 0.003 percent per degree; with Pyrex, the change is about one third of this value. Clearly, variations in the volume of equipment as the result of changes in temperature need be considered only for the most exacting work.

The coefficient of expansion for dilute aqueous solutions is approximately 0.025 percent per degree. The magnitude of this figure is such that a temperature variation of about 5 degrees will measurably affect the precision of ordinary volumetric measurements.

★EXAMPLE. A 40.00-ml sample is taken from a liquid refrigerated at 5° C. The volume this sample will occupy at 20° C is sought.

$$V_{20°} = V_{5°} + 0.00025(20 - 5)(40.00) \qquad (10\text{-}1)$$
$$= 40.00 + 0.15$$
$$= 40.15 \text{ ml}$$

Volumetric measurements must be referred to some standard temperature; in order to minimize the need for calculations such as these, 20.0° C, the average room temperature, has been chosen for this reference point. Since the ambient temperature in most laboratories is within a few degrees of this, the need seldom arises for a temperature correction in ordinary analytical work. The coefficient of cubic expansion for many organic liquids, however, is considerably greater than that for water or dilute aqueous solutions. Good precision in the measurement of these liquids may require corrections for temperature variations of a degree or less.

TYPES OF VOLUMETRIC APPARATUS

The reliable measurement of volume is the common purpose of the *pipet*, the *buret*, and the *volumetric flask*. These can be calibrated either to *deliver* or, alternatively, to *contain* a specified volume. Volumetric equipment is marked by the manufacturer to indicate not only the manner of calibration (usually with a TD, for "to deliver"; or a TC, for "to contain)" but also the temperature to which the calibration strictly refers. Ordinarily, pipets and burets are designed and calibrated to deliver specified volumes while volumetric flasks are calibrated on a to-contain basis.

10.2   Apparatus for Volumetric Measurements

PIPETS

All pipets are designed for the transfer of known volumes of liquid from one container to another. Some deliver a single, fixed volume; these are called *volumetric*, or *transfer pipets*. Others, known as *measuring pipets*, are calibrated in convenient units so that any volume up to the maximum capacity can be delivered.

TABLE 10-1

Pipets

Name	Type of Calibration	Function	Available Capacities, ml	Type of Drainage
Volumetric	TD	delivery of a fixed volume	1–200	free drainage
Mohr	TD	delivery of a variable volume	1–25	drain to lower calibration line
Serological	TD	same	0.1–10	blow out last drop
Serological	TD	same	0.1–10	drain to lower calibration line
Ostwald-Folin	TD	delivery of a fixed volume	0.5–10	blow out last drop
Lambda	TC	to contain a fixed volume	0.001–2	wash out with suitable solvent
Lambda	TD	delivery of a fixed volume	0.001–2	blow out last drop

While all pipets are filled to an initial calibration mark at the outset, the manner in which the transfer is completed is subject to considerable variation. Because of the attraction between most liquids and glass, a drop tends to remain in the tip of a drained pipet. This drop is blown from some pipets, but not others. Table 10-1 summarizes the several varieties most likely to be encountered in an analytical laboratory.

BURETS

Burets, like measuring pipets, enable the analyst to deliver any volume up to the maximum capacity. The precision attainable with a buret is appreciably better than that with a measuring pipet.

In general, a buret consists of a calibrated tube containing the liquid and a valve arrangement by which flow from a tip can be controlled. Principal differences among burets are to be found in the type of valve employed. The Bunsen valve is the simplest, consisting of a closely fitting glass bead within a short length of rubber tubing. Only when the rubber tubing is deformed can liquid flow past the bead.

Burets equipped with glass stopcocks rely upon a lubricant between the ground-glass surfaces of stopcock and barrel for a liquid tight seal. Some solutions, notably bases, will cause a stopcock to freeze upon long contact; thorough cleaning is indicated after each use.

Valves made of plastics have appeared in recent years. These are inert to attack by most common reagents and require no lubricant.

More elaborate burets are designed so that they may be filled and leveled automatically; these are of particular value in routine analysis.

VOLUMETRIC FLASKS

Volumetric flasks are available with capacities ranging from 5 ml to 5 liters, and are usually calibrated to contain the specified volume when filled to the line etched on the neck. They are used in the preparation of standard solutions and in the dilution of samples to known volumes prior to taking aliquot portions with a pipet. Some are also calibrated on a "to-deliver" basis; these are readily distinguishable by two reference lines. If delivery of the stated volume is desired, the flask is filled to the upper of the two lines.

10.3   The Measurement of Volume—Techniques and Operations

Only clean glass surfaces will support a uniform film of liquid; the presence of dirt or oil will tend to cause breaks in this film. The appearance of water breaks is a certain indication of an unclean surface. Volumetric glassware is carefully cleansed by the manufacturer before being supplied with markings, and in order for these to have meaning the equipment must be kept equally clean when in use.

As a general rule, the heating of calibrated glass equipment should be avoided. Too rapid cooling can permanently distort the glass and cause a change in volume.

When a liquid is confined in a narrow tube such as a buret or a pipet, the surface ordinarily exhibits a marked curvature called a *meniscus*. It is common practice to use the bottom of the meniscus in calibrating and using volumetric ware. This minimum can often be established more exactly if an opaque card or piece of paper is held behind the graduations.

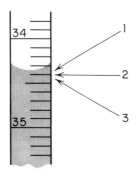

Fig. 10.1 The Liquid in a Buret, Showing the Meniscus. Volume indicated is 34.36 ml.

In reading volumetric ware the eye must be level with the liquid; otherwise an error due to *parallax* will arise. Thus if one's eye level is above that of the liquid, it will appear that a smaller volume has been taken than is actually the case. An error in the opposite direction can be expected if the point of observation is too low (see Figure 10.1).

DIRECTIONS FOR THE USE OF A PIPET

The following instructions pertain specifically to the manipulation of transfer pipets, but with minor modifications they may be used for other types as well. Liquids are usually drawn into pipets through the application of a slight vacuum. The mouth should not be used for suction owing to the danger of accidentally ingesting liquids. Use of a rubber suction bulb or a rubber tube connected to an aspirator pump is strongly recommended (see Figure 10.2).

★PROCEDURE

Cleaning. Pipets may be cleaned with a warm solution of detergent or with tepid cleaning solution (see page 88). Draw in sufficient liquid to fill the bulb to about one third of its capacity. While holding it nearly horizontal, carefully rotate the pipet so that all interior surfaces are covered. Drain, and then rinse thoroughly with distilled water. Inspect for water breaks, and repeat the cleaning cycle if necessary.

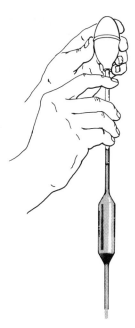

(a) Draw liquid past the graduation mark.

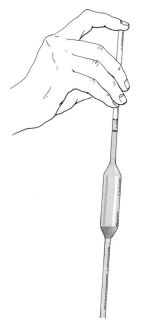

(b) Use forefinger to maintain liquid level above the graduation mark.

(c) Tilt pipet slightly and wipe away any drops on the outside surface.

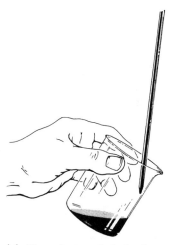

(d) Allow pipet to drain freely.

Fig. 10.2 Technique for the Use of a Volumetric Pipet.

Measurement of an Aliquot. As in cleaning, draw in a small quantity of the liquid to be sampled and thoroughly rinse the interior surfaces; repeat this with at least two more portions. Then carefully fill the pipet somewhat past the graduation mark. Quickly place a forefinger over the upper end of the pipet to arrest the outflow of liquid. Make certain that there are no air bubbles in the bulk of the liquid or foam at the surface. Tilt the pipet slightly from the vertical and wipe the exterior free of adhering liquid. Touch the tip of the pipet to the wall of a glass vessel (not the actual receiving vessel) and slowly allow the liquid level to drop by partially releasing the forefinger. Halt further flow as the bottom of the meniscus coincides exactly with the graduation mark. Place the tip of the pipet well into the receiving vessel and allow the sample to drain. When free flow ceases, rest the tip against an inner wall for a full 10 seconds. Finally, withdraw the pipet with a rotating motion to remove any droplet still adhering to the tip. *The small volume remaining inside the tip is not to be blown or rinsed into the receiving vessel.*

This sequence is illustrated in Figure 10.2.

NOTES:

1. The liquid can best be held at a constant level in the pipet if one's forefinger is slightly moist; too much moisture, however, makes control difficult.

2. It is good practice to avoid handling the pipet by the bulb.

3. Pipets should be thoroughly rinsed with distilled water after use.

DIRECTIONS FOR THE USE OF A BURET

Before being placed in service, a buret must be scrupulously clean. In addition, it must be established that the valve is liquid-tight.

★PROCEDURE

Lubrication of a Stopcock Buret. Carefully remove all of the old grease from the stopcock and barrel. Lightly grease the stopcock, taking care to avoid the area near the hole. Insert the stopcock into the barrel and rotate it vigorously. When the proper amount of lubricant has been used, the area of contact between stopcock and barrel appears nearly transparent, the seal is liquid-tight, and no grease has worked its way into the tip.

Cleaning. Thoroughly clean the tube with detergent and a long brush. If water breaks persist after rinsing, clamp the buret in an inverted position with the end dipped in a beaker of cleaning solution. Connect a hose from the buret tip to a vacuum line. Gently pull the cleaning solution into the buret, stopping well short of the stopcock. Allow to stand for 10 to 15 minutes and then drain. Rinse thoroughly with distilled water and again inspect for water breaks. Repeat the treatment if necessary.

NOTES:

1. Cleaning solution often disperses more stopcock lubricant than it oxidizes and leaves a buret more heavily coated with film than before the treatment. For this reason the cleaning solution should *not* be allowed to come in contact with lubricated stopcock assemblies.

2. Grease films may yield to treatment with such organic solvents as acetone or benzene. Thorough washing with detergent should follow such treatment.

3. As long as the flow of liquid is not impeded, fouling of the buret tip with lubricant is not a serious matter. Removal is best accomplished with organic solvents.

4. Before returning a buret to service after reassembly, it is advisable to test for leakage. Simply fill the buret with water and establish that the volume reading does not change with time.

Filling. Make certain that the stopcock is closed. Add 5 to 10 ml of solution and carefully rotate the buret to wet the walls completely; allow the liquid to drain through the tip. Repeat this procedure two more times. Then fill the buret well above the zero mark. Free the tip of air bubbles by rapidly rotating the stopcock and allowing small quantities of solution to pass. Finally, lower the level of the solution to, or somewhat below, the zero marking; after allowing about a minute for drainage, take an initial volume reading.

Titration. Figure 10.3 illustrates the preferred method for manipulation of a stopcock. Any tendency for lateral movement of the stopcock will be in the direction of firmer seatings.

With the tip well within the titration vessel, introduce solution from the buret in increments of a milliliter or so. Swirl (or stir) the sample constantly to assure efficient mixing. Reduce the volume of the additions as the titration progresses; in the immediate vicinity of the end point, the reagent should be added a drop at a time. When it is judged that only a few more drops are needed, rinse down the walls of the titration vessel before completing the titration. Allow about a minute to elapse between the last addition of reagent and the reading of the buret.

NOTES:

1. If a particular titration is unfamiliar, many analysts prepare an extra sample. No care is lavished on its titration since its only functions are to reveal the nature of the end point and to provide a rough estimate of titrant requirements. This deliberate sacrifice of one sample often results in an over-all saving of time.

2. Instead of rinsing near the end of the titration, the flask can be carefully tipped and rotated so that the bulk of the liquid picks up any droplets adhering to the walls.

3. Volume increments smaller than a normal drop may be taken by allowing a small volume of liquid to form on the tip of the buret and then touching the tip to the wall of the flask. This droplet is then combined with the bulk of the solution as in Note 2.

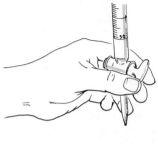

Fig. 10.3 Recommended Technique for Manipulation of a Buret Stopcock.

DIRECTIONS FOR THE USE OF A VOLUMETRIC FLASK

Before use, volumetric flasks should be washed with detergent and, if necessary, cleaning solution; only rarely need they be dried. Should drying be required, however, it is best accomplished by clamping the flasks in an inverted position and employing a mild vacuum to circulate air through them.

★PROCEDURE

Weighing Directly into a Volumetric Flask. Direct preparation of a standard solution requires that a known weight of solute be introduced into a volumetric flask. In order to minimize the possibility of loss during transfer, insert a funnel into the neck of the flask. The funnel is subsequently washed free of solid.

Dilution to the Mark. After transferring the solute, fill the flask about half full and swirl the contents to achieve solution. Add more solvent, and again mix well. Bring the liquid level almost to the mark, and allow time for drainage. Then use a medicine dropper to make such final additions of solvent as are necessary. Firmly stopper the flask and invert repeatedly to assure uniform mixing. Finally, transfer the solution to a dry storage bottle.

NOTE:

If, as sometimes happens, the liquid level accidentally exceeds the calibration mark, the solution can be saved by correcting for the excess volume. Use a gummed label to mark the actual position of the meniscus. After the flask has been emptied, carefully refill to the mark with water. Then, using a buret, measure the volume needed to duplicate the actual volume of the solution. This volume, of course, should be added to the nominal value for the flask when calculating the concentration of the solution.

10.4 Calibration of Volumetric Ware

The reliability of a volumetric analysis depends upon agreement between the volumes actually and purportedly contained (or delivered) by the apparatus. Calibration simply verifies this agreement if such already exists, or provides the means for attaining agreement if it is lacking. The latter involves either the assignment of more reliable numerical values to the existing volume markings or the striking of new markings that agree with the existing numerical values.

In general, a calibration consists of determining the mass of a liquid of known density contained (or delivered) by the apparatus. Although this appears to be a straightforward process, a number of important variables must be controlled.

Principal among these is the temperature which influences a calibration in two ways. First and most important, the volume occupied by a given mass of liquid varies with temperature. Second, the volume of the apparatus itself is variable, owing to the tendency of the glass to expand or contract with changes in temperature.

In Chapter 5 we noted that weighing data must be corrected, under some circumstances, for the volume of air displaced by weights and objects alike, and that the effect of buoyancy upon results becomes most pronounced when the density of the object is significantly lower than that of the weights. As a general rule a buoyancy correction must be applied to weighing data relating to a calibration.

Finally, the liquid employed for calibration requires consideration. Water is the liquid of choice for most work. Mercury is also useful, particularly where small volumes are involved. Because it does not wet glass surfaces, the volume of mercury contained by the apparatus will be identical with that which is delivered. In addition, the convex meniscus of mercury gives rise to a small correction that must be applied to give the corresponding volume for a liquid forming a concave meniscus. The magnitude of this correction is dependent upon the diameter of the apparatus at the graduation mark.

The calculations associated with calibrations, while not difficult, are somewhat involved. The raw weighing data are first corrected for buoyancy by means of the equation

$$W_1 = d_{air} W_2 \left(\frac{1}{d_1} - \frac{1}{d_2} \right) + W_2 \tag{10-2}$$

where W_1 is the corrected mass of the object, d_1 is its density, and W_2 and d_2 are the mass and density of the weights.

The volume of the apparatus at the temperature (t) of calibration is next obtained by dividing the density of the liquid at that temperature into the corrected weight.

Finally, this volume is corrected to the standard temperature of 20° C by means of equation (10-1), page 191.

★EXAMPLE. A 25-ml volumetric pipet was calibrated against brass weights at 23° C; it was found to deliver an average of 25.08 grams of water. We wish to compute the volume delivered at this temperature and at 20° C.

At 23° C, the density of water is 0.9975; the density of brass is approximately 8.4. For all but the most refined work the density of air can be taken as 0.0012 gram/ml. Introducing these quantities into equation (10-2) we find

$$W_1 = (0.0012)(25.08) \left(\frac{1}{0.9975} - \frac{1}{8.4} \right) + 25.08$$

$$= 0.027 + 25.08 = 25.11 \text{ grams}$$

This is the weight of water delivered by the pipet at the temperature of the test. The volume corresponding to this weight is

$$V_{23°} = \frac{25.11}{0.9975} = 25.17 \text{ ml}$$

To determine the volume delivered by this pipet at 20° C, we make use of equation (10-1), taking 0.000025 as the coefficient of cubic expansion for glass.

$$V_{20°} = 25.17 + (0.000025)(20 - 23)(25.17)$$

$$= 25.17 - 0.0019 \cong 25.17 \text{ ml}$$

Table 10-2 is provided to ease the computational burden of calibration. It tabulates the volume occupied by 1.000 gram of water at various temperatures, as computed by equation (10-2). Provided that brass weights are

TABLE 10-2

**Volume (at 20° C) Occupied by 1.000 Gram of Water in a Glass Container
That Has Been Weighed in Air against Brass Weights
at Various Temperatures**

Temperature (°C)	Volume ml	Temperature (°C)	Volume ml	Temperature (°C)	Volume ml
10	1.0016	17	1.0023	24	1.0036
11	1.0017	18	1.0025	25	1.0038
12	1.0018	19	1.0026	26	1.0041
13	1.0019	20	1.0028	27	1 0043
14	1.0020	21	1.0030	28	1.0046
15	1.0021	22	1.0032	29	1.0048
16	1.0022	23	1.0034	30	1.0051

used in calibration, the corresponding volume is obtained simply by multiplying the weight of water taken by the appropriate factor from this table.

> ★EXAMPLE. A 10-ml pipet was found to deliver 9.861 grams of water when calibrated against brass weights at 17° C. We need to know the volume this pipet delivers at 20° C.
> From Table 10-2 we find that 1 gram of water at 17° C occupies 1.0023 ml at 20° C. Therefore, the volume delivered by the pipet at this temperature will be

$$V_{20°} = (9.861)(1.0023) = 9.88 \text{ ml}$$

GENERAL DIRECTIONS FOR CALIBRATION WORK

All volumetric apparatus should be painstakingly freed of water breaks before being tested. Burets and pipets need not be dried; volumetric flasks should be thoroughly drained.

The water used for calibration should be drawn well in advance of use in order to allow it to reach thermal equilibrium with its surroundings. This condition is best established by noting the temperature of the water at frequent intervals and waiting until no further changes are observed.

An analytical balance is used for calibrations involving 50 ml or less; weighing to the nearest milligram is sufficient for all volumes in excess of 1 ml. Weighing bottles or small, well-stoppered Erlenmeyer flasks are convenient receivers for small volumes.

A two-pan laboratory balance is employed for the calibration of apparatus holding volumes larger than can be accommodated by an analytical balance. Since the arm lengths of such a balance can no longer be assumed to be equal, weighing by substitution is the preferred method.

CALIBRATION OF A VOLUMETRIC PIPET

Determine the empty weight of the receiver. Introduce an aliquot from the pipet, weigh receiver and contents to the nearest milligram, and evaluate the weight of water delivered from the difference in these weights. Repeat the calibration several times.

CALIBRATION OF A BURET

Fill the buret, making certain that no bubbles are entrapped in the tip. Withdraw water until the level is at, or just below, the zero mark. Touch the tip to the wall of a beaker to remove any adhering drop. After allowing time for drainage, take an initial reading of the meniscus, estimating to the nearest 0.01 ml. Allow the buret to stand for 5 minutes and recheck the reading; if the stopcock is tight, there should be no noticeable change. During this interval, weigh (to the nearest mg) a 125-ml Erlenmeyer flask fitted with a rubber stopper.

Once tightness of the stopcock has been established, run approximately 10 ml into the flask at a rate of flow of about 10 ml per minute. Touch the tip to the wall of the flask. Wait 1 minute, record the volume, and refill the buret. Weigh the flask and its contents to the nearest 5 mg; the difference between this and the initial weight gives the mass of water actually delivered. Convert this mass into terms of volume using Table 10-2. Compute the correction in this interval by subtracting the apparent volume from that actually delivered.

Starting again from the zero mark, repeat the calibration using about 20 ml. Test the buret at 10-ml intervals over its entire length. Prepare a plot of the correction to be applied as a function of the volume delivered.

NOTE:

Any correction larger than 0.10 ml should be verified by duplicate determinations before being accepted.

CALIBRATION OF A VOLUMETRIC FLASK

Weigh the clean, dry flask, placing it on the right-hand pan of a laboratory balance. Set a beaker on the left pan and add lead shot until balance is achieved. Remove the flask, and in its place substitute known weights until the same point of balance is reached. Carefully fill the flask with water of known temperature until the meniscus coincides with the graduation mark. Return the flask to the right-hand pan and the beaker to the left. Repeat the process of counterweighing with lead shot followed by substituting weights for the flask. The difference between the two weighings gives the mass of water contained by the apparatus; calculate the corresponding volume with the aid of Table 10-2.

NOTE:

A glass tube with one end drawn to a tip is useful in making final adjustments of the liquid level.

CALIBRATION OF A VOLUMETRIC FLASK RELATIVE TO A PIPET

The calibration of a flask relative to a pipet makes possible an excellent method for partitioning a sample into aliquots. The following directions pertain specifically to a 50-ml pipet and a 500-ml flask; other combinations are equally convenient.

With a 50-ml pipet, carefully transfer 10 aliquots to a 500-ml volumetric flask. Mark the location of the meniscus with a gummed label; coat the label with paraffin to assure permanence. When a sample has been diluted to this mark, an aliquot taken with the same 50-ml pipet will constitute exactly one tenth of the total sample.

(11)

Precipitation Titrations

Volumetric methods based on the formation of a slightly soluble precipitate are called *precipitation titrations*. These are among the oldest analytical procedures as attested by the association of such names as Gay-Lussac, Mohr, and Volhard with specific volumetric-precipitation procedures. Aside from their historical interest, precipitation titrations are important because they provide excellent methods for the analysis of the halides and pseudo-halides as well as for the determination of certain metal ions.

11.1   Titration Curves for Precipitation Reactions

DERIVATION

The curves presented in Chapter 9 illustrate the changes in reactant concentration that occur during the course of a titration. These are particularly useful in indicating the conditions prevailing at and near the equivalence point; they are thus valuable aids in deciding not only whether a particular substance can be titrated, but also in determining the magnitude of error to be expected from the application of a given indicator system.

To illustrate the derivation of a typical curve, consider the titration of 50.0 ml of 0.1 F sodium chloride with a 0.1 F solution of silver nitrate. A plot of either pAg or pCl with respect to the volume of silver nitrate added will yield a titration curve for the process. The solubility-product constant for silver chloride is 1.82×10^{-10} mol²/liter² at 25° C.

At the outset, the concentration of chloride ion is 0.1 M; pCl will thus be 1.00. Since none has yet been introduced, the silver ion concentration is zero, and pAg is indeterminate. After the addition of, say, 10.0 ml of silver nitrate solution, the chloride ion concentration will be decreased not only because of precipitate formation, but also because of the increase in volume of the solution; it will be given by

$$[Cl^-] = \frac{(50.0 \times 0.1 - 10.0 \times 0.1)}{60} + [Ag^+]$$

The first term in this equation would express the concentration of chloride ion only if the precipitate were absolutely insoluble. In fact, of course, silver chloride is slightly soluble, yielding equal quantities of silver and chloride ions to the solution as a consequence. The second term in the equation accounts for the chloride ion contribution from this source.

Substituting this expression for $[Cl^-]$ into the solubility-product expression for AgCl will provide an exact solution for the silver ion concentration; however, a quadratic equation must be solved. Actually, we can arrive at an entirely satisfactory answer by assuming that the silver ion concentration is numerically small with respect to the chloride ion concentration; under these circumstances

$$[Cl^-] \cong \frac{(50.0 \times 0.1 - 10.0 \times 0.1)}{60} = 6.7 \times 10^{-2} \text{ mol/liter}$$

Substituting this value into the solubility-product expression we find that

$$[Ag^+] = \frac{1.82 \times 10^{-10}}{6.7 \times 10^{-2}} = 2.7 \times 10^{-9} \text{ mol/liter}$$

The magnitude of this answer confirms that we were justified in making the simplifying assumption. The respective p functions may now be calculated as follows:

$$p\text{Cl} = -\log 6.7 \times 10^{-2} = 2 - \log 6.7 = 1.17$$

$$p\text{Ag} = -\log 2.7 \times 10^{-9} = 9 - \log 2.7 = 8.57$$

After 20.0 ml of silver nitrate solution have been added, we find that

$$[Cl^-] = \frac{(50.0 \times 0.1 - 20.0 \times 0.1)}{70} + [Ag^+] \cong 4.3 \times 10^{-2} \text{ mol/liter}$$

Thus

$$[Ag^+] = \frac{1.82 \times 10^{-10}}{4.3 \times 10^{-2}} = 4.1 \times 10^{-9} \text{ mol/liter}$$

Therefore

$$pCl = 2 - \log 4.3 = 1.37$$

$$pAg = 9 - \log 4.1 = 8.39$$

In this manner, then, we can calculate the equilibrium concentrations of chloride ion and silver ion resulting from the addition of any volume of silver nitrate short of the equivalence point. The chloride ion concentration is determined directly, the small contribution from the dissolved silver chloride being considered negligibly small except in the immediate region of the equivalence point; the silver ion concentration is calculated from the solubility-product expression.

At the equivalence point we have added an amount of silver ion identical to the amount of chloride ion in the sample; the system here consists simply of a saturated solution of silver chloride. The concentrations of the two ions are therefore identical and are readily calculated from the solubility-product expression.

$$[Ag^+][Cl^-] = [Ag^+]^2 = 1.82 \times 10^{-10}$$

$$[Ag^+] = [Cl^-] = 1.35 \times 10^{-5} \text{ mol/liter}$$

$$pAg = pCl = 5 - \log 1.35 = 4.87$$

Beyond the equivalence point, we can evaluate the silver ion concentration directly, it now being present in excess; the chloride ion concentration is computed from the solubility-product expression. Thus, for example, after 52.5 ml of silver nitrate solution have been introduced,

$$[Ag^+] = \frac{(52.5 \times 0.1 - 50.0 \times 0.1)}{102.5} + [Cl^-]$$

Here the first term gives the silver ion concentration due to the excess of reagent present, while the second represents that due to the solubility of the precipitate. The assumption that the latter is vanishingly small with respect to the former is justified; after making this approximation, we find that

$$[Ag^+] = \frac{0.25}{102.5} = 2.4 \times 10^{-3} \text{ mol/liter}$$

Thus

$$[Cl^-] = \frac{1.82 \times 10^{-10}}{2.4 \times 10^{-3}} = 7.6 \times 10^{-8} \text{ mol/liter}$$

and

$$pAg = 3 - \log 2.4 = 2.62$$

$$pCl = 8 - \log 7.6 = 7.12$$

FACTORS AFFECTING TITRATION CURVES

Reagent Concentrations. Table 11-1 is a compilation of data for this titration as well as for two others involving the same reactants at lower concentrations. We see that the sum of pAg and pCl is a constant for each point, being equal to the negative logarithm of the solubility-product constant. It is also clear that the equivalence point for each of

TABLE 11-1

p Functions for Several Titrations of Chloride with Silver Ion

Volume AgNO$_3$ added, ml	50.0 ml of 0.1 F Cl$^-$ titrated with 0.1 F AgNO$_3$		50.0 ml of 0.01 F Cl$^-$ titrated with 0.01 F AgNO$_3$		50.0 ml of 0.001 F Cl$^-$ titrated with 0.001 F AgNO$_3$	
	pAg	pCl	pAg	pCl	pAg	pCl
0	—	1.00	—	2.00	—	3.00
10	8.57	1.17	7.57	2.17	6.57	3.17
20	8.37	1.37	7.37	2.37	6.37	3.37
30	8.14	1.60	7.14	2.60	6.14	3.60
40	7.79	1.95	6.79	2.95	5.79	3.95
45	7.46	2.28	6.46	3.28	5.50*	4.24
47.5	7.15	2.59	6.15	3.50	5.27*	4.47
49.0	6.76	2.98	5.78*	3.96	5.05*	4.69
49.9	5.74	4.00	5.05*	4.69	4.88*	4.86
50.0	4.87	4.87	4.87	4.87	4.87	4.87
50.1	4.00	5.74	4.69	5.05*	4.86	4.88*
51	3.00	6.74	4.20	5.54*	4.64	5.10*
52.5	2.62	7.12	3.62	6.12	4.48	5.26*
55.0	2.32	7.42	3.32	6.42	4.20	5.54*

* Value computed using no approximations.

these titrations is characterized by invariant silver and chloride ion concentrations; end points for this titration are based on this fact.

The pAg data for these titrations are plotted in Figure 11.1 as a function of the volume of silver nitrate added. It is noteworthy that all the curves have the same general shape. The most obvious characteristic is the abrupt change in pAg occurring in the vicinity of the equivalence point; we know from the previous discussion that pCl will show a similar rapid change in the opposite direction. The break in the titration curve becomes more pronounced with increasing reactant concentrations. This factor is of considerable importance from the practical standpoint of end-point detection, since the most satisfactory indicator behavior is observed in titrations whose curves display sharp breaks in the region of the equivalence point.

Completeness of Reaction. Figure 11.2 illustrates curves obtained when 0.1 F solutions of several anions are titrated with 0.1 F silver nitrate.

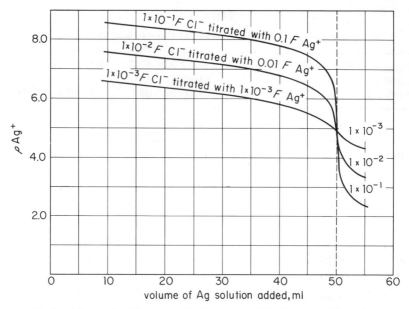

Fig. 11.1 Theoretical Curves for the Titration of Chloride Ion with Silver Ion. Plots of pAg as a function of the volume of AgNO$_3$ added. Note the effect of reagent concentration upon the shape of the curves.

Inspection of these curves reveals a definite relationship between the sharpness of the end-point break and the solubility of the precipitate formed in the reaction. The greatest change in pAg accompanies the titration of iodide ion which, of all the anions considered, forms the least soluble silver salt and hence represents the most complete reaction. The poorest break is observed for the reaction that is least complete—that is, in the titration of bromate ion. Those reactions that produce silver salts having solubilities intermediate between these extremes yield titration curves that are also of intermediate character.

To summarize, the change in p function in the vicinity of the equivalence point is dependent not only upon reagent concentration, but also upon the

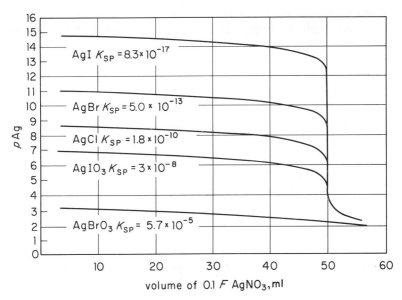

Fig. 11.2 Theoretical Curves for the Titration of Several Anions with Silver Ion. Plots of pAg with respect to the volume of 0.100 F AgNO₃ added to 50.0 ml of solution in which the anion concentration is 0.100 F.

completeness of the reaction. The most pronounced breaks are thus observed where the solutions titrated are of relatively high concentration and the chemical reactions proceed to essential completion.

11.2   End-point Detection

END POINTS BASED UPON INDICATORS

A chemical *indicator* is a substance that can react with one of the participants of the volumetric reaction in such a way as to produce an observable change in the appearance of the solution; ordinarily this change involves an alteration in color. The indicator substance, by virtue of its tendency to react with the reagent or the substance titrated, competes with one of the participants of the reaction for the other. In order to minimize the titration error, the reaction involving the indicator must suddenly become either highly favorable or highly unfavorable at the equivalence point as a consequence of the change in p function. Thus, the most satisfactory indicator behavior is observed with the most abrupt changes in solution composition at the equivalence point. For example, consider an indicator that shows a perceptible color change as pAg varies from 4.5 to 5.5. Referring again to Figure 11.1 we see that each of these titrations requires a different volume of titrant to encompass this range; this varies from less than 0.1 ml of 0.1 F silver solution to about 7.5 ml of 0.001 F reagent. Clearly, in the first case a pronounced color change will occur in the region of the equivalence point; in the other, the change will be too gradual to be of use. With 0.01 F silver solutions approximately 0.5 ml will be required and the end point will not be sharp.

Consider now the effectiveness of this same indicator in detecting the equivalence points for the titrations represented by the curves in Figure 11.2. No change will be observed during the bromate titration, and there will be a very gradual and somewhat premature change in an iodate titration. The indicator will be satisfactory for the titration of bromide and iodide although the change in color occurs after the point of chemical equivalence; these curves are so steep that the resulting error will be negligible for most purposes.

The Formation of a Second Precipitate; the Mohr Method. The formation of a second precipitate of distinctive color is the basis for end-point detection with the *Mohr method*. This procedure has been widely applied to the titration of chloride ion and bromide ion with standard silver nitrate. Chromate ion is the indicator, the end point being signaled by the appearance of brick-red silver chromate, Ag_2CrO_4.

Calculation of the formal solubility of silver chromate from its solubility product constant (1.1×10^{-12}) reveals that this compound is several times more soluble than silver chloride. Thus the latter precipitate tends to form first in the titration mixture employed in the Mohr method. By adjusting the chromate concentration to a suitable level, formation of the silver chromate can be retarded until the silver ion concentration in the mixture rises to the level corresponding to the theoretical equivalence point. The data in Table 11-1 show that the equivalence point pAg is 4.87, from which the silver ion concentration is calculated to be 1.35×10^{-5} M. The chromate concentration required to initiate precipitation of silver chromate under these conditions can be computed as follows:

$$[CrO_4^{2-}] = \frac{K_{sp}}{[Ag^+]^2} = \frac{1.1 \times 10^{-12}}{(1.35 \times 10^{-5})^2} = 6 \times 10^{-3} \text{ mol/liter}$$

In principle, then, the amount of chromate ion necessary to give this concentration could be added, and the red color of silver chromate would signal the appearance of the first excess of silver ion over its equivalence concentration. In fact, however, a chromate concentration of 6×10^{-3} M imparts such an intense yellow color to the solution that formation of silver chromate is not easily seen. As a result an indicator concentration smaller than 5×10^{-3} M must be employed. Lowering the chromate concentration requires a silver concentration greater than $1.35 \times 10^{-5} M$ to produce a red precipitate. In addition, a finite amount of silver nitrate must be added to produce a detectable quantity of the precipitate. Thus an overconsumption of reagent is observed at the end point. These difficulties are most serious where dilute solutions are involved. With $0.1 N$ solutions they do not give rise to serious error. A correction may be made by determining an indicator blank—that is, by determining the silver ion consumption for a suspension of chloride-free calcium carbonate in about the same volume and with the same quantity of indicator as the sample. The blank titration mixture serves as a convenient color standard for subsequent titrations. An alternative that largely eliminates the indicator error is to use the Mohr method to standardize the silver nitrate solution against pure sodium chloride; the "working normality" obtained for the solution will compensate not only for this effect but also for the acuity of the analyst in detecting the color change.

Attention must be paid to the acidity of the medium because the equilibrium

$$2CrO_4^{2-} + 2H^+ \rightleftharpoons Cr_2O_7^{2-} + H_2O$$

is displaced to the right as the hydrogen ion concentration is increased; since silver dichromate is considerably more soluble than the chromate, the indicator reaction in acid solution requires far higher silver ion concentrations, if indeed it occurs at all. If the medium is made strongly alkaline, there is danger that silver will precipitate as its oxide.

$$2Ag^+ + 2OH^- \rightleftharpoons 2AgOH \rightleftharpoons Ag_2O + H_2O$$

Thus, the determination of chloride by the Mohr method must be carried out in a medium that is neutral or nearly so (pH 7 to 10). The addition of either sodium bicarbonate or of borax to the solution tends to maintain the hydrogen ion concentration within suitable limits.

Formation of a Colored Complex; the Volhard Method. A standard solution of thiocyanate may be used to titrate silver ion by the Volhard method.

$$Ag^+ + SCN^- \rightleftharpoons AgSCN$$

Iron (III) ammonium sulfate serves as the indicator, imparting a red coloration to the solution with the first slight excess of thiocyanate

$$Fe^{3+} + SCN^- \rightleftharpoons \underset{\text{red}}{Fe(SCN)^{2+}}$$

The titration must be carried out in acid solution to prevent hydrolysis of the iron (III). The titration error in the Volhard method is small because the indicator is highly sensitive to thiocyanate ions. Thus, 1 or 2 ml of a saturated iron (III) ammonium sulfate solution (about 40 percent) will impart a faint orange color to 100 ml of solution that also contains about 0.1 ml of 0.01 N thiocyanate. In order to avoid a premature end point in the titration, however, the solution must be shaken vigorously and the titration continued until the indicator color is permanent. This precaution is necessitated by the strong tendency of silver thiocyanate to adsorb silver ions from the solution, thus inhibiting the rate at which they combine with the thiocyanate.

The most important application of the Volhard method is for the indirect determination of chloride, as well as the other halide ions. A measured excess of standard silver nitrate solution is added to the sample, and the excess is determined by back titration with a standard thiocyanate solution. The requirement of a strongly acid environment represents a distinct advantage for the Volhard technique over other methods for halide analysis because such ions as carbonate, oxalate, and arsenate, which form insoluble silver salts in neutral media, do not interfere at high hydrogen ion concentrations.

An interesting problem in connection with the Volhard determination of chloride ion stems from the greater solubility of silver chloride as compared with silver thiocyanate. As a consequence, the reaction

$$AgCl + SCN^- \rightleftharpoons AgSCN + Cl^-$$

will tend to occur when a silver chloride precipitate is exposed to a solution containing an excess of thiocyanate ion. In a Volhard chloride determination this condition will exist at the end point, and will cause the thiocyanate back titration to be too high and the resulting percentage of chloride to be too low.

The equilibrium constant for this reaction can be obtained by dividing the solubility-product expression for silver chloride by that for silver thiocyanate; that is,

$$K = \frac{[Cl^-]}{[SCN^-]} = \frac{[Ag^+][Cl^-]}{[Ag^+][SCN^-]} = 1.65 \times 10^2$$

As mentioned earlier, about 0.1 ml of 0.01 N thiocyanate is required to produce a color in 100 ml of solution when the usual amount of indicator is employed. Thus the thiocyanate concentration must be 10^{-5} F to give a detectable end point. The equilibrium chloride ion concentration of the solution at this point is then

$$[Cl^-] = K[SCN^-] = 1.65 \times 10^2 \times 10^{-5}$$
$$= 1.6 \times 10^{-3} \text{ mol/liter}$$

Insofar as this chloride concentration results primarily from reaction between the thiocyanate reagent and the silver chloride, we can readily calculate the volume of the overtitration that results. Thus, with a 0.1 N thiocyanate solution and a total volume of 100 ml at the end point

$$\frac{1.6 \times 10^{-3} \times 100}{0.1} = 1.6 \text{ ml}$$

In actual practice the overconsumption of reagent is often greater.

A number of schemes have been developed to circumvent this source of error. Filtration, followed by titration of an aliquot of the filtrate, yields excellent results provided the precipitated silver chloride is first briefly digested; the time required for filtration is, of course, a disadvantage. Probably the most widely employed modification is that of Caldwell and Moyer[1] which consists of coating the silver chloride precipitate with nitrobenzene, thereby substantially removing it from contact with the solution. The coating is accomplished by shaking the titration mixture with a few milliliters of the organic liquid prior to back titration.

The Volhard method may be applied to the analysis of any anions that form slightly soluble salts with silver nitrate. Steps must be taken to prevent interference from precipitates that are more soluble than silver thiocyanate.

Adsorption Indicators. Substances that impart a distinctive color to the surface of a precipitate are known as *adsorption indicators*. Under proper circumstances, the adsorption (or the reverse desorption process) can be made to occur at or near the equivalence point in the titration; thus the appearance or disappearance of a color on the precipitate signals the end point.

An example of an adsorption indicator is the organic dye, *fluorescein*, which is employed as an indicator for the titration of chloride ion with silver nitrate. In aqueous solution this compound partially dissociates into hydrogen ions and negatively charged fluoresceinate ions which impart a yellowish-green color to the medium. The fluoresceinate ion forms a highly colored silver salt of limited solubility; in its application as an indicator, however, the concentration of the dye is *never large enough to exceed the solubility product for silver fluoresceinate.*

In the early stages of a titration of chloride with silver ions, the dye anion is not appreciably adsorbed by the precipitate; it is, in fact, repelled from the surface by the negative charge resulting from adsorbed chloride ions. When the equivalence point is passed, however, the precipitate particles become positively charged by virtue of the strong adsorption of

[1] J. R. Caldwell and H. V. Moyer, *Ind. Eng. Chem., Anal. Ed.*, **7**, 38 (1935).

excess silver ions; under these conditions, retention of the fluoresceinate ions in the counter-ion layer is observed. This adsorption of silver fluoresceinate is marked by the appearance of the red silver-fluoresceinate color *on the surface of the precipitate.* This is an *adsorption,* not a precipitation, process inasmuch as the solubility product of the silver fluoresceinate is not exceeded. The process is reversible, the dye being desorbed upon back titration with chloride ion.

We may distinguish four requirements of dye and precipitate upon which successful indicator action depends.

(1) Since this is a surface phenomenon, the precipitate should be produced in a highly dispersed state; this is one of the few instances where the analytical chemist is interested in producing and preserving a colloid.

(2) The precipitate must strongly adsorb its own ions. We have seen (Chapter 7) that this is usually the case.

(3) The dye must be strongly held by the primarily adsorbed ion. In general, strong adsorption correlates with low solubility of the salt formed between dye and lattice ion. At the same time, the solubility of the dye salt must be sufficiently great to prevent its precipitation.

(4) Since most adsorption indicators are anions of weak acids, the dye concentration will be dependent upon the pH of the solution in which it is contained. In general then, these indicators can only be used in solutions that are not too acid. A few cationic adsorption indicators are known, however, that can be employed in strongly acid solutions. With these, adsorption of the dye and coloration of the precipitate occurs in the presence of an excess of the anion of the precipitate (that is, when the precipitate particles are negatively charged).

Titrations involving adsorption indicators are rapid, accurate, and reliable. At the same time, however, their application is limited to a relatively small number of precipitation reactions in which a colloidal precipitate is rapidly formed. Furthermore, the indicators are pH sensitive and care must be taken to control the acidity of the solution in which they are used. In the presence of high electrolyte concentrations, end points with these indicators tend to be less satisfactory owing to coagulation of the precipitate and the consequent reduction of surface on which adsorption can occur. Finally, in the case of titrations with silver ion, some adsorption indicators sensitize the precipitate toward photodecomposition; this may also lead to errors.

Miscellaneous Indicators. If the precipitation reaction is accompanied by the consumption or release of hydrogen ions, or if the precipitating agent is an acid or a base, an acid-base indicator may be useful in detecting the end point. Similarly, oxidation-reduction indicators may be employed where the precipitating agent possesses oxidizing or reducing properties.

OTHER METHODS OF END-POINT DETECTION

The cessation of precipitation is sometimes used as an end point in a precipitation titration. The *Gay-Lussac method* for the titration of chloride requires sufficient time between additions of silver ion to allow the precipitate to settle; the titration is continued until further additions of reagent fail to produce a turbidity. This is called the *clear point*. An objection to the use of the clear point in a chloride titration is that a perceptible turbidity attends the addition of either silver ion or chloride ion to a saturated solution of silver chloride; thus, the clear point actually occurs slightly beyond the equivalence point. The *Mulder* modification of the Gay-Lussac method takes advantage of the fact that equal turbidity results from treatment of a saturated solution of silver chloride with either silver ion or chloride ion, provided only that the concentrations and volumes of these solutions are the same. Here, small quantities of supernatant liquid are withdrawn from the titrated solution and divided, each half being treated with identical volumes of a solution of one of the ions; the equivalence point is taken when equal turbidity is observed. This is the most reliable of all volumetric methods for the determination of chloride; because it is time consuming, however, it is employed only where the greatest accuracy is required.

With more insoluble precipitates, the clear point often provides a practical indication of the equivalence point.

In a later chapter we shall describe an electroanalytical method whereby end points for some precipitation reactions may be detected.

11.3 Applications of Precipitation-titration Analysis

Many volumetric precipitation methods make use of a standard solution of silver nitrate. The term *argentometry* refers to the employment of this reagent in volumetric analysis. Table 11-2 provides an indication of the variety of argentometric methods available to the analyst.

Table 11-3 lists applications of other precipitating agents to volumetric analysis.

11.4 Precipitation Analysis with Silver Ion

Following are specific directions for the argentometric determination of chloride ion by the Mohr, the Volhard, and the Fajans methods. These may be used with little or no modification for the titration of other anions; Table 11-2 will serve as a guide in this respect.

TABLE 11-2

Argentometric Precipitation Methods

Substance Determined	End Point	Remarks
AsO_4^{3-}, Br^- I^-, CNO^-, SCN^-	Volhard	
CO_3^{2-}, CrO_4^{2-}, CN^-, Cl^- $C_2O_4^{2-}$, PO_4^{3-}, S^{2-}	Volhard	removal of silver salt required before back titration of excess Ag^+
BH_4^-	modified Volhard	basis: titration of excess Ag^+ following $$BH_4^- + 8Ag^+ + 8OH^- \rightleftharpoons 8Ag + H_2BO_3^- + 5H_2O$$
Epoxide	Volhard	basis: titration of excess Cl^- following hydrohalogenation
K^+	modified Volhard	basis: precipitation of K^+ with known excess of $B(C_6H_5)_4^-$, addition of excess Ag^+ which precipitates $AgB(C_6H_5)_4$ and back titration of this excess
Br^-, Cl^-	Mohr	
I^-	clear point	
Br^-, Cl^-, I^-, SeO_3^{2-}	Fajans	
$V(OH)_4^+$, fatty acids, mercaptans	electroanalytical	direct titration with Ag^+

SILVER NITRATE AND ITS SOLUTIONS

Silver nitrate may be obtained in primary-standard purity. It has a high equivalent weight (169.89) and is readily soluble in water. Both the solid and aqueous solutions must be scrupulously protected from dust and other organic materials, and from sunlight. Metallic silver is produced by chemical reduction in the former instance, and by photodecomposition in the latter. The reagent is relatively expensive.

Silver nitrate crystals may be freed of surface moisture by drying at 110° C for about an hour. Some discoloration of the solid may result, but the amount of decomposition occurring in this time is ordinarily negligible.

★PROCEDURE

Preparation of Standard 0.1 N Silver Nitrate. Use a laboratory balance to weigh approximately 17 grams of silver nitrate into a clean, dry weighing bottle. Heat bottle and contents for 1 hour at 110° C; store in a desiccator. When cooled, determine the weight to the nearest mg with an analytical balance. Carefully transfer the bulk

TABLE 11-3

Volumetric Precipitation Methods

Precipitating Agent	Element Determined	Product	End-point Detection	Remarks
$K_4Fe(CN)_6$	Zn In, Ga Ag, Co, Ni, Mn Hg (II)	$K_2Zn_3[Fe(CN)_6]_2$ $M_4[Fe(CN)_6]_3$ $Hg_4[Fe(CN)_6]$	diphenylamine electroanalytical starch I_2 electroanalytical	reverse titration also feasible
$Hg_2(NO_3)_2$	Cl^-, Br^- $Fe(CN)_6^{3-}$	Hg_2X_2 $KHg_2Fe(CN)_6$	diphenylcarbazone electrometric	titrate in 20-percent ethanol
$HgCl_2$	I^-	HgI_2	starch I_2	
$Pb(NO_3)_2$	SO_4^{2-}		Fajans	erythrosin B indicator
$Pb(OAc)_2$	PO_4^{3-}, $C_2O_4^{2-}$			dibromofluorescein for PO_4^{3-}, fluorescein for $C_2O_4^{2-}$
$Th(NO_3)_4$	F^- $C_2O_4^{2-}$		Fajans	sodium alizarin sulfonate indicator alizarin red indicator

of the solid to a 1-liter volumetric flask and dilute to the mark; reweigh the bottle and residual solid. From the difference in weights compute the normality of the solution.

NOTES:

1. Weighing silver nitrate to only the nearest milligram will incur a maximum error of 1 part in 17,000 upon the value of the normality; since uncertainties in the subsequent analyses commonly exceed this figure, more accurate weighing is of little value.

2. If desired, silver nitrate solutions prepared to approximately the desired strength can be standardized against sodium chloride.

3. Once prepared, and when not actually in use, the solution should be stored in a dark place.

DETERMINATION OF CHLORIDE BY THE MOHR METHOD

★PROCEDURE. Carefully weigh 0.25 to 0.35-gram samples to the nearest 0.1 mg; dissolve each in about 100 ml of water. Add a pinch of sodium bicarbonate, making further additions, if necessary, until no further effervescence is noted. Then introduce 1 to 2 ml of 5-percent potassium chromate and titrate with standard silver nitrate solution to the first permanent appearance of a buff color due to silver chromate. Determine an indicator blank by suspending a small quantity of $CaCO_3$ in about 100 ml of water containing 1 to 2 ml of 5-percent K_2CrO_4; use the color developed in this determination as a standard for judgment of the end point in the actual titrations.

NOTE:

The solubility of silver chromate increases with rising temperatures; its sensitivity as an indicator in this titration undergoes a corresponding decrease. Satisfactory results using the Mohr method require titration at room temperature.

DETERMINATION OF CHLORIDE BY THE VOLHARD METHOD

As applied to the analysis of chloride ion, the Volhard method is an indirect method involving the addition of a measured excess of standard silver nitrate solution to the sample and back titration of the excess with a standard potassium thiocyanate solution.

★PROCEDURE

Preparation and Standardization of 0.1 N Potassium Thiocyanate. Dissolve approximately 9.8 grams of KSCN in about 1 liter of water. Mix well.

Accurately measure 25 to 30-ml samples of standard $AgNO_3$ solution into Erlenmeyer flasks and dilute to approximately 100 ml. Add about 2 ml of concentrated HNO_3, followed by 2 ml of a saturated solution of iron (III) ammonium sulfate (Note 3). Titrate with the KSCN solution, with vigorous swirling of the flask, until the red-brown color of $FeSCN^{2+}$ is permanent for 1 minute. Calculate the normality of the KSCN solution. Results from duplicate standardizations should show agreement within 2 to 3 parts per thousand; if this precision has not been attained, perform further standardization titrations.

NOTES:

1. Potassium thiocyanate is usually somewhat moist; the direct preparation of a standard solution is not ordinarily attempted. However, Kolthoff and Lingane[2] report that gentle fusion followed by storage over calcium chloride yields a product that can be used for the direct preparation of standard solutions.

2. A potassium thiocyanate solution retains its titer over extended periods of time.

3. The indicator is readily prepared by placing some lumps of iron (III) ammonium sulfate, $NH_4Fe(SO_4)_2 \cdot 12H_2O$, in a bottle and shaking with dilute nitric acid. The acid prevents hydrolysis of the iron (III) ion.

★PROCEDURE

The Analysis of Chloride. Dry the sample at 100° to 110° C for 1 hour. Weigh several 0.25 to 0.35-gram samples to the nearest 0.1 mg into numbered 250-ml Erlenmeyer flasks. Dissolve each sample in 100 ml of distilled water. Introduce an excess of standard silver nitrate, being sure to note the volume taken. Acidify with 2 ml of concentrated nitric acid; add 2 ml of iron (III) indicator and 5 ml of chloride-free nitrobenzene. Shake vigorously. Titrate the excess silver with standard thiocyanate until the color of $FeSCN^{2+}$ is permanent for 1 minute.

NOTES:

1. With the concurrence of the instructor, a larger quantity of unknown can be weighed into a volumetric flask and diluted to known volume. The determination can then be made upon aliquot portions of this solution.

2. To obtain an approximation of the volume of standard $AgNO_3$ constituting an excess, calculate the amount that would be required for one of the samples assuming that it contains 100-percent NaCl. When actually adding silver solution to the sample, swirl the flask vigorously, and add 3 or 4 ml in excess of the volume required to produce the clear point.

[2] I. M. Kolthoff and J. J. Lingane, *J. Am. Chem. Soc.*, **57**, 2126 (1935).

3. Nitric acid is introduced in order to improve observation of the clear point. Since the lower oxides of nitrogen tend to attack thiocyanate, the acid should be freshly boiled.

4. Nitrobenzene is a hazardous chemical and must be handled with respect. Poisoning can result not only from prolonged breathing of its vapors, but also from absorption of the liquid through the skin. In the event of spillage on one's person, the affected areas should be promptly and thoroughly washed with soap and warm water. Clothing soaked with the liquid should be removed and laundered.

5. At the outset of the back titration an appreciable quantity of silver ion is adsorbed on the surface of the precipitate. As a result there is a tendency for a premature appearance of the end-point color. Since success of the method depends upon an accounting for all of the excess silver ion, thorough and vigorous agitation is essential to bring about desorption of this ion from the precipitate.

Other Applications and Limitations of the Volhard Method. As indicated in Table 11-2, the Volhard method may be employed for the determination of a fairly extensive variety of substances. Where the solubility of the silver salt formed is increased by the presence of strong acid, a filtration is mandatory prior to back titration. The use of nitrobenzene or of filtration can be omitted in the few instances where the salts formed are less soluble than silver thiocyanate in acid media; silver bromide and silver iodide are the only common examples.

The method cannot be employed in the presence of oxidizing agents because of the susceptibility of thiocyanate to attack. It is often possible to eliminate this source of interference by prior treatment of the sample with a reducing agent. The method also fails in the presence of cations that form slightly soluble thiocyanates, notably palladium and mercury. Again, preliminary treatment may eliminate these sources of interference.

DETERMINATION OF CHLORIDE BY THE FAJANS METHOD

The Fajans method employs a direct titration with organic substance, dichlorofluorescein, as indicator. Only a standard silver nitrate solution is required.

★PROCEDURE. Dry the unknown for 1 hour at 100° to 110° C. Weigh individual 0.20 to 0.29-gram samples (to the nearest 0.1 mg) into 500-ml flasks. Dissolve in 175 to 200 ml of distilled water. Introduce 10 drops of dichlorofluorescein solution and about 0.1 gram of dextrin; immediately titrate with standard silver nitrate to the first permanent appearance of the pink color of the indicator.

NOTES:

1. Kolthoff[3] states that the chloride concentration should be within the range of 0.025 to 0.005 M; these directions yield solutions approaching this maximum concentration only when the sample taken is pure sodium chloride at the upper weight limit. If the approximate percentage of chloride in the sample is known, a corresponding decrease in volume or increase in sample size can be tolerated.

2. Silver chloride is particularly sensitive to photodecomposition in the presence of the indicator; the titration will fail if attempted in direct sunlight. Where this problem exists, the approximate equivalence point should first be ascertained in a trial titration, this value being used to calculate the volume of silver nitrate required for the other samples; the addition of indicator and dextrin should be delayed until the bulk of the silver nitrate has been added to subsequent samples, after which the titration should be completed without further delay.

3. The use of polyethylene glycol is reportedly superior to dextrin for stabilizing the colloid.[4] The *indicator* may be prepared in a 50-percent aqueous solution of this preparation. In contrast to dextrin, polyethylene glycol is not susceptible to attack by microorganisms.

4. The indicator solution may be prepared as a 0.1-percent solution of dichlorofluorescein in 70-percent alcohol, or as a 0.1-percent aqueous solution of the sodium salt.

Problems

1. A standard $AgNO_3$ solution is prepared by diluting 4.675 grams of the pure salt to exactly 1 liter. This solution is to be used for the titration of soluble Cl^- samples; express its concentration in terms of its
   (a) normality
   (b) titer, as mg Cl^-/ml
   (c) titer, as mg NaCl/ml

2. Calculate the normality of an $AgNO_3$ solution if 39.80 ml were required to titrate 0.1497 gram of pure NaCl.

3. What is the normality of an $AgNO_3$ solution for which the titer is 1.0 mg of Cl^-/ml? What weight of pure $AgNO_3$ would be required to produce 2 liters of this solution?

[3] I. M. Kolthoff, W. M. Lauer, and C. J. Sunde, *J. Am. Chem. Soc.*, **51**, 3273 (1929).
[4] R. B. Dean, W. C. Wiser, G. E. Martin, and D. W. Barnum, *Anal. Chem.*, **24**, 1638 (1952).

4. Samples of impure NaCl are to be determined by the Volhard method. Calculate the minimum volume of 0.0800 N AgNO$_3$ that must be added to 0.200-gram samples in order to assure an excess of the reagent.

5. A 50.00-ml aliquot of 0.0492 N AgNO$_3$ was introduced to a 0.410-gram sample of impure KBr. Titration of the excess Ag$^+$ required 7.50 ml of 0.0600 N KSCN. Calculate the percentage of KBr in the sample.

6. The effluent from a manufacturing process is to be analyzed for its Cl$^-$ content by a Fajans titration. This will ordinarily range from 0.40 to 0.75 mg/ml, expressed as NaCl. Titration of 100-ml aliquots should not exceed 40 ml of standard AgNO$_3$.
   (a) What should be the normality of the AgNO$_3$ solution?
   (b) What will be its titer, expressed as mg NaCl/ml?
   (c) What is the minimum volume of this solution that will ordinarily be required?

7. Silver ion readily replaces a hydrogen attached to an acetylenic carbon atom according to the reaction

$$HC{\equiv}CR + 2Ag^+ + NO_3^- \rightleftharpoons AgC{\equiv}CR \cdot AgNO_3 + H^+$$

The sample is treated with an excess of AgNO$_3$ in an ammoniacal medium; the product is essentially insoluble in water (and violently explosive when dry). The analysis is completed by titration of the excess Ag$^+$ in the supernatant liquid. Calculate the percentage of 3-butyne-1-ol (gfw 70) in a crude sample on the basis of the following information:

weight of sample taken	0.1860 gram
volume of 0.1120 N AgNO$_3$ used	50.00 ml
volume of 0.1080 N KSCN required for back titration	7.40 ml

8. A K$_4$Fe(CN)$_6$ solution was standardized against a 0.1830-gram sample of ZnO, 38.80 ml being required for the titration. The same solution was then used to determine the percentage of zinc carbonate in a 0.2380-gram sample of the mineral smithsonite; this titration required 30.60 ml. Both processes may be represented by the reaction

$$2Fe(CN)_6^{4-} + 3Zn^{2+} + 2K^+ \rightleftharpoons K_2Zn_3[Fe(CN)_6]_2$$

Calculate the percent ZnCO$_3$.

$$\left(\begin{array}{c} 12 \end{array} \right)$$

Volumetric Methods Based on
Complex-formation Reactions

Metal ions can act as electron-pair acceptors, reacting with electron donors to form coordination compounds or complex ions. The donor species, or *ligand*, must have at least one pair of unshared electrons to form the bond; the water molecule, ammonia, the chloride ion, and the cyanide ion are common examples of simple ligands that form complexes with many metal ions.

While exceptions are known, a given cation normally forms coordination bonds to a maximum of two, four, or six, its *coordination number* being a statement of this maximum. The species produced as a consequence of coordination bonding can be electrically positive, neutral, or negative. For example, copper (II) ion, with a coordination number of four, forms a cationic complex with ammonia, $Cu(NH_3)_4^{2+}$, a neutral compound with glycine, $Cu(H_2NCH_2COO)_2$, and is incorporated in an anionic complex with chloride ion, $CuCl_4^{2-}$.

Complex-formation reactions have been used to advantage in quantitative analysis for at least a century. The truly remarkable growth in analytical applications is of recent origin, however, and is due to a particular class of coordination compounds known as *chelates*. These compounds result from the reaction between a metal ion and a ligand that contains two or more donor groups; the properties of chelates frequently differ markedly from the parent cation.

A chelating agent containing two groups that coordinate with the metal ion is classified as *bidentate*, while one with three such groups is called

223

terdentate. Quadri-, *quinque-*, and *sexadentate* chelating agents are also encountered.

12.1   Titration Curves for Complex-formation Reactions

Any point in a titration is characterized by a condition of equilibrium among the species participating in the reaction. If constants for the equilibria involved are known, we can derive titration curves that relate the concentration of one of the reactants to the volume of titrant introduced. For complex ions, numerical values for equilibrium constants will be found tabulated in the literature either as *instability constants* or as the reciprocally related *formation* (or *stability*) *constants*. These constants were defined in Chapter 2.

Consider the equilibrium between a metal ion M, possessing a coordination number of four, and the quadridentate ligand D;

$$MD \rightleftharpoons M + D$$

We have intentionally avoided supplying either species with electrostatic charge since, for present purposes, these are not of importance.

In a similar manner, the equilibrium between M and the bidentate ligand B can be represented by

$$MB_2 \rightleftharpoons M + 2B$$

Here, however, the equation and the equilibrium constant derived from it refer to the *over-all* process, whereas the actual dissociation involves the intermediate formation of the substance MB. Thus,

$$MB_2 \rightleftharpoons MB + B \qquad\qquad (12\text{-}1)$$

$$MB \rightleftharpoons M + B \qquad\qquad (12\text{-}2)$$

Instability constants can be expressed for these individual processes.

$$K_1 = \frac{[MB][B]}{[MB_2]} \qquad K_2 = \frac{[M][B]}{[MB]}$$

Addition of equations (12-1) and (12-2) yields the expression for the over-all process. The equilibrium constant for the over-all reaction is given by the product of the individual steps.

$$K_{\text{over-all}} = \frac{[M][B]^2}{[MB_2]} = K_1 K_2$$

The complex produced between M and the simple ligand A results in the over-all equilibrium

$$MA_4 \rightleftharpoons M + 4A$$

Again, this process occurs in a stepwise fashion; the equilibrium constant for the over-all reaction is therefore numerically equal to the product of the constants for the four constituent processes.

Unless otherwise noted, instability- (or formation-) constant data tabulated in the literature refer to the over-all reaction. This is of paramount importance when considering a system as the basis of a titration.

DERIVATION OF TITRATION CURVES

For the derivation of a titration curve we shall use the least involved type of complex formation—namely, a system in which the reactants combine in a 1:1 ratio. Specifically, consider the titration of 60.0 ml of a 0.02 F solution of M ion with a 0.02 F solution of the quadridentate ligand D. The equilibrium-constant expression for the system can be expressed as

$$K_{inst} = \frac{[M][D]}{[MD]}$$

If the numerical value for this instability constant is 1×10^{-20} mol/liter, we can compute the equilibrium concentrations of all species at any point in the titration from the volume of titrant added. A plot of pM or pD against the volume of D will yield the desired titration curve. We shall use pM.

Before the addition of any reagent, the concentration of M is 2×10^{-2} molar. The initial pM for the system is thus equal to 1.70.

After 10.0 ml of D have been added, the volume of the solution will have increased to 70 ml. The solution will contain relatively large quantities of M and MD, but the concentration of D will be small since its only source will be the dissociation of the complex. We may express the concentration of M as

$$[M] = \frac{60 \times 0.02 - 10 \times 0.02}{70} + [D]$$

Assuming that D is small with respect to the first quantity, we find that

$$[M] \cong \frac{1.2 - 0.2}{70} = 1.43 \times 10^{-2} \text{ mol/liter}$$

Thus the value for pM at this point is

$$pM = -\log 1.43 \times 10^{-2} = 2 - \log 1.43$$

$$= 1.84$$

In order to check the assumption employed in this calculation, we must estimate a value for D. The concentration of the complex may be evaluated from the expression

$$[MD] = \frac{10 \times 0.02}{70} - [D]$$

$$\cong \frac{0.20}{70} = 2.86 \times 10^{-3} \text{ mol/liter}$$

The concentration of D may then be found from the instability-constant expression

$$[D] = K_{inst} \frac{[MD]}{[M]} = \frac{1 \times 10^{-20} \times 2.86 \times 10^{-3}}{1.43 \times 10^{-2}}$$

$$= 2 \times 10^{-21} \text{ mol/liter}$$

This is indeed small when compared with the concentration of either M or MD.

The value of pM may be calculated in this way for any point short of the equivalence point; this provides the means for defining the initial portion of the titration curve.

At the equivalence point the system consists of a 0.01 F solution of MD. Dissociation of the complex is the sole source of both M and D ions; consequently, they are present in equal concentration.

$$[M] = [D]$$

$$[MD] = 0.01 - [M] \cong 1 \times 10^{-2} \text{ mol/liter}$$

Substituting into the instability expression

$$\frac{[M]^2}{1 \times 10^{-2}} = 1 \times 10^{-20}$$

$$[M] = 1 \times 10^{-11} \text{ mol/liter}$$

and

$$pM = -\log 1 \times 10^{-11} = 11$$

After passing the equivalence point, values for pM can be calculated from the formal concentration of excess D and the instability constant. For example, after 70 ml of a 0.02 F solution of D have been introduced,

$$[D] = \frac{70 \times 0.02 - 60 \times 0.02}{130} + [M]$$

Assuming [M] to be much smaller than the first term

$$[D] \cong \frac{0.2}{130} = 1.5 \times 10^{-3} \text{ mol/liter}$$

$$[MD] = \frac{60 \times 0.02}{130} - [M]$$

$$\cong \frac{1.2}{130} = 9.2 \times 10^{-3} \text{ mol/liter}$$

Introducing these values into the instability-constant expression gives

$$[M] = \frac{1.0 \times 10^{-20} \times 9.2 \times 10^{-3}}{1.5 \times 10^{-3}}$$

$$= 6.2 \times 10^{-20} \text{ mol/liter}$$

and

$$pM = 19.2$$

In view of the very small value for [M], the assumptions made in this calculation appear valid.

The curve for this titration appears in Figure 12.1. As in the case of precipitation titrations, the equivalence-point region is characterized by a

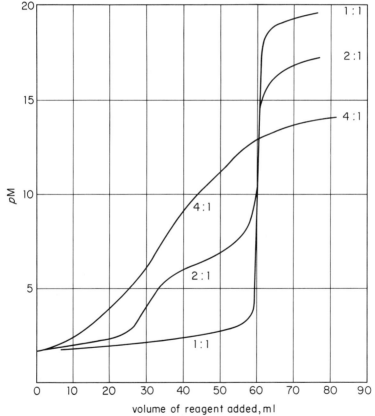

Fig. 12.1 Theoretical Titration Curves for Typical Complex Formation Reactions. Plots of pM as a function of the volume of 0.100 F solutions of simple, bidentate, and quadridentate ligands added to 60.0 ml aliquots of 0.100 F M. For each process the over-all equilibrium constant is 1×10^{-20}.

marked change in the p function. Shown also are curves representing the titration of M with the bidentate ligand B to produce a $2:1$ complex

$$K_1 = 1 \times 10^{-8}, \qquad K_2 = 1 \times 10^{-12}$$

and with the unidentate A to yield a $4:1$ complex

$$K_1 = 1 \times 10^{-2}, \qquad K_2 = 1 \times 10^{-4}, \qquad K_3 = 1 \times 10^{-6}, \qquad K_4 = 1 \times 10^{-8}$$

Although the units vary, the numerical value for the over-all equilibrium constant is 1×10^{-20} in each of the three cases. Thus for any given value of the over-all equilibrium constant, the single-step process gives the most definite change in pM at the equivalence point; the presence of intermediate species of varying stability tends to diminish the magnitude of this break. It is in this respect that chelating agents show great superiority over other complexing agents, since fewer intermediate complexes are involved.

12.2   Methods of End-point Detection

We have seen that end-point detection is based upon the establishment of auxiliary equilibria that yield a tangible indication of the marked change in p function, or upon the physiochemical measurement of some property of the system. We shall consider examples from the former only and defer discussion of the latter to later chapters.

FORMATION OR DISAPPEARANCE OF A SOLID PHASE

The *Liebig* determination of cyanide provides an example of an end point based upon the appearance of a solid phase. Addition of standard silver nitrate solution leads to formation of the soluble complex, $Ag(CN)_2^-$. As long as any free cyanide is present, the complex is formed exclusively, and the silver ion concentration remains at a low level. At the equivalence point, however, a rapid increase in silver ion concentration occurs, and reaction between this species and the complex then produces the slightly soluble silver cyanide, AgCN (or $Ag[Ag(CN)_2]$). The end point, then, is signaled by the appearance of the first faint turbidity in the solution. The equations for the titration are

$$Ag^+ + 2CN^- \rightleftharpoons Ag(CN)_2^- \qquad \text{(analytical reaction)}$$

$$Ag^+ + Ag(CN)_2^- \rightleftharpoons Ag[Ag(CN)_2] \qquad \text{(indicator reaction)}$$
white precipitate

The disappearance of turbidity can also be employed as an end point in a complex-formation titration. For example, the routine titration of nickel may be performed with a standard solution of potassium cyanide. The analysis is carried out in an ammoniacal medium containing just enough suspended silver iodide to impart a slight turbidity to the solution; the end point is signaled by the disappearance of this turbidity, resulting from the rapid increase in the cyanide concentration. The reactions may be formulated as

$$Ni(NH_3)_4^{2+} + 4CN^- \rightleftharpoons Ni(CN)_4^{2-} + 4NH_3 \qquad \text{(analytical reaction)}$$

$$AgI + 2CN^- \rightleftharpoons Ag(CN)_2^- + I^- \qquad \text{(indicator reaction)}$$

Since the end point and equivalence point do not coincide exactly, it is advisable to standardize the cyanide reagent against a known quantity of nickel.

ACID-BASE INDICATORS

The electron-donor groups of most common ligands tend to combine not only with metallic ions but, to a lesser extent, with protons as well. As a consequence, the equivalence point in a complex-formation titration is often accompanied by a marked change in pH which can be detected with an acid-base indicator. For example, the tetrasodium salt of ethylenediaminetetraacetic acid, a widely used complexing reagent, can be employed to titrate several cations, the analytical reaction being

$$Y^{4-} + M^{2+} \rightleftharpoons MY^{2-}$$

where MY^{2-} is the soluble complex ion. When the equivalence point has been passed, the solution becomes basic as a result of the reaction between the excess Y^{4-} ions and water

$$Y^{4-} + H_2O \rightleftharpoons HY^{3-} + OH^-$$

$$HY^{3-} + H_2O \rightleftharpoons H_2Y^{2-} + OH^-$$

etc.

The consequent rise in hydroxyl ion concentration can be detected with an acid-base indicator.

FORMATION OR DISAPPEARANCE OF A SOLUBLE COMPLEX

In Chapter 11 we noted that the Volhard method utilizes the formation of a colored complex to signal the end point. Analogous indicator reactions are often employed for complex-formation titrations. In recent years, a large number of reagents that form colored complexes with certain metal ions have been developed expressly for use as indicators in these titrations.

Metal-indicator systems function in two ways. If the cation being titrated produces a color with the indicator, the end point will be characterized by the disappearance of this color. Where this cation does not give a colored complex, a second cation that does is introduced; the first excess of titrant then decolorizes this complex. Clearly, the complex formed in the analytical reaction must be sufficiently stable to prevent decomposition of the indicator-metal complex until the equivalence point has been passed.

The selection of a metal indicator for a particular titration is often a matter of trial and error—the principal reason being the formidable number of equilibria that exert an appreciable influence upon the course of the titration and the behavior of the indicator. The active species in both titrant and indicator are often pH dependent; the hydronium ion concentration of the medium is thus an important experimental variable. Provided numerical values for all constants are known, it is possible to predict in advance whether a given metal indicator will provide a satisfactory color change. Reilley and Schmid[1] describe in detail a method for ascertaining the optimum reaction conditions for the use of metal indicators in chelate titrations.

12.3   Application of Organic Chelating Reagents to Volumetric Analysis

A number of tertiary amines containing carboxylic acid groups form remarkably stable complexes with a variety of metal ions. These compounds are marketed under such trade names as Complexones or Versenes (Dow Chemical Co.). Their application to analysis was first suggested by Schwarzenbach in 1945; since that time the amount of investigative effort devoted to their application has been truly phenomenal. We must therefore consider titrations employing these reagents in some detail.

REAGENTS

Ethylenediaminetetraacetic acid—often abbreviated EDTA—has the structure

$$\begin{matrix} HOOC—CH_2 & & & CH_2—COOH \\ & \diagdown & & \diagup & \\ & N—CH_2—CH_2—N & \\ & \diagup & & \diagdown & \\ HOOC—CH_2 & & & CH_2—COOH \end{matrix}$$

---

[1] C. N. Reilley and R. W. Schmid, *Anal. Chem.*, **31**, 887 (1959).

EDTA is the most widely used of this class of compounds. It is a weak acid for which $pK_1 = 2.0$, $pK_2 = 2.67$, $pK_3 = 6.16$, and $pK_4 = 10.26$.[2] These values indicate that the first two protons are lost much more readily than the remaining two. In addition to the four acidic hydrogens, each nitrogen atom has an unshared pair of electrons; the molecule thus has six potential sites for bonding with a metal ion.

The abbreviations H_4Y, H_3Y^-, H_2Y^{2-}, and so on, are often employed in referring to EDTA and its ions.

Because of its limited solubility, the free acid, H_4Y, is not often employed for the preparation of standard solutions. Likewise, the tetrasodium salt, Na_4Y is not very satisfactory owing to its extensive hydrolysis in solution and the resulting high alkalinity. The disodium salt, Na_2H_2Y, is most useful for analytical purposes, being obtainable in high purity as the dihydrate. Recrystallization of a commercial preparation of this salt is advisable before considering it to be of primary standard quality.[3] Solutions of this substance are stable for months when stored in plastic or borosilicate glass containers.

Another common reagent is nitrilotriacetic acid—abbreviated NTA—which has the structure

$$HOOC-CH_2 \qquad CH_2-COOH$$
$$\diagdown \qquad \diagup$$
$$N$$
$$\diagdown$$
$$CH_2-COOH$$

Aqueous solutions of this quadridentate ligand are prepared from the free acid.

Many related substances have also been investigated; these have not been widely employed for volumetric analysis, however. We shall confine our discussion to the applications of EDTA.

REACTIONS OF EDTA WITH METAL IONS

In general, 1:1 complexes are formed with metallic ions; the reactions of EDTA, for example, can be summarized as follows:

$$M^{2+} + H_2Y^{2-} \rightleftharpoons MY^{2-} + 2H^+$$

$$M^{3+} + H_2Y^{2-} \rightleftharpoons MY^- + 2H^+$$

$$M^{4+} + H_2Y^{2-} \rightleftharpoons MY + 2H^+$$

---

[2] The negative logarithm of an equilibrium constant is called its pK. Thus, in this instance, $K_1 = 1.00 \times 10^{-2}$, and therefore $pK_1 = 2.0$.

[3] W. J. Blaedel and H. T. Knight, *Anal. Chem.*, **26**, 743 (1954).

Obviously the extent to which these complexes form is markedly affected by pH. In addition, there is a rough correlation between charge on the cation and stability of the resultant complex. Welcher states this relationship as follows:[4] (1) the complexes of EDTA with divalent cations are very stable in basic or slightly acidic solutions; (2) complexes of the trivalent cations are stable in the pH range of 1 to 2; and (3) complexes of quadrivalent cations are often stable at a pH less than one.

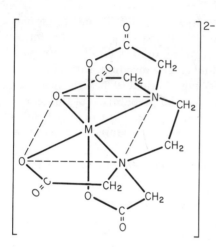

Fig. 12.2 Proposed Structure of a Metal-EDTA Chelate.

The Versenes are remarkable from the standpoint of the high stability of their metal adducts and the ubiquity of their complexes. All cations react, at least to some extent; with the exception of the alkali metals, the complexes formed are sufficiently stable to form the basis for volumetric analysis. Undoubtedly this great stability arises from the several complexing groups within the molecule giving rise to structures that effectively surround and isolate the cation. This is depicted in Figure 12.2.

TITRATION METHODS USING EDTA

Several procedures are employed in the application of EDTA to volumetric analysis. The most common of these are considered in the following paragraphs.

Direct-titration Procedure. Direct titration of metal ions by a standard solution of EDTA is feasible when a suitable method for end-point detection is available. For example, magnesium and a number of other

[4] F. J. Welcher, *The Analytical Uses of Ethylenediaminetetraacetic Acid.* Princeton, N.J.: D. Van Nostrand Company, Inc., 1958.

divalent ions can be determined in this way by using the metal indicator *Eriochrome black T*. The titration is carried out in somewhat basic solution, the reaction being

$$Mg^{2+} + H_2Y^{2-} \rightleftharpoons MgY^{2-} + 2H^+$$

The indicator is a complex organic chelating agent. In neutral or somewhat basic solutions it is a doubly dissociated ion, HIn^{2-}, that is blue in color. This ion forms red chelate complexes with several metallic ions including magnesium. Displacement of hydrogen accompanies chelation of magnesium or other cations

$$Mg^{2+} + \underset{\text{blue}}{HIn^{2-}} \rightleftharpoons \underset{\text{red}}{MgIn^-} + H^+$$

When a direct titration of magnesium is performed with Eriochrome black T, the solution is initially red due to the large magnesium ion concentration (low pMg). At the equivalence point there is sharp increase in pMg (see Figure 12.1), and this equilibrium is shifted to the left. Clearly, the stability of the metal-indicator complex must be such that EDTA can compete favorably with it for the magnesium ions.

Acid-base indicators are also employed in direct titrations in which Na_4Y is the reagent (see page 229).

Back Titrations. Back-titration procedures are useful for the analysis of metallic ions that form very stable complexes with EDTA and for which a satisfactory indicator is not available. In these instances the excess EDTA is determined by back titration with a standard magnesium solution using Eriochrome black T as the indicator. The metal-EDTA complex must be more stable than the magnesium-EDTA complex; otherwise the back titrant could displace the metal ion.

This technique is also useful for the analysis of metals in the presence of anions that form insoluble precipitates with the metal under the conditions of the analysis; the presence of EDTA prevents their precipitation.

Displacement Titrations. In displacement titrations an excess of a solution containing EDTA in the form of a magnesium or zinc complex is introduced; if the metal ion forms a more stable complex than that of magnesium or zinc, the following reaction occurs:

$$MgY^{2-} + M^{2+} \rightleftharpoons MY^{2-} + Mg^{2+}$$

The liberated magnesium is then titrated with a standard EDTA solution. This technique is useful where no satisfactory indicator is available for the metal ion being determined.

Alkalimetric Titrations. In alkalimetric titrations an excess of Na_2H_2Y is added to a neutral solution of the metallic ion; the liberated hydrogen ions are then titrated with a standard solution of a base.

SCOPE OF COMPLEXOMETRIC TITRATIONS

Complexometric titrations with EDTA have been reported for the analysis of nearly all the metallic ions.[5] Because of the tendency of the reagent to complex most cations, EDTA would appear at first glance to be totally lacking in specificity. In fact, however, considerable control over the behavior of this reagent, and other chelating agents as well, can be achieved through pH regulation. Thus, for example, it is generally possible to determine trivalent cations without interference from divalent species by performing the titration in a medium having a pH of about 1. Under these circumstances the less stable divalent complexes do not form while the trivalent ions are quantitatively complexed. Similarly, cadmium, which forms a more stable EDTA complex than magnesium, can be determined in the presence of that ion by buffering the mixture to pH 7 before titration. Eriochrome black T serves as an indicator for the cadmium end point without interference from magnesium because the magnesium-indicator chelate is not formed at this pH. Finally, interference from a particular cation can sometimes be eliminated through addition of a suitable *masking agent*. This is simply an auxiliary ligand that preferentially forms highly stable complexes with the potential interference and thereby prevents involvement of that ion in equilibria associated with either the titrant or the indicator. The cyanide ion, alone or in combination with other substances, finds wide use as a masking agent.

The following directions illustrate some of the techniques employed for EDTA titrations.

REAGENTS AND SOLUTIONS

Preparation of 0.01 *F* EDTA Solution—Direct Method. Dry the purified dihydrate ($Na_2H_2Y \cdot 2H_2O$, gfw = 372.2) at 80° C to remove superficial moisture. After cooling, weigh about 3.8 grams (to the nearest milligram) into a 1-liter volumetric flask and dilute to the mark.

NOTES:

1. Specific instructions for the purification of commercial preparations of the disodium salt are to be found in reference 3, page 231.

2. Direct preparation of standard solutions requires the total exclusion of polyvalent cations. If any doubt exists regarding the quality

---

[5] For further information regarding specific methods of analysis, the interested reader should consult the works of Welcher, cited previously; S. Chaberek and A. E. Martell, *Organic Sequestering Agents*. New York: John Wiley and Sons, Inc., 1959; and G. Schwarzenbach, *Complexometric Titrations*. London: Methuen and Co. Ltd., 1957.

of the distilled water, a pretreatment by passage through a cation-exchange resin is recommended.

3. If desired, the anhydrous salt (gfw = 336.1) may be employed instead of the dihydrate. The weight taken should be adjusted accordingly.

4. If desired, an EDTA solution of approximately the desired concentration may be prepared and standardized against a Mg^{2+} solution of known strength.

Preparation of the Magnesium Complex of EDTA, 0.1 F Solution. To 37.2 grams of $Na_2H_2Y \cdot 2H_2O$ in 500 ml of distilled water add an equivalent quantity (24.65 grams) of $MgSO_4 \cdot 7H_2O$. Introduce a few drops of phenolphthalein followed by sufficient sodium hydroxide to turn the solution faintly pink. Dilute the solution to 1 liter. When properly prepared, portions of this solution should assume a dull violet color when treated with pH-10 buffer and a few drops of Eriochrome black T (Erio T) indicator. Furthermore, a single drop of 0.01 F Na_2H_2Y should cause a color change to blue, while an equal quantity of 0.01 F Mg^{2+} should cause a change to red. The composition of the solution should be adjusted by addition of Mg^{2+} or Na_2H_2Y until these criteria are met.

Preparation of Eriochrome Black T Solution. Dissolve 200 mg of the solid in a solution consisting of 15 ml of triethanolamine and 5 ml of absolute ethanol.

Preparation of Buffer, pH 10. Dilute 570 ml of aqueous NH_3 (sp gr 0.90) and 70 grams of NH_4Cl to approximately 1 liter.

APPLICATIONS

Determination of Magnesium by Direct Titration. The sample will be issued as an aqueous solution; transfer it to a clean 500-ml volumetric flask. Dilute to the mark. Take 50.00-ml aliquots, treating each with 1 to 2 ml of pH-10 buffer and 2 to 4 drops of Erio T indicator solution. Titrate with 0.01 F Na_2H_2Y to a color change from red to blue. Express the results of the analysis in terms of milligrams of Mg^{2+}/liter of solution.

NOTES:

1. The color change of the indicator is slow in the vicinity of the end point. Care must be taken to avoid overtitration.

2. Other alkaline earths, if present, will also be titrated with magnesium and should be removed prior to the analysis. $(NH_4)_2CO_3$ is a suitable reagent for this. Most polyvalent cations also interfere, and should be precipitated as hydroxides.

3. Since this reaction may be expressed as

$$Mg^{2+} + H_2Y^{2-} \rightleftharpoons MgY^{2-} + 2H^+$$

the normality of the chelating solution is twice its formal concentration. For a 40-ml titration, each aliquot should contain about 10 mg of magnesium ion.

Determination of Calcium by Substitution Titration. Weigh the sample into a 500-ml volumetric flask and dissolve in a minimum quantity of dilute HCl. Neutralize the solution with sodium hydroxide (Note 2) and dilute to the mark. Take 50.00-ml aliquots for titration, treating each as follows: add approximately 2 ml of pH-10 buffer, 1 ml of the magnesium-chelate solution, and 2 to 4 drops of Erio T indicator. Titrate with standard $0.01\ F$ Na_2H_2Y to a color change from red to blue. Report the percentage of calcium oxide in the sample.

NOTES:

1. The weight of sample taken should be such as will contain about 150 to 160 mg of Ca^{2+}.

2. To neutralize the solution, introduce a few drops of methyl red and add base until the red color is discharged.

3. The amount of MgY^{2-} solution added is not critical. Its presence is required because the indicator does not exhibit a satisfactory color change when Ca^{2+} is present alone. Since the calcium chelate is more stable, the reaction

$$Ca^{2+} + MgY^{2-} \rightleftharpoons CaY^{2-} + Mg^{2+}$$

takes place. Introduction of titrant leads to the preferential formation of the calcium chelate for the same reason. At the equivalence point, the reaction is actually between H_2Y^{2-} and Mg^{2+}, for which Erio T is an excellent indicator.

4. Interferences with this method are substantially the same as with the direct determination of magnesium, and are eliminated in the same way.

Determination of Calcium and Magnesium in Hard Water. Acidify 100-ml aliquots with a few drops of HCl and boil gently for a few minutes to remove CO_2. Cool, add a few drops of methyl red, and neutralize the solution with NaOH. Introduce 2 ml of pH-10 buffer, 2 to 4 drops of Erio T indicator, and titrate with standard $0.01\ F$ Na_2H_2Y to a color change from red to blue. Report results of the analysis in terms of milligrams of $CaCO_3$/liter of water.

NOTE:

If the color change of the indicator is sluggish, the absence of magnesium is indicated. In this event 1 to 2 ml of standard $0.1\ F$ MgY^{2-} solution should be added.

Determination of Calcium by Back Titration. Prepare the sample as directed for the substitution analysis of calcium. To each 50.0-ml aliquot taken add about 2 ml of pH-10 buffer and 2 to 4 drops of Erio T indicator. Run in an excess of $0.01\ F$ Na_2H_2Y solution from a buret and record the volume taken. Titrate the excess chelating agent to a color change from blue to red with standard 0.01 F $MgSO_4$ solution.

NOTE:

The magnesium sulfate solution is conveniently prepared by dissolving about 2.5 grams of the heptahydrate in 1 liter of distilled water. The equivalence of this solution with respect to the Na_2H_2Y solution should be determined by a direct titration.

Problems

1. A solution is prepared by dissolving 5.200 grams of KCN in water and diluting to 1 liter. Express the concentration of this solution in terms of its
   (a) formality
   (b) normality with respect to the reaction $Ag^+ + 2CN^- \rightleftharpoons Ag(CN)_2^-$
   (c) normality with respect to the reaction $Ni^{2+} + 4CN^- \rightleftharpoons Ni(CN)_4^{2-}$
   (d) titer, in terms of mg Ag^+/ml
   (e) titer, in terms of mg Ni^{2+}/ml

2. A solution contains 18.60 grams of $Na_2H_2Y \cdot 2H_2O$ (gfw = 372) per liter. Express the concentration of this solution in terms of its
   (a) formality
   (b) normality with respect to the reaction $Ca^{2+} + H_2Y^{2-} \rightleftharpoons CaY^{2-} + 2H^+$
   (c) titer, in terms of mg Ca^{2+}/ml

3. The excess cyanide in a silver-plating bath was determined by titration with standard $AgNO_3$ solution. A 50.00-ml aliquot required 23.4 ml of 0.0920 N Ag^+. Calculate the weight of free potassium cyanide present per liter of this solution.

4. Another 50-ml sample of the plating bath in Problem 3 was heated with HNO_3 to expel all of the cyanide as HCN. The residual $AgNO_3$ was rendered ammoniacal, after which 23.6 ml of 0.105 F KCN were introduced; this was sufficient to produce a clear solution. Titration of the excess KCN required 1.62 ml of 0.0920 N Ag^+. On the basis of the data in this and the preceding problem calculate
   (a) the weight of Ag^+ present per liter of the plating solution
   (b) the total KCN content of this solution (in grams per liter)

5. The Ni in a 1.020-gram alloy sample was titrated with 28.40 ml of KCN solution. A 25.00-ml aliquot of solution containing 3.94 mg Ni^{2+}/ml required 36.30 ml of this cyanide solution. Calculate
   (a) the formal concentration of the KCN solution
   (b) the titer of the KCN solution in mg Ni^{2+}/ml
   (c) the normality of the standard Ni^{2+} solution
   (d) the formal concentration of the standard Ni^{2+} solution

(e) the normality of the cyanide solution with respect to this reaction

(f) the percentage of Ni in the alloy

6. A standard Ca^{2+} solution was prepared by dissolving 0.4644 gram of $CaCO_3$ in HCl and diluting to 1 liter. Calculate the concentration of this solution in terms of parts Ca^{2+}/million.

7. A 50.00-ml aliquot of the solution in Problem 6 was titrated with 31.40 ml of an EDTA solution. Express the titer of this solution in terms of mg Ca^{2+}/ml EDTA.

8. A 50.00-ml aliquot of hard water required 19.80 ml of the EDTA solution in Problem 7. Express the hardness of the water in terms of parts Ca^{2+}/million.

$$\left(\textbf{13} \right)$$

Theory of Neutralization
Titrations of Simple Systems

The end points employed in neutralization titrations are ordinarily based upon the abrupt change in pH that occurs in the vicinity of the equivalence point. The pH range over which such a change is observed depends upon the nature and concentration of the substance titrated as well as the titrant. Proper selection of an indicator for any given case requires a knowledge of the general features of the titration curve for the system. Thus we need to consider how such curves are derived.

13.1   Acid-base Equilibria—pH Calculations

Aqueous solutions always contain hydronium ions as well as hydroxyl ions as a consequence of the dissociation of water.

$$2H_2O \rightleftharpoons H_3O^+ + OH^-$$

Certain solutes, however, cause tremendous changes in the concentrations of the two species, often with profound effects as far as the chemical behavior of the solution is concerned.

ION PRODUCT CONSTANT FOR WATER

As shown on page 22, application of the mass law to the dissociation of water leads to the expression

$$K_w = [H_3O^+][OH^-]$$

where K_w is a constant called the *ion product constant* for water. At 25° C the numerical value of this constant is 1.0×10^{-14} mol²/liter². The dissociation of water is an endothermic process; the extent to which it occurs, therefore, increases with temperature. Thus at 60° C the value of K_w is approximately 1×10^{-13} mol²/liter²; at 100° C it has increased to about 5×10^{-13}.

In pure water or in the presence of a solute that does not react to give hydronium or hydroxyl ions, the concentrations of these two species are identical, and therefore their concentrations must equal the square root of the ion product constant—that is, 1.0×10^{-7} mol/liter at 25° C. A solution in which the hydronium and hydroxyl ion concentrations are the same is said to be *neutral*. The hydronium and hydroxyl ion concentrations of a neutral solution increase with temperature.

A solution is said to be *acidic* when the hydronium ion concentration exceeds that of the hydroxyl ions; it is *basic* when the reverse is the case. Such changes arise as a result of the presence of a solute that reacts to produce or consume one of the two ions.

A useful relationship is obtained by taking the negative logarithm of both sides of the ion product constant expression. Thus

$$- \log K_w = - \log [H_3O^+][OH^-] = - \log [H_3O^+] - \log [OH^-]$$

from which it follows that

$$- \log K_w = pH + pOH$$

at 25° C, $- \log K_w$, or pK_w, is equal to fourteen and we may write

$$pH + pOH = 14$$

★EXAMPLE. Calculate the pH and pOH of a solution having a hydronium ion concentration of 2.0×10^{-3}.

$$[H_3O^+] = 2.0 \times 10^{-3} \text{ mol/liter}$$
$$pH = - \log 2.0 \times 10^{-3} = - \log 2 - \log 10^{-3}$$
$$= -0.3 - (-3) = 2.7$$
$$pOH = 14 - 2.7 = 11.3$$

SOLUTIONS OF STRONG ACIDS AND STRONG BASES

A strong acid is one that reacts completely with the solvent to give the conjugate acid of the solvent. For example, when gaseous hydrogen chloride is dissolved in water the acid-base reaction

$$HCl + H_2O \rightarrow H_3O^+ + Cl^-$$

$$\text{acid}_1 \quad \text{base}_1 \quad \text{acid}_2 \quad \text{base}_2$$

is complete, the product H_3O^+ being the conjugate acid of the solvent water.

Strong bases, such as sodium hydroxide, are ionic in the solid state and remain in this form upon solution in a solvent such as water.

The calculation of the pH or pOH of aqueous solutions of strong acids or bases is a straightforward matter since the hydronium or hydroxyl ion concentration can be calculated directly from the formal concentration of the solute. In such calculations, the number of hydronium ions or hydroxyl ions produced by the dissociation of water is ordinarily so small, compared with that introduced from the added strong acid or base, that it is unnecessary to take this equilibrium into account.

★EXAMPLE. Calculate the pH and pOH of a 0.050 F solution of HCl.

Since this acid is completely dissociated, the hydronium ion concentration is numerically equal to the formal concentration of HCl in the solution.

$$[H_3O^+] = 0.05 = 5 \times 10^{-2} \text{ mol/liter}$$

Here the hydronium ions arising from the dissociation of water are negligible in comparison with the large number from the HCl. Then

$$pH = -\log 5 \times 10^{-2} = 1.3$$

$$pOH = 14 - 1.3 = 12.7$$

★EXAMPLE. Calculation of the pH, and pOH of a 3.2×10^{-4} F solution of $Ba(OH)_2$ will serve as another example.

$Ba(OH)_2$ is a strong base containing 2 mols of hydroxyl ions for each formula weight of base. Thus

$$[OH^-] = 2 \times 3.2 \times 10^{-4} = 6.4 \times 10^{-4} \text{ mol/liter}$$

$$pOH = -\log 6.4 \times 10^{-4} = 3.19$$

$$pH = 14 - 3.19 = 10.81$$

SOLUTIONS OF WEAK ACIDS AND BASES

Weak acids and bases react incompletely with the solvent; as a consequence the hydronium or hydroxyl ion concentration in such solutions will be less than the formal reagent concentration. Calculation of the pH or pOH requires a knowledge of the magnitude of the equilibrium constant for the reaction of the substance with water.

Calculation of the pH of Solutions of Weak, Monoprotic Acids. When the weak acid, HA, is dissolved in water, the reaction

$$HA + H_2O \rightleftharpoons H_3O^+ + A^-$$

is incomplete and the resulting equilibrium relationship is described by the equation

$$K_a = \frac{[H_3O^+][A^-]}{[HA]} \qquad (13\text{-}1)$$

where K_a is the *ionization constant* or *dissociation constant* of the acid. The only other independent equilibrium in such a solution is

$$2H_2O \rightleftharpoons H_3O^+ + OH^-$$

for which

$$K_w = [H_3O^+][OH^-] \qquad (13\text{-}2)$$

In addition to (13-1) and (13-2), two more algebraic expressions can be readily derived from mass-balance and charge-balance considerations. Since the number of negative charges in the system must equal the number of positive ones, we may write

$$[H_3O^+] = [OH^-] + [A^-] \qquad (13\text{-}3)$$

Furthermore the sum of the concentrations of all species containing A must be equal to the formal concentration of HA, it being the only source of these species. Therefore

$$F_{HA} = [A^-] + [HA] \qquad (13\text{-}4)$$

We now have four algebraic equations containing the four unknowns, $[H_3O^+]$, $[OH^-]$, $[A^-]$, and $[HA]$; provided we know F_{HA} and K_a, the concentrations of all the species can therefore be calculated.

For nearly every case we will encounter, it will be permissible to make an approximation that reduces the number of algebraic expressions and unknowns to three, and greatly simplifies the calculation of pH. This approximation is that the hydroxyl ion concentration is so much smaller than the concentration of A^- that it need not be considered in equation (13-3); therefore

$$[H_3O^+] \cong [A^-] \qquad (13\text{-}5)$$

This approximation is ordinarily valid because K_w is inherently small; the hydronium ions from HA repress the dissociation of water even further.

Having invoked this approximation, there are three unknowns, $[H_3O^+]$, $[A^-]$, and $[HA]$ and three equations, (13-1), (13-4), and (13-5). For convenience, let x equal $[H_3O^+]$; from (13-5)

$$[H_3O^+] = [A^-] = x$$

According to (13-4) we may write

$$[HA] = (F_{HA} - x) \qquad (13\text{-}6)$$

Substituting into (13-1) we find

$$\frac{x^2}{(F_{HA} - x)} = K_a \tag{13-7}$$

which can be rearranged to give

$$x^2 + K_a x - K_a F_{HA} = 0$$

The solution to this quadratic equation is then

$$x = [H_3O^+] = \frac{-K_a + \sqrt{K_a^2 + 4K_a F_{HA}}}{2} \tag{13-8}$$

Calculation of the hydronium ion concentration of a weak acid solution can often be further simplified without introducing a serious error. By assuming that the concentration of undissociated acid is not greatly different from its formal concentration—that is, that x is small compared to F_{HA}—equation (13-6) becomes

$$[HA] \cong F_{HA} \text{ when } x \ll F_{HA}$$

Equation (13-7) then simplifies to

$$\frac{x^2}{F_{HA}} = K_a$$

and

$$x = [H_3O^+] = \sqrt{K_a F_{HA}} \tag{13-9}$$

The magnitude of the error introduced by this assumption will become greater as the concentration of acid becomes smaller and as the dissociation constant of the acid becomes larger. This is illustrated by the data in Table 13-1.

TABLE 13-1
Errors Introduced by Assuming x Small Relative to F_{HA} in Equation (13-7)

Value of K_a	Value of F_{HA}	Value for $x = [H_3O^+]$ using assumption	Value for $x = [H_3O^+]$ by more exact equation
1×10^{-2}	1×10^{-5}	3.16×10^{-4}	$0.1 \ \times 10^{-4}$
	1×10^{-3}	3.16×10^{-3}	0.92×10^{-3}
	1×10^{-1}	3.16×10^{-2}	2.70×10^{-2}
1×10^{-4}	1×10^{-5}	3.16×10^{-5}	0.92×10^{-5}
	1×10^{-3}	3.16×10^{-4}	2.70×10^{-4}
	1×10^{-1}	3.16×10^{-3}	3.11×10^{-3}
1×10^{-6}	1×10^{-5}	3.16×10^{-6}	2.70×10^{-6}
	1×10^{-3}	3.16×10^{-5}	3.11×10^{-5}
	1×10^{-1}	3.16×10^{-4}	3.16×10^{-4}

In general, it is good practice to make this assumption and obtain a trial value for x that may be compared with F_{HA} in equation (13-7). If this trial value alters [HA] by an amount smaller than the allowable error in the calculation, the solution may be considered satisfactory. Otherwise the quadratic equation must be solved to give a more exact value for x.

★EXAMPLE. Calculate the hydronium ion concentration of a $4.00 \times 10^{-2} F$ solution of formic acid.

The equilibrium for formic acid is

$$HCOOH + H_2O \rightleftharpoons HCOO^- + H_3O^+$$

From Table A-6 of the Appendix

$$K_a = \frac{[H_3O^+][HCOO^-]}{[HCOOH]} = 1.74 \times 10^{-4}$$

Now, let $x = [H_3O^+]$. From a consideration of charge balance in the solution

$$x = [H_3O^+] = [HCOO^-] + [OH^-] \cong [HCOO^-]$$

This assumption is probably valid since the $[OH^-]$ of this acidic solution will be very small. Then, material balance requires that

$$[HCOOH] = (F_{HCOOH} - x) = (4.00 \times 10^{-2} - x)$$

Substituting into the dissociation-constant expression, we find

$$\frac{x^2}{(4.00 \times 10^{-2} - x)} = 1.74 \times 10^{-4}$$

We shall first assume x is small relative to 4.00×10^{-2} and obtain a trial value of x; that is,

$$x^2 = 4.00 \times 10^{-2} \times 1.74 \times 10^{-4}$$

$$x = 2.64 \times 10^{-3}$$

We may now test the assumption by comparing 2.64×10^{-3} with 4.00×10^{-2}; we see that the former value is about 7 percent of the latter, which gives a maximum value for the error in the trial value of x. If a more accurate figure were needed, solution of the quadratic equation would give a value of 2.55×10^{-3} mol/liter.

Calculation of the *pH* of Solutions of Weak Bases. The techniques discussed in the previous sections are readily adaptable to the calculation of the hydroxyl ion concentration in solutions of weak bases; from this, the *p*H can be obtained. In contrast to the large variety of common weak acids, the number of weak bases is quite small, consisting of ammonia, several organic amines, and a few miscellaneous compounds. Of these only ammonia is generally encountered by the chemist.

Aqueous solutions of ammonia are basic by virtue of the reaction

$$NH_3 + H_2O \rightleftharpoons NH_4^+ + OH^-$$

The predominant species in these solutions has been clearly demonstrated to be NH_3. Despite this, such solutions are frequently called ammonium hydroxide, this terminology being vestigial from the time when the substance NH_4OH rather than NH_3 was believed to be the undissociated form of the base. Application of the mass law to this equilibrium yields the expression

$$K_b = \frac{[NH_4^+][OH^-]}{[NH_3]}$$

By analogy to the case of the weak acid, K_b is commonly called a *basic ionization* or *basic dissociation constant* despite the fact that this latter terminology does not describe the reaction very well. The magnitude of this constant is independent of the formula used in the denominator, be it the more correct NH_3 or the historical NH_4OH.

Equilibrium constants for other weak bases are formulated in a similar fashion. For example, the equilibrium for dimethylamine can be written

$$(CH_3)_2NH + H_2O \rightleftharpoons (CH_3)_2NH_2^+ + OH^-$$

for which

$$K_b = \frac{[(CH_3)_2NH_2^+][OH^-]}{[(CH_3)_2NH]}$$

The hydroxyl ion concentration in a solution of a weak base is readily calculated from its dissociation constant by the same techniques and assumptions as used for weak acids.

★EXAMPLE. Calculate the pH of a 0.075 F solution of NH_3. From the table of basic ionization constants (Table A-7, Appendix)

$$K_b = 1.86 \times 10^{-5} = \frac{[NH_4^+][OH^-]}{[NH_3]}$$

In this instance, we shall let $x = [OH^-]$. The condition of electrical neutrality demands that

$$[NH_4^+] + [H_3O^+] = [OH^-] = x$$

Since $[H_3O^+] \ll [NH_4^+]$ in the system we may write

$$[NH_4^+] \cong [OH^-] = x$$

From the standpoint of material balance

$$[NH_4^+] + [NH_3] = 7.5 \times 10^{-2}$$

$$[NH_3] = (7.5 \times 10^{-2} - x)$$

Substituting these quantities into the dissociation-constant expression gives

$$\frac{x^2}{(7.5 \times 10^{-2} - x)} = 1.86 \times 10^{-5}$$

Finally, we shall assume that x is small relative to 7.5×10^{-2}. Then

$$x^2 \cong 7.5 \times 10^{-2} \times 1.86 \times 10^{-5} = 13.95 \times 10^{-7}$$

$$x = [OH^-] = 1.18 \times 10^{-3} \text{ mol/liter}$$

Comparing this result with 7.5×10^{-2}, we see that the maximum error in x will be less than 2 percent. Were a better value for x desired, it could be obtained by solution of the quadratic equation.

To obtain pH, we first compute pOH.

$$p\text{OH} = -\log 1.18 \times 10^{-3} = 2.93$$

Then

$$p\text{H} = 14 - 2.93 = 11.07$$

Calculation of the pH of Dilute Solutions of Very Weak Acids. In determining the pH of a weak acid solution by these techniques the assumption was made that the concentration of hydronium ion resulting from the dissociation of the acid so far exceeded the concentration arising from the dissociation of water that the latter contribution could be neglected. A similar assumption was made regarding calculation of the hydroxyl ion concentration of weak base solutions. As shown by the following example, this assumption is not valid when dealing with dilute solutions of very weak acids or bases.

★EXAMPLE. Calculate the pH of a $5 \times 10^{-5}\, F$ solution of phenol ($K_a = 1.05 \times 10^{-10}$).

First we shall employ the techniques already developed for the calculation of the pH of such a solution.

Using ROH as the symbol for phenol we write

$$H_2O + ROH \rightleftharpoons RO^- + H_3O^+$$

$$K_a = 1.05 \times 10^{-10} = \frac{[H_3O^+][RO^-]}{[ROH]}$$

and assuming that the only source of hydronium ions is the phenol, we can say

$$x = [H_3O^+] = [RO^-]$$

$$(5 \times 10^{-5} - x) \cong [ROH]$$

Then substituting these values into the dissociation-constant expression and solving in the usual way, we find

$$x = [H_3O^+] = 7.25 \times 10^{-8} \text{ mol/liter}$$

Here the hydronium ion concentration resulting from dissociation of phenol is comparable in magnitude to that contributed by the solvent; as a consequence a more refined calculation that accounts for the hydronium ions from water as well as phenol is desirable. We can arrive at a more exact description of the system by writing an equation based on the electrical neutrality of the solution—namely,

$$[H_3O^+] = [RO^-] + [OH^-]$$

Remembering that $[H_3O^+][OH^-] = K_w$, we may write

$$[RO^-] = ([H_3O^+] - [OH^-]) = \left([H_3O^+] - \frac{K_w}{[H_3O^+]}\right)$$

Since the phenol is present either as ROH or RO$^-$

$$[ROH] + [RO^-] = 5 \times 10^{-5}$$

We shall assume that [RO$^-$] is small and that

$$[ROH] \cong 5 \times 10^{-5}$$

Substituting into the equilibrium expression, we obtain

$$\frac{[H_3O^+]\left([H_3O^+] - \frac{K_w}{[H_3O^+]}\right)}{5 \times 10^{-5}} = 1.05 \times 10^{-10}$$

$$[H_3O^+]^2 - K_w = 5.25 \times 10^{-15}$$

$$[H_3O^+] = 1.23 \times 10^{-7} \text{ mol/liter}$$

$$pH = 6.91$$

This same technique can be applied to the calculation of the pH of a solution of a very weak base.

When confronted with problems involving very dilute solutions—particularly of weak acids or bases—the chemist should always check the validity of the assumption that the solute is the only significant source of hydronium ions or hydroxyl ions. This may be done by computing a trial value using ordinary assumptions and comparing this value with the hydronium or hydroxyl ion content of pure water. If the two figures are of the same order of magnitude, a recalculation, as shown above, should be made.

SOLUTIONS OF SALTS OF WEAK ACIDS AND BASES

As we have pointed out earlier, the salt of a weak acid is the conjugate base of the acid; upon being dissolved in water such a substance reacts with the solvent to give hydroxyl ions and the undissociated weak acid. Thus a solution of sodium acetate is basic by virtue of the equilibrium

$$OAc^- + H_2O \rightleftharpoons OH^- + HOAc$$

The extent to which such reactions proceed is inversely related to the strength of the weak acid formed. When the acid is very weak, the anion is a good proton acceptor and thus a relatively strong base. On the other hand salts of stronger acids react to a lesser extent with the solvent and are, therefore, weaker bases.

A basic equilibrium constant for the conjugate base of a weak acid is formulated in the same way as other basic equilibrium constants. Thus for the generalized reaction

$$A^- + H_2O \rightleftharpoons OH^- + HA$$

we may write

$$K_b = \frac{[OH^-][HA]}{[A^-]}$$

It is easily shown that the constant K_b is inversely related to the ionization constant K_a of the acid formed in the reaction. Thus

$$K_b = \frac{K_w}{K_a} = \frac{[\cancel{H_3O^+}][OH^-]}{\dfrac{[\cancel{H_3O^+}][A^-]}{[HA]}}$$

$$K_b = \frac{K_w}{K_a} = \frac{[HA^-][OH^-]}{[A^-]} \tag{13-10}$$

Analogous considerations apply to the salts of a weak base. For example, ammonium ion is the conjugate acid of ammonia; a solution of an ammonium salt is thus acidic as a consequence of the reaction

$$NH_4^+ + H_2O \rightleftharpoons NH_3 + H_3O^+$$

An acid equilibrium constant for this reaction can be written in the usual way

$$K_a = \frac{[NH_3][H_3O^+]}{[NH_4^+]}$$

By analogous reasoning it is easily shown that

$$K_a = \frac{K_w}{K_b} \tag{13-11}$$

where K_b is the basic ionization constant for ammonia. The above relationship shows that salts of bases weaker than ammonia (that is, bases with smaller values of K_b) will be stronger acids.

Because of the simple algebraic relationships between equilibrium constants for conjugate base-acid pairs, shown in equations (13-10) and (13-11), tabulations seldom, if ever, include equilibrium constants for both species of the pair. Ordinarily only ionization constants for the parent acid or base are recorded; thus in calculations dealing with the pH of solutions of salts, the appropriate constant must be computed.

It is well to emphasize that calculation of the pH for a weak acid and for the conjugate acid of a weak base is fundamentally the same process; the primary difference is that a value for the equilibrium constant is directly obtainable from tables in the one instance, while it must be computed, as above, in the other. The same is true for solutions of a weak base and the conjugate base of a weak acid.

Considering again the equilibrium established when the salt of a weak acid is dissolved in water

$$A^- + H_2O \rightleftharpoons HA + OH^-$$

we can write an algebraic expression relating the equilibrium concentrations of the various species. Since the anion of the salt will be present as A^- or HA, material balance requires that

$$F_{NaA} = [A^-] + [HA] \tag{13-12}$$

We may also write an equation to account for the electrical neutrality of the solution; namely,

$$[Na^+] + [H_3O^+] = [OH^-] + [A^-]$$

But the concentration of sodium ions in the solution is equal to the formal concentration of the salt, inasmuch as these ions in no way react with water. Thus we may write

$$F_{NaA} + [H_3O^+] = [OH^-] + [A^-] \tag{13-13}$$

Subtracting equation (13-13) from (13-12) and rearranging, we find

$$[HA] = [OH^-] - [H_3O^+] \tag{13-14}$$

If reaction occurs to an appreciable extent the hydroxyl ion concentration will be sufficiently large with respect to the hydronium ion concentration to permit simplification of (13-14) to

$$[HA] \cong [OH^-] \tag{13-15}$$

If we now set x equal to the equilibrium hydroxyl ion concentration, (13-15) becomes

$$x = [OH^-] = [HA]$$

Equation (13-12) then rearranges to

$$[A^-] = (F_{NaA} - x)$$

and by substituting these values into (13-10) we obtain

$$K_b = \frac{K_w}{K_a} = \frac{x^2}{(F_{NaA} - x)} \tag{13-16}$$

This equation is similar in form to equation (13-7) on page 243 and, as in that case, an exact solution can be found by solving the quadratic equation. If, as is frequently the case, K_w/K_a is small or if F_{NaA} is large, the assumption may be made that x is small with respect to F_{NaA}, whereupon (13-16) becomes

$$\frac{K_w}{K_a} = \frac{x^2}{F_{NaA}}$$

Solving for x we find

$$x = [OH^-] = \sqrt{\frac{K_w}{K_a} F_{NaA}} \qquad (13\text{-}17)$$

Here, again, a trial value for x via equation (13-17) is advisable before undertaking a more rigorous solution to the problem. We can then readily determine whether or not the assumption was justified.

★EXAMPLE. Calculate the pH of a 0.100 F solution of NaCN.
  Cyanide ion is the conjugate base of the acid, HCN; its behavior as a base is described by the equilibrium

$$CN^- + H_2O \rightleftharpoons HCN + OH^-$$

for which

$$K_b = \frac{K_w}{K_a} = \frac{[HCN][OH^-]}{[CN^-]}$$

The dissociation constant for HCN is 2.1×10^{-9}.
Setting $x = [OH^-]$, we may write

$$x = [OH^-] \cong [HCN]$$

and

$$(0.1 - x) = [CN^-]$$

Therefore,

$$\frac{x^2}{(0.1 - x)} = \frac{1.0 \times 10^{-14}}{2.1 \times 10^{-9}} = 4.8 \times 10^{-6}$$

If we now assume $x \ll 0.1$, then

$$\frac{x^2}{0.1} = 4.8 \times 10^{-6}$$

$$x = [OH^-] = 6.9 \times 10^{-4} \text{ mol/liter}$$

We see that x is indeed small relative to 0.1, and this approximate solution is entirely adequate.

$$pOH = -\log 6.9 \times 10^{-4} = 3.16$$

$$pH = 14 - 3.16 = \underline{10.84}$$

Salts of Weak Bases. The calculation of pH for a solution of a salt of a weak base is analogous to the calculation just completed.

★EXAMPLE. Calculate the pH of a 0.200 F solution of NH_4Cl. The equilibrium in this instance can be written

$$H_2O + NH_4^+ \rightleftharpoons NH_3 + H_3O^+$$

for which

$$K_a = \frac{K_w}{K_b} = \frac{[NH_3][H_3O^+]}{[NH_4^+]}$$

where K_b is the basic ionization constant for NH_3.

If we combine a material-balance equation and a charge-balance equation as in the previous section, we find that

$$[NH_3] = [H_3O^+] - [OH^-]$$

and since $[OH^-] \ll [H_3O^+]$

$$[NH_3] = [H_3O^+] = x$$

Also

$$[NH_4^+] = (0.200 - x)$$

Substituting these quantities into the equilibrium expression

$$\frac{x^2}{(0.2 - x)} = \frac{1.0 \times 10^{-14}}{1.86 \times 10^{-5}}$$

Assuming, further, x to be small relative to 0.2

$$\frac{x^2}{0.2} = \frac{1.0 \times 10^{-14}}{1.86 \times 10^{-5}}$$

and

$$x = [H_3O^+] = 1.04 \times 10^{-5} \text{ mol/liter}$$

$$pH = 4.98$$

Salts of a Weak Acid and a Weak Base. When the salt derived from reaction between a weak acid and a weak base is dissolved in water, two reactions occur that affect the pH. For example, in a solution of ammonium acetate, both the following equilibria exist:

$$OAc^- + H_2O \rightleftharpoons HOAc + OH^-$$

$$H_2O + NH_4^+ \rightleftharpoons NH_3 + H_3O^+$$

Whether the resulting solution is basic or acidic depends upon which of these equilibria is predominant. Calculation of the pH of such a solution must take both processes into account.

SOLUTIONS OF A WEAK ACID AND ITS SALT OR A WEAK BASE AND ITS SALT

Addition of a salt of a weak acid to a solution of that acid has the effect of markedly lowering the hydronium ion concentration of the solution.

This effect is predicted by the principle of Le Chatelier. Thus, if a salt NaA is added to a solution of HA, the equilibrium

$$H_2O + HA \rightleftharpoons H_3O^+ + A^-$$

will be displaced to the left. As a result, a decrease in the hydronium ion concentration occurs. Similarly, additions of ammonium chloride to an aqueous solution of ammonia will shift the equilibrium

$$NH_3 + H_2O \rightleftharpoons NH_4^+ + OH^-$$

in such a direction as to remove hydroxyl ions from the solution. The magnitude of these effects is readily calculated.

Calculation of the pH of a Solution of a Weak Acid and Its Salt. Consider a solution having a formal acid concentration F_{HA} and a formal salt concentration F_{NaA}. The important equilibrium in this solution involves dissociation of the acid, the constant for which is

$$K_a = \frac{[H_3O^+][A^-]}{[HA]}$$

We shall first set $x = [H_3O^+]$, and then express the concentrations of A^- and HA in terms of their respective formal concentrations and x. Since the substance A is present either as the ion A^- or as HA, material balance requires that

$$F_{NaA} + F_{HA} = [A^-] + [HA] \tag{13-18}$$

From electrical neutrality considerations we may write

$$[Na^+] + [H_3O^+] = [A^-] + [OH^-]$$

But

$$[Na^+] = F_{NaA}$$

Therefore,

$$F_{NaA} + [H_3O^+] = [A^-] + [OH^-] \tag{13-19}$$

Subtracting equation (13-19) from (13-18), we find

$$F_{HA} - [H_3O^+] = [HA] - [OH^-] \tag{13-20}$$

On the *assumption* that $[OH^-]$ is small relative either to $[A^-]$ or to $[HA]$, equations (13-19) and (13-20) can be rearranged and written

$$[A^-] = F_{NaA} + x \tag{13-21}$$

$$[HA] = F_{HA} - x \tag{13-22}$$

It is important to appreciate the significance of the last two equations. The first states that the anion concentration $[A^-]$ is equal to the formal concentration of the salt plus the concentration of A⁻ resulting from dissociation of the acid (which is equal numerically to $[H_3O^+]$). The undissociated acid concentration [HA], on the other hand, is equal to the formal concentration of the acid minus that lost by dissociation (also equal to $[H_3O^+]$).

Substituting equations (13-21) and (13-22) into the dissociation-constant expression, we obtain

$$K_a = \frac{x(F_{NaA} + x)}{(F_{HA} - x)} \tag{13-23}$$

In nearly every case the solution of (13-23) can be greatly simplified by assuming that x is small relative to either F_{NaA} or F_{HA}; then (13-23) becomes

$$K_a = x\frac{F_{NaA}}{F_{HA}}$$

where $x \ll F_{NaA}$ and F_{HA} or

$$x = [H_3O^+] = K_a\frac{F_{HA}}{F_{NaA}} \tag{13-24}$$

As in the earlier calculations of this chapter, this assumption should always be made; the provisional value for x is then used to test the validity of the assumption.

Within limits imposed by the assumptions made in its derivation, equation (13-24) states that the hydronium ion concentration of a solution of a weak acid and its salt is dependent only upon the ratio of the formal concentrations of the two components of the solution. Furthermore, this ratio remains *independent of the dilution* of the solution since the concentration of each component changes in a proportionate manner upon dilution. Thus *the hydronium ion concentration of a solution containing appreciable quantities of a weak acid and its salt is independent of dilution and depends only upon the ratio of the number of formula weights of each component present.* In this respect solutions composed of a mixture of a weak acid and its salt differ from solutions containing either of the components alone.

The following example will illustrate the technique for calculating the pH of a solution of this type.

★EXAMPLE. What is the pH of a solution that is 4.00×10^{-2} F in formic acid and 0.100 F in sodium formate?

The equilibrium governing the hydronium ion concentration in this solution is

$$H_2O + HCOOH \rightleftharpoons H_3O^+ + HCOO^-$$

for which

$$K_a = \frac{[H_3O^+][HCOO^-]}{[HCOOH]} = 1.74 \times 10^{-4}$$

Let x equal the equilibrium hydronium ion concentration $[H_3O^+]$. Then

$$[HCOO^-] = (0.100 + x)$$

$$[HCOOH] = (0.0400 - x)$$

and

$$\frac{x(0.100 + x)}{(0.0400 - x)} = 1.74 \times 10^{-4}$$

Making the assumption that x is small compared with 0.1 and 0.04, the equation simplifies to

$$\frac{x(0.1)}{(0.04)} = 1.74 \times 10^{-4}$$

and

$$x = [H_3O^+] = 6.96 \times 10^{-5} \text{ mol/liter}$$

Comparing this value with 0.04 and 0.1, we see that the assumption is quite reasonable for most purposes. Thus

$$pH = - \log 6.96 \times 10^{-5} = 4.16$$

If we compare the pH of this solution with that of a solution which is 0.04 F in formic acid only (see page 244), we see that the addition of the formate has raised the pH from 2.6 to 4.16 as a result of the common ion effect.

Calculation of the pH of a Solution of a Weak Base and Its Salts. The following example will show that the calculation of pH in this instance is analogous to that discussed in the previous section.

★EXAMPLE. Calculate the pH of a solution that is 0.28 F in NH_4Cl and 0.070 F in NH_3. The equilibrium of interest is

$$NH_3 + H_2O \rightleftharpoons NH_4^+ + OH^-$$

for which $K_b = 1.86 \times 10^{-5}$.

The concentration of NH_4^+ will be equal to the formal concentration of the salt plus any NH_4^+ formed in the equilibrium reaction. Thus if we let $x = [OH^-]$, we may write

$$[NH_4^+] = (0.28 + x)$$

The NH_3 concentration will be equal to its formal concentration minus the amount needed to establish equilibrium.

$$[NH_3] = (0.07 - x)$$

Substituting these values into the equilibrium-constant expression

$$\frac{x(0.28 + x)}{(0.07 - x)} = 1.86 \times 10^{-5}$$

If we now assume $x \ll 0.28$ and 0.07, then

$$\frac{0.28x}{0.07} = 1.86 \times 10^{-5}$$

$$x = [\text{OH}^-] = 4.65 \times 10^{-6} \text{ mol/liter}$$

$$p\text{OH} = - \log 4.65 \times 10^{-6} = 5.33$$

$$p\text{H} = 14 - 5.33 = 8.67$$

Here again, the assumption regarding the magnitude of x was justified.

13.2 Buffer Solutions

Solutions composed of weak acids or bases and their corresponding salts are types of *buffer solutions* or *buffers*. These are of great importance in chemistry because they have the property of resisting changes in $p\text{H}$ both upon dilution and upon addition of strong acids or bases. This impor-

TABLE 13-2

**Effect of Dilution and Addition of Strong Acid or Base
to Buffered and Unbuffered Solutions**

	Composition	Initial $p\text{H}$	10-fold dilution	addition of 1.0 ml of 0.1 F HCl to 100 ml	addition of 1.0 ml of 0.1 F NaOH to 100 ml
				$p\text{H}$ after	
Unbuffered solutions	H_2O	7.00	7.00	3.00	11.00
	0.1 F HCl	1.00	2.00	1.00	1.01
	0.1 F NaOH	13.00	12.00	12.99	13.00
	0.1 F HOAc	2.88	3.38	2.72	3.05
	0.1 F NaOAc	8.83	8.38	6.75	11.00
Buffered solutions	0.1 F HOAc 0.1 F NaOAc	4.76	4.76	4.75	4.77
	0.1 F HOAc 0.01 F NaOAc	3.76	3.76	3.70	3.80
	0.01 F HOAc 0.1 F NaOAc	5.76	5.76	5.71	5.80
	0.1 F NH$_3$ 0.1 F NH$_4$Cl	9.27	9.27	9.26	9.28

tant characteristic is illustrated in Table 13-2 which contrasts the behavior of several buffered and unbuffered solutions under various circumstances.

PROPERTIES OF BUFFER SOLUTIONS

We have already indicated in the previous section that dilution of a buffered solution has little effect upon its pH because the concentrations of both the salt and the acid or base are altered in a proportionate way by the addition of solvent. The changes caused by the addition to small amounts of strong base or strong acid are shown in the examples that follow.

★EXAMPLE. Compare the pH before and after the addition of 10 mfw of NaOH to 1 liter of a buffer solution that is 0.100 F in HOAc and 0.200 F in NaOAc.

$$\frac{[H_3O^+][OAc^-]}{[HOAc]} = 1.75 \times 10^{-5}$$

The pH prior to addition of the strong base is readily found by assuming that $[OAc^-]$ and $[HOAc]$ are equal to their formal concentrations. Then

$$\frac{0.2x}{0.1} = 1.75 \times 10^{-5}$$

$$x = [H_3O^+] = 8.75 \times 10^{-6} \text{ mol/liter}$$

$$p\text{H} = 5.06$$

Upon addition of base, some of the HOAc will be neutralized; as a result, the concentration of weak acid will be diminished while that of the salt will be increased. We can obtain the pH of the solution after first calculating the new formal concentrations. The number of milliformula weights of HOAc will be equal to the original number less the number of milliformula weights of base added; that is,

$$\text{no. mfw HOAc} = 1000 \times 0.1 - 10 = 90$$

and

$$F_{\text{HOAc}} = \frac{90}{1000} = 0.090$$

The number of milliformula weights of NaOAc will have increased by this number. Thus

$$\text{no. mfw NaOAc} = 1000 \times 0.2 + 10 = 210$$

and

$$F_{\text{NaOAc}} = \frac{210}{1000} = 0.210$$

We may now calculate the pH of this solution using the same technique as before; that is,

$$\frac{0.210x}{0.090} = 1.75 \times 10^{-5}$$

$$x = [H_3O^+] = 7.5 \times 10^{-6} \text{ mol/liter}$$

$$pH = 5.12$$

★EXAMPLE. Calculate the pH of 1 liter of the same buffer solution after addition of 10 meq of HCl.

We may predict an increase in the concentration of undissociated acetic acid as well as a decrease in the acetate concentration owing to the reaction between the latter and the hydronium ions from the added HCl. As before, we can readily calculate the pH of the solution after first calculating the new formal concentrations of acetic acid and acetate ion. Thus

$$F_{\text{HOAc}} = \frac{0.1000 \times 1000 + 10}{1000} = 0.110$$

$$F_{\text{NaOAc}} = \frac{1000 \times 0.2 - 10}{1000} = 0.190$$

We can then calculate $[H_3O^+]$ as above

$$[H_3O^+] = 1.01 \times 10^{-5} \text{ mol/liter}$$

$$pH = 4.99$$

In these examples we considered 1 liter of solution containing 0.1 mol of acetic acid and 0.2 mol of sodium acetate. Since the pH of a buffer is governed by the ratio between acid and salt, we would expect a solution in which the concentrations were ten times those of the example to have substantially the same pH; the same should be true for a solution having concentrations one tenth as great. The number of equivalents of acid or base that each of these could tolerate without material alteration of the pH will vary appreciably, however. For example, we have seen that 1 liter of the original buffer changes pH from 5.06 to 5.12 upon addition of 10 milliequivalents of sodium hydroxide; 100 milliequivalents of the strong base could be added before the same pH change would occur in 1 liter of the more concentrated buffer. On the other hand, the most dilute of the three buffers would require only 1 meq of base to cause an identical pH change. Thus, while the three solutions have the same pH, they are quite different in what is called their *buffer capacity*—that is, in the quantity of acid or base they are capable of consuming.

In more quantitative terms, buffer capacity is often defined as *the number of mols of strong base required to cause a unit increase in pH in 1 liter of a buffer solution.* This quantity can be calculated if the composition of the buffer is known.

Ordinarily a high buffer capacity is desirable, and one obvious way of achieving this is by using high reagent concentrations. Less apparent, perhaps, but also effective is the proper choice of the buffering system. Generally, the maximum buffer capacity is achieved when the dissociation constant of the weak acid is numerically identical to the desired hydronium ion concentration. Under these circumstances the ratio of the concentration of the salt to the concentration of the acid approaches unity. It can easily be shown that the maximum in buffer capacity is associated with this 1:1 ratio.

PREPARATION OF BUFFER SOLUTIONS

When faced with the need for preparing a buffer solution, the chemist ordinarily has available a host of reagents from which to pick. In making a choice among these he will try to avoid substances that will react with other components of the system he wishes to buffer. Insofar as possible, he will also attempt to attain the maximum buffer capacity for a given concentration of reagent by employing a system in which the formal ratio of salt to acid or base is near unity.

Recipes for preparation of buffer solutions are readily available in chemical handbooks and reference works.[1] Because of their widespread employment, two buffer systems deserve specific mention. McIlvaine buffers cover a pH range from about 2 to 8 and are prepared by mixing solutions of citric acid with disodium hydrogen phosphate. Clark and Lubs buffers, which include a pH range from 2 to 10, make use of three systems—namely, phthalic acid, potassium hydrogen phthalate; potassium dihydrogen phosphate, dipotassium hydrogen phosphate; and boric acid, sodium borate.

13.3   Acid-base Indicators

There are substances whose color in solution depends upon the pH of the medium. Many occur naturally in various plants; their properties have been recognized and used for thousands of years for the determination of the alkalinity or acidity of water. These compounds, called *acid-base indicators*, are widely employed by the modern chemist to estimate the pH of solutions and to signal the end point in acid-base titrations. We must consider briefly the theory of their behavior.

THEORY OF INDICATOR BEHAVIOR

Acid-base indicators are generally complex organic compounds of high molecular weight. In water or other solvents they behave as weak acids

---

[1] See, for example, I. M. Kolthoff and C. Rosenblum, *Acid-Base Indicators*, 239. New York: The Macmillan Company, 1937.

or bases and thus participate in equilibrium reactions involving the hydronium ion. Accompanying the dissociation or association reactions of these compounds are complex, internal structural rearrangements that result in changes in color.

Without discussing the nature of the structural rearrangements we can symbolize the association or dissociation reaction of an acid-base indicator as follows:

$$H_2O + \underset{\text{(acid color)}}{HIn} \rightleftharpoons H_3O^+ + \underset{\text{(base color)}}{In^-}$$

or

$$\underset{\text{(base color)}}{In} + H_2O \rightleftharpoons \underset{\text{(acid color)}}{InH^+} + OH^-$$

In the first instance the indicator (which may be ionic or molecular in constitution) behaves as a weak acid that yields an anion, In^-, and a hydronium ion upon dissociation. In the second case, the indicator acts as a weak base capable of combining with hydronium ions to form the conjugate acid of the base. In either case, the two species involved in these equilibria differ from one another in color. Which species, and hence which color, predominates depends upon the pH. Thus, in the first instance, HIn will be the major constituent in strongly acid solutions and will be responsible for the "acid color" of the indicator, whereas In^- will represent its "basic color"; in the second case the species In will predominate in basic solutions and thus be responsible for the "basic color" of this indicator, while InH^+ will constitute the "acid color."

Equilibrium expressions for these processes take the following forms:

$$K_a = \frac{[H_3O^+][In^-]}{[HIn]}$$

and

$$K_b = \frac{[InH^+][OH^-]}{[In]}$$

Rearrangement of these expressions will illustrate the dependence of the ratio of indicator species not only upon the value for the equilibrium constant but also upon the hydronium ion concentration; in this respect, indicators behave as typical weak acids and bases.

The color of an indicator will vary according to the pH of its environment. Experiments show that the change will occur gradually over a range that typically embraces 2 pH units. The ability of the human eye to discriminate between colors is not overly acute, and therefore something on the order of a tenfold excess of one of the forms of the indicator is needed before the observer can state that the color due to this form predominates. In other words, the subjective "color change" of the indicator typically involves a major alteration in the position of the indicator equilibrium from a tenfold excess of one of the species to a similar excess of the other. Using HIn as an example, we may write that the indicator exhibits its acid color to the average observer when

$$\frac{[\text{In}^-]}{[\text{HIn}]} \leqq \frac{1}{10}$$

and its basic color when

$$\frac{[\text{In}^-]}{[\text{HIn}]} \geqq \frac{10}{1}$$

At ratios between these two values the color appears to be intermediate. These numerical estimates, of course, represent average behavior only; some indicators require smaller ratio changes and others larger. Furthermore, considerable variation in the ability to judge colors exists among observers, the extreme being the case of the color-blind person.

If we now substitute the two concentration ratios into the dissociation-constant expression for the indicator, we can find the variation of hydronium ion concentration necessary to effect the indicator color change. Thus for the acid color

$$\frac{[\text{H}_3\text{O}^+][\text{In}^-]}{[\text{HIn}]} = \frac{[\text{H}_3\text{O}^+]1}{10} = K_a$$

$$[\text{H}_3\text{O}^+] = 10 \, K_a$$

and, similarly, for the basic color

$$\frac{[\text{H}_3\text{O}^+]10}{1} = K_a$$

$$[\text{H}_3\text{O}^+] = \frac{1}{10} K_a$$

Converting these to pH, we get

$$p\text{H} = -1 - \log K_a \text{ for the acid color}$$

$$p\text{H} = +1 - \log K_a \text{ for the basic color}$$

or

$$p\text{H range} = pK_a \pm 1$$

Thus an indicator having an acid dissociation constant of 1×10^{-5} would show a color change when the pH of the solution in which it was dissolved changed from 4 to 6. A similar relationship is easily derived for an indicator of the basic type.

TYPES OF ACID-BASE INDICATORS

A list of compounds having acid-base indicator properties is very large and comprises a variety of organic structures. An indicator covering almost any desired pH range can ordinarily be found. A few of the most common indicators are given in Table 13-3.

The large majority of acid-base indicators can be classified into perhaps half a dozen categories based upon structural similarities.[2] Three of these classes are described below.

TABLE 13-3

Some Important Acid-base Indicators[3]

Common Name	Transition Range, pH	Color Change		Indicator Type[4]
		Acid	Base	
Methyl violet	0.5 — 1.5	yellow	blue	
Thymol blue	1.2 — 2.8	red	yellow	2
	8.0 — 9.6	yellow	blue	
Methyl yellow	2.9 — 4.0	red	yellow	3
Methyl orange	3.1 — 4.4	red	yellow	3
Bromcresol green	3.8 — 5.4	yellow	blue	2
Methyl red	4.2 — 6.3	red	yellow	3
Chlorophenol red	4.8 — 6.4	yellow	red	2
Bromthymol blue	6.0 — 7.6	yellow	blue	2
Phenol red	6.4 — 8.0	yellow	red	2
Neutral red	6.8 — 8.0	red	yellow-orange	
Cresol purple	7.4 — 9.0	yellow	purple	2
	1.2 — 2.8	red	yellow	
Phenolphthalein	8.0 — 9.6	colorless	red	1
Thymolphthalein	9.3 — 10.5	colorless	blue	1
Alizarin yellow	10.1 — 12.0	colorless	violet	3

[3] Taken from I. M. Kolthoff and H. A. Laitinen, *pH and Electro Titrations*, 29. New York: John Wiley and Sons, Inc., 1941.

[4] See text: 1. phthalein; 2. sulfonphthalein; 3. azo.

Phthalein Indicators. Most phthalein indicators are colorless in moderately acidic solutions and exhibit a variety of colors in alkaline media. In strongly alkaline solutions their colors tend to fade slowly; in some applications this is an inconvenience. As a group the phthaleins are

---

[2] See I. M. Kolthoff and C. Rosenblum, *Acid-Base Indicators*, Chap. 5. New York: The Macmillan Company, 1937.

insoluble in water but quite soluble in alcohol; the latter is the preferred solvent in preparing solutions of these indicators.

The best-known example of a phthalein indicator is *phenolphthalein*, whose structures may be represented as

The last equilibrium in this series predominates in the pH range 8.0 to 9.8. A major structural change involving the formation of a quinoid structure is associated with this reaction; it is this quinoid structure that is responsible for the red color imparted to the solution.

The other phthalein indicators differ in that the phenolic rings contain various additional functional groups. In the case of *thymolphthalein*, for example, there are two alkyl groups on each ring. The basic structural changes associated with the color change of this indicator are no different from phenolphthalein.

Sulfonphthalein Indicators. Many of the sulfonphthaleins exhibit two useful color-change ranges. One color change occurs in rather acidic solutions and the other in neutral or moderately basic media. In contrast to the phthaleins, the basic color shows good stability toward strong alkali.

Indicator solutions of these compounds can be prepared in approximately 20-percent alcohol; however, such reagents are often sufficiently acidic to alter slightly the pH of the media into which they are introduced. To avoid this problem, the sodium salt of the indicator is frequently prepared by dissolving a weighed quantity of the solid indicator in a suitable volume of dilute aqueous sodium hydroxide.

The simplest sulfonphthalein indicator is *phenolsulphonthalein* or *phenol red*. The principal equilibria for this compound is

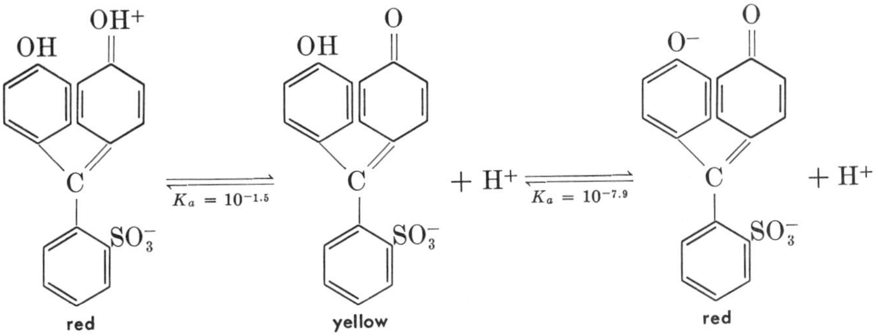

Only the second of the two color changes, occurring in the pH range 6.4 to 8.0, is commonly employed.

Substitution of halogens or alkyl groups for the hydrogens in the phenolic rings of the parent compound leads to a large variety of indicators that differ in color and pH range.

Azo Indicators. Most of the azo indicators exhibit a color change from red to yellow with increasing basicity. Their transition range is generally on the acid side. The best-known compounds in this class are *methyl orange* and *methyl red;* the behavior of the former is shown below

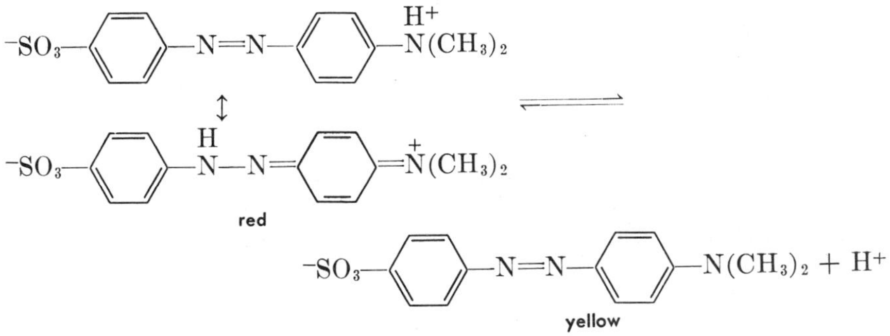

Methyl red is similar to methyl orange with the exception that the sulfonic acid group is replaced by a carboxylic acid group. Variations in the substituents on the amino nitrogen and in the rings give rise to a series of indicators with slightly different properties.

VARIABLES THAT INFLUENCE THE BEHAVIOR OF INDICATORS

Several factors play a part in determining the pH interval over which a given indicator exhibits a color change. Among these are temperature, electrolyte concentration, the presence of organic solvents, and the presence of colloidal particles. Some of these effects, particularly the last two, can cause a shift in the color range of one or more pH units. A discussion of these effects is beyond the scope of this book.[5]

13.4   Titration Curves for Simple Neutralization Reactions

For neutralization reactions, titration curves customarily consist of a plot of pH as the ordinate and volume of reagent as the abscissa. The reagent, for reasons that will become apparent, is always a standard solution of a strong acid or a strong base. The curves vary considerably in character depending upon the concentration of the reactants and the completeness of the reaction.

TITRATION OF SOLUTIONS OF STRONG ACIDS AND BASES

The simplest neutralization titrations are encountered in the analysis of strong acids and bases. The reaction is described by

$$H_3O^+ + OH^- \rightleftharpoons 2H_2O$$

and only this equilibrium need be considered in the derivation of titration curves.

Titration Curves of Strong Acids. To illustrate how a curve may be derived let us consider the titration of 50.0 ml of a 0.100 N solution of hydrochloric acid with a standard 0.100 N solution of sodium hydroxide.

> **Calculation of Initial pH.** Before addition of base the solution is 0.100 N in HCl. Therefore the pH is 1.00.

---

[5] For a further discussion see H. A. Laitinen, *Chemical Analysis*, 50–55. New York: McGraw-Hill Book Co., Inc., 1960.

Calculation of pH After Addition of 10 ml of Base. We may write

no. meq HCl remaining $= 50 \times 0.1 - 10 \times 0.1 = 4.0$

thus

$$N_{HCl} = [H_3O^+] = \frac{4.0}{60}$$

$$pH = -\log \frac{4}{60} = 1.18$$

In these calculations, the dissociation of water has been neglected since the contribution of hydronium ions from that source is negligible compared with the high concentration from the strong acid.

TABLE 13-4

Changes in pH During the Titration of 50 ml of 0.100 N HCl
with 0.100 N NaOH

Volume NaOH Added, ml	pH
0.0	1.00
10.0	1.18
25.0	1.48
40.0	1.95
49.0	3.00
49.9	4.00
49.99	5.00
Equivalence → 50.00	7.00
point 50.01	9.00
50.1	10.00
51.0	11.00
60.0	11.96
75.0	12.30
100.0	12.52

Calculations analogous to this provided the data in Table 13-4 for all additions short of the equivalence point.

Calculation of pH After Addition of 50.0 ml of Base. When 50.0 ml of base have been added, the titration is at the equivalence point; in this system neither acid nor base is present in excess. Therefore the pH is 7.00.

Calculation of *p*H After Addition of 50.01 ml of Base. The addition of 50.01 ml of base produces a slight excess of base in the solution; we can obtain the *p*H from its concentration.

$$N_{\text{NaOH}} = [OH^-] = \frac{50.01 \times 0.1 - 50.0 \times 0.1}{100.01}$$

$$= 1.00 \times 10^{-5}$$

$$p\text{OH} = 5.00$$

$$p\text{H} = 14.00 - 5.00 = 9.00$$

Additional calculations such as this yielded the remaining data shown in Table 13-4. Clearly the equivalence point is signaled by a very marked *p*H change. Thus a 0.02 ml addition of reagent in this region causes the

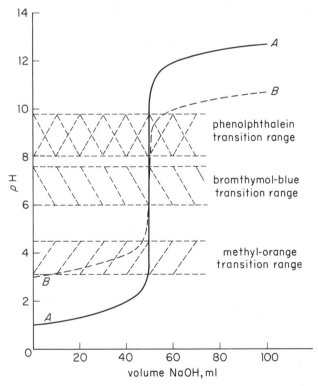

Fig. 13.1 Curves for the Titration of 50.0 ml Aliquots of Hydrochloric Acid with Sodium Hydroxide. Plots of pH as a function of the volume of NaOH added. *A.* Reactant concentrations are 0.100 N; *B.* Reactant concentrations are 0.00100 N.

pH to rise from 5 to 9 which corresponds to a ten-thousandfold change in hydronium ion concentration. These data are plotted as Curve *A* of Figure 13.1 which further emphasizes the equivalence-point behavior characteristic of the system.

Effect of Concentration. Curve *B* of Figure 13.1 is the theoretical titration curve for 50 ml of 0.001 *N* hydrochloric acid with 0.001 *N* base. It is apparent that a reduction in reactant concentration results in a decrease in the pH change associated with the equivalence point.

Indicator Choice. The transition intervals of three common acid-base indicators are also shown in Figure 13.1. Any of the three should produce a sharp end point with a negligible error in the titration of the 0.1 *N* reactants; this is no longer true, however, with the titration involving 0.001 *N* solutions. Here, only *bromthymol blue* could be employed, and even with this indicator the end point would be indistinct. It can be established by calculation that the pH of the system undergoes a change from 6.0 to 8.0 in the volume interval between 49.9 and 50.1 ml of titrant. Thus, nearly 0.2 ml of reagent is required to produce a change in color. Clearly, titrations of solutions more dilute than this cannot be performed with accuracy.

Titration Curves of Strong Bases. The uppermost curve of Figure 13.4 is typical for titration of a strong base with a strong acid. The derivation of this curve is analogous to that for a strong acid, involving only the calculation of the concentration of excess acid or base at any point in the titration.

TITRATION OF SOLUTIONS OF WEAK ACIDS OR BASES

The derivation of a titration curve for a solution of a weak acid or base is somewhat more complicated because the dissociation equilibrium of the acid or base must be taken into account. In arriving at a complete titration curve, four types of calculations must be employed, corresponding to four distinct parts of the curve. At the outset, the solution contains only a weak acid or a weak base and the calculation is based on the formal concentration of that substance. Addition of various increments of the reagent (in amounts up to but not including an equivalent amount) gives rise to a series of buffers; the pH of each can be calculated from the formal concentrations of the salt produced and the residual weak acid or base. At the equivalence point, the solution contains simply the salt of the weak acid or base being titrated, and the pH can be calculated from the formal concentration of that substance. Finally, beyond the equivalence point an excess of strong acid or base exists; this represses the basic or acidic character of the salt. Thus, the pH is governed largely by the concentration of the excess reagent.

Titration Curves of Weak Acids. To illustrate, consider the derivation of a curve depicting the titration of 50.0 ml of 0.100 N acetic acid ($K_a = 1.75 \times 10^{-5}$) with 0.100 N sodium hydroxide.

Initial pH. Here we must calculate the pH of a 0.1 N solution of HOAc; using the method shown on page 244, we obtain a value of 2.88.

pH After Addition of 10 ml of Reagent. A buffer solution consisting of NaOAc and HOAc has now been produced; to calculate the pH we must know the formal concentrations of the two constituents. These can be ascertained as follows:

$$F_{HOAc} = \frac{50 \times 0.1 - 10 \times 0.1}{60} = \frac{4.0}{60}$$

$$F_{NaOAc} = \frac{10 \times 0.1}{60} = \frac{1.0}{60}$$

Then letting $x = [H_3O^+]$, and substituting appropriate numbers for the various terms in the dissociation-constant expression for acetic acid, we obtain

$$\frac{x \cdot \frac{1}{60}}{\frac{4}{60}} = K_a = 1.75 \times 10^{-5}$$

$$x = [H_3O^+] = 7.0 \times 10^{-5} \text{ mol/liter}$$

$$pH = 4.15$$

Calculations similar to this will delineate the curve in the entire buffer region. Data from such calculations are given in Table 13-5. Note that when the acid has been 50 percent neutralized—in this particular titration, after an addition of exactly 25.0 ml of base—the formal concentrations of acid and salt are identical; within the limits of the approximations ordinarily used, so also are their molar concentrations. Thus these terms cancel one another out in the equilibrium-constant expression, and the hydronium ion concentration is numerically equal to the dissociation constant; that is, the pH is equal to the pK_a. This relationship can be used to ascertain quickly the pH at the midpoint in the titration of a weak acid. In the case of a weak base, the hydroxyl ion concentration is equal numerically to the dissociation constant of the base at the midpoint in the titration.

Equivalence Point pH. At the equivalence point in the titration the acetic acid has been converted to sodium acetate; the solution is therefore similar to one formed by dissolving that salt in water. After calculation of the formal concentration of the salt, the pH calculation is identical to that described on page 250; that is,

$$F_{NaOAc} = \frac{50 \times 0.100}{100.0} = 0.05$$

TABLE 13-5

Changes in pH During the Titration of 50 ml of 0.100 N Acetic Acid with
0.100 N NaOH

Volume NaOH Added, ml	pH
0.0	2.88
10.0	4.15
25.0	4.76
40.0	5.36
49.0	6.45
49.9	7.45
50.0	8.73
50.1	10.0
51.0	11.00
60.0	11.96
75.0	12.30
100.0	12.52

The equilibrium that determines the pH at this point is

$$OAc^- + H_2O \rightleftharpoons HOAc + OH^-$$

and letting $x = [OH^-]$ we find

$$\frac{x^2}{(0.05 - x)} \cong \frac{x^2}{0.05} = \frac{1 \times 10^{-14}}{1.75 \times 10^{-5}}$$

$$x = [OH^-] = 5.36 \times 10^{-6} \text{ mol/liter}$$

$$p\text{OH} = 5.27$$

$$p\text{H} = 8.73$$

pH After Addition of 50.10 ml of Base. When 50.10 ml of base have
been added, we can write

$$F_{NaOH} = \frac{50.10 \times 0.1 - 50.00 \times 0.1}{100.1} = 1.0 \times 10^{-4}$$

In this solution hydroxyl ions arise both from the excess of sodium hydroxide and the reaction of the acetate ion with water. The contribution of the
latter is small enough to be neglected, however, since the excess base will
tend to repress this reaction. This becomes evident when we consider
that the hydroxyl ion concentration was only 5.36×10^{-6} mol/liter when
no excess base was present. Once an excess of strong base has been added,

the contribution from the reaction of the acetate will be even smaller, so that we may say

$$[OH^-] \cong F_{\text{NaOH}} = 1.0 \times 10^{-4}$$

$$pOH = 4.0$$

$$pH = 10.0$$

Thus the titration curves for a weak acid and a strong acid become identical in the region slightly beyond the equivalence point. This is confirmed by the identical data found in Tables 13-4 and 13-5 for the final points in the titrations.

Before discussing the curve just derived, we should consider the calculation of the pH beyond the equivalence point under circumstances where the contribution of the salt to the pH cannot be neglected. This would be the situation if the excess of base were very small, or if the basic equilibrium constant of the salt were relatively large.

★EXAMPLE. Calculate the pH of a mixture of 50.00 ml of 0.100 N HA ($K_a = 1.0 \times 10^{-7}$) and 50.05 ml of 0.100 N NaOH.

The formal concentrations of the constituents are given by

$$F_{\text{NaA}} = \frac{50.0 \times 0.100}{100.05} = 0.0500$$

$$F_{\text{NaOH}} = \frac{50.05 \times 0.100 - 50.00 \times 0.100}{100.05} = 5.0 \times 10^{-5}$$

Inasmuch as HA is a rather weak acid, we might suspect that a significant fraction of the OH^- ions would arise from reaction of A^- with water. If we let y be the concentration of HA formed as a result of this reaction, we can express the equilibrium concentrations of the various species as follows:

$$[HA] = y$$

$$[A^-] = 0.0500 - y$$

$$[OH^-] = (5 \times 10^{-5} + y)$$

The last equation simply states that hydroxyl ions originate both from two sources—the excess of strong base ($5 \times 10^{-5} N$) and the reaction of A^- with water (y). Substituting into the equilibrium expression

$$\frac{y(5 \times 10^{-5} + y)}{(0.0500 - y)} = \frac{1 \times 10^{-14}}{1 \times 10^{-7}}$$

gives, on rearrangement,

$$y^2 + 5.01 \times 10^{-5} y - 5.0 \times 10^{-9} = 0$$

Solving this quadratic equation for y,

$$y = [HA] = 5.0 \times 10^{-5} \text{ mol/liter}$$
$$[OH^-] = (5 \times 10^{-5} + y) = 1.0 \times 10^{-4} \text{ mol/liter}$$
$$pOH = 4.0$$
$$pH = 10.0$$

The data from Table 13-5 are plotted as Curve A in Figure 13.2. Contrasting this with the curve for a strong acid, we see that one obvious difference lies in the pH at the equivalence point, which is about 8.7 for the weak acid and 7.0 for the strong. Furthermore, the pH of the solution is higher for comparable points prior to the equivalence point. The net

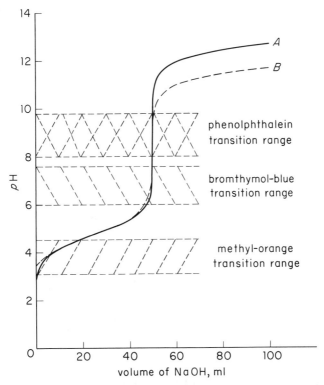

Fig. 13.2 Curves for the Titration of 50.0-ml Aliquots of Acetic Acid with Sodium Hydroxide. **A.** Reactant concentrations are 0.100 N; **B.** Reactant concentrations are 0.0100 N.

effect is to reduce the magnitude of the pH change occurring in the equivalence-point region.

Effect of Concentration. Curve B in Figure 13.2 is the theoretical curve for the titration of a 0.01 N solution of acetic acid with 0.01 N base.

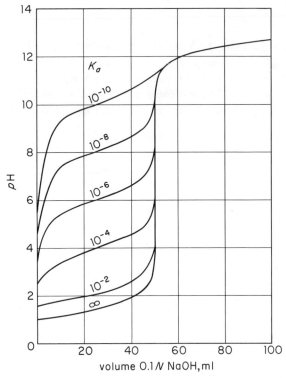

Fig. 13.3 Titration Curves for Acids of Various Strengths. Each curve represents titration of 50.0 ml of 0.100 N acid with 0.100 N NaOH.

For this system the initial pH is higher; in the buffer region, however, the two curves are identical because the pH of buffer solutions is nearly independent of dilution. The equivalence point pH for the more dilute solution can be shown to be about half a unit lower, or 8.2, while beyond the equivalence point the two curves differ by about one pH unit. Thus the change in pH associated with the equivalence point becomes smaller with dilution.

Indicator Choice; Feasibility of Titration. These curves clearly indicate that the choice of indicators for the titration of a weak acid is more limited than for a strong acid. *Methyl orange* is totally unsuited for this titration; nor would *bromthymol blue* be satisfactory, since its color change requires the addition of 1 or 2 ml of reagent. Only an indicator having a transition range in the basic region would be appropriate; *phenol-phthalein* is an excellent example.

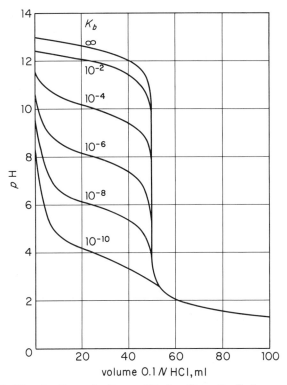

Fig. 13.4 Titration Curves for Bases of Various Strengths. Each curve represents titration of 50.0 ml of 0.100 N base with 0.100 N HCl.

Figure 13.3 illustrates that the end-point problem becomes more critical for weaker acids; in this figure are shown titration curves for a series of weak acids of differing strengths. Because of the limited sensitivity of the eye to color changes, we might conclude that 0.1 N solutions of acids with dissociation constants much less than 1×10^{-6} could not be titrated accurately; actually, the limiting figure for errors of ± 0.2 percent is about 5×10^{-7}. Somewhat weaker acids can be titrated by preparing a color standard to compare against the solution being titrated. The standard should have about the same volume and the same quantity of indicator as the solution being analyzed; obviously the pH of the standard must be that of the equivalence point. With these added precautions, 0.1 N solutions of acids with dissociation constants as low as 1×10^{-8} can be determined with an error no greater than about 0.2 percent. By working with more concentrated solutions titration of even weaker acids is possible.

Titration Curves of Weak Bases. Figure 13.4 shows the theoretical titration curves for a series of bases of differing strengths. These were derived by techniques similar to those employed in calculating the curve for acetic acid. With weak bases, an indicator having an acid transition range is obviously required.

TITRATION OF SOLUTIONS OF SALTS OF WEAK ACIDS AND BASES

Salts of sufficiently weak acids can be titrated with standard solutions of a strong acid, the product being the undissociated weak acid; that is,

$$A^- + H_3O^+ \rightleftharpoons HA + H_2O$$

Derivation of a curve for this titration involves the same four types of calculations. Initially, the solution contains only the salt, and the pH is calculated from its concentration. Addition of a strong acid produces a buffer; the pH can be obtained from the formal concentrations of the residual salt and the weak acid formed. At the equivalence point, the solution consists of a weak acid plus the salt of the strong acid. Since the latter has no appreciable effect, the pH can be calculated from the formal concentration of the weak acid. Finally, beyond the equivalence point the solution is composed of a mixture of a weak and a strong acid. When the concentration of the latter becomes sufficiently great, the dissociation of the weak acid is repressed to the point where the pH can be calculated directly from the formal concentration of the strong acid.

Titration Curves of Salts of Weak Acids. By way of illustration, consider the titration of 50 ml of 0.1 F sodium cyanide with 0.1 N hydrochloric acid. Hydrogen cyanide is a weak acid with a dissociation constant of 2.1×10^{-9}.

Initial pH. By the technique shown on page 250 the calculated pH will be 10.84.

Buffer Region pH. Additions of HCl to the solution result in the formation of HCN, thus giving a buffer mixture. For example, after the addition of 10 ml of HCl, we may write

$$F_{HCN} = \frac{10 \times 0.1}{60} = \frac{1}{60}$$

$$F_{NaCN} = \frac{50 \times 0.100 - 10 \times 0.100}{60} = \frac{4.0}{60}$$

The pH of this buffer mixture is obtained in the usual way and has a value of 9.28.

Equivalence Point pH. At the equivalence point the salt has been converted to the weak acid; thus we may say

$$F_{\text{HCN}} = \frac{50 \times 0.100}{100.0} = 0.0500$$

Calculation of the pH of a 0.0500 F solution of HCN will give 4.99.

Postequivalence Point pH. When 50.01 ml of reagent have been added

$$F_{\text{HCl}} = \frac{50.01 \times 0.1000 - 50.00 \times 0.1000}{100.01} = 1.0 \times 10^{-5}$$

$$F_{\text{HCN}} = \frac{50.0 \times 0.1000}{100.01} = 5.0 \times 10^{-2}$$

Hydronium ions are present from the excess HCl and from the dissociation of the HCN. If we let x be the concentration of cyanide arising from dissociation, we may write

$$[\text{CN}^-] = x$$

$$[\text{H}_3\text{O}^+] = 1.0 \times 10^{-5} + x$$

$$[\text{HCN}] = 0.05 - x$$

$$\frac{(1.0 \times 10^{-5} + x)(x)}{(0.05 - x)} = 2.1 \times 10^{-9}$$

If we assume x to be small relative to 0.05 and 1.0×10^{-5}, we obtain a trial value of 1×10^{-5}; clearly we must solve the quadratic equation

$$x^2 + 1.0 \times 10^{-5}x - 1.05 \times 10^{-10} = 0$$

This gives

$$x = [\text{CN}^-] = 0.64 \times 10^{-5} \text{ mol/liter}$$

$$[\text{H}_3\text{O}^+] = 1.0 \times 10^{-5} + 0.64 \times 10^{-5} = 1.64 \times 10^{-5} \text{ mol/liter}$$

$$p\text{H} = 4.78$$

As the excess of HCl increases, the contribution of HCN to the acidity rapidly becomes smaller and the pH can be calculated from the formality of the HCl alone. Thus after the addition of 50.5 ml of acid, the formality of HCl is 4.78×10^{-5}. By assuming this to be the hydronium ion concentration, a pH of 3.32 is obtained.

Figure 13.5 illustrates the titration curve derived from these calculations. Clearly none of the indicators shown is well suited for the titrations; *methyl red* (transition range 4.1 to 6.2) would, however, be satisfactory.

Curve B illustrates the effect of dilution. Obviously a solution of this salt more dilute than 0.01 F cannot be titrated with a high degree of accuracy.

We have already demonstrated that end points become less sharp for solutions of weaker acids or bases. A similar situation applies in the case of salts. As the equilibrium constant for the salt becomes smaller (that is, as the dissociation constant of the parent acid or base becomes larger) the titration curves are the less well defined. In other words, the salts of very

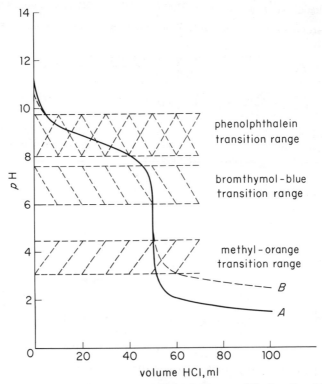

Fig. 13.5 Curves for the Titration of 50.0 ml Aliquots of Sodium Cyanide Solutions with Hydrochloric Acid. A. Reactant concentrations are 0.100 N; B. Reactant concentrations are 0.0100 N.

weak acids or bases can be titrated successfully, while those of stronger reagents cannot. Titration curves for a series of salts of acids with differing basic equilibrium constants will have an appearance similar to the curves in Figure 13.4. Only those salts having constants larger than about 10^{-7} are readily titrated with a high degree of accuracy. These, of course, would be salts of acids that have dissociation constants smaller than about 10^{-7}.

These observations also apply to the titration of salts of the weaker bases with a standard solution of a strong base. In such titrations end points occur in basic solutions, the curves being similar in appearance to those for the weak acids shown in Figure 13.3. Good end points are observed only where the salt is derived from a fairly weak base—that is, a base with a dissociation constant of 10^{-7} or smaller.

Problems

1. The value for K_w at $0°$, $50°$, and $100°$ C is 1.15×10^{-15}, 9.61×10^{-14}, and 5.13×10^{-13}, respectively. Calculate the pH of a neutral solution at each of these temperatures.   ans. $pH = 7.47$ at $0°$ C

2. Calculate the $[H_3O^+]$, $[OH^-]$, pH, and pOH of (a) 0.200 N $HClO_4$ and (b) 0.0035 F KOH.
     ans. (a) $[H_3O^+] = 0.200$; $[OH^-] = 5 \times 10^{-14}$; $pH = 0.7$; $pOH = 13.3$

3. Calculate the $[H_3O^+]$, $[OH^-]$, pH, and pOH of (a) 0.0084 F $Ba(OH_2)$, (b) 3.7×10^{-4} N $Ba(OH)_2$, and (c) 3.7×10^{-4} N NaOH.

4. What is the pH of a 0.500 N KOH solution at $0°$ C (K_w at $0°$ C $= 1.15 \times 10^{-15}$)?

5. Calculate the pH of a 2.0 F HCl solution.

6. What is the $[H_3O^+]$ of a solution having (a) a pH of 3.42, (b) a pH of 9.67, (c) a pOH of 13.16?   ans. (a) $[H_3O^+] = 3.8 \times 10^{-4}$ mol/liter

7. What is the pH of a solution containing 0.0731 gram of NaOH in 1 liter?

8. What is the pH of a solution prepared by mixing 17.4 ml of 0.200 N $HClO_4$ with 36.0 ml of 0.109 N NaOH?   ans. $pH = 11.92$

9. What is the pH of a mixture of 30.0 ml of 0.0300 N HCl and 6.4 ml of 0.080 N KOH?

10. Calculate the pH of a 1.0×10^{-7} N solution of HCl.   ans. $pH = 6.8$

11. Calculate the pH of a 2.0×10^{-7} F solution of NaOH.

12. Calculate the pH of a 0.050 F solution of the weak acid HA which has a dissociation constant of 3.5×10^{-6}.   ans. $pH = 3.38$

13. What is the pH of a 0.100 F solution of hydroxylamine?   ans. $pH = 9.51$

14. Calculate the pH of a 0.0020 F solution of formic acid.   ans. $pH = 3.30$

15. What is the pH of a 1.50×10^{-4} F solution of methylamine?

16. By how many units will pH of the following solutions change upon twofold and upon one-hundredfold dilution: (a) a 0.010 F solution of HCl and (b) a 0.010 F solution of HOAc?

17. What is the pH of a solution that is 0.0200 F in sodium benzoate and 0.0100 F in benzoic acid?   ans. $pH = 4.5$

18. What is the pH of a solution that is 0.710 F in NH_4Cl?   ans. pH = 4.71

19. Calculate the pH of a buffer prepared by mixing 50 ml of 1.07 F NH_3 with 100 ml of 0.25 F NH_4Cl.

20. Describe the preparation of 1 liter of a buffer of pH 4.0 from 1.0 F solutions of HOAc and NaOAc.

ans. Mix 149 ml of the NaOAc with 851 ml of the HOAc

21. How many grams of NH_4Cl should be added to 2 liters of 0.30 F NH_3 to give a buffer having a pH of 9.0?

22. What is the pH of a 0.0010 F solution of aniline hydrochloride?

ans. pH = 3.79

23. To 400 ml of 1.00 F formic acid were added 21 grams of sodium formate. What was the pH of the resultant buffer?

24. How many milliliters of 1.0 N NaOH should be added to 1.0 liter of 0.60 F HOAc to give a buffer having a pH of 5.0?

25. What is the pH at the equivalence point in the titration of 0.200 F NH_3 with 0.200 F HCl?

26. What is the pH in the titration in Problem 25 when half the NH_3 has been neutralized?

27. What is the pH of the solution obtained by mixing 19.0 ml of 0.20 F sodium benzoate with 20 ml of 0.050 F HCl and diluting to 100 ml?

28. What is the pH of a mixture of 100 ml of 0.100 F formic acid to which 0.2 ml of 1.00 F HCl has been added?   ans. pH = 2.29

29. A mixture containing HOAc and NaOAc had a pH of 4.12. Calculate the ratio of the formal concentrations of the two species.

ans. $\dfrac{F_{NaOAc}}{F_{HOAc}} = 0.231$

30. A 1.00-liter mixture of NH_4Cl and NH_3 had a pH of 9.64. The total number of formula weights of the two substances was 0.80. Calculate the formal concentration of each in the solution.

31. A buffer is 0.500 F in NaOAc and 0.75 F in HOAc. To 1 liter of this is added 1.0 ml of 1.0 N NaOH. Calculate the change in pH of the solution.

32. To 1 liter of the buffer in Problem 31 is added 1.0 ml of 1.5 N HCl. Calculate the change in pH.

33. Calculate the pH of
   (a) 10.0 ml of 0.0100 N $Ba(OH)_2$ and 5.0 ml of 0.0200 N HCl
   (b) 10.0 ml of 0.0100 F $Ba(OH)_2$ and 5.0 ml of 0.0200 N HCl
   (c) 10.0 ml of 0.0100 N $Ba(OH)_2$ and 10.0 ml of 0.0200 N HCl
   (d) 10.0 ml of 0.150 N formic acid
   (e) 10.0 ml of 0.150 N formic acid and 10.0 ml of 0.100 N NaOH

(f) 10.0 ml of 0.150 N formic acid and 15.0 ml of 0.100 N NaOH

(g) 10.0 ml of 0.150 N formic acid and 20.0 ml of 0.100 N NaOH

34. Calculate the pH of the solutions obtained by the addition of the following volumes of 0.100 N HCl to 25.0 ml of 0.200 F methylamine:
    (a) 0.0 ml
    (b) 10.0 ml
    (c) 25.0 ml
    (d) 45.0 ml
    (e) 49.9 ml
    (f) 50.0 ml
    (g) 50.1 ml
    (h) 51.0 ml
    (i) 60.0 ml

35. Sketch a titration curve from the data obtained in Problem 34 and choose an indicator from Table 13-3 that would be suitable for this titration.

36. For 25.0 ml of 0.100 N HA ($K_a = 1.0 \times 10^{-7}$) with 0.100 N KOH derive a theoretical titration curve. Suggest an indicator for this titration.

37. Calculate the pH of the solutions obtained by mixing the following volumes of 0.150 N HCl with 30.0 ml of 0.100 F NaOCl:
    (a) 0.0 ml
    (b) 5.0 ml
    (c) 10.0 ml
    (d) 19.0 ml
    (e) 19.9 ml
    (f) 20.0 ml
    (g) 21.0 ml
    (h) 25.0 ml

38. Sketch a titration curve from the data in Problem 37 and suggest an indicator for this titration.

39. Derive a theoretical titration curve for the titration of 20.0 ml of 0.100 F pyridinum chloride with 0.0500 N NaOH. Suggest an indicator for the titration.

40. Calculate the pH of the solution 0.1 ml before and 0.1 ml after the equivalence point in the following titrations:
    (a) 25.0 ml of 0.200 N HNO$_2$ with 0.100 N KOH
    (b) 25.0 ml of 0.00200 N NaOH with 0.00180 N HClO$_4$
    (c) 30.0 ml of 0.0300 F NaCN with 0.0500 N HCl
    (d) 25.0 ml of 0.0100 N NH$_3$ with 0.0100 N HCl

41. What is the pH of a solution which is 0.100 F in ZnCl$_2$ and saturated with Zn(OH)$_2$?

$$\left(\, 14 \,\right)$$

Theory of Neutralization Titrations
in Complex Systems

In the previous chapter our consideration of equilibrium behavior was focused upon simple acid-base systems—that is, upon solutes that yield but a single hydronium or hydroxyl ion per molecule in their reaction with water. There are, of course, numerous substances that provide two or more of these ions when dissolved; in general, titration curves for such solutes will possess greater complexity than the curves we have derived thus far. Limitations of space preclude an examination of the many possibilities that result from the ability of a substance to enter into a stepwise dissociation. Nevertheless, we can extend our present knowledge to those acid or base systems in which each succeeding dissociation is significantly less favorable than the one preceding it. For such a system it is necessary to employ but one calculation in addition to those we have already used in order to derive a reasonably satisfactory titration curve.

14.1 Calculation of the pH of Solutions of Acid Salts

Solutions of weak-acid salts of the type NaHA present a unique problem in equilibrium calculations in that the anion may react with the solvent in two ways

$$HA^- + H_2O \rightleftharpoons H_2A + OH^-$$

and

$$H_2O + HA^- \rightleftharpoons H_3O^+ + A^{2-}$$

One of these reactions produces hydronium ions while the other yields hydroxyl ions. Whether the solution is acidic or basic will be determined by the relative magnitude of the equilibrium constants for these processes.

$$K_b = \frac{K_w}{K_1} = \frac{[H_2A][OH^-]}{[HA^-]} \tag{14-1}$$

$$K_2 = \frac{[H_3O^+][A^{2-}]}{[HA^-]} \tag{14-2}$$

If K_b is greater than K_2, the solution will be basic; otherwise it will be acidic.

Equations describing the solution in terms of material balance and charge balance can be written. Thus we may state

$$F_{NaHA} = [HA^-] + [H_2A] + [A^{2-}] \tag{14-3}$$

and

$$[Na^+] + [H_3O^+] = [HA^-] + 2[A^{2-}] + [OH^-]$$

Since the sodium ion concentration is equal to the formal concentration of the salt, we may rewrite the last equation as

$$F_{NaHA} = [HA^-] + 2[A^{2-}] + [OH^-] - [H_3O^+] \tag{14-4}$$

Often we cannot neglect either the hydroxyl or the hydronium ion concentration in solutions of this type, and we need, therefore, a fifth equation to take care of the five unknowns. The ion-product constant for water will serve this purpose.

$$K_w = [H_3O^+][OH^-]$$

The derivation of a rigorous expression for the hydronium ion concentration from these five equations is difficult; however, a reasonably good approximation, applicable in most cases, can be obtained fairly easily. Equating (14-4) with (14-3) yields

$$[H_2A] = [A^{2-}] + [OH^-] - [H_3O^+]$$

With the aid of (14-1) and (14-2) we can express $[H_2A]$ and $[A^{2-}]$ in terms of $[HA^-]$; that is,

$$\frac{K_w[HA^-]}{K_1[OH^-]} = \frac{K_2[HA^-]}{[H_3O^+]} + [OH^-] - [H_3O^+]$$

Replacing $[OH^-]$ by the equivalent expression $K_w/[H_3O^+]$ gives

$$\frac{[H_3O^+][HA^-]}{K_1} = \frac{K_2[HA^-]}{[H_3O^+]} + \frac{K_w}{[H_3O^+]} - [H_3O^+]$$

Multiplying through by $[H_3O^+]$ and rearranging yields

$$[H_3O^+]^2 \left(\frac{[HA^-]}{K_1} + 1 \right) = K_2[HA^-] + K_w$$

This is easily converted to

$$[H_3O^+] = \sqrt{\frac{K_1K_2[HA^-] + K_1K_w}{[HA^-] + K_1}} \qquad (14\text{-}5)$$

Equation (14-5) is useful only where the following is valid:

$$[HA^-] \cong F_{NaHA} \qquad (14\text{-}6)$$

This is a reasonable assumption provided that neither of the two equilibria involving HA^- is favorable and provided that the formality of the salt is not too low.

Substituting (14-6) into (14-5) yields

$$[H_3O^+] = \sqrt{\frac{K_1K_2F_{NaHA} + K_1K_w}{F_{NaHA} + K_1}} \qquad (14\text{-}7)$$

K_1 will often be so much smaller than F_{NaHA} that it can be neglected in the denominator, thus permitting further simplification of equation (14-7). Furthermore, K_1K_w will frequently be much smaller than $K_1K_2F_{NaHA}$. When both of these conditions exist, equation (14-7) simplifies to

$$[H_3O^+] = \sqrt{K_1K_2} \qquad (14\text{-}8)$$

when

$$K_1 \ll F_{NaHA} \quad \text{and} \quad K_1K_w \ll K_1K_2F_{NaHA}$$

Thus, in many instances, the pH of a solution of a salt of the type NaHA will be independent of the salt concentration over a considerable concentration range.

★EXAMPLE. Calculate the hydronium ion concentration of a 0.100 F solution of $NaHCO_3$.

We must first examine the assumptions necessary to use equation (14-8). From the table of dissociation constants we find that K_1 for H_2CO_3 is 4.6×10^{-7} and K_2 is 4.4×10^{-11}. Obviously K_1 is much smaller than F_{NaHA}; K_1K_w is equal to 4.6×10^{-21}, while $K_1K_2F_{NaHA}$ has the value of about 2×10^{-18}; we can therefore use the simplified equation.
Thus

$$[H_3O^+] = \sqrt{4.6 \times 10^{-7} \times 4.4 \times 10^{-11}}$$

$$[H_3O^+] = 4.5 \times 10^{-9} \text{ mol/liter}$$

★EXAMPLE. Calculate the hydronium ion concentration of a 1.0×10^{-3} F solution of Na_2HPO_4.

Here we are concerned with the acid salt HPO_4^- for which the pertinent dissociation constants (those containing $[HPO_4^-]$) are K_2 and K_3 for H_3PO_4. These have the values of 6.2×10^{-8} and 4.8×10^{-13}, respectively. Considering again the assumptions implicit in equation (14-8), we find that 6.2×10^{-8} is indeed much smaller than the formality of the salt. On the other hand, K_2K_w is by no means much smaller than $K_2K_3F_{Na_2HPO_4}$, the former having a value of 6.2×10^{-22} and the latter of about 3×10^{-23}. We should, therefore, make use of equation (14-7).

$$[H_3O^+] = \sqrt{\frac{6.2 \times 10^{-8} \times 4.8 \times 10^{-13} \times 1.0 \times 10^{-3} + 6.2 \times 10^{-22}}{1.0 \times 10^{-3} + 6.2 \times 10^{-8}}}$$

$$= 8.1 \times 10^{-10} \text{ mol/liter}$$

Use of equation (14-8) would have yielded a value of 1.7×10^{-10} mol/liter.

★EXAMPLE. Find the hydronium ion concentration of a 0.0100 F solution of NaH_2PO_4.

In this case the two dissociation constants of importance are K_1 and K_2 for H_3PO_4; these have values of 7.5×10^{-3} and 6.2×10^{-8}. Because K_1 is not much smaller than $F_{NaH_2PO_4}$, we again must make use of equation (14-7).

$$[H_3O^+] = \sqrt{\frac{7.5 \times 10^{-3} \times 6.2 \times 10^{-8} \times 1.0 \times 10^{-2} + 7.5 \times 10^{-17}}{0.0075 + 0.010}}$$

$$= 1.6 \times 10^{-5} \text{ mol/liter}$$

14.2   Titration Curves for Complex Systems

We shall consider the derivation of titration curves for three types of complex systems. The first involves a weak acid of the type H_2A which, upon solution in water undergoes a stepwise dissociation.

$$H_2O + H_2A \rightleftharpoons H_3O^+ + HA^- \qquad K_1 = \frac{[H_3O^+][HA^-]}{[H_2A]}$$

$$H_2O + HA^- \rightleftharpoons H_3O^+ + A^{2-} \qquad K_2 = \frac{[H_3O^+][A^{2-}]}{[HA^-]}$$

The second involves titration of a solution containing two monoprotic acids, HA and HX, that differ in their degree of dissociation. Here we will need to consider the equilibria

$$H_2O + HA \rightleftharpoons H_3O^+ + A^- \qquad K_1 = \frac{[H_3O^+][A^-]}{[HA]}$$

$$H_2O + HX \rightleftharpoons H_3O^+ + X^- \qquad K_2 = \frac{[H_3O^+][X^-]}{[HX]}$$

The third system consists of salts of the type Na_2A that may be titrated with a standard solution of a strong acid. The significant equilibria governing such a system are

$$A^{2-} + H_2O \rightleftharpoons HA^- + OH^- \qquad K_1' = \frac{[HA^-][OH^-]}{[A^{2-}]}$$

$$HA^- + H_2O \rightleftharpoons H_2A + OH^- \qquad K_2' = \frac{[H_2A][OH^-]}{[HA^-]}$$

Throughout this discussion we shall limit ourselves to those systems for which the ratio K_1/K_2 is equal to or greater than 10^3—that is, where the one acidic or basic group is at least one thousand times stronger than the second. This limitation will permit the derivation of titration curves with the techniques that we have already described.

POLYPROTIC ACIDS

As an example let us consider the titration of 25.00 ml of 0.100 F maleic acid with a 0.100 F solution of sodium hydroxide. Maleic acid is a typical dibasic organic acid having the empirical formula $H_2C_4H_2O_4$; for the sake of simplicity, we will use H_2M to symbolize the free acid. The dissociation equilibria and their constants are as follows:

$$H_2O + H_2M \rightleftharpoons H_3O^+ + HM^- \qquad K_1 = 1.5 \times 10^{-2}$$

$$H_2O + HM^- \rightleftharpoons H_3O^+ + M^{2-} \qquad K_2 = 2.6 \times 10^{-7}$$

Initial pH. There are three sources of hydronium ions in an aqueous solution of maleic acid: (1) dissociation of the solvent, water, (2) dissociation of the maleic acid, H_2M, and (3) further dissociation of HM^- to give hydronium ions and M^{2-}. An exact statement of the pH would require taking into account the equilibria associated with all three of these processes. As in the case of monoprotic acids (Chapter 13), however, we can generally neglect the contribution of water to the acidity since the number of protons from this source is negligible with respect to the far larger contribution from the first dissociation step of the acid. Furthermore, provided the ratio of K_1/K_2 is high—say greater than 1000—we can also neglect the hydronium ions formed by dissociation of HM^- without introducing a serious error. As in the case of the dissociation of water, the hydronium ions formed from the H_2M will, by the LeChatelier principle, repress the further dissociation of the HM^- and keep the concentration from this source at a negligible level. With these two assumptions, the calculation of the pH of a solution of maleic acid becomes identical to the calculation for a monoprotic acid with a K_a of 1.5×10^{-2}. Thus

$$x \cong [H_3O^+] \cong [HM^-]$$

$$0.1 - x \cong [H_2M]$$

and

$$\frac{x^2}{0.1 - x} = 1.5 \times 10^{-2}$$

Solution of this quadratic equation leads to a value for x of 3.2×10^{-2} mol/liter or a pH of 1.5.

First Buffer Region. Addition of base to the maleic acid solution results in conversion of a part of the acid to hydrogen maleate. A buffer is thus formed consisting of the weak acid H_2M and its salt NaHM. Again, we can neglect the dissociation of HM^- to M^{2-} and treat the system as a simple buffer provided that K_1/K_2 is greater than 10^3. Thus

$$F_{H_2M} = \frac{(25.0 \times 0.1) - (5.0 \times 0.100)}{30.0} = 6.67 \times 10^{-2}$$

$$F_{NaHM} = \frac{5.00 \times 0.1}{30.0} = 1.67 \times 10^{-2}$$

Then

$$x = [H_3O^+]$$

$$[H_2M] = 6.67 \times 10^{-2} - x$$

$$[HM^-] = 1.67 \times 10^{-2} + x$$

Assuming x to be small with respect to the two formal concentrations and substituting into the equilibrium-constant expression leads to a tentative value of 6.0×10^{-2} mol/liter for x; it is clear that this approximation is not reasonable and the more rigorous treatment must be followed. That is,

$$\frac{x(1.67 \times 10^{-2} + x)}{(6.67 \times 10^{-2} - x)} = 1.5 \times 10^{-2}$$

Solution of the resulting quadratic expression gives a value for $[H_3O^+]$ of 1.95×10^{-2} mol per liter; the pH is 1.71.

Additional points in the first buffer region can be computed in a similar way. The dissociation of HM^- begins to assume importance within a few tenths of a milliliter of the first equivalence point (corresponding to the formation of NaHM) and the simplified calculation for pH becomes subject to appreciable error. As a practical matter, however, this region of uncertainty is so small that the titration curve can be readily defined without the necessity of calculating any points within it.

First Equivalence Point. When 25.0 ml of base have been added, the solution is $0.0500 \ F$ with respect to the acid salt NaHM. The pH is calculated by means of equation (14-7) on page 282; the value is 4.26.

Second Buffer Region. Further additions of base to the solution of hydrogen maleate gives rise to a new buffer consisting of the weak acid HM^- and its salt M^{2-}. The pH can be calculated in the usual way employing the second dissociation constant, K_2. In doing this, it is assumed that the reaction

$$HM^- + H_2O \rightleftharpoons H_2M + OH^-$$

has a negligible effect on the hydronium ion concentration compared with the effect produced by the dissociation of HM^- to hydronium ions and M^{2-}. This assumption will be valid provided that K_2 is weaker than K_1 by a factor of a thousand or more.

With the introduction of 25.5 ml of NaOH, for example, the number of milliformula weights of Na_2M is numerically equal to the number of milliformula weights of base in excess of the amount required to form NaHM, namely $(25.5 - 25.0)0.100$, and

$$F_{Na_2M} = \frac{(25.5 - 25.0)0.100}{50.5} = \frac{0.050}{50.5}$$

The number of milliformula weights of NaHM remaining will be equal to the amount present at the first equivalence point (25.0×0.100) minus the number of milliformula weights of Na_2M subsequently produced; here

$$F_{NaHM} = \frac{(25.0 \times 0.100) - (25.5 - 25.0)0.100}{50.5}$$

$$= \frac{2.45}{50.5}$$

Expressing $[H_3O^+]$ as x we may write

$$\frac{x[(0.050/50.5) + x]}{[(2.45/50.5) - x]} = 2.6 \times 10^{-7}$$

A trial solution neglecting x in the parenthetic terms yields a value of 1.29×10^{-5}; this answer is certainly reliable enough for present purposes.

Similar calculations will yield data to establish the form of the curve up to the second equivalence point.

Second Equivalence Point. After addition of 50 ml of base, the solution is 0.0333 F in Na_2M; calculation of the pH of this solution will require consideration of the equilibria

$$M^{2-} + H_2O \rightleftharpoons HM^- + OH^-$$

$$HM^- + H_2O \rightleftharpoons H_2M + OH^-$$

The equilibrium constants are

$$\frac{K_w}{K_2} = \frac{[HM^-][OH^-]}{[M^{2-}]} = 3.84 \times 10^{-8}$$

and

$$\frac{K_w}{K_1} = \frac{[H_2M][OH^-]}{[HM^-]} = 6.67 \times 10^{-13}$$

The degree to which the second reaction influences the pH is reduced by the hydroxyl ions formed from the first. As a consequence, only the first need be taken into account in determining the hydroxyl ion concentration of the solution. An assumption of this sort can generally be made in those instances where the second equilibrium constant is less than one one-thousandth of the first. We proceed then by letting x be the hydroxyl ion concentration and

$$x = [OH^-] \cong [HM^-]$$

$$(0.0333 - x) = [M^{2-}]$$

and substituting into the equilibrium-constant expression

$$\frac{x^2}{(0.0333 - x)} = \frac{1 \times 10^{-14}}{2.6 \times 10^{-7}} = 3.84 \times 10^{-8}$$

Solving for x gives a value of 3.58×10^{-5} mol/liter for $[OH^-]$. The pH is 9.55.

pH Beyond the Second Equivalence Point. Further additions of strong base repress the reaction of M^{2-} with water and the pH can be calculated from the amount of NaOH added in excess of that required for total neutralization of H_2M.

TITRATION CURVES

Figure 14.1 depicts the titration curve for a solution of maleic acid from data obtained as shown in the previous section. Two end points are apparent; through the judicious choice of indicator either one or both of the available acidic hydrogens could be titrated. The second end point is clearly the better one to use, however, inasmuch as the pH change is more pronounced.

Figure 14.2 shows titration curves for three other dibasic acids; these data illustrate that a well-defined end point corresponding to the first equivalence point is observed only where the degree of dissociation of the two acids is considerably different.

The ratio of K_1 to K_2 for oxalic acid (curve B) is approximately one thousand. Here the titration curve shows a distinct inflection corresponding to the first equivalence point. The magnitude of the pH change at this point is not sufficiently great, however, to allow an accurate location of this equivalence point; thus, only the second equivalence point can be used for analytical purposes.

Curve A illustrates the theoretical titration curve for the tribasic phosphoric acid. The ratio of K_1 to K_2 here is approximately 10^5. This is about 100 times greater than that for oxalic acid, and two well-defined end points are observed, either of which is satisfactory for analytical purposes.

With an indicator having an acid transition range, one equivalent of base will be consumed per mol of acid; with an indicator exhibiting a basic color change, two equivalents of base will be used. The third hydrogen of phosphoric acid is so slightly dissociated ($K_3 = 4.8 \times 10^{-13}$) that it does not yield an end point of any practical value. The effect of the third dissociation

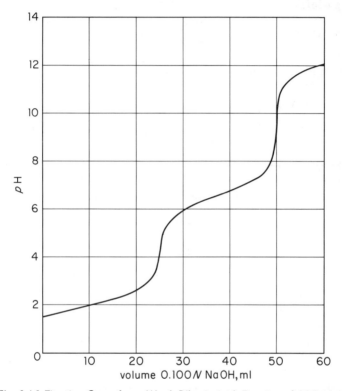

Fig. 14.1 Titration Curve for a Weak Dibasic Acid. Titration of 25.0 ml of 0.100 F maleic acid ($K_1 = 1.5 \times 10^{-2}$, $K_2 = 2.6 \times 10^{-7}$) with 0.100 N NaOH.

is noticeable in curve A, however, causing the pH to be lower than that for the other two acids in the region beyond their second equivalence points.

In general, the titration of polyfunctional acids or bases yields individual end points that are of practical value only where the ratio of the two dissociation constants is at least 10^5. If the ratio is much less than this, the pH change at the first equivalence point will be too small for accurate detection—only the second end point will prove satisfactory for analysis.

A judicious choice of indicators may make possible the analysis of the individual components of certain mixtures. Consider, for example, a solution containing phosphoric acid and a dihydrogen phosphate salt. If an aliquot is titrated with an indicator having a transition interval in the range of pH 4, the milliequivalents of base consumed will be equal to the

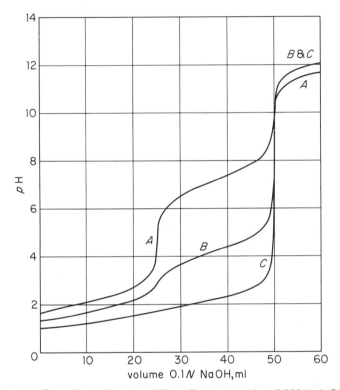

Fig. 14.2 Curves for the Titration of Three Polybasic Acids. A 0.100 N NaOH solution is used to titrate: A. 25.0 ml of 0.100 F H_3PO_4 ($K_1 = 7.5 \times 10^{-3}$, $K_2 = 6.2 \times 10^{-8}$); B. 25.0 ml of 0.100 F oxalic acid ($K_1 = 6.5 \times 10^{-2}$, $K_2 = 6.1 \times 10^{-5}$); C. 25.0 ml of 0.100 F H_2SO_4 ($K_2 = 1.2 \times 10^{-2}$).

number of milliformula weights of phosphoric acid alone. Titration of another aliquot with an indicator such as phenolphthalein, on the other hand, requires an amount of base corresponding to the number of milliformula weights of the dihydrogen phosphate salt present plus twice the milliformula weights of the acid. From these data the quantity of each of the constituents in the mixture can be readily computed.

MIXTURES OF ACIDS

The techniques involved in the derivation of titration curves for solutions containing more than one acid component do not differ greatly from those just discussed since a solution of a dibasic acid can be thought of simply as an equiformal mixture of two acids with different dissociation constants.

Titration Curves for Strong and Weak Acid Mixtures. The derivation of a theoretical titration curve for a mixture of a strong and a weak acid is quite straightforward when the weak acid has a dissociation constant less than 1×10^{-4}. The pH of the solution at any point up to the first equivalence point is found from the formal concentration of the strong acid by using the method described on page 264. Neutralization of the strong acid is complete at the first equivalence point; for purposes of pH calculation, the solution is then treated as a simple weak acid. The remainder of the titration curve is therefore characteristic of the weak acid.

Curves with two inflection points are obtained for a mixture of this type. Where the weak acid has a dissociation constant smaller than approximately 10^{-5}, the pH change at the first equivalence point is well marked; by the proper choice of indicator the concentration of each of the components is readily found. When the weak acid has a dissociation constant much greater than 10^{-5}, however, only the total acid content of the solution can be determined.

Titration Curves for Mixtures of Two Weak Acids. The derivation of a theoretical titration curve for a mixture of two weak acids is more complex than for a weak dibasic acid inasmuch as the formal concentrations of the two acids are no longer related to each other. Where the ratio of the dissociation constants is greater than about 10^3 or 10^4 and the ratio of the initial acid concentrations does not differ greatly from one, a curve can be obtained in a fashion analogous to that described for the dibasic weak-acid system. In the region preceding the first equivalence point, the dissociation of the weaker acid is disregarded; beyond this point, hydrolysis of the salt of the stronger acid is not considered. Thus the titration curve approaches a composite of the individual titration curves for each of the acids. It can be shown that the pH at the first equivalence point is approximated by means of the expression[1]

$$[\text{H}_3\text{O}^+] = \sqrt{K_l K_m \frac{F_m}{F_l}}$$

where K_l and K_m are the dissociation constants of the stronger and weaker acids, respectively, and F_l and F_m are their initial formal concentrations.

[1] J. E. Ricci, *Hydrogen Ion Concentration*, 180. Princeton, New Jersey: Princeton University Press, 1952.

When the initial concentrations are identical, this equation reduces to equation (14-8) (page 282).

SALTS OF POLYBASIC ACIDS

Several salts of polybasic acids are important in volumetric analysis; since the derivation of titration curves for this class of compounds involves no new principles we need not treat the technique in detail.

As an example, consider the titration of a solution of sodium carbonate with standard hydrochloric acid. The important equilibrium constants are

$$H_2O + H_2CO_3 \rightleftharpoons H_3O^+ + HCO_3^- \qquad K_1 = 4.6 \times 10^{-7}$$

$$H_2O + HCO_3^- \rightleftharpoons H_3O^+ + CO_3^{2-} \qquad K_2 = 4.4 \times 10^{-11}$$

The reaction of the carbonate ion with water governs the initial pH of the solution; the technique shown on page 286 is used in the pH calculation.

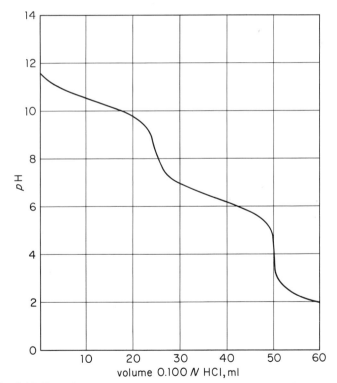

Fig. 14.3 Curve for the Titration of 25.0 ml of 0.100 F Sodium Carbonate with 0.100 N Hydrochloric Acid.

With the first additions of acid a carbonate-bicarbonate buffer develops, and the hydronium ion concentration is found from K_2. Sodium bicarbonate is the principal solute species at the first equivalence point; equation (14-8) will give the pH of this solution. With the further introductions of acid, a bicarbonate-carbonic acid buffer governs the pH, and here the hydronium ion content is obtained from K_1. Upon reaching the second equivalence point, the solution consists of carbonic acid and sodium chloride; the hydronium ion concentration is estimated in the usual way for a simple weak acid. Finally, an excess hydrochloric acid is introduced, the dissociation of the weak acid is soon repressed to a point where the hydronium ion concentration is essentially that of the formal concentration of the strong acid.

Figure 14.3 illustrates a titration curve for a solution of sodium carbonate; two end points are observed, the second being a good deal sharper than the first. Clearly, the stoichiometry of the analytical reaction depends upon the transition interval of the indicator chosen for the titration. It is also apparent that mixtures of sodium carbonate and sodium bicarbonate can be analyzed by neutralization methods. Thus, titration to a phenolphthalein end point would yield the number of milliformula weights of carbonate present, while titration to a methyl-orange color change would require an amount of acid equal to twice the number of milliformula weights of carbonate plus the number of milliformula weights of bicarbonate in the sample.

Problems

1. Calculate the pH of
   (a) a 0.0500 F solution of H_3PO_4 ans. 1.80
   (b) a 0.100 F solution of phthalic acid   ans. 1.97
   (c) a 0.100 F solution of salicylic acid
   (d) a solution that is 0.0100 F in HCl and 0.0200 F in phthalic acid

   ans. 1.92

   (e) a solution that is 0.0100 F in HCl and 0.100 F in oxalic acid
   (f) a 0.0100 F solution of H_2SO_4
   (g) a solution that is 0.0100 F in H_2SO_4 and 0.0100 F in HCl   ans. 1.63
   (h) a solution that is 0.100 F in acetic acid and 0.100 F in boric acid

2. Calculate the pH of
   (a) a buffer solution that is 0.100 F in NaH_2PO_4 and 0.200 F in Na_2HPO_4

   ans. 7.51

   (b) a buffer that is 1.00 F in NaH_2PO_4 and 2.00 F in H_3PO_4 ans. 1.82
   (c) a buffer prepared by mixing 50.0 ml of 0.200 F tartaric acid and 50.0 ml
       of 0.0800 F NaOH   ans. 2.85

    (d) a buffer prepared by adding 200 ml of 0.0800 F NaOH to 50.0 ml of 0.200 F tartaric acid   ans. 4.71

    (e) a buffer prepared by adding 1.00 ml of 10.0 N HCl to 100 ml of 0.300 F Na_2CO_3

    (f) a mixture of 1.00 liter of 0.250 F potassium hydrogen phthalate and 1.00 liter of 0.100 F NaOH

    (g) a mixture of 1.00 liter of 0.250 F potassium hydrogen phthalate and 1.00 liter of 0.0500 F HCl

    (h) a solution that was 0.100 F in H_2SO_4 and 0.100 F in $NaHSO_4$

3. Calculate the pH of

    (a) a 0.200 F solution of potassium hydrogen phthalate   ans. 4.15

    (b) a 0.0100 F solution of NaHS   ans. 9.62

    (c) a 0.0400 F solution of Na_2HPO_4

    (d) a 0.0100 F solution of $NaHSO_3$

    (e) a 0.0100 F solution of NaH_2PO_4

4. Calculate the pH of

    (a) a 0.100 F solution of Na_2CO_3 ans. 11.68

    (b) a solution that is 0.100 F in Na_2CO_3 and 0.0100 F in NaOH   ans. 12.08

    (c) a 0.0100 F solution of Na_3PO_4

5. How many ml of 1.00 N HCl must be added to a liter of a 0.100 F solution of Na_2CO_3 to give a buffer having a pH of 10.0?   ans. 69.4 ml

6. How many ml of 1.00 N HCl must be added to 1.00 liter of 0.100 F Na_2CO_3 to give a buffer having a pH of 6.00?

7. How many grams of $NaH_2PO_4 \cdot H_2O$ (gfw = 138) should be added to 1.00 liter of 0.500 F H_3PO_4 to give a buffer of pH 2.00?   ans. 51.8 grams

8. How many grams of potassium hydrogen phthalate must be added to 2.00 liters of 0.400 N NaOH to produce a buffer of pH 7.00?

9. A solution containing 0.500 gram formula weight of H_3PO_4 was brought to a pH of 4.00 with NaOH and then diluted to 1.00 liter. Calculate the equilibrium concentration of each of the phosphate-containing species.

$$\text{ans. } [H_3PO_4] = 6.6 \times 10^{-3} \text{ mol/liter}$$
$$[H_2PO_4^-] = 0.493 \text{ mol/liter}$$
$$[HPO_4^{2-}] = 3.1 \times 10^{-4} \text{ mol/liter}$$
$$[PO_4^{3-}] = 1.5 \times 10^{-12} \text{ mol/liter}$$

10. Calculate the equilibrium concentrations of each of the phosphate-containing species in a solution of pH 8.00 and in which the total concentration of these species is 0.100 F.

11. Calculate the equilibrium concentrations of each of the phosphate-containing species in a series of solutions in which the total concentration of these species is 0.100 F and the pH is: 1.0, 2.0, 3.0, 4.0, 5.0, 6.0, 7.0, 8.0, 9.0, 10.0, 11.0, 12.0, and 13.0.

    On a single sheet of graph paper plot the percentage concentration of each of the species as a function of pH.

12. Calculate the ratios of the various carbonate species in a sample of human blood having a pH of 7.3.

13. Exactly 25.0 ml of 0.100 F Na_2CO_3 was titrated with 0.100 N HCl. Calculate the pH of the solution after addition of the following volumes of reagent: 0.0, 5.0, 12.5, 20.0, 24.0, 25.0, 26.0, 30.0, 37.5, 45.0, 49.0, 50.0, 51.0, 55.0. Plot the data.

14. Calculate the pH of the solution resulting from mixture of
    (a) 100 ml of 0.125 F tartaric acid and 50.0 ml of 0.098 N NaOH
    (b) 100 ml of 0.125 F tartaric acid and 100 ml of 0.125 F NaOH
    (c) 100 ml of 0.125 F tartaric acid and 50.0 ml of 0.300 F NaOH
    (d) 100 ml of 0.125 F tartaric acid and 100.0 ml of 0.300 F NaOH

15. Calculate the pH of the solution resulting from mixture of
    (a) 100 ml of 0.0500 F potassium hydrogen phthalate and 20.0 ml of 0.100 N HCl
    (b) 100 ml of 0.0500 F potassium hydrogen phthalate and 100 ml of water
    (c) 100 ml of 0.0500 F potassium hydrogen phthalate and 100 ml of 0.0500 N HCl
    (d) 100 ml of 0.0500 F potassium hydrogen phthalate and 100 ml of 0.0500 N NaOH

16. Calculate the pH of solutions produced by mixing the following with 50 ml of 0.100 F Na_2HPO_4:
    (a) 20 ml of 0.200 N HCl
    (b) 40 ml of 0.200 N HCl
    (c) 200 ml of water
    (d) 20 ml of 0.200 N NaOH
    (e) 25 ml of 0.200 N NaOH

17. A solution that was 0.100 F in acetic acid and 0.100 F in HCl was titrated with a standard 0.100 N solution of KOH. Calculate the pH after the following additions of reagent if the original volume of the acid mixture was 30.0 ml: 0.0, 15.0, 25.0, 29.0, 29.9, 30.0, 30.1, 31, 35, 45.0, 55.0, 59.0, 59.9, 60.0, 60.1, 61.0, 65.0. Construct a titration curve from these data.

18. Calculate the hydronium ion concentration of a 1.00 and a 0.0100 F solution of H_2SO_4.

$$\left(\, 15 \, \right)$$

Applications of Neutralization
Titrations

Methods based upon neutralization reactions are widely used in volumetric analysis. In general, a standard solution of acid or of base is used to titrate the hydroxyl or hydronium ions liberated upon solution of the sample in water; in other instances the preliminary treatment of the substance being analyzed results in the evolution of an equivalent amount of one of these ions which is then titrated.

Although space limitations restrict this discussion to neutralizations occurring in aqueous solution, we should recognize that the acidic or basic character of a solute is determined in part by the nature of the liquid in which it is dissolved and that the use of solvents other than water can result in marked changes in these properties. As a result, acids and bases that are too weakly dissociated for titration in water can often be determined successfully and accurately by titration in nonaqueous media.

15.1 Reagents for Neutralization Titrations

Strong acids or bases are employed as reagents in neutralization titrations. Standard solutions of the former are commonly prepared from hydrochloric, sulfuric, or perchloric acid. Because of their high solubility, sodium hydroxide and potassium hydroxide are preferred in the preparation of the latter; in addition, barium hydroxide may be used for dilute basic solutions.

PREPARATION OF INDICATOR SOLUTIONS

Many indicators are available for end-point detection in neutralization titrations. Specific directions for the preparation of several of the more common of these follow.

Stock solutions generally contain 0.5 to 1.0 gram of indicator per liter of solution.

Methyl Orange and Methyl Red. Dissolve the sodium salt directly in distilled water.

Phenolphthalein and Thymolphthalein. Dissolve the solid indicator in a solution that is 80 percent by volume in ethyl alcohol.

Sulfonthaleins. Dissolve the sulfonthaleins in water by adding sufficient NaOH to react with the sulfonic acid group of the indicator. To prepare stock solutions of these, triturate 100 mg of the solid indicator with the specified volume of 0.1 N NaOH; then dilute to 100 ml with distilled water. The volumes in milliliters of base required are as follows: *bromcresol green*, 1.45; *bromthymol blue*, 1.6; *bromphenol blue*, 1.5; *thymol blue*, 2.15; *cresol red*, 2.65; *phenol red*, 2.85.

PREPARATION OF STANDARD SOLUTIONS OF ACID

Hydrochloric acid is the most commonly employed volumetric acid reagent. Dilute solutions of this substance are indefinitely stable, and the reagent can be used in the presence of most cations without interference due to precipitate formation. It is reported that 0.1 N solutions of the reagent can be boiled for as long as 1 hour without loss of acid provided the evaporated water is replaced periodically; 0.5 N solutions are stable for at least 10 minutes at boiling temperature.

Standard solutions of sulfuric or perchloric acid also make satisfactory acid reagents. They may be used to advantage when chloride ion causes precipitation problems. Nitric acid is seldom used because of its oxidizing properties.

There are several ways to prepare acid solutions of known composition, the most common involving suitable dilution of the concentrated reagent followed by standardization against a primary-standard base. In addition, the normality of a concentrated acid can be determined by careful density measurements; less concentrated solutions of known normality are then prepared by diluting weighed quantities to an exact volume.[1] Finally, stock solutions of some acids may be prepared by distillation of the commercial reagents under specified conditions; so-called *constant boiling* HCl

---

[1] See I. M. Kolthoff and V. A. Stenger, *Volumetric Analysis*, **2**, 64. New York: Interscience Publishers, Inc., 1947.

is prepared in this way. To obtain this reagent, the concentrated acid is distilled at atmospheric pressure, the first three quarters of the distillate being rejected. The final quarter has a constant and definite composition, its acid content being dependent only upon the atmospheric pressure.

Preparation of Approximately 0.1 *N* HCl. Add about 8 ml of concentrated HCl to approximately 1 liter of distilled water (Note): mix thoroughly, and store in a glass-stoppered bottle. Standardize according to the directions that follow.

NOTE:

If a very dilute HCl solution is required, boil the water to expel CO_2 and cool to room temperature before introducing the HCl.

STANDARDIZATION OF ACIDS

Dilute acid solutions are standardized in several ways. One method involves determining the anion content of the solution by a gravimetric procedure. Thus, for hydrochloric acid, a silver chloride precipitate may be used; for sulfuric acid, standardization by precipitation of barium sulfate is feasible. These methods assume, of course, that the anion concentration is equivalent to the hydrogen ion concentration.

More commonly, acids are standardized by titration against a weighed quantity of a primary-standard base. There are several such substances available, the most common being sodium carbonate.

Standardization of Acids with Sodium Carbonate. Sodium carbonate is available commercially in sufficient purity for most purposes; it can also be prepared by heating a good grade of sodium bicarbonate for 1 hour at 270° to 300° C.

$$2NaHCO_3 \rightarrow Na_2CO_3 + H_2O + CO_2$$

A titration curve for a solution of sodium carbonate is shown in Figure 14.3 (page 291). Of the two possible end points, the second, occurring in acid solution, is always employed in standardization procedures since it is a good deal sharper than the first. As a matter of fact, the simple expedient of heating to decompose the reaction product, carbonic acid, sharpens the *p*H change in the end-point region even further. One of the several ways of doing this involves titration of the solution at room temperature until an acidic indicator (such as bromcresol green, methyl orange, or bromphenol blue) just begins to exhibit its acid color. At this point, a small quantity of unreacted bicarbonate remains in the solution in addition to a large amount of carbonic acid. All of the latter is removed when the solution is boiled for a few minutes.

$$H_2CO_3 \rightarrow CO_2 + H_2O$$

During this process the pH rises to a slightly alkaline level owing to the residual bicarbonate. After cooling, the titration is completed; now, however, the pH change accompanying the final increments of reagent is considerably larger and, as a consequence, the end point is more accurately located.

An alternative method is to run in enough acid initially to provide a small excess. The solution is then boiled to remove the carbon dioxide and the excess acid is back titrated with a dilute solution of base. Any of the indicators suited to a strong acid-base titration can then be employed. Obviously, the combining capacity of the base for the acid must also be determined in order to make a correction for the back titration.

> ★PROCEDURE. Dry a quantity of primary-standard sodium carbonate for 2 hours at 150° C and cool in a desiccator. For standardization of 0.1 N solutions, weigh 0.2- to 0.25-gram portions of the salt (to the nearest 0.1 mg) into 250-ml flasks and dissolve in 25 to 50 ml of water. Add 3 drops of bromcresol green and titrate until the solution just begins to change from blue to green. Boil the solution for 2 to 3 minutes, cool to room temperature under a water tap, and complete the titration. During the heating process the indicator should change back to blue. If it does not, an excess of acid was added originally; back titrate this excess with standard base. Determine an indicator blank by titrating a similar volume of water containing approximately the same amounts of sodium chloride and indicator as are present at the end point in the solution being titrated.

Other Primary Standards for Acids. Several other primary-standard compounds are recommended for standardization of acids. Among these is sodium tetraborate decahydrate, $Na_2B_4O_7 \cdot 10H_2O$, which can be formed by recrystallization of borax from water followed by washing with alcohol and ether. The air-dried product is then stored in tightly stoppered bottles. The stoichiometry of its reaction with acid is expressed by the equation

$$B_4O_7^{2-} + 2H^+ + 5H_2O \rightarrow 4H_3BO_3$$

Sodium oxalate can also be employed; it is readily obtained in a pure state. Weighed quantities of this compound are ignited in platinum crucibles; the sodium carbonate produced is then titrated by the methods already described. The following equation expresses the ignition reaction:

$$Na_2C_2O_4 \rightarrow Na_2CO_3 + CO$$

Detailed descriptions of the use of these and other standards can be found in the reference work of Kolthoff and Stenger.[2]

[2] I. M. Kolthoff and V. A. Stenger, *Volumetric Analysis*, **2**, 74–93. New York: Interscience Publishers, Inc., 1947.

PREPARATION OF STANDARD SOLUTIONS OF BASES

Sodium hydroxide is the most common basic reagent, although potassium and barium hydroxides are also employed. None of these is obtainable in primary-standard quality; standardization of the solutions after preparation is always necessary. The solutions are all reasonably stable provided care is taken to protect them from atmospheric contamination.

Effect of Carbon Dioxide on Standard-base Solutions. The hydroxides of sodium, potassium, and barium, either in solid or solution form, rapidly absorb carbon dioxide from the atmosphere with the production of the corresponding carbonate.

$$CO_2 + 2OH^- \rightarrow CO_3^{2-} + H_2O$$

This process consumes 2 mols of hydroxyl ions per mol of carbon dioxide; thus we might expect exposure to the atmosphere to alter the combining capacity of a standard-base solution. This is true under some circumstances but not in others.

With barium hydroxide solutions, the absorption of carbon dioxide results in precipitation of the slightly soluble barium carbonate. Clearly, a loss in normality of the base results. On the other hand, the carbonates of sodium and potassium are soluble and quite capable of reacting with hydrogen ions. The number of ions consumed, however, is variable and depends upon the type of indicator used in conjunction with the reagent. If the indicator has an acidic transition range (such as methyl orange), the carbonate ion reacts with two hydrogen ions of the acid being titrated; because this is chemically equivalent to the amount of base required to produce the carbonate ion, the solution will have the same combining capacity for hydrogen ions as before the absorption. If, on the other hand, the analysis calls for an indicator with a basic transition range (such as phenolphthalein), the carbonate ion will have reacted with only one hydrogen ion to form bicarbonate when color change occurs. Here the combining capacity of the base will be diminished as a consequence of contamination by carbon dioxide. In order to avoid this potential decrease in normality care is taken to protect standard solutions of base from contact with the carbon dioxide of the atmosphere.

Another facet of the carbonate problem arises from the presence of that ion in the solids used to prepare standard solutions of base. The extent of contamination is frequently great, even in the best quality of solid reagent, due to absorption of carbon dioxide from the atmosphere; as a result a freshly prepared solution may contain an appreciable concentration of carbonate. The presence of carbonate need not lead to errors in analysis provided care is taken to employ the same indicator used in the standardization; this may often be inconvenient, however, and much of the versatility of the reagent is lost.

Carbonate contamination is also troublesome because it leads to poorly defined end points. This is particularly true where an indicator such as phenolphthalein must be employed (see Figure 14.3).

In the interests of eliminating these *carbonate errors*, it is common practice to prepare standard alkali solutions in such a way that none of the contaminant is present initially and to protect them from absorption of atmospheric carbon dioxide during storage.

Preparation and Storage of Standard Solutions of Base. Several methods are available for the preparation of carbonate-free solutions of base. Barium hydroxide may be employed as the reagent; the carbonate is insoluble, particularly in the presence of a neutral barium salt such as the chloride or nitrate. A barium salt may also be dissolved in a sodium or potassium hydroxide solution in order to remove the carbonate. Often, however, the presence of barium ion is undesirable since it forms precipitates with a number of anions that may be present in the sample to be analyzed. Carbonate-free solutions of the alkali-metal hydroxides may be prepared by direct solution of the clean metals; here precautions must be taken to avoid explosion during the solution process.

One convenient method for the preparation of sodium hydroxide solutions takes advantage of the very low solubility of sodium carbonate in concentrated solutions of the alkali. An approximately 50-percent solution of sodium hydroxide is prepared; after the sodium carbonate has settled out, the supernatant liquid is decanted and diluted to produce a reagent of the desired concentration. An alternative method calls for removal of the sodium carbonate by filtration through a sintered glass crucible. Details of this procedure follow.

In preparing carbonate-free base the distilled water used must be free of carbon dioxide. Water that is in equilibrium with the atmosphere contains only 1.5×10^{-5} formula weight of carbon dioxide per liter, a negligible concentration in most applications. Often, however, distilled water is supersaturated with respect to carbon dioxide, and removal is essential. This is readily accomplished by boiling for a few minutes. The water is then cooled to room temperature before introduction of the base since hot alkali solutions absorb carbon dioxide avidly.

An arrangement for the storage of standard-base solutions so that contamination by carbon dioxide of the air will not occur is shown in Figure 15.1; the air entering the storage vessel is passed over Ascarite—a solid absorbent consisting of sodium hydroxide deposited on asbestos. With this arrangement some contamination of the base by atmospheric carbon dioxide will occur while the solution is being transferred to the buret; the extent, however, is generally small. Finally, absorption by the solution in the open buret is also to be expected. Covering the top of the buret with a small beaker or test tube will minimize this.

Solutions of the alkalies should not be stored in glass-stoppered containers, nor should they be left in burets any longer than necessary because the stopper or the stopcock will tend to stick. Rubber stoppers are generally used with containers of alkali. Another problem is the slow attack

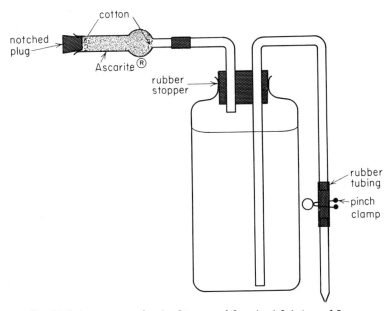

Fig. 15.1 Arrangement for the Storage of Standard Solutions of Base.

of glass containers by solutions of base. Where the reagents are to be kept for extended periods, paraffin-lined bottles or polyethylene ware should be employed.

Preparation of Carbonate-free 0.1 *N* NaOH. Prepare a bottle for protected storage as in Figure 15.1. Boil approximately 1 liter of distilled water and cool to room temperature. Prepare a Gooch crucible and wash thoroughly (page 99).

Use a platform balance to weigh approximately 10 grams of NaOH pellets into a 125-ml Erlenmeyer flask. Promptly introduce 10 ml of distilled water and swirl to hasten solution of the base (caution!). Allow flask and contents to cool; filter through the Gooch crucible and collect the clear filtrate in a clean test tube placed in the filter flask. Pour about 4 to 5 ml of this into the cooled water and mix thoroughly. Immediately transfer the solution to the storage bottle.

STANDARDIZATION OF SOLUTIONS OF BASE

Several excellent primary standards are available for alkali solutions. Most of these are weak organic acids that require the use of an indicator with a basic transition range.

Potassium Hydrogen Phthalate, $KHC_8H_4O_4$. The acid salt of phthalic acid is a nonhygroscopic crystalline substance that is readily obtained in a state of high purity. For the most accurate work, analyzed samples of this compound are available from the National Bureau of Standards. For most purposes, however, the commercial analytical-grade reagent can be used without further purification.

★PROCEDURE

> **Standardization of 0.1 *N* NaOH.** Dry the $KHC_8H_4O_4$ for 1 to 2 hours at 110° C and cool. Accurately weigh (to the nearest 0.1 mg) 0.7- to 0.9-gram samples into 250-ml Erlenmeyer flasks and dissolve in 25 to 50 ml of distilled water (preferably freshly boiled and cooled). Add 2 drops of phenolphthalein and titrate with the base to the first pink color that persists for a half minute.

Other Primary Standards for Alkalies. Among the other primary standards for bases is benzoic acid, $HC_7H_5O_2$, a substance obtainable in pure form from the National Bureau of Standards. The compound is not very soluble in water and is ordinarily dissolved in a little ethyl alcohol before titration. Another useful standard is the dihydrate of oxalic acid, $H_2C_2O_4 \cdot 2H_2O$. Rather careful preparation and storage of this compound are necessary to ensure its containing exactly 2 mols of water per mol of acid. Potassium hydrogen iodate, $KH(IO_3)_2$, is an excellent nonhygroscopic primary standard of high equivalent weight. In contrast to the other standards mentioned, it is a strong acid; thus the standardization can be made with any indicator showing a color change in the *p*H range between 4 and 10.

15.2   Some Applications of Neutralization Titrations

This section contains detailed descriptions of typical applications of neutralization analysis. In all of these experiments an acid-base indicator is used to estimate the equivalence point in the titration. Other means of detecting the equivalence point are available, however, the most important being based upon measurement of the potential of a *p*H-sensitive electrode immersed in the solution being titrated. Such measurements give the *p*H directly. From a plot of these data against the volume of added reagent, the equivalence points can be determined. This useful procedure is described in greater detail in Chapter 19; the instructor may choose to substitute this technique for the suggested indicator in one or more of the experiments.

A PRELIMINARY EXPERIMENT

A useful preliminary exercise consists of determining the combining ratio for a solution of a strong acid and a strong base. This permits the student to become familiar with acid-base end points; additionally, the data obtained may be used to calculate the concentration of one of the reagents from the normality of the other.

> ★PROCEDURE. Prepare approximately 0.1 *N* solutions of HCl and carbonate-free NaOH as instructed on pages 297 and 301. Fill burets with each of the reagents, and place a small beaker or test tube over the one containing the base. Run a 35- to 40-ml portion of the acid into a 250-ml Erlenmeyer flask, touch the inside of the flask with the buret tip and rinse down with a little water. Add 2 drops of phenolphthalein and run in the NaOH until the solution turns distinctly pink. Now add the HCl dropwise until the solution is decolorized, rinse down the sides of the flask, and carefully add base until the faintest pink color that persists for 30 seconds is observed. In making the final adjustment, add fractional drops of the base by forming a part of a drop on the buret tip, touching this to the side of the flask, and rinsing down with distilled water. The end point will slowly fade as carbon dioxide is absorbed from the atmosphere.
>
> Repeat the experiment and calculate the ratio of the volume of acid to the volume of base. Duplicate runs should agree to within 2 to 3 parts per thousand.
>
> Repeat this experiment with an indicator that shows an acidic transition range, such as bromcresol green. In this particular case, adjust the solution until the faintest tinge of green is imparted to the solution.

ANALYSIS OF WEAK ACIDS

The experiments in this section make use of a standard solution of a strong base. In each analysis a weak acid is being titrated; thus, an indicator with a basic transition range must be employed. Directions for preparation and standardization of base solutions are given on page 301. Although a solution of hydrochloric acid is not absolutely necessary for these titrations, it is very helpful. With this acid the end point may be located with greater certainty; in addition, an overtitrated sample can be saved. The combining capacity of the acid for the base must be determined as described in the previous section.

Determination of Potassium Hydrogen Phthalate. The sample is a mixture of potassium hydrogen phthalate and a neutral salt; the percentage of the former is to be determined.

> ★PROCEDURE. Dry the sample for 2 hours at 110° C and weigh out suitable-sized samples into 250-ml Erlenmeyer flasks. Add 50 ml of boiled water and 2 drops of phenolphthalein to each. Titrate with standard NaOH to the first pale pink color that persists for 30 seconds. If a standard HCl solution is available, run in a slight excess of base and find the end point exactly by addition of small increments of acid and base.
>
> Calculate the percent potassium hydrogen phthalate, $KHC_8H_4O_4$, in the sample. The duplicate analyses should agree to within 3 to 4 parts per thousand.

Determination of the Equivalent Weight of an Acid. The equivalent weight of a weak acid is useful for identification purposes; it is readily determined by titration of a weighed quantity of the pure compound.

> ★PROCEDURE. Weigh 0.3-gram samples of the purified acid into 250-ml flasks and dissolve in 25 to 50 ml of boiled water. In some cases heating may be required to dissolve the sample. If necessary, use ethyl alcohol or an alcohol-water mixture as a solvent.
>
> Add 2 drops of phenolphthalein and titrate with standard 0.100 N base to the first persistent pink color. Calculate the equivalent weight of the acid.

Determination of the Acid Content of Vinegar. The total acid content of vinegar is conveniently determined by titration with standard base. Even though other acids are also present the results of the analysis are ordinarily reported in terms of acetic acid, the principal acidic constituent. Vinegars assay approximately 4 percent acid, expressed as acetic acid.

> ★PROCEDURE. Pipet 25 ml of vinegar into a 250-ml volumetric flask and dilute to the mark with boiled and cooled distilled water. Mix thoroughly and pipet 50-ml aliquots into 250-ml flasks. Add 50 ml of water, 2 drops of phenolphthalein, and titrate to the first permanent pink color with standard 0.1 N NaOH.
>
> Calculate the grams of acetic acid per 100 ml of sample.

ANALYSIS OF CARBONATE MIXTURES

An interesting application of neutralization titrations is found in the qualitative and quantitative determination of the constituents of a solution containing sodium carbonate, sodium bicarbonate, and sodium hydroxide alone or admixed. No more than two of these components can exist in appreciable concentrations in any solution, inasmuch as reaction will occur to eliminate the third. For example, the addition of sodium hydroxide to a solution of sodium bicarbonate results in formation of sodium carbonate until either the sodium hydroxide or the sodium bicarbonate is exhausted. In the former case, a mixture of bicarbonate and carbonate will result; in the latter, the solution will contain only carbonate and hydroxide ions in analytical concentrations.

In order to analyze solutions of this sort, two titrations with a standard acid are performed on identical samples. One titration employs an indicator

TABLE 15-1

Volume Relationship in the Analysis of
Carbonate—Bicarbonate—Hydroxide Mixtures

Constituents Present	Relationship between Volume of Acid to Reach a Phenolphthalein End Point, V_{ph}, and a Methyl Orange End Point, V_{mo}
NaOH	$V_{ph} = V_{mo}$
Na_2CO_3	$V_{ph} = \frac{1}{2}V_{mo}$
$NaHCO_3$	$V_{ph} = 0$
NaOH, Na_2CO_3	$V_{ph} > \frac{1}{2}V_{mo}$
Na_2CO_3, $NaHCO_3$	$V_{ph} < \frac{1}{2}V_{mo}$

such as phenolphthalein with a transition interval at a pH of about 9. The other makes use of an indicator that has an acidic range—methyl orange, for example. As shown in Table 15-1, the constitution of the solution can then be judged from the relative volumes of acid required for the two titrations. After deduction of the qualitative constitution of the solution from the data, the concentrations of the component or components originally present can be derived from the normality of the acid and the volumes of reagent.

Sample Calculation. A solution contained one or more of the following constituents: Na_2CO_3, $NaHCO_3$, and NaOH. A 50.0-ml portion required 22.1 ml of 0.100 N HCl when titrated to a phenolphthalein end point. Methyl orange was then added to the solution and the titration continued, the solution being boiled near the second equivalence point in order to remove CO_2. An additional 26.3 ml of the HCl was used. What was the formal composition of the original solution?

Had the solution contained only NaOH, no appreciable volume of acid would have been required for titration from the phenolphthalein to the methyl-orange end point (that is, $V_{ph} \cong V_{mo}$). On the other hand, if only NaHCO$_3$ had been present, the solution would have been acidic to the phenolphthalein at the outset, and acid would have been used only in the second titration. Finally, if Na$_2$CO$_3$ were the sole constituent, the volume of acid to reach the phenolphthalein end point would have been exactly one half the total volume required to achieve a methyl-orange end point (that is, $V_{ph} = \frac{1}{2}V_{mo}$). In fact, however, a total of 48.4 ml was required. Since less than half of this amount was involved in the first titration, the solution must have contained some NaHCO$_3$ in addition to Na$_2$CO$_3$. We can now calculate the concentration of the two constituents. When the phenolphthalein end point was reached, the CO$_3^{2-}$ originally present was converted to HCO$_3^-$; thus we may say that

$$\text{no. mfw Na}_2\text{CO}_3 = 22.1 \times 0.100 = 2.21$$

The titration from the phenolphthalein to the methyl-orange end point involved both the bicarbonate ion originally present and that formed by titration of the carbonate; thus,

$$\text{no. mfw NaHCO}_3 + \text{no. mfw Na}_2\text{CO}_3 = 26.3 \times 0.1$$

Hence

$$\text{no. mfw NaHCO}_3 = 2.63 - 2.21 = 0.42$$

From these data we calculate the formal concentrations:

$$F_{\text{Na}_2\text{CO}_3} = \frac{2.21}{50.0} = 0.0442 \text{ gfw/liter}$$

$$F_{\text{NaHCO}_3} = \frac{0.42}{50} = 0.0084 \text{ gfw/liter}$$

The analysis cited for this example is not entirely satisfactory because the first end point, involving the formation of the bicarbonate ion, cannot be fixed with certainty; no indicator will give a sharp end point over the small pH change associated with this equivalence point (Figure 14.3, page 291). In order to minimize the titration error, the color of the solution being titrated can be matched against a comparison solution that contains an identical concentration of indicator and an approximately equivalent concentration of sodium bicarbonate. Even with this precaution, errors of 1 percent or more are to be expected.

The slight solubility of barium carbonate can be used to improve the titration of carbonate-hydroxide or carbonate-bicarbonate mixtures. The *Winkler* method for the determination of carbonate-hydroxide mixtures involves titration of both components in an aliquot using an indicator with an acidic transition range; this titration will closely resemble the standardization of an acid against sodium carbonate (page 298). An excess of neutral barium chloride is then added to a second aliquot to remove all of the carbonate ion, following which the hydroxide ion is titrated to a phenolphthalein end point. If the concentration of the excess barium ion is approximately 0.1 M, the solubility of the barium carbonate will be too low to offer interference in this titration.

To achieve an accurate analysis of a carbonate-bicarbonate mixture, the total equivalence of the two components is measured by titration with a standard acid following the procedure for an acid standardization against carbonate (page 298). The bicarbonate concentration is then determined in a second aliquot by the addition of a large excess of barium chloride and a measured excess of standard base. Precipitation of the carbonate ion from the original salt as well as that formed by reaction of the bicarbonate with the base leaves only the unreacted sodium hydroxide. This sodium hydroxide can be determined by a back titration with standard acid. Filtration of the barium carbonate is unnecessary if an indicator such as phenolphthalein is employed; the end point is easily discerned in the presence of the white solid.

Analysis of a Sample of Impure Sodium Carbonate. This method is suitable for a sample containing sodium carbonate and various neutral salts.

> ★PROCEDURE. Dry the sample for 2 hours at 150° C and then cool in a desiccator. Weigh samples of the proper size (see instructor) into 250-ml Erlenmeyer flasks. Dissolve in 25 to 50 ml of boiled water and add 2 drops of bromcresol-green indicator. Titrate with standard 0.1 N HCl until the indicator just begins to change to its green color. Boil the solution for 2 to 3 minutes, cool, and complete the titration. If additional acid is not required after boiling, the end point may have been passed. In this case discard the sample; alternatively, determine the excess acid by a back titration with a standard alkali solution.
>
> Calculate the percentage of sodium carbonate in the sample.

This analysis is conveniently carried out at the same time as the standardization of the acid (page 298).

Analysis of a Sodium Carbonate—Sodium Bicarbonate Mixture. The following instructions are for a sample containing both sodium carbonate and sodium bicarbonate as well as inert neutral salts.

> ★PROCEDURE. If the sample is a solid, weigh dried portions and dissolve in 25 to 50 ml of water. Transfer the solutions quantitatively to 250-ml volumetric flasks and dilute to the mark with boiled and cooled water. If the sample is a solution, pipet suitable aliquots into 250-ml volumetric flasks and dilute to volume. Mix thoroughly.

To determine the total number of milliequivalents of the two components, transfer a 25-ml aliquot of each of the diluted solutions to 250-ml Erlenmeyer flasks and titrate with standard 0.1 N HCl following the directions given in the previous section for a sodium carbonate sample.

To determine the bicarbonate content of the sample, pipet a second 25-ml portion of each solution into an Erlenmeyer flask and add a carefully measured volume of standard 0.1 N NaOH to the solution (conveniently 50.00 ml). Immediately add 10 ml of 10-percent $BaCl_2$ and 2 drops of phenolphthalein indicator. Titrate the excess NaOH at once with a standard 0.1 N HCl solution to the disappearance of the pink color. Titrate a blank consisting of 25 ml of water, 10 ml of the $BaCl_2$ solution, and *exactly* the same volume of NaOH as used with the samples. The difference in volume of HCl for the blank and sample corresponds to the $NaHCO_3$ present.

Calculate the percentage of $NaHCO_3$ and of Na_2CO_3 in the sample.

Analysis of a Sodium Carbonate—Sodium Hydroxide Mixture.

The sample is an aqueous solution containing sodium carbonate and sodium hydroxide.

★PROCEDURE. Transfer the sample to a 250-ml volumetric flask immediately upon receipt and dilute to the mark with boiled and cooled distilled water. Keep the flask tightly stoppered to avoid absorption of CO_2.

Pipet 25-ml aliquots of the sample solution into 250-ml Erlenmeyer flasks, add 2 drops of bromcresol green, and titrate with 0.1 N HCl following the procedure given on page 307 for the analysis of carbonate. This will give the total number of milliequivalents of NaOH and Na_2CO_3.

To determine the quantity of NaOH present, transfer a 25-ml aliquot of the sample solution into a 250-ml Erlenmeyer flask. Slowly add 10 ml of a neutral 10-percent $BaCl_2$ solution and 2 drops of phenolphthalein. Titrate immediately with standard 0.1 N HCl. To avoid contamination of the samples by atmospheric CO_2, complete this part of the analysis as rapidly as possible.

Calculate the weight of NaOH and Na_2CO_3 in the original sample.

ANALYSIS OF AMMONIUM SALTS

Neutralization methods provide a simple means for determining the concentration of ammonium salts. Three steps are involved in the process: first the compound is decomposed with an excess of strong base; the liberated ammonia is then distilled from the mixture and collected quantitatively; finally the amount of ammonia is determined by neutralization titration. Since few substances other than ammonium salts give a volatile basic compound under the conditions employed, the method is relatively specific.

Distillation of Ammonia. Figure 15.2 illustrates a distillation apparatus for the analysis of ammonia. The long-necked, round-bottomed flask, called a *Kjeldahl flask*, is connected to a spray trap that serves to prevent small droplets of the strongly alkaline solution from being carried over in the vapor stream. A water-cooled condenser is provided; during distillation the end of the adapter tube extends below the surface of an acidic solution in the receiving flask.

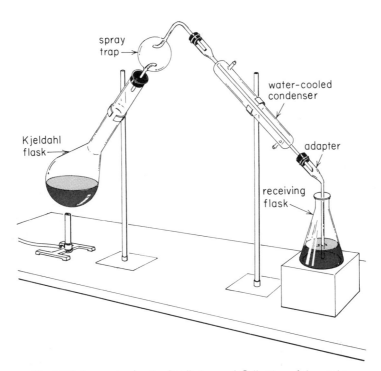

spray
trap

water-cooled
condenser

Kjeldahl
flask

adapter

receiving
flask

Fig. 15.2 Apparatus for the Distillation and Collection of Ammonia.

Titration of Ammonia. One method of completing the analysis is to place a measured quantity of standardized strong acid in the receiving flask of the apparatus. After the distillation is complete, the excess acid is back titrated with a standard solution of base, using an indicator with an acidic transition interval. An indicator with a neutral or basic range is not suitable because of the presence of ammonium ion.

A convenient modification of the procedure—it requires only a single standard reagent—employs an unmeasured quantity of very weak

acid solution to retain the ammonia; a 4-percent solution of boric acid
($K_a = 5.8 \times 10^{-10}$) serves this purpose very well.

$$NH_3 + HBO_2 \rightleftharpoons NH_4^+ + BO_2^-$$

Because it is the salt of a very weak acid, the borate formed may be titrated
with a standard solution of hydrochloric acid.

$$BO_2^- + H^+ \rightleftharpoons HBO_2$$

At the equivalence point, the solution contains boric acid and ammonium chloride; an indicator with an acidic transition interval is therefore
required.

★PROCEDURE. The sample should contain 2 to 4 meq of ammonium salt. Introduce the sample into a 500-ml Kjeldahl flask and
add enough water to give a total volume of about 200 ml.

Set up a distillation apparatus similar to that shown in Figure
15.2. Use a buret or pipet to measure precisely 50 ml of 0.1 N HCl
into the receiver flask; clamp the flask so that the tip of the adapter
reaches just below the surface of the standard acid. Start the cooling
water through the jacket of the condenser.

For each sample prepare a solution containing approximately
45 grams of NaOH in about 75 ml of water. Cool this solution to
room temperature before use. With the Kjeldahl flask tilted, slowly
pour the caustic down the side of the container so that little mixing
occurs with the solution in the flask (Note 1). Add several pieces of
granulated zinc (Note 2) and a small piece of litmus paper. *Immediately* connect the flask to the spray trap; very *cautiously* mix the
solution by gentle swirling. After mixing is complete, the litmus
paper should indicate that the solution is basic.

Immediately bring the solution to a boil and distill at a steady
rate until one half to one third of the original solution remains.
Watch the rate of heating during this period to prevent the receiver
acid from being sucked back into the distillation flask. After the
distillation is judged complete, lower the receiver flask until the tip
of the adapter is well out of the standard acid; then remove the
flame, disconnect the apparatus, and rinse the inside of the condenser with a small amount of water. Disconnect the adapter and
rinse it thoroughly. Add 2 drops of bromcresol green or methyl red
and titrate the distillate with standard 0.1 N NaOH to the color
change of the indicator.

This procedure can be modified to use about 50 ml of 4-percent
boric acid solution in place of the standard HCl in the receiver flask.
The distillation is then carried out in an identical fashion; when
complete, the ammonium borate present is titrated with a standard
0.1 N HCl solution using 2 to 3 drops of bromcresol-green indicator.

Calculate the percent nitrogen in the sample.

NOTES:

1. The more dense caustic solution should form a second layer on the bottom of the flask. Mixing is avoided at this point in order to prevent loss of the volatile ammonia; manipulations should be carried out as rapidly as possible.

2. The granulated zinc is added to reduce bumping during the distillation. It reacts slowly with the alkali to give small bubbles of hydrogen gas that minimize superheating of the liquid.

Analysis of Nitrates. An important modification of the method just discussed makes possible the analysis of inorganic nitrates. Here the nitrate is reduced to an ammonium salt which is then determined by the distillation and titration procedure. The most common reducing agent for this purpose is Devarda's alloy which consists of 50-percent copper, 45-percent aluminum, and 5-percent zinc. The finely powdered metal is introduced into a strongly alkaline solution of the sample; the ammonia is distilled after allowing time for the evolution of hydrogen to cease. Arnd's alloy, containing 60-percent copper and 40-percent magnesium, can also be used for the reduction.

DETERMINATION OF NITROGEN IN ORGANIC COMPOUNDS; THE KJELDAHL METHOD

Nitrogen occurs in a variety of important organic substances including proteins, peptides, synthetic drugs, and fertilizers. As a consequence, procedures for the analysis of this element find widespread use in industry and research.

Methods for Nitrogen Analysis. Basically two methods are employed for the determination of nitrogen in organic compounds—the *Dumas* and the *Kjeldahl* methods. The former, which is suitable for the analysis of nearly all types of organic nitrogen compounds, consists of mixing the sample with powdered copper (II) oxide and igniting in a stream of carbon dioxide in a combustion tube. At elevated temperatures the organic substance is oxidized to carbon dioxide and water by the copper (II) oxide. Any nitrogen in the compound is converted primarily to the elemental state although nitrogen oxides may also result. These oxides are reduced to elemental nitrogen by passing the gases over a bed of hot copper. The products of the ignition are then swept into a gas buret filled with highly concentrated potassium hydroxide; this completely absorbs the carbon dioxide, water, and other products of the combustion, such as sulfur dioxide and hydrochloric acid. The elemental nitrogen remains undissolved in the caustic, however, and its volume is directly measured.

The second method, for which there are a number of modifications, bears the name of its inventor, Kjeldahl. The procedure, first conceived in 1883, has undoubtedly been one of the most widely used of all analyses. In its original form, oxidation of the sample was accomplished with hot concentrated sulfuric acid; it was presumed that the organic nitrogen was completely converted to ammonium sulfate. The latter compound was then decomposed with strong base, the liberated ammonia being distilled into a standard acid solution where it was determined by back titration with standard base.

The Kjeldahl procedure is in much wider use than the Dumas method because it requires no special equipment and because it is more easily adapted to the routine analysis of large numbers of samples. It has become the standard method for determining the protein nitrogen of grains, meats, and other biological materials.

Sample Oxidation in the Kjeldahl Method. Undoubtedly the most critical step in the Kjeldahl procedure is the sulfuric acid oxidation of the organic compound. During this operation the carbon in the sample is converted to carbon dioxide and the hydrogen to water; the fate of the nitrogen is, however, highly dependent upon the form in which it occurs in the original compound. Where the element is bound as an amide or an amine, as in proteinaceous materials, quantitative conversion to ammonium ion nearly always results, and it is retained as such in the sulfuric acid. On the other hand, where the nitrogen occurs in a more highly oxidized form, such as in nitro, azo, or azoxy groups, losses of the element result because the oxidation product is elemental nitrogen or nitrogen oxides; certain heterocyclic nitrogen compounds behave similarly. In these cases, the Kjeldahl method leads to erroneously low results unless the precaution of introducing a reducing agent prior to the digestion step is taken; this assures conversion of the element to an oxidation state that gives ammonium ion upon treatment with the sulfuric acid. One method for prereduction calls for the addition of sodium thiosulfate and salicylic acid to the concentrated sulfuric acid solution containing the sample; the digestion is then carried out in the usual way.

Rate of the Kjeldahl Oxidation. The most time-consuming step in the Kjeldahl analysis is the oxidation process, which may require several hours to complete; numerous modifications have been proposed to improve the kinetics of the process. One such modification, involving the introduction of a neutral salt such as potassium sulfate, is now almost universally employed. This very simple expedient, proposed by Gunning, is effective because it raises the boiling point of the sulfuric acid and thus the temperature at which the oxidation can be carried out. Care is necessary, however, for oxidation of the ammonium ion can occur if the salt concentration is too great—a serious problem if evaporation of the sulfuric acid is excessive during digestion.

Catalysts of many sorts have been suggested as a means of hastening the digestion process, the most common of these including elemental mercury, copper, selenium, or compounds of these elements. Mercury or mercury compounds appear to be the most effective. The ions of mercury or copper, if present, should be precipitated as sulfides prior to the distillation step; otherwise some ammonia remains as an ammine complex of the metallic ion.

Attempts to hasten the Kjeldahl oxidation by the addition of stronger oxidizing agents such as perchloric acid, potassium permanganate, and hydrogen peroxide have failed because oxidation of the ammonium ion to volatile nitrogen oxides occurs.

The procedure that follows is suitable for the analysis of protein nitrogen in samples such as blood meal or wheat flour. Prereduction is unnecessary. A simple modification will allow the analysis of samples that contain oxidized forms of nitrogen.[3]

★PROCEDURE. Weigh out three samples of 0.25 to 2.5 grams, depending upon the nitrogen content, and wrap each in a 9-cm filter paper. Drop each into a 500-ml Kjeldahl flask (the paper wrapping will prevent the sample from clinging to the neck of the flask). Add 25 ml of concentrated sulfuric acid and 10 grams of powdered K_2SO_4. Add catalyst (Note 1) and clamp the flask in an inclined position in a hood. Heat the mixture carefully until the H_2SO_4 is boiling. Continue the heating until the solution becomes colorless or light yellow; this may take as much as 2 to 3 hours. If there is much reduction in the volume of acid, replace that lost by evaporation.

Remove the flame and allow the flask to cool; swirl the flask if the contents begin to solidify. Cautiously dilute with 200 ml of water and cool under a water tap to room temperature. If mercury or copper was used as the catalyst, introduce 25 ml of a 4-percent sodium sulfide solution. Then proceed as in paragraph 2 of the procedure on page 310 for the analysis of an inorganic ammonium salt.

Calculate the percent nitrogen in the samples.

NOTES:

1. As a catalyst, one may use a drop of mercury, 0.5 gram of HgO, a crystal of $CuSO_4$, 0.1 gram of Se, or the catalyst may be omitted.

2. For best results, a blank should also be carried through all steps of the analysis.

---

[3] See *Official and Tentative Methods of Analysis*, 5th ed., 27. Washington, D.C.: Association of Official Agricultural Chemists, 1940.

Problems

1. Describe the preparation of
   (a) 5 liters of approximately 0.01 N $Ba(OH)_2$
   (b) 500 ml of approximately 0.3 N HCl from the concentrated reagent (sp gr = 1.18; percent HCl = 37)
   (c) 2 liters of about 0.2 N H_2SO_4 from the concentrated reagent (sp gr = 1.83; percent H_2SO_4 = 96)
   (d) 10 liters of approximately 0.05 N KOH from the solid reagent
   (e) 5 liters of 0.2 N carbonate-free NaOH from a 50-percent solution of the reagent (sp gr = 1.53)
   (f) 1 liter of about 0.1 N NaOH from metallic Na
   (g) 1 liter of exactly 0.0500 N $HClO_4$ from a 0.275 N solution of the acid
   ans. (a) Dissolve 4.3 grams $Ba(OH)_2$ in 5 liters of water
(b) Dilute 12.5 ml of the reagent to 500 ml

2. A solution of $HClO_4$ was standardized against 0.2127 gram of pure Na_2CO_3. Exactly 35.00 ml of the acid was added, the solution was boiled, and the excess acid was back titrated with 1.84 ml of NaOH. In a separate titration, 27.10 ml of the NaOH was found to be equivalent to 25.00 ml of the $HClO_4$. Calculate the normality of the acid and the base.
   ans. 0.1205 N $HClO_4$; 0.1112 N NaOH

3. A solution of HCl was standardized against 0.1750 gram of pure Na_2CO_3. Exactly 47.00 ml of the acid was added to the carbonate; the solution was then boiled to remove the CO_2. The excess acid was back titrated with 2.12 ml of 0.01740 N NaOH to a bromcresol-green end point. What was the normality of the acid?
   ans. 0.06947 N HCl

4. Exactly 2.000 grams of Na_2CO_3 were dissolved in water and diluted to 250.0 ml. A 50.05-ml aliquot of this solution was titrated with a solution of HCl; CO_2 was removed by boiling near the end point. Calculate the normality of the acid if 30.15 ml were required to produce a methyl-orange end point.

5. A second 50.05-ml aliquot of the Na_2CO_3 solution in Problem 4 was treated with 35.00 ml of a solution of $HClO_4$. After boiling, the excess acid was titrated with 1.45 ml of a solution of NaOH (1.000 ml NaOH = 1.097 ml of the $HClO_4$). Calculate the normality of the $HClO_4$.

6. Exactly 34.10 ml of a solution of HCl were required to titrate 0.5000 gram of borax, $Na_2B_4O_7 \cdot 10\ H_2O$. What was the normality of the acid?

7. A 0.3320-gram sample of $Na_2C_2O_4$ was decomposed to Na_2CO_3 and titrated with 24.76 ml of HCl to a methyl-orange end point. What is the normality of the acid?

8. A 0.2031-gram sample of potassium hydrogen phthalate required 47.63 ml of a $Ba(OH)_2$ solution to reach a phenolphthalein end point. What was the normality of the base?

9. A 1.00-gram sample of a carbonate was analyzed by titration with 0.202 N HCl. The solution was boiled near the end point to remove CO_2. (a) Calculate the percent CO_2 in the sample if 24.2 ml of acid were required. (b) What would be the error in parts per thousand if the end point were exceeded by 0.15 ml?

ans. (a) 10.8 percent
(b) 6.2 parts/1000

10. Suggest a range of sample weights for the standardization of 0.2 N NaOH against potassium hydrogen phthalate.

11. 50.0 ml of a solution of HCl yielded a 0.964-gram precipitate of AgCl.
(a) What was the normality of the acid?
(b) How many ml of this acid would be required to prepare 1 liter of 0.0500 N acid?

12. A 50.0-ml sample of vinegar (density = 1.06) was diluted to 250 ml and a 25.0-ml aliquot titrated with 0.136 N NaOH to a phenolphthalein end point. If 28.1 ml of base were required, what was the percent acetic acid in the sample?

13. A 0.0770-gram sample of a pure amine was dissolved and titrated with a 0.0820 N solution of $HClO_4$. If 10.1 ml of acid were required, what was the equivalent weight of the organic compound? ans. 93 grams/equivalent

14. A 1.500-gram sample of substance containing $CaCO_3$ was boiled with 50.0 ml of a solution of HCl. The excess acid was back titrated with 13.1 ml of 0.292 N NaOH. From a separate titration it was learned that 1.000 ml of the HCl was equivalent to 1.407 ml of the NaOH.
(a) Calculate the percent $CaCO_3$ in the sample.
(b) Calculate the percent CaO in the sample.
(c) What volume of CO_2 in ml (STP) was liberated from the sample?

15. A 0.167-gram sample of pure organic acid was titrated with 15.2 ml of 0.202 N NaOH. What was the equivalent weight of the acid?

16. What weight of sample should be taken for the analysis of Na_2CO_3 so that the volume of 0.2760 N $HClO_4$ used will equal the percent Na_2CO_3 in the sample?

ans. 1.46 grams

17. Calculate the percent NH_3 in a crude ammonium salt analyzed by treating a 0.500-gram sample with concentrated NaOH, distilling the NH_3 into 40.0 ml of 0.116 N HCl, and back-titrating the excess HCl with 0.97 ml of 0.143 N NaOH.

18. Compute the percent $(NH_4)_2SO_4$ in the sample described in Problem 17.

19. A 0.746-gram sample of crude urea, $CO(NH_2)_2$ was analyzed by the Kjeldahl procedure. The liberated NH_3 was collected in 50.0 ml of 0.200 N H_2SO_4. The excess acid required 4.24 ml of 0.100 N base. Calculate the percent urea in the sample.

20. A 1.00-gram sample of an organic mixture containing the compound $C_6H_{12}N_4$ was analyzed by the Kjeldahl procedure. The liberated NH_3, collected in

boric acid, was titrated with 27.1 ml of 0.320 N HCl. Calculate the percent $C_6H_{12}N_4$ (gfw = 140) in the sample.

21. A 0.500-gram organic sample was burned in a stream of O_2 in a combustion tube. The SO_2 formed was collected in a solution of H_2O_2 which resulted in quantitative formation of H_2SO_4. The latter was titrated with 37.7 ml of 0.262 N NaOH. Calculate the percent S in the sample.

22. A fertilizer sample is to be analyzed for nitrogen by the Kjeldahl method using boric acid to absorb the ammonia. Assuming the sample contains 5-percent N what range of sample weights could be taken in order that the volume of 0.150 N HCl used would be between 25 and 40 ml?

23. A 100-ml sample of a natural water when titrated to a methyl-orange end point consumed 31.2 ml of 0.0138 N acid. A similar sample consumed 1.80 ml of the acid to reach a phenolphthalein end point. Calculate the mg per liter of CO_3^{2-} and HCO_3^- in the water.   ans. 14.9 mg/liter CO_3^{2-}; 232 mg/liter HCO_3^-

24. A series of solutions known to contain one or more of the following was analyzed: Na_2CO_3, $NaHCO_3$, and NaOH. 100-ml aliquots of the solution were titrated with 0.100 N HCl. Given below are the volumes of acid required to reach the phenolphthalein and the methyl-orange end points, respectively, in each case. Calculate the grams per liter of each constituent.
   (a) 27.3 and 30.7   ans. 0.36 gram/liter Na_2CO_3; 0.96 gram/liter NaOH
   (b) 0.0 and 18.1   ans. 1.52 grams/liter $NaHCO_3$
   (c) 4.60 and 12.2
   (d) 27.1 and 27.1
   (e) 15.1 and 30.2
   (f) 15.6 and 48.1
   (g) 20.2 and 49.6

25. A 5.000-gram sample of a mixture containing Na_2CO_3, $NaHCO_3$, and inert substances was dissolved in water and diluted to exactly 250 ml. A 25.0-ml aliquot was treated with 50.0 ml of 0.120 N HCl and boiled to remove CO_2. The excess acid was back titrated with 7.60 ml of 0.100 N NaOH to a bromcresol-green end point. A second 50.0-ml aliquot was treated with 50.0 ml of the base and an excess of neutral $BaCl_2$ which precipitated all of the carbonate as $BaCO_3$. The excess base was back titrated to a phenolphthalein end point with 26.2 ml of the 0.120 N acid. Calculate the percent $NaHCO_3$ and Na_2CO_3 in the sample.   ans. percent Na_2CO_3 = 45.6
                                                            percent $NaHCO_3$ = 15.6

26. A 3.50-gram sample containing both NaOH and Na_2CO_3 was dissolved and diluted to 250 ml. A 50.0-ml aliquot required 41.7 ml of 0.0860 N HCl to reach a methyl-orange end point. A second 50.0-ml aliquot was treated with excess of $BaCl_2$ to precipitate all of the carbonate. The solution then required 7.60 ml of the acid to reach a phenolphthalein end point. Calculate the percentage of each of the constituents.

27. A solution containing both H_3PO_4 and HCl was analyzed by titration of two 25.0-ml aliquots with 0.0500 N base. To reach an end point at a pH of 4 to 5 required 28.6 ml, while 46.1 ml were required to reach an end point at pH 9 to 10. What was the formal concentration of each of the acids in the sample?

28. A solution containing both H_3PO_4 and NaH_2PO_4 was titrated in the manner described in Problem 27. Two 25-ml aliquots required 12.2 and 39.1 ml of 0.0500 N base to reach the end points at pH 4 to 5 and 9 to 10, respectively. What were the formal concentrations of the two constituents?

29. A series of solutions known to contain one or more of the following constituents was titrated with 0.100 N base: HCl, H_3PO_4, and NaH_2PO_4. The data provided give the volumes of reagent required to reach an end point at pH 4 to 5 (product NaH_2PO_4) and pH 9 to 10 (product Na_2HPO_4) when 25.0-ml aliquots were titrated. Calculate the composition of each solution in milligrams per 100 ml.
    (a) 10.2 and 20.4
    (b) 10.2 and 10.2
    (c) 10.2 and 30.7
    (d) 0.0 and 19.1
    (e) 20.2 and 27.6

30. A sample containing both HPO_4^{2-} and $H_2PO_4^-$ was analyzed by titration of two 25.0-ml portions. The first was titrated with 0.197 N HCl using methyl-orange indicator until the color matched that of a solution containing the same amount of indicator and KH_2PO_4. 17.4 ml of acid were required. The second aliquot was titrated with 0.174 N NaOH using thymolphthalein as an indicator. The end point was taken when the color matched that of a solution of Na_2HPO_4 containing the indicator. 30.7 ml of base were required. Calculate the formal concentrations of HPO_4^{2-} and $H_2PO_4^-$.

(16)

Equilibrium in Oxidation-reduction Systems

Many chemical processes are characterized by the transfer of electrons between the reacting species; these are known as *oxidation-reduction*, or *redox*, reactions. More volumetric analytical methods are based upon reactions of this type than any other; for this reason we must examine the application of the equilibrium law to these processes in some detail.

Oxidation involves the loss of electrons by a substance, and *reduction* the gain of electrons. In any oxidation-reduction reaction the ratio of mols of substance oxidized to mols of substance reduced is such that the number of electrons lost by the one species is equal to the number gained by the other. This fact must always be taken into account when balancing equations for oxidation-reduction reactions.

Separating an oxidation-reduction reaction into its two component parts—that is, into *half reactions*—is a convenient way to indicate clearly which species gains electrons and which loses them. The electrons symbolized in these equations are, of course, cancelled out when the two half reactions are combined. For example, consider the reaction that occurs when a piece of metallic zinc is immersed in a solution of copper (II) sulfate. The over-all reaction is expressed by the equation

$$Zn + Cu^{2+} \rightleftharpoons Zn^{2+} + Cu$$

which can be resolved into two half reactions, the one depicting the oxidation of zinc metal

$$Zn \rightleftharpoons Zn^{2+} + 2e$$

and the other indicating the reduction of copper (II) ions

$$Cu^{2+} + 2e \rightleftharpoons Cu$$

The same rules apply to balancing equations for half reactions as for ordinary reactions; that is, the number of atoms of each element as well as the number of charges on either side of the equation must be equal.

The tendency of various substances to gain or lose electrons differs immensely. Those substances possessing a strong affinity for electrons cause other substances to be oxidized by abstracting electrons from them. Reagents that function in this manner are called *oxidizing agents*. In acting as oxidizing agents the substances are themselves reduced. In the above reaction, for example, the copper (II) ion acts as the oxidizing agent and is consequently reduced to metallic copper. Similarly potassium permanganate functions as an oxidizing agent in acid solution, by being reduced to manganese (II)

$$MnO_4^- + 8H^+ + 5e \rightleftharpoons Mn^{2+} + 4H_2O$$

Reducing agents are substances that readily give up electrons and thereby cause some other species to be reduced. In this process the reducing agent is itself oxidized. Metallic zinc acts as a reducing agent in the presence of copper (II) ion; iron (II) often behaves similarly

$$Fe^{2+} \rightleftharpoons Fe^{3+} + e$$

Most of the oxidation-reduction reactions that we shall consider are reversible and thus subject to the law of mass action. The position of equilibrium in any case is determined by the relative tendencies of the reactants to acquire or lose electrons. Thus the mixture of a strong oxidizing agent with a strong reducing agent will lead to an equilibrium in which the products are overwhelmingly favored. A less complete reaction results when weaker reagents react. The relative tendencies of substances to gain or lose electrons can be measured in quantitative terms; the data from such measurements have great utility because they lead directly to equilibrium constants for oxidation-reduction reactions.

Oxidation-reduction reactions may result from the direct transfer of electrons from the donor to the acceptor. Thus, upon immersing a piece of zinc in a copper (II) sulfate solution, copper (II) ions migrate to and are reduced at the surface of the metal. One unique aspect of these reactions, however, is that the transfer of electrons—and hence the same over-all reaction—can be accomplished when the donor and acceptor are quite remote from one another. With an arrangement such as illustrated in Figure 16.1 (page 320), direct contact between the metallic zinc and copper (II) ions is prevented by a porous barrier. Despite this separation, electrons are transferred by means of the external metallic conductor. The half reactions here are the same as before, electrons being transferred from the metallic zinc to the copper (II) ions. This transfer can be expected to continue until the copper (II) and zinc ion concentrations achieve levels corresponding to equilibrium for the reaction

$$Zn + Cu^{2+} \rightleftharpoons Zn^{2+} + Cu$$

When this point is reached no further net flow of electrons will be observed. *The reaction and its position of equilibrium is the same regardless of the manner in which the process is carried out.*

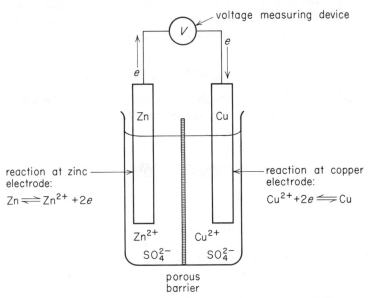

Fig. 16.1 Schematic Diagram of a Simple Electrochemical Cell.

The device illustrated in Figure 16.1 is, of course, an electrochemical cell; it is capable of producing electric energy because of the tendency of the reacting species to transfer electrons and thereby achieve the condition of equilibrium. The electrical potential existing between the zinc and the copper electrodes is a measure of this driving force and is easily evaluated by a voltmeter, V, placed in the circuit as shown in Figure 16.1. We shall see that the voltage produced by an electrochemical cell is directly related to the equilibrium constant for the particular oxidation-reduction process involved and that, in fact, measurement of such potentials constitutes an important source of numerical values for these constants. It is desirable, therefore, to examine more closely the construction and behavior of electrochemical cells as well as the measurement of the potentials they develop.

16.1 Fundamentals of Electrochemistry

CELLS

A *cell* consists of a pair of conductors or electrodes, usually metallic, immersed in an electrolyte. When the electrodes are connected by an external conductor and a passage of current ensues, a chemical oxidation occurs at the surface of one electrode and a reduction at the surface of the other.

Galvanic and Electrolytic Cells. When a cell is operated in such a way as to produce electric energy, it is called a *galvanic*, or sometimes, a *voltaic* cell. A cell that consumes electric energy is termed an *electrolytic* cell. Thus the cell shown in Figure 16.1 is capable of behaving as a galvanic cell. When the two electrodes are connected by a wire, electric energy is produced, and a spontaneous flow of electrons from the zinc electrode to the copper occurs.

The same cell could also be operated as an electrolytic cell. To do this it would be necessary to introduce a battery in the external circuit that would force electrons to flow in the opposite direction through the cell. Under these circumstances, zinc would deposit and copper would dissolve; these processes would consume energy from the battery.

Passage of Current Through a Cell. We have seen that the electrode reactions that occur in the galvanic cell in Figure 16.1 are

$$Zn \rightleftharpoons Zn^{2+} + 2e$$

$$Cu^{2+} + 2e \rightleftharpoons Cu$$

As a result, the solution in the cell compartment containing the zinc electrode shows an increase in concentration of zinc ions, while the solution surrounding the copper electrode is depleted in copper (II) ions. If no internal contact existed between the two parts of the cell, a charge imbalance in the neighborhood of the electrodes would result, an excess of positive ions being found near the zinc and an excess of negative ions near the copper. Such a charge inhomogeneity within the solutions would prevent the further flow of current in the external circuit by virtue of the electrostatic forces set up between these charges and the electrons within the metal.

In an actual cell, redistribution of ions can occur as a result of their mobility within the electrolyte solution. As a result, regions of unbalanced charge do not develop. In the above example, for instance, zinc ions as well as other cations can migrate from the solution surrounding the zinc electrode toward the copper electrode; anions can also migrate but will do so in the opposite direction. The result of these ionic movements is to rectify the imbalance of charge in the two compartments and thus allow a continued flow of current.

The passage of current through a cell, then, involves a migration of ions within the solution, and the current may be considered as conveyed by these ions. Not only the electrode-reactive ions but all of the ions in the solution participate in carrying the current, the contribution of each being determined by its relative concentration and inherent mobility in the medium. Only at the electrode surface—the site of transfer of electrons from solution to metallic conductor—is the current passage limited to the reacting species.

ELECTRODE PROCESSES

We have thus far considered a cell as being composed of two *half cells*, each of which is associated with the process occurring at one of the electrodes. This treatment forms an extremely useful approach to many of the problems encountered in electrochemistry. In using it, however, we run the risk of thinking of individual half cells as real, separate entities, capable of independent existence. This, of course, is not so; it is impossible to operate a half cell in the absence of a second half cell, nor is it feasible to measure the potential of a half cell without reference to another.

Anode and Cathode. *In either a galvanic or electrolytic cell, the electrode at which oxidation occurs is called the anode, whereas the electrode at which reduction takes place is the cathode.*

Some Typical Cathodic Reactions. Common types of cathodic half reactions include:

1. Deposition of metals on an electrode surface. Examples would include the formation of copper or silver metal according to the half reactions

$$Cu^{2+} + 2e \rightleftharpoons Cu$$

$$Ag^+ + e \rightleftharpoons Ag$$

Many metal ions can be removed from solution in this way.

2. Formation of hydrogen gas. The evolution of hydrogen gas is often observed at inert electrodes in cells that do not contain other more easily reduced species. The half reaction for this process is

$$2H^+ + 2e \rightleftharpoons H_2$$

3. Change in oxidation state of an ion in solution. A common reaction at nonreactive metal electrodes is the reduction of an ion to a lower oxida-

tion state. Thus, for example, iron (III) can acquire an electron at a platinum electrode

$$Fe^{3+} + e \rightleftharpoons Fe^{2+}$$

Some Common Anodic Reactions. Several types of reactions are listed below.

1. Oxidation of a metal electrode. Where a readily oxidized metal is used as an anode, consumption of the electrode frequently occurs. For example

$$Cd \rightleftharpoons Cd^{2+} + 2e$$
$$Zn \rightleftharpoons Zn^{2+} + 2e$$

2. Oxidation of halide ions. Oxidation of halide ions, at an inert metal anode is common. As an example

$$2Cl^- \rightleftharpoons Cl_2 + 2e$$

3. Change in oxidation state of an ion in solution. Often the anode reaction in a cell involves oxidation of an ion to a higher oxidation state. This will take place at a nonreactive metal electrode. The oxidation of iron (II) ion is typical of this process.

$$Fe^{2+} \rightleftharpoons Fe^{3+} + e$$

4. Evolution of oxygen. In the absence of easily oxidizable species, oxidation of water may occur at the anode giving oxygen as a product.

$$2H_2O \rightleftharpoons O_2 + 4H^+ + 4e$$

Electrode Signs. A positive or a negative sign is customarily assigned to an electrode to indicate the direction of flow of electrons as the electrode operates as part of a cell. Unfortunately some ambiguities are associated with this practice, particularly when attempts are made to relate these signs to anodic or cathodic processes. In the case of a galvanic cell, the negative electrode is the one from which electrons are obtained. For the cell shown in Figure 16.1, the electrons would be produced at the zinc *anode*. In the case of an electrolytic cell the negative electrode is the one into which electrons are forced. Thus in a cell used for removal of cadmium by electrolysis, the negative electrode is the one upon which metallic cadmium is deposited; that is, the *cathode*. Clearly, the sign assumed by, say, the cathode depends upon whether we are dealing with an electrolytic or a galvanic cell. Irrespective of sign, the anode is the electrode at which oxidation occurs and the cathode is the site for reduction; use of these terms, rather than positive and negative, in describing electrodes is un-ambiguous and much preferred.

ELECTRODE POTENTIAL

Turning again to the galvanic cell shown in Figure 16.1 we see that the driving force for the chemical reaction

$$Zn + Cu^{2+} \rightleftharpoons Cu + Zn^{2+}$$

manifests itself in the form of measurable electric force or voltage between the two electrodes. We may consider this force as being the sum of two forces or potentials, called *half-cell potentials* or single-electrode potentials; one of these is associated with the half reaction occurring at the anode and the other with the half reaction taking place at the cathode.

It is not difficult to see how we might obtain information regarding the *relative* magnitudes of half-cell potentials. For example, by replacing the left-hand side of the cell in Figure 16.1 with a cadmium electrode immersed in a solution of cadmium ions, the voltmeter reading would be approximately 0.4 volt less than that of the original cell. Since the copper cathode remains unchanged, we logically ascribe this voltage decrease to the alteration in the anode reaction; thus we conclude that the half-cell potential for the oxidation of cadmium is 0.4 volt less than for the oxidation of zinc. Other substitutions in the left-hand side of the cell would make possible the comparison of the chemical driving forces of a variety of half reactions by means of simple electrical measurements.

Such a technique does not lead to absolute values for half-cell potentials; indeed, there is no way to determine such quantities since all voltage-measuring devices must make contact both with the electrode in question and also with the solution. This latter contact, however, inevitably involves a solid-solution interface and hence acts as a second half cell at which a chemical reaction must also take place. Thus we do not obtain a measurement of the desired half-cell potential but rather a sum consisting of the potential of interest and the half-cell potential for the contact between the voltage measuring device and the solution.

Relative Half-cell Potentials. Our inability to measure absolute potentials for half-cell processes is not a serious handicap because relative half-cell potentials are just as useful for our purposes. These relative potentials can be combined to give cell potentials; in addition they are useful for the calculation of equilibrium constants for oxidation-reduction processes.

The Standard Hydrogen Electrode. To obtain consistent relative half-cell potential data, it is necessary to compare all electrodes against a common reference. This reference electrode should be relatively easy to construct, should exhibit reversible behavior, and should give constant and reproducible potentials for a given set of experimental conditions. The standard hydrogen electrode meets these requirements, and is used almost universally as such a reference. Figure 16.2 illustrates a typical hydrogen electrode. It consists, in essence, of a piece of platinum immersed in a solution with a hydrogen ion activity of one. Hydrogen gas is bubbled across the surface of the platinum in an uninterrupted stream to assure that the electrode is continuously in contact with both the solution and the gas; in order to achieve the largest possible surface area, the electrode is

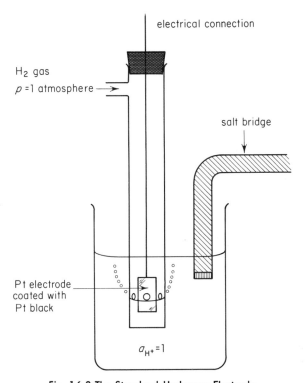

Fig. 16.2 The Standard Hydrogen Electrode.

coated with a finely divided layer of platinum called *platinum black*. The partial pressure of hydrogen is maintained at one atmosphere above the liquid phase.

An electrode of this type is called a *gas electrode*. The platinum takes no part in the electrochemical reaction, serving only as an aid in the transfer of electrons. The half-cell reaction responsible for the transmission of current across the interface is

$$H_2 \text{ (gas)} \rightleftharpoons 2H^+ + 2e$$

The hydrogen electrode may act as anode or cathode depending upon the type of half cell with which it is coupled. In the one case, oxidation of the hydrogen gas to hydrogen ions occurs; in the other, the reverse reaction takes place. Under proper conditions, then, the hydrogen electrode is reversible in its behavior.

The potential of the hydrogen electrode is dependent upon temperature, the concentration of hydrogen ions in the solution, and the pressure of the hydrogen gas at the surface of the electrode. Values for these parameters

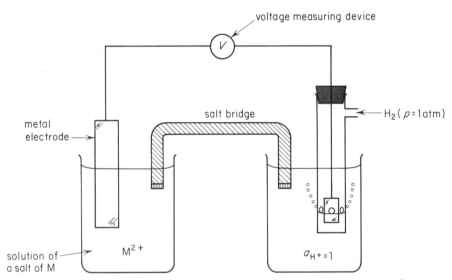

Fig. 16.3 Schematic Diagram of an Apparatus for Measurement of Electrode Potentials Against the Standard Hyrogen Electrode.

must be carefully defined in order for the half-cell process to serve as a reference. Specifications for a *standard* (known also as a *normal) hydrogen* electrode call for a hydrogen-ion activity of 1.00 mol/liter and a partial pressure of 1.00 atm for hydrogen gas. *Quite arbitrarily* the potential of this half cell is assigned the value of exactly zero volts at all temperatures.

Measurement of Electrode Potentials. Electrode potentials relative to the standard hydrogen electrode can be measured by means of a cell such as that shown in Figure 16.3. Here, one half of the cell consists of the standard hydrogen electrode and the other half is the electrode whose potential is to be determined. Connecting the two cells is a salt bridge, a device that consists of a tube containing a concentrated solution of an electrolyte—most often a saturated potassium chloride solution. This bridge provides electric contact between the two halves of the cell while preventing mixture of the contents of the half cells; the passage of current takes place by ionic migration, as previously described. In general, the effect of a salt bridge upon the cell voltage is vanishingly small.

The half cell in Figure 16.3 consists of a pure metal in contact with a solution of its ions. The electrode reaction then is

$$M \rightleftharpoons M^{2+} + 2e$$

If the metal is cadmium and the solution is approximately 1 molar in cadmium ions, the voltage indicated by the measuring device V will be about 0.4 volt. Further the metal electrode will behave as an anode so that electrons tend to flow from the metal electrode to the hydrogen electrode via the external circuit. Thus the half-cell reactions for the galvanic cell can be written as

$$Cd \rightleftharpoons Cd^{2+} + 2e \qquad \text{anode}$$
$$2H^+ + 2e \rightleftharpoons H_2 \qquad \text{cathode}$$

The over-all reaction is the sum of these, or

$$Cd + 2H^+ \rightleftharpoons Cd^{2+} + H_2$$

If the cadmiun electrode were replaced by a zinc electrode immersed in a solution of zinc ions, a potential of slightly less than 0.8 volt would be observed on the voltmeter. Again the metal electrode would behave as the anode. The larger voltage developed reflects the greater tendency of zinc to be oxidized; the difference between this potential and the one observed for cadmium gives a quantitative measure of the relative strengths of these two metals as reducing agents.

As mentioned earlier, a value of zero is assigned as the potential for the hydrogen electrode. The electrode potentials for the two half cells thus become 0.4 and 0.8 volt with respect to this reference. Since this is an arbitrary assignment, however, these so-called half-cell or electrode potentials are actually potentials of cells involving the hydrogen electrode as a common reference.

If the half cell in Figure 16.3 were a copper electrode in a 1-molar solution of copper (II) ions, we would find the potential of the cell to be about 0.3 volt. However, we would note a marked difference in behavior of this electrode as compared with two earlier examples. Here, the copper would be plated out and the external electron flow would be from the hydrogen electrode to the copper electrode. Obviously the spontaneous cell reaction is the reverse of the two earlier cases.

$$Cu^{2+} + H_2 \rightleftharpoons Cu + 2H^+$$

Thus metallic copper is a much less effective reducing agent than either the zinc or the cadmium. As before, the observed potential is a quantitative measure of this strength; in comparing this potential with those for the half reactions of zinc and cadmium, however, it becomes necessary to indicate the differences in behavior of the electrode systems relative to the reference electrode. This can be done conveniently by assigning a positive or negative sign to the potentials thus making the sign of the potential for the copper half reaction opposite to that of the other two.

Sign Conventions for Electrode Potentials. Two possible sign conventions can be applied to electrode potentials. For example we could say above that the potential for the oxidation of cadmium is $+0.4$ volt and that for copper is -0.3 volt, or the reverse notation could be used. Unfortunately chemists have not been able to agree on a single convention and this often leads to confusion.

We shall call the potential of an electrode reaction positive if the reaction, as written, proceeds spontaneously relative to the standard hydrogen electrode. A nonspontaneous reaction will have a negative potential. Thus for the three half reactions already considered we would write

$$Zn^{2+} + 2e \rightleftharpoons Zn \qquad E = -0.8 \text{ volt}$$

$$Cd^{2+} + 2e \rightleftharpoons Cd \qquad E = -0.4 \text{ volt}$$

$$Cu^{2+} + 2e \rightleftharpoons Cu \qquad E = +0.3 \text{ volt}$$

The reaction involving reduction of copper (II) ion to copper is spontaneous relative to the standard hydrogen electrode and is, therefore, given a positive sign. Within this same sign convention we may also write

$$Zn \rightleftharpoons Zn^{2+} + 2e \qquad E = +0.8 \text{ volt}$$

$$Cd \rightleftharpoons Cd^{2+} + 2e \qquad E = +0.4 \text{ volt}$$

$$Cu \rightleftharpoons Cu^{2+} + 2e \qquad E = -0.3 \text{ volt}$$

In this case the negative sign for copper indicates the nonspontaneity of the oxidation of copper relative to the hydrogen half cell. The positive sign for the zinc and cadmium potentials indicates that these reactions proceed spontaneously as written; that is, that the reaction

$$M + 2H^+ \rightleftharpoons M^{2+} + H_2$$

takes place in a galvanic cell under the prescribed conditions. The first set of potential data given above can be called *reduction potentials;* the second set, consisting of the same half-cell reactions written in the opposite sense are *oxidation potentials*. The two differ only in signs.

Clearly, an electrode potential datum has significance only when the half reaction to which it refers is explicitly indicated. This information is usually conveyed by writing the half reaction, as above, beside the potential of the half cell.[1] Note also that, the sign of the electrode potential is employed here to indicate the direction of the spontaneous chemical reaction. *This sign should not be confused with the sign used to indicate the polarity of the actual physical electrode in a galvanic or electrolytic cell.*

Effect of Concentration on Electrode Potentials. The electrode potential is a measure of the chemical force tending to drive a half reaction toward equilibrium. Consequently the potential is zero only when a system is at equilibrium, and becomes larger with departures from this state. Thus the potential of a piece of metallic zinc immersed in pure water is large relative to a piece of the same metal immersed in a 1 formal solution of zinc sulfate. In general, then, the concentration of the reactants and products of a half reaction will have a marked effect on electrode potentials, and the quantitative aspects of this effect must now be considered.

Consider the generalized, reversible half-cell reaction

$$aA + bB + \cdot\cdot\cdot + ne \rightleftharpoons cC + dD + \cdot\cdot\cdot$$

where the capital letters represent formulas of reacting species (whether charged or uncharged), e represents electrons, and the remaining uncapitalized letters indicate the number of mols of each species participating in the reaction. It can be shown theoretically as well as experimentally that the potential E for this electrode process is governed by the relation

$$E = E^\circ - \frac{RT}{nF} \ln \frac{[C]^c[D]^d \cdot\cdot\cdot}{[A]^a[B]^b \cdot\cdot\cdot} \qquad (16\text{-}1)$$

where E° = a constant characteristic of the particular half reaction
R = the gas constant = 8.314 volt coulombs/°K/mol
T = the absolute temperature
n = number of electrons participating in the reaction as defined by the equation describing the half-cell reaction
F = the faraday = 96,493 coulombs
$\ln$ = the natural logarithm = 2.303 $\log_{10}$

Substituting numerical values for the various constants into (16-1) and converting to base 10 logarithms, equation (16-1) becomes, at 25° C

$$E = E^\circ - \frac{0.059}{n} \log \frac{[C]^c[D]^d \cdot\cdot\cdot}{[A]^a[B]^b \cdot\cdot\cdot} \qquad (16\text{-}2)$$

---

[1] The International Union of Pure and Applied Chemistry has proposed the convention that the term "electrode potential" be reserved for half reactions written as reductions. Thus the electrode potential for a zinc electrode is the potential for the reaction

$$\text{Zn}^{2+} + \text{H}_2 \rightleftharpoons \text{Zn} + 2\text{H}^+$$

Because this reaction is not spontaneous the sign of the electrode potential for zinc is negative.

The symbols in brackets represent the activities of the reacting species. As in the case of equilibrium-constant expressions (Chapter 2) certain approximations for these activities are useful. Thus where the substances are dissolved in a solvent

$$[\ ] \cong \text{concentration in mols/liter}$$

If the reactant is a gas,

$$[\ ] \cong \text{partial pressure of the gas in atmospheres}$$

If the reactant exists in a second phase as a pure solid or liquid, then by definition[2]

$$[\ ] = 1$$

Finally if the solvent, water, is also involved in the half-cell process

$$[H_2O] = 1$$

Compared with the other reactants, the amount of water present is enormous, and its concentration can thus be considered to remain substantially unchanged despite its participation in the reaction. The constant activity of water is included in the constant, $E°$.

Equation 16-1 is often called the *Nernst equation* in honor of a nineteenth-century electrochemist. Application of the Nernst equation, and the approximations associated with it, is illustrated in the following examples.

1. $Zn^{2+} + 2e \rightleftharpoons Zn$ $E = E° - \dfrac{0.059}{2} \log \dfrac{1}{[Zn^{2+}]}$

Here the activity of the elemental zinc is unity; the electrode potential varies with the logarithm of the molar concentration of zinc ions in the solution.

2. $Fe^{3+} + e \rightleftharpoons Fe^{2+}$ $E = E° - \dfrac{0.059}{1} \log \dfrac{[Fe^{2+}]}{[Fe^{3+}]}$

The electrode potential, in this instance, could be measured with an inert metal electrode immersed in a solution containing iron (II) and iron (III). The potential is dependent upon the ratio of the molar concentrations of these ions.

3. $2H^+ + 2e \rightleftharpoons H_2$ $E = E° - \dfrac{0.059}{2} \log \dfrac{p_{H_2}}{[H^+]^2}$

---

[2] The arbitrary assignment of unity to the activity of the second phase was also made in arriving at the solubility-product expression (page 21). In either case, this assumes that the concentration of the substance in the second phase is constant and the equilibrium is unaffected by the *quantity* of this second phase.

In this example, p_{H_2} represents the partial pressure of hydrogen gas, expressed in atmospheres, at the surface of the electrode. Ordinarily this will be very close to the atmospheric pressure.

4. $Cr_2O_7^{2-} + 14H^+ + 6e \rightleftharpoons 2Cr^{3+} + 7H_2O$

$$E = E^\circ - \frac{0.059}{6} \log \frac{[Cr^{3+}]^2}{[Cr_2O_7^{2-}][H^+]^{14}}$$

Here the potential is dependent not only on the concentration of the chromium (III) and dichromate ions but also on the pH of the solution.

5. $AgCl + e \rightleftharpoons Ag + Cl^-$ $\qquad E = E^\circ - \frac{0.059}{1} \log \frac{[Cl^-]}{1}$

In this case the activities of both metallic silver and silver chloride are constant and equal to one; the potential of the silver electrode varies as the chloride ion concentration changes.

The Standard Electrode Potential, E°. An examination of equation (16-1) or (16-2) reveals that the constant, E°, is equal to the half-cell potential when the logarithmic term is zero. This occurs whenever the activity quotient is equal to unity, one instance being when the activities of all of the reactants and products are unity; thus the *standard electrode potential may be defined as the potential of a half-cell reaction versus the standard hydrogen electrode when the reactants and products are at unit activity.*

The standard electrode potential is a fundamental physical constant that gives a quantitative description of the relative driving force of a half-cell reaction. Several facts should be kept in mind regarding it. First, a standard electrode potential is temperature dependent; if it is to have significance, the temperature at which it is determined must be specified. Second, the standard electrode potential is a relative quantity in the sense that it is really a cell potential where one of the electrodes is a carefully specified reference electrode—that is, the standard hydrogen electrode whose potential is assigned a value of zero volts. Third, a standard electrode potential is given a sign that depends upon the direction of the spontaneous reaction with respect to the standard hydrogen electrode under the specified conditions of activity. We may encounter standard oxidation potentials and standard reduction potentials; for a given half reaction these will differ only in sign from one another. Thus the numerical value for a standard electrode potential is of no use unless the direction of the reaction and the sign convention being used are specified. Finally, the value of a standard potential is a measure of the intensity of the driving force of a half reaction. As such, it is independent of the notation employed to express the half-cell process. Thus the potential for the reaction

$$Ag^+ + e \rightleftharpoons Ag \qquad E^\circ = +0.799 \text{ volt}$$

while dependent upon the *concentration* of silver ions, is the same regardless of whether we write the reaction as above, or as

$$100Ag^+ + 100e \rightleftharpoons 100Ag \qquad E° = +0.799 \text{ volt}$$

Standard electrode potentials are available for numerous half reactions. Many of these have been determined directly from voltage measurements of various cells in which the standard hydrogen electrode constitutes one of the electrodes. It is possible, however, to calculate values for this important constant from equilibrium studies of oxidation-reduction reactions and from thermochemical data relating to such reactions. Many of the values found in the literature were so obtained. W. M. Latimer[3] published

TABLE 16-1
Standard Reduction Potentials
(See Appendix for a more extensive list.)

Reaction	$E°$ at 25° C, volts
$Zn^{2+} + 2e \rightleftharpoons Zn$	-0.763
$Cr^{3+} + e \rightleftharpoons Cr^{2+}$	-0.41
$Cd^{2+} + 2e \rightleftharpoons Cd$	-0.403
$2H^+ + 2e \rightleftharpoons H_2$	0.000
$Ag(S_2O_3)_2^{3-} + e \rightleftharpoons Ag + 2S_2O_3^{2-}$	$+0.010$
$AgCl + e \rightleftharpoons Ag + Cl^-$	$+0.222$
$I_3^- + 2e \rightleftharpoons 3I^-$	$+0.536$
$Fe^{3+} + e \rightleftharpoons Fe^{2+}$	$+0.771$
$Ag^+ + e \rightleftharpoons Ag$	$+0.799$
$Cl_2 + 2e \rightleftharpoons 2Cl^-$	$+1.359$
$MnO_4^- + 8H^+ + 5e \rightleftharpoons Mn^{2+} + 4H_2O$	$+1.51$

a definitive work that is to be recommended as an authoritative source for standard electrode potential data.

A few standard reduction potentials are given in Table 16-1; a more comprehensive list is found in the appendix (page 507). In these tabulations the species in the lower left side of the equations are most easily reduced as evidenced by the large positive $E°$ values; they are therefore the most effective oxidizing agents. Proceeding up the table, each succeeding species

---

[3] W. M. Latimer, *The Oxidation States of the Elements and Their Potentials in Aqueous Solutions*, 2d ed. Englewood Cliffs, N.J.: Prentice-Hall, Inc., 1952.

is a less effective acceptor of electrons than the one below it. The half-cell reactions at the head of the table have little tendency to take place as written. On the other hand, they do tend to occur in the opposite sense, as oxidations; the most effective reducing agents, then, are those species that appear in the upper right-hand portion of the table of standard reduction potentials.

A compilation of standard potentials provides the chemist with a qualitative picture regarding the extent and direction of electron transfer reactions between the tabulated species. On the basis of Table 16-1, for example, we see that zinc is more easily oxidized than cadmium; we conclude, then, that a piece of zinc immersed in a solution of cadmium ions results in the deposition of metallic cadmium. On the other hand cadmium has little tendency to reduce zinc ions. Also from Table 16-1 we see that iron (III) is a better oxidizing agent than the triiodide ion. We may therefore predict that in a solution containing an equilibrium mixture of iron (III), iodide, iron (II), and triiodide ions, the latter pair will predominate.

Calculation of Half-cell Potentials from $E°$ Values. We must now consider some applications of the Nernst equation to the calculation of various half-cell potentials.

★EXAMPLE. What is the potential for the half reaction involving a cadmium electrode in a solution that is 0.0100 F in Cd^{2+}?
From Table 16-1 we find

$$Cd^{2+} + 2e \rightleftharpoons Cd \qquad E° = -0.403 \text{ volt}$$

and we write

$$E = E° - \frac{0.059}{2} \log \frac{1}{[Cd^{2+}]}$$

Substituting the Cd^{2+} concentration into the equation we get

$$E = -0.403 - \frac{0.059}{2} \log \frac{1}{(0.01)}$$

$$= -0.403 - \frac{0.059}{2} (+2)$$

$$= -0.462 \text{ volt}$$

The sign for the potential simply indicates the direction of the half reaction when this half cell is coupled with the standard hydrogen electrode. The fact that it is negative shows that the reverse reaction

$$Cd + 2H^+ \rightleftharpoons H_2 + Cd^{2+}$$

would occur spontaneously. Note that the calculated potential is a larger negative number than the standard electrode potential itself. This follows from equilibrium considerations since the half reaction, as written, has less tendency to occur with the lower cadmium ion concentration. Note also that an identical value—except for sign—would be obtained had we used the standard oxidation potential for the calculation; that is,

$$Cd \rightleftharpoons Cd^{2+} + 2e \qquad E^\circ = +0.403$$

$$E = +0.403 - \frac{0.059}{2} \log [Cd^{2+}]$$

Substituting 0.01 for $[Cd^{2+}]$, we obtain

$$E = +0.462 \text{ volt}$$

Electrode Potentials in the Presence of Precipitation and Complex-forming Reagents. Reagents that react with the participants of an electrode process have a marked effect on the potential for that process. For example the standard electrode potential for the reaction $Ag^+ + e \rightleftharpoons Ag$ is $+0.799$ volt. This is the potential of a piece of silver metal immersed in a solution of silver ions at unit activity measured with respect to the standard hydrogen electrode. Addition of chloride ions to such a solution will materially alter the silver ion concentration and hence the electrode potential. This is illustrated in the following example.

★EXAMPLE. Calculate the potential of a silver electrode in a solution that is saturated with silver chloride and has a chlorideion activity of exactly 1.00.

$$Ag^+ + e \rightleftharpoons Ag \qquad E^\circ_{Ag^+ \to Ag} = +0.799 \text{ volt}$$

$$E = E^\circ_{Ag^+ \to Ag} - 0.059 \log \frac{1}{[Ag^+]}$$

We may calculate $[Ag^+]$ from the solubility-product constant

$$[Ag^+] = \frac{K_{sp}}{[Cl^-]}$$

Substituting this into the Nernst equation

$$E = E^\circ_{Ag^+ \to Ag} - \frac{0.059}{1} \log \frac{[Cl^-]}{K_{sp}}$$

This may be rewritten as

$$E = E^\circ_{Ag^+ \to Ag} + 0.059 \log K_{sp} - 0.059 \log [Cl^-] \qquad (16\text{-}3)$$

If we substitute 1.00 for $[Cl^-]$ and use a value of 1.82×10^{-10} for K_{sp}, we obtain

$$E = +0.222 \text{ volt}$$

This calculation shows that the half-cell potential for the reduction of silver becomes smaller in the presence of chloride ions. Qualitatively, this is what we expect since removal of silver ions would decrease the tendency of the silver ions to be reduced.

Equation (16-3) relates the potential of a silver electrode to the chloride ion concentration of a solution that is also saturated with silver chloride. When the chloride ion activity is unity, the potential is the sum of two constants; this sum can be called the standard electrode potential for the half reaction

$$AgCl + e \rightleftharpoons Ag + Cl^- \qquad E^\circ_{AgCl \to Ag} = +0.222 \text{ volt}$$

where

$$E^\circ_{AgCl \to Ag} = E^\circ_{Ag^+ \to Ag} + 0.059 \log K_{sp}$$

Thus, when in contact with a solution saturated with silver chloride, the potential of a silver electrode can be described either in terms of the silver ion concentration using the standard electrode potential for the simple silver half reaction or in terms of the chloride ion concentration using the standard potential for the silver-silver chloride half reaction.

In an analogous fashion to the foregoing, we can treat the behavior of a silver electrode in a solution of an ion that forms a soluble complex with silver ion. For example, in a solution of thiosulfate ion, the half reaction is

$$Ag(S_2O_3)_2^{3-} + e \rightleftharpoons Ag + 2S_2O_3^{2-}$$

The standard electrode potential for this half reaction would be the electrode potential when both the complex and the complexing anion are at unit activity. Using the same approach as in the previous example, we find that

$$E^\circ_{Ag(S_2O_3)_2^{3-} \to Ag} = E^\circ_{Ag^+ \to Ag} + 0.059 \log K_{inst}$$

where K_{inst} is the dissociation constant for the complex ion.

Data for the potential of the silver electrode in the presence of a variety of ions are given in the table of standard electrode potentials (page 507). Similar information is given for other electrode systems. Such data often simplify the calculation of half-cell potentials.

CELLS AND CELL POTENTIALS

Schematic Representation of Cells. In order to simplify the description of cells, chemists frequently use a shorthand notation. For example, the cell shown in Figure 16.1 can be represented as

$$Zn \mid ZnSO_4(C_1) \mid CuSO_4(C_2) \mid Cu$$

the anode process being listed on the left. The single vertical lines represent phase boundaries in the cell; potential differences arising across these are included in the measured cell potential. The potential difference across the interface between the two solutions—a $ZnSO_4$ solution of concentration C_1 and a $CuSO_4$ solution of concentration C_2—is known as a *liquid junction potential*. Often, the magnitude of this potential can be made to approach zero by interposing between the two solutions a *salt bridge* consisting of a saturated solution of potassium chloride. The presence of a salt bridge is symbolized by vertical double lines. Using this notation the cell in Figure 16.3 can be written as

$$M \mid M^{2+}(C_1) \parallel H^+(a = 1) \mid H_2(p = 1 \text{ atm})Pt$$

Here the hydrogen ion activity a and the partial pressure of hydrogen p are given in parentheses. Some chemists prefer to replace the single vertical lines with semicolons or colons.

Calculation of Cell Potentials. One of the important uses of standard electrode potentials is the calculation of the theoretical potential obtainable from a galvanic cell or required to operate an electrolytic cell. Voltages such as these are for cells through which there is essentially no passage of current; additional considerations are necessary where a current flow occurs.

Consider the cell

$$Zn \mid ZnSO_4(1.00 \ F) \parallel CuSO_4(1.00 \ F) \mid Cu$$

The two half reactions involve oxidation of zinc to zinc ions and reduction of the copper (II) ions to the metal. Standard electrode potentials for these half reactions are available; however, these are actually potentials for cells in which the chemical reactions are

$$Zn + 2H^+ \rightleftharpoons Zn^{2+} + H_2 \qquad E° = +0.763 \text{ volt}$$

$$Cu^{2+} + H_2 \rightleftharpoons Cu + 2H^+ \qquad E° = +0.337 \text{ volt}$$

Here we have reversed the direction of the zinc-zinc ion half reaction from the way it appears in the table of standard potentials; as a consequence, the sign of the standard potential has also been changed. Because the hydrogen electrode acts in the opposite sense in the two cases, the potential of a cell with a zinc anode and copper cathode is obtained by adding these two potentials together. Any effect due to the hydrogen electrodes is cancelled out and we get

$$Zn + Cu^{2+} \rightleftharpoons Cu + Zn^{2+} \qquad E = 1.100 \text{ volts}$$

The calculated potential will be for a cell in which the copper (II) and zinc ion activities are unity; this should be reasonably close to the potential for the actual cell in question where the concentrations are given as one formal.

A certain amount of care is needed in calculations of this type in order to avoid a confusion of the signs. The procedure that follows is strongly recommended.

1. Calculate the two half-cell potentials using standard oxidation or reduction potentials and the Nernst equation.

2. Write one of the half reactions as an oxidation and the other as a reduction; also write the potentials for each, being sure that the signs are appropriate for the half reactions *as written*.

3. Add the potentials and the equations for the half reactions. A positive cell potential will indicate that the cell reaction is spontaneous as written; a negative sign, on the other hand, will mean that a potential greater than this must be applied to the cell in order to cause the reaction to proceed in the manner indicated. Provided we know the reaction direction, we may also deduce which electrode behaves as the anode and which as the cathode.

★EXAMPLE. Calculate the theoretical potential of the following cell:

$$\text{Pt, } H_2(0.8 \text{ atm}) \mid HCl(0.20 \text{ } F), AgCl(\text{saturated}) \mid Ag$$

The two half-cell reactions and standard reduction potentials are

$$2H^+ + 2e \rightleftharpoons H_2 \qquad\qquad E° = 0.000 \text{ volt}$$

$$AgCl + e \rightleftharpoons Ag + Cl^- \qquad E° = +0.222 \text{ volt}$$

For the hydrogen electrode

$$E = 0.000 - \frac{0.059}{2} \log \frac{0.8}{(0.2)^2} = -0.038 \text{ volt}$$

For the silver-silver chloride electrode

$$E = +0.222 - 0.059 \log 0.20 = +0.263 \text{ volt}$$

This half reaction may be written as

$$2AgCl + 2e \rightleftharpoons 2Ag + 2Cl^-(0.2 \text{ } M) \qquad E = +0.263 \text{ volt}$$

By reversing the other half reaction and changing the sign for its potential

$$H_2(0.8 \text{ atm}) \rightleftharpoons 2H^+(0.2 \text{ } M) + 2e \qquad E = +0.038 \text{ volt}$$

we obtain on addition

$$H_2 + 2AgCl \rightleftharpoons 2H^+ + 2Cl^- + 2Ag \qquad E_{cell} = +0.301 \text{ volt}$$

The positive sign shows that this equation describes the *spontaneous* cell reaction and that the hydrogen electrode is the anode of the galvanic cell.

16.2   Chemical Equilibrium in Cells; Equilibrium Constants from Standard Electrode Potentials

An Important Condition at Equilibrium. Consider once again the galvanic cell shown in Figure 16.1 where the electrode reactions are

$$Zn \rightleftharpoons Zn^{2+} + 2e$$

$$Cu^{2+} + 2e \rightleftharpoons Cu$$

We have shown that the potential for this cell is equal to the sum of the half-cell potentials as written; that is,

$$E_{cell} = E_{Zn \rightarrow Zn^{2+}} + E_{Cu^{2+} \rightarrow Cu}$$

When current is drawn from this cell, there is an increase in the zinc ion concentration and a decrease in the copper (II) ion concentration of the solutions surrounding the electrodes. The effect of this is to lower the potentials of each of the half reactions as they occur in this cell

$$E_{Zn \rightarrow Zn^{2+}} = E^{\circ}_{Zn \rightarrow Zn^{2+}} - \frac{0.059}{2} \log [Zn^{2+}]$$

$$E_{Cu^{2+} \rightarrow Cu} = E^{\circ}_{Cu^{2+} \rightarrow Cu} - \frac{0.059}{2} \log \frac{1}{[Cu^{2+}]}$$

Thus as current is drawn, the cell potential will decrease and eventually become zero. When this occurs, the cell is said to be completely discharged; at this point, *the cell reaction*

$$Zn + Cu^{2+} \rightleftharpoons Zn^{2+} + Cu$$

is at chemical equilibrium; that is, the driving force for the forward reaction has become equal to that of the reverse reaction. We may say, then, that *at chemical equilibrium*

$$E_{cell} = 0 = E_{Zn \rightarrow Zn^{2+}} + E_{Cu^{2+} \rightarrow Cu}$$

or, writing both half-cell potentials as reductions and rearranging, that

$$E_{Zn^{2+} \rightarrow Zn} = E_{Cu^{2+} \rightarrow Cu}$$

This illustrates an important and quite general relationship—*for an oxidation-reduction system at chemical equilibrium, the reduction potentials (or the oxidation potentials) of the two half reactions of the system will be equal.*

Equilibrium Constants for Oxidation-reduction Reactions. Consider the oxidation-reduction equilibrium

$$aA_{red} + bB_{oxid} \rightleftharpoons aA_{oxid} + bB_{red}$$

where the half reactions may be written

$$aA_{\text{oxid}} + ne \rightleftharpoons aA_{\text{red}}$$

$$bB_{\text{oxid}} + ne \rightleftharpoons bB_{\text{red}}$$

When the components of this system are at chemical equilibrium

$$E_A = E_B$$

where E_A and E_B are the reduction potentials for the two half cells. Applying the Nernst equation we may write

$$E_A^\circ - \frac{0.059}{n} \log \frac{[A_{\text{red}}]^a}{[A_{\text{oxid}}]^a} = E_B^\circ - \frac{0.059}{n} \log \frac{[B_{\text{red}}]^b}{[B_{\text{oxid}}]^b}$$

Upon rearranging and combining the log terms

$$E_B^\circ - E_A^\circ = \frac{0.059}{n} \log \frac{[A_{\text{oxid}}]^a [B_{\text{red}}]^b}{[A_{\text{red}}]^a [B_{\text{oxid}}]^b}$$

The concentrations here are equilibrium concentrations; the quotient containing these is the equilibrium constant for the reaction. Thus, we may write

$$\log K_{\text{equil}} = \frac{n(E_B^\circ - E_A^\circ)}{0.059}$$

★EXAMPLE. Calculate the equilibrium constant for the reaction

$$MnO_4^- + 5Fe^{2+} + 8H^+ \rightleftharpoons Mn^{2+} + 5Fe^{3+} + 4H_2O$$

From the table of standard reduction potentials (page 332) we find

$$5Fe^{3+} + 5e \rightleftharpoons 5Fe^{2+} \qquad\qquad E_{Fe^{3+}}^\circ = +0.771 \text{ volt}$$

$$MnO_4^- + 8H^+ + 5e \rightleftharpoons Mn^{2+} + 4H_2O \qquad E_{MnO_4^-}^\circ = +1.51 \text{ volts}$$

Since, at equilibrium

$$E_{Fe^{3+}} = E_{MnO_4^-}$$

then

$$E_{Fe^{3+}}^\circ - \frac{0.059}{5} \log \frac{[Fe^{2+}]^5}{[Fe^{3+}]^5} = E_{MnO_4^-}^\circ - \frac{0.059}{5} \log \frac{[Mn^{2+}]}{[MnO_4^-][H^+]^8}$$

Rearranging

$$\frac{0.059}{5} \log \frac{[Mn^{2+}][Fe^{3+}]^5}{[MnO_4^-][Fe^{2+}]^5[H^+]^8} = E_{MnO_4^-}^\circ - E_{Fe^{3+}}^\circ$$

$$\log K_{\text{equil}} = \frac{(1.51 - 0.77)5}{0.059}$$

$$= 62.7$$

$$K_{\text{equil}} = 10^{62.7} = 5 \times 10^{62}$$

★EXAMPLE. A piece of metallic copper is placed in a $0.05\,F$ solution of $AgNO_3$. The equilibrium composition of the solution is sought.
    The reaction is

$$Cu + 2Ag^+ \rightleftharpoons Cu^{2+} + 2Ag$$

We first calculate the equilibrium constant for the reaction and then determine the solution composition from this. From a table of standard potentials (page 507), we find

$$2Ag^+ + 2e \rightleftharpoons 2Ag \qquad E^\circ_{Ag^+} = +0.799 \text{ volt}$$

$$Cu^{2+} + 2e \rightleftharpoons Cu \qquad E^\circ_{Cu^{2+}} = +0.337 \text{ volt}$$

Since, at equilibrium

$$E_{Cu^{2+}} = E_{Ag^+}$$

then

$$E^\circ_{Cu^{2+}} - \frac{0.059}{2} \log \frac{1}{[Cu^{2+}]} = E^\circ_{Ag^+} - \frac{0.059}{2} \log \frac{1}{[Ag^+]^2}$$

$$\log \frac{[Cu^{2+}]}{[Ag^+]^2} = \frac{2(E^\circ_{Ag^+} - E^\circ_{Cu^{2+}})}{0.059}$$

and

$$\frac{[Cu^{2+}]}{[Ag^+]^2} = K = 4.6 \times 10^{15}$$

From the size of the equilibrium constant, we conclude that the reaction goes far to the right as written and that nearly all of the Ag^+ is used up. Let the concentration of residual silver ions be x. The Cu^{2+} concentration will be just one half of the concentration of Ag^+ consumed by the reaction; that is,

$$[Cu^{2+}] = \tfrac{1}{2}(0.05 - x)$$

Since the reaction goes nearly to completion it is probably safe to assume that x is small; then

$$[Cu^{2+}] \cong \tfrac{1}{2}(0.05) = 0.025$$

Substituting

$$\frac{(0.025)}{x^2} = 4.6 \times 10^{15}$$

$$x = [Ag^+] = 2.3 \times 10^{-9} \text{ mol/liter}$$

$$[Cu^{2+}] = \tfrac{1}{2}(0.05 - 2.3 \times 10^{-9}) \cong 0.025 \text{ mol/liter}$$

Problems

1. For each of the following indicate the oxidizing agent and write a balanced equation for its half reaction. Do the same for the reducing agent. It may be necessary to supply H^+, OH^-, and H_2O in balancing these half reactions.

Reactants	Products
(a) Cl_2, I^-	I_3^-, Cl^-
(b) Cd, Ag^+	Ag, Cd^{2+}
(c) H_2, Fe^{3+}	H^+, Fe^{2+}
(d) $Cr_2O_7^{2-}$, U^{4+}	Cr^{3+}, UO_2^{2+}
(e) $V(OH)_4^+$, V^{3+}	VO^{2+}
(f) HNO_2, MnO_4^-	NO_3^-, Mn^{2+}
(g) O_2, I^-	H_2O, I_3^-
(h) IO_3^-, I^-	I_2
(i) $H_2C_2O_4$, Ce^{4+}	CO_2, Ce^{3+}
(j) Ag, Br^-, Sn^{4+}	AgBr, Sn^{2+}

ans. (a) Oxidizing agent $Cl_2 + 2e \rightleftharpoons 2Cl^-$
Reducing agent $3I^- \rightleftharpoons I_3^- + 2e$

2. Give the equivalent weight of each oxidizing agent in Problem 1.

$$\text{ans. (1-a) eq wt } Cl_2 = \frac{\text{gfw } Cl_2}{2}$$

3. Write balanced equations for each of the reactions in Problem 1.

4. Calculate the reduction potentials of the following half cells against the standard hydrogen electrode.

(a) Ag | Ag^+ (0.0100 M)	ans. $E = +0.681$ volt
(b) Ni | Ni^{2+} (0.712 M)	$E = -0.254$ volt
(c) Pt, H_2 (1 atm) | HCl (10^{-5} F)	$E = -0.295$ volt
(d) Pt | Fe^{3+} (1.00×10^{-4} M), Fe^{2+} (0.100 M)	$E = +0.594$ volt
(e) Ag | AgBr (sat'd), Br^- (3.00 M)	$E = +0.067$ volt

5. Calculate the reduction potentials of the following half cells against the standard hydrogen electrode.
(a) Cr \| Cr^{3+} (0.00100 M)
(b) Pb \| Pb^{2+} (1.00×10^{-5} M)
(c) Pt, H_2 (1.00 atm) \| HCl (4.00 F)
(d) Pt \| V^{3+} (0.100 M), V^{2+} (0.0500 M)
(e) Hg \| Hg_2Cl_2 (sat'd), Cl^- (0.0300 M)

6. Calculate the reduction potentials for the following systems against the standard hydrogen electrode.
(a) Pt \| V^{3+} (1.00×10^{-3} M), VO^{2+} (1.00 M), HCl (0.100 F)

ans. $E = +0.420$ volt

(b) Pt \| MnO_4^- (0.300 M), Mn^{2+} (0.100 M), H^+ (0.200 M)

ans. $E = +1.45$ volts

7. Calculate the reduction potentials for the following systems against the standard hydrogen electrode.

(a) Pt | UO_2^{2+} (0.010 M), U^{4+} (0.100 M), H^+ (0.100 M)

(b) Pt | TiO^{2+} (0.500 M), Ti^{3+} (0.100 M), H^+ (1.00 × 10^{-3} M)

8. Indicate whether the following half cells would behave as the anodes or cathodes of the galvanic cells formed in conjunction with a standard hydrogen electrode.

(a) Co | Co^{2+} (1.00 M)   ans. anode

(b) Ag | AgCl (sat'd), Cl^- (1.00 M)   ans. cathode

(c) Pb | Pb^{2+} (1.00 × 10^{-4} M)

(d) Pt, H_2 (1 atm) | H^+ (1.00 × 10^{-5} M)

(e) Ag | AgI (sat'd), I^- (1.00 M)

(f) Pt | Sn^{4+} (10^{-5} M), Sn^{2+} (10^{-5} M)

(g) Pt | CuI (sat'd), I^- (1.00 × 10^{-10} M)

9. Arrange the following substances in their order of decreasing strength as oxidizing agents: $Fe(CN)_6^{3-}$, Fe^{3+}, $Ag(CN)_2^-$ in 1 F KCN, F_2, Al^{3+}, H^+ (in 1 F acid), Ce^{4+}, Cd^{2+}, O_2 (in 1 F acid), Cr^{3+}.

10. Arrange the following substances in their order of decreasing strength as reducing agents: Cl^-, Fe^{2+}, Ni, Ag (in 1 F KI), V^{2+}, Pb, Ti^{3+}, $Na_2S_2O_3$, KI, H_2.

11. Indicate in which direction the following reactions will proceed if all substances are initially at unit activity.

(a) $Fe^{3+} + Ag \rightleftharpoons Fe^{2+} + Ag^+$ ans. left

(b) $Sn^{4+} + 2Ag + 2Cl^- \rightleftharpoons Sn^{2+} + 2AgCl$ ans. left

(c) $2Tl + Cd^{2+} \rightleftharpoons 2Tl^+ + Cd$

(d) $2Ce^{4+} + 2Br^- \rightleftharpoons 2Ce^{3+} + Br_2$

(e) $5Cl_2 + I_2 + 6H_2O \rightleftharpoons 2IO_3^- + 10Cl^- + 12H^+$

(f) $Ag(CN)_2^- + Cr^{2+} \rightleftharpoons Ag + Cr^{3+} + 2CN^-$

(g) $Ba + 2Na^+ \rightleftharpoons Ba^{2+} + 2Na$

(h) $2Ag + Hg_2Cl_2 \rightleftharpoons 2Hg + 2AgCl$

(i) $4Ce^{4+} + 2H_2O \rightleftharpoons 4Ce^{3+} + O_2 + 4H^+$

12. In 1-F acid solution which is the better oxidizing agent, I_2 or H_3AsO_4? In neutral solution? Explain your answers.

13. Calculate the theoretical potentials of the following cells. Indicate which electrode would act as anode when current is drawn from the cell.

(a) Pb | Pb^{2+} (0.100 M) || Cd^{2+} (0.0010 M) | Cd

(b) Pt | I_3^- (0.0100 M), I^- (0.1 M), AgI (sat'd) | Ag

(c) Pt, H_2 (1 atm) | H^+ (1.0 × 10^{-5} M), KCl (0.1 F), AgCl (sat'd) | Ag

(d) Pt | Tl^{3+} (1.0 M), Tl^+ (0.01 M) || Zn^{2+} (0.01 M) | Zn

ans. (a) 0.335 volt, Cd electrode anode

(b) 0.658 volt, Ag electrode anode

(c) 0.576 volt, Pt electrode anode

(d) 2.13 volts, Zn electrode anode

14. Calculate the theoretical cell potentials for the following. Indicate which electrode would behave as the negative electrode (anode) of a galvanic cell.

(a) Ag | AgBr (sat'd), Br⁻ (0.01 *M*), H⁺ (10 *M*) | H₂ (1 atm) Pt

(b) Pt | Fe³⁺ (0.2 *M*), Fe²⁺ (0.01 *M*) ‖ Cl⁻ (0.1 *M*), Hg₂Cl₂ (sat'd) | Hg

(c) Cd | Cd²⁺ (0.305 *M*) ‖ H⁺ (0.01 *M*) | O₂ (1 atm) Pt

(d) Pt | UO₂²⁺ (0.510 *M*), U⁴⁺ (0.100 *M*), H⁺ (0.01 *M*) ‖ Ni²⁺ (0.4 *M*) | Ni

15. Calculate the potentials of the following cells. Indicate which electrode is the anode of a galvanic cell.

(a) Ag | AgCl (sat'd), KCl (1.0 *F*) ‖ KCl (0.001 *F*), AgCl (sat'd) | Ag

(b) Pt, H₂ (1 atm) | HCl (0.5 *F*) ‖ HCl (1.0 × 10⁻⁴ *F*) | H₂ (1 atm) Pt

16. In order to determine the solubility product for the salt AgX, the following cell was prepared:

$$\text{Ag | AgX (sat'd), X}^- \text{ (0.1 } M\text{), H}^+ \text{ (1.0 } M\text{) | H}_2 \text{ (1 atm) Pt}$$

The cell had a potential of 0.122 volt and the silver electrode behaved as the anode. Calculate the silver ion concentration of the solution and the solubility product of AgX.   ans. [Ag⁺] = 2.5 × 10⁻¹⁶ mol/liter

$$K_{sp} = 2.5 \times 10^{-17}$$

17. From the standard potentials

$$\text{Tl}^+ + e \rightleftharpoons \text{Tl} \qquad\qquad E° = -0.336 \text{ volt}$$
$$\text{TlCl} + e \rightleftharpoons \text{Tl} + \text{Cl}^- \qquad E° = -0.557 \text{ volt}$$

calculate the solubility-product constant for TlCl.   ans. $K_{sp} = 1.8 \times 10^{-4}$

18. Calculate the solubility product for Mn(OH)₂ from the following data:

$$\text{Mn}^{2+} + 2e \rightleftharpoons \text{Mn} \qquad\qquad\quad E° = -1.18 \text{ volts}$$
$$\text{Mn(OH)}_2 + 2e \rightleftharpoons \text{Mn} + 2\text{OH}^- \qquad E° = -1.55 \text{ volts}$$

19. The solubility product for Tl₂S is 1.2 × 10⁻²². Calculate $E°$ for the reaction

$$\text{Tl}_2\text{S} + 2e \rightleftharpoons 2\text{Tl}^+ + \text{S}^{2-}.$$

20. Calculate the instability constant for Ni(CN)₄²⁻ from the data:

$$\text{Ni}^{2+} + 2e \rightleftharpoons \text{Ni} \qquad\qquad\qquad E° = -0.250 \text{ volt}$$
$$\text{Ni(CN)}_4^{2-} + 2e \rightleftharpoons \text{Ni} + 4\text{CN}^- \qquad E° = -0.82 \text{ volt}$$

21. The half cell

$$\text{Pt, H}_2 \text{ (1 atm) | HA (0.2 } F\text{), NaA (0.1 } F\text{)}$$

behaves as an anode when coupled with a standard hydrogen electrode. Its potential is 0.443 volt. Calculate the dissociation constant for the weak acid HA.   ans. $K_a = 1.5 \times 10^{-8}$

22. The half cell

$$\text{Pt, H}_2 \text{ (1 atm) | HY (0.12 } F\text{), NaY (0.36 } F\text{)}$$

develops an anode potential of 0.107 volt against the standard hydrogen electrode. What is the dissociation constant for HY?

23. Compute the equilibrium constant for the reaction

$$Br_2 + 2Fe^{2+} \rightleftharpoons 2Br^- + 2Fe^{3+}$$ ans. $\dfrac{[Br^-]^2[Fe^{3+}]^2}{[Br_2][Fe^{2+}]^2} = 1.0 \times 10^{10}$

24. Calculate the equilibrium constant for the reaction

$$O_2 + 4I^- + 4H^+ \rightleftharpoons 2I_2 + 2H_2O$$

25. Calculate the equilibrium constant for the reaction

$$IO_3^- + 8I^- + 6H^+ \rightleftharpoons 3I_3^- + 3H_2O$$

26. An excess of iron filings are shaken in a 0.02 F solution of $CdSO_4$. What is the equilibrium concentration of Cd^{2+}?

27. Calculate equilibrium constants for the following reactions (unbalanced).
   (a) $MnO_4^- + Tl^+ \rightleftharpoons Mn^{2+} + Tl^{3+}$
   (b) $VO^{2+} + 2I^- \rightleftharpoons V^{3+} + I_2$
   (c) $TiO^{2+} + V^{2+} \rightleftharpoons Ti^{3+} + V^{3+}$

$$\left(\mathbf{17} \right)$$

Theory of Oxidation-reduction Titrations

The successful application of an oxidation-reduction reaction to volumetric analysis requires, among other things, the means for detecting the equivalence point. We must therefore examine the changes that occur in the course of such a titration, paying particular attention to those variations that are most pronounced in the region of the equivalence point.

17.1   Titration Curves

In the titration curves so far considered the logarithm of the concentration of one of the reacting species has been plotted against the volume of reagent added. The species chosen for plotting in each case has been the one to which the indicator for the reaction is sensitive. Most of the indicators used for oxidation-reduction titrations are themselves oxidizing or reducing agents that respond not to the changes in concentration of any particular ion in the solution but rather to the change in oxidation potential of the substrate. For this reason, the usual practice is to use a half-cell potential as the ordinate in oxidation-reduction titration curves rather than the logarithm of a concentration. To illustrate, for the volumetric reaction

$$Ce^{4+} + Fe^{2+} \rightleftharpoons Ce^{3+} + Fe^{3+}$$

a typical titration curve will consist of the oxidation or reduction potential for the cerium (IV)-cerium (III) system or the iron (III)-iron (II) system plotted as a function of the volume of the reagent. Because the two half reactions are in equilibrium throughout the entire titration, *the reduction potentials for the two systems are numerically identical at every point on the curve.*

EQUIVALENCE-POINT POTENTIAL

Of the data that can be computed for an oxidation-reduction system the most useful is the potential at chemical equivalence. The calculation of this quantity can be illustrated with the foregoing reaction.

$$Ce^{4+} + e \rightleftharpoons Ce^{3+}$$

$$Fe^{3+} + e \rightleftharpoons Fe^{2+}$$

and we may write

$$E = E^\circ_{Ce^{4+}} - 0.059 \log \frac{[Ce^{3+}]}{[Ce^{4+}]}$$

$$E = E^\circ_{Fe^{3+}} - 0.059 \log \frac{[Fe^{2+}]}{[Fe^{3+}]}$$

Because the system is at equilibrium, the two values for E must be identical; thus, upon addition we get

$$2E = E^\circ_{Ce^{4+}} + E^\circ_{Fe^{3+}} - 0.059 \log \frac{[Ce^{3+}][Fe^{2+}]}{[Ce^{4+}][Fe^{3+}]}$$

We know, from the stoichiometric equation, that *at the equivalence point*

$$[Fe^{3+}] = [Ce^{3+}]$$

$$[Fe^{2+}] = [Ce^{4+}]$$

so that

$$2E = E^\circ_{Ce^{4+}} + E^\circ_{Fe^{3+}} - 0.059 \log \frac{[Ce^{3+}][Fe^{2+}]}{[Ce^{4+}][Fe^{3+}]}$$

and

$$E = \frac{E^\circ_{Ce^{4+}} + E^\circ_{Fe^{3+}}}{2}$$

The E obtained in this way represents the reduction potential (against the standard hydrogen electrode) of either the cerium (IV)-cerium (III) or the iron (III)-iron (II) system with concentrations corresponding to those existing at the equivalence point. In common with all other phases of the titration the same value for E would be obtained through application of the Nernst equation to *either* of the half-cell processes involved. Such an approach would require a preliminary calculation, employing the equilibrium constant, to obtain a numerical value for either $[Ce^{4+}]$ or $[Fe^{2+}]$, however.

Now consider the somewhat more complicated case

$$5Fe^{2+} + MnO_4^- + 8H^+ \rightleftharpoons 5Fe^{3+} + Mn^{2+} + 4H_2O$$

The respective half reactions may be written

$$Fe^{3+} + e \rightleftharpoons Fe^{2+}$$

$$MnO_4^- + 8H^+ + 5e \rightleftharpoons Mn^{2+} + 4H_2O$$

The equilibrium potential of this system is given by either

$$E = E^\circ_{Fe^{3+}} - \frac{0.059}{1} \log \frac{[Fe^{2+}]}{[Fe^{3+}]}$$

or

$$E = E^\circ_{MnO_4^-} - \frac{0.059}{5} \log \frac{[Mn^{2+}]}{[MnO_4^-][H^+]^8}$$

It is necessary to multiply the second equation through by 5 to permit the combination of logarithmic terms.

$$5E = 5E^\circ_{MnO_4^-} - 0.059 \log \frac{[Mn^{2+}]}{[MnO_4^-][H^+]^8}$$

After addition we find that

$$6E = E^\circ_{Fe^{3+}} + 5E^\circ_{MnO_4^-} - 0.059 \log \frac{[Fe^{2+}][Mn^{2+}]}{[Fe^{3+}][MnO_4^-][H^+]^8}$$

The stoichiometry at the equivalence point requires that

$$[Fe^{3+}] = 5[Mn^{2+}]$$

$$[Fe^{2+}] = 5[MnO_4^-]$$

Substituting

$$E = \frac{E^\circ_{Fe^{3+}} + 5E^\circ_{MnO_4^-}}{6} - \frac{0.059}{6} \log \frac{5[MnO_4^-][Mn^{2+}]}{5[Mn^{2+}][MnO_4^-][H^+]^8}$$

$$= \frac{E^\circ_{Fe^{3+}} + 5E^\circ_{MnO_4^-}}{6} - \frac{0.059}{6} \log \frac{1}{[H^+]^8}$$

This is an example of a reaction for which the equivalence-point potential is dependent upon the pH. There are instances where the concentration of other ions also affect the equivalence potential—for example

$$6Fe^{2+} + Cr_2O_7^{2-} + 14H^+ \rightleftharpoons 6Fe^{3+} + 2Cr^{3+} + 7H_2O$$

Proceeding as before we obtain the expression

$$7E = E^\circ_{Fe^{3+}} + 6E^\circ_{Cr_2O_7^{2-}} - 0.059 \log \frac{[Fe^{2+}][Cr^{3+}]^2}{[Fe^{3+}][Cr_2O_7^{2-}][H^+]^{14}}$$

At the equivalence point

$$[Fe^{2+}] = 6[Cr_2O_7^{2-}]$$

$$[Fe^{3+}] = 3[Cr^{3+}]$$

Upon substituting these, we find that

$$E = \frac{E^\circ_{Fe^{3+}} + 6E^\circ_{Cr_2O_7^{2-}}}{7} - \frac{0.059}{7} \log \frac{2[Cr^{3+}]}{[H^+]^{14}}$$

In general, the equivalence-point potential will depend upon the concentration of one of the participants in the reaction whenever a molar ratio other than unity exists between the species containing that participant as a reactant and product. Dependence upon the hydrogen ion concentration will also be observed whenever this ion takes part in the reaction.

The equilibrium concentrations of the reacting species can be readily calculated from the equivalence-point potential.

★EXAMPLE. Calculate the concentration of the various reactants and products at the equivalence point in the titration of a 0.1 *N* solution of Fe^{2+} with 0.1 *N* Ce^{4+} at 25° C.

From the foregoing discussion we have seen that the equivalence-point potential in this titration is

$$E = \frac{E^\circ_{Ce^{4+}} + E^\circ_{Fe^{3+}}}{2}$$

Substituting E° values we obtain

$$E = \frac{+1.44 + 0.771}{2} = +1.11 \text{ volts}$$

The concentrations of Fe^{2+} and Fe^{3+} can be computed by first evaluating their molar ratio at the equivalence point. This is done with the Nernst equation

$$E = E^\circ_{Fe^{3+}} - 0.059 \log \frac{[Fe^{2+}]}{[Fe^{3+}]}$$

Substituting

$$+1.11 = +0.77 - 0.059 \log \frac{[Fe^{2+}]}{[Fe^{3+}]}$$

$$\log \frac{[Fe^{2+}]}{[Fe^{3+}]} = - \frac{0.34}{0.059} = -5.77$$

$$\frac{[Fe^{2+}]}{[Fe^{3+}]} = 1.7 \times 10^{-6}$$

From the size of this ratio we see that most of the Fe^{2+} has been converted to Fe^{3+} at the equivalence point, and as a consequence the Fe^{3+} concentration will be approximately one half the original Fe^{2+} concentration (because of dilution); that is,

$$[Fe^{3+}] = 0.05 - [Fe^{2+}] \cong 0.05 \text{ mol/liter}$$

Then

$$[Fe^{2+}] = 1.7 \times 10^{-6} \times 0.05$$

$$= 8.5 \times 10^{-8} \text{ mol/liter}$$

Finally, the stoichiometry of the reaction requires that

$$[Ce^{4+}] \cong 8.5 \times 10^{-8} \text{ mol/liter}$$

$$[Ce^{3+}] \cong 0.05 \text{ mol/liter}$$

DERIVATION OF TITRATION CURVES

The shape of the titration curve for an oxidation-reduction reaction depends upon the nature of the system under consideration. The derivation of several typical curves will serve to illustrate this.

Titration of Iron (II) with Quadrivalent Cerium. As an example we will consider the titration of 100 ml of 0.100 F solution of iron (II) with 0.100 F solution of quadrivalent cerium.

1. *Initial potential*. At the outset the solution contains no cerium ions; in addition to the iron (II) ions there will, however, be a small but finite quantity of iron (III) present as a consequence of air oxidation. Because the concentration of the latter is uncertain, we cannot calculate an initial potential that has significance.

2. *Potential after addition of 10 ml of oxidizing agent*. With the introduction of a volume of the oxidizing agent, the solution acquires appreciable concentrations of three of the participating ions; that for the fourth, the cerium (IV) ion, will be small. Setting this last quantity equal to x, we may write

$$[Ce^{4+}] = x$$

$$[Ce^{3+}] = \frac{10 \times 0.1}{110} - x \cong \frac{1}{110} \text{ mol/liter}$$

$$[Fe^{3+}] = \frac{10 \times 0.1}{110} - x \cong \frac{1}{110} \text{ mol/liter}$$

$$[Fe^{2+}] = \frac{100 \times 0.1 - 10 \times 0.1}{110} + x \cong \frac{9}{110} \text{ mol/liter}$$

Since the equilibrium lies reasonably far to the right, the approximation that the concentration of cerium (IV) ion (x) is negligibly small should be satisfactory. Its numerical value could be found from the equilibrium constant for the reaction; however, we need only recognize that it is very small since the potential for the system can be calculated with the aid of *either of the two equations*

$$E = E^\circ_{Ce^{4+}} - 0.059 \log \frac{[Ce^{3+}]}{[Ce^{4+}]}$$

$$= E^\circ_{Fe^{3+}} - 0.059 \log \frac{[Fe^{2+}]}{[Fe^{3+}]}$$

The second equation is the more convenient since we know, within acceptable limits, the two ionic concentrations. Therefore, substituting for the iron (III) and iron (II) concentration

$$E = +0.77 - 0.059 \log \frac{9/110}{1/110}$$

$$= +0.77 - 0.059 \log 9$$

$$E = +0.71 \text{ volt}$$

Had we used the standard potential for the cerium (IV)-cerium (III) system and the equilibrium concentrations of these ions, an identical potential would have been obtained.

3. *Additional pre-end-point potentials.* Further values for the potentials necessary to define a curve up to the end point can be calculated in a fashion strictly analogous to that in (2). Table 17-1 contains a number of these. The student should check one or two to be sure he understands completely how they were obtained.

4. *Equivalence-point potential.* We have seen that the potential at the equivalence point in this titration is given by

$$E = \frac{E^\circ_{Ce^{4+}} + E^\circ_{Fe^{3+}}}{2}$$

Substituting standard potentials in this equation yields a numerical value of $+1.11$ volts.

5. *Potential after addition of 100.1 ml of reagent.* The solution now contains an excess of quadrivalent cerium in addition to equivalent quantities of iron (III) and cerium (III) ions. The concentration of iron (II) will now be very small; if we set its value equal to y, then

$$[Fe^{2+}] = y$$

$$[Fe^{3+}] = \frac{100 \times 0.1}{200.1} - y \cong \frac{10}{200.1} \text{ mol/liter}$$

$$[Ce^{3+}] = \frac{100 \times 0.1}{200.1} - y \cong \frac{10}{200.1} \text{ mol/liter}$$

$$[Ce^{4+}] = \frac{100.1 \times 0.1 - 100 \times 0.1}{200.1} + y \cong \frac{0.01}{200.1} \text{ mol/liter}$$

These approximations should be reasonably good in view of the favorable equilibrium constant. As before we could calculate the desired potential from the value for the iron (III)-iron (II) system; at this stage in the titration, however, it is more convenient to use the cerium (IV)-cerium (III)

TABLE 17-1

Reduction Potentials during Titrations of Iron (II) Solutions
(100 ml of 0.1 F Fe²⁺, [H⁺] = 1.00)

Volume of 0.1 N Reagent, ml	Potential, Volts vs the Standard Hydrogen Electrode	
	Titration with Ce⁴⁺	Titration with MnO₄⁻
0.0	—	—
10.0	+0.71	+0.71
30.0	+0.75	+0.75
50.0	+0.77	+0.77
70.0	+0.79	+0.79
90.0	+0.83	+0.83
99.0	+0.89	+0.89
99.9	+0.95	+0.95
100.0	+1.11 ← equivalence point → +1.39	
100.1	+1.26	+1.47
101	+1.32	+1.48
110	+1.38	+1.49
130	+1.40	+1.50

potential since the concentrations of these species are immediately available. Thus

$$E = + 1.44 - 0.059 \log \frac{[Ce^{3+}]}{[Ce^{4+}]}$$

$$= + 1.44 - 0.059 \log \frac{10/200.1}{0.01/200.1}$$

$$= + 1.26 \text{ volts}$$

The additional postequivalence-point potentials shown in Table 17-1 were calculated in a similar fashion.

A curve for this titration is shown in Figure 17.1. Its shape is quite analogous to the curves encountered in neutralization, precipitation, and complex-formation titrations, the equivalence point being signaled by a large change in the ordinate function. This particular curve is symmetric about the equivalence point as a consequence of the equimolar combining ratio between oxidant and reductant. From the calculations we see that the potential values are all independent of dilution; thus a curve involving 0.01 F reactants will be, for all practical purposes, identical with the one that was derived.

Titration of Iron (II) with Permanganate. As a second example consider the derivation of a curve for the titration of 100 ml of 0.100 F iron (II) with 0.100 N potassium permanganate. To simplify the calculations we will assume that the hydrogen ion concentration of the solution is maintained at 1 M throughout the titration.

The chemical reaction is

$$5Fe^{2+} + MnO_4^- + 8H^+ \rightleftharpoons 5Fe^{3+} + Mn^{2+} + 4H_2O$$

In all of the computations, the formal concentrations of the manganese species must be employed. Note that these are one fifth of the normal concentrations.

1. *Pre-equivalence-point potentials.* The pre-equivalence-point potentials are most easily calculated from the concentrations of iron (II) and iron (III) in the solution; their values will be substantially identical to those computed for the previous titration with cerium (IV) ion.

2. *Equivalence-point potential.* The equivalence-point potential in this case is given by the equation (page 347)

$$E = \frac{E^\circ_{Fe^{3+}} + 5E^\circ_{MnO_4^-}}{6} - \frac{0.059}{6} \log \frac{1}{[H^+]^8}$$

Substituting standard potentials and introducing a value of 1 for the hydrogen ion concentration gives

$$E = \frac{+0.77 + 5(+1.51)}{6} - \frac{0.059}{6} \log \frac{1}{(1)^8}$$

$$= +1.39 \text{ volts}$$

3. *Postequivalence-point potentials.* When 100.1 ml of the 0.1 N potassium permanganate have been added, the stoichiometry requires that

$$[Fe^{2+}] = x$$

$$[Fe^{3+}] = \left(\frac{100 \times 0.1}{200.1} - x\right) \cong \frac{10}{200.1} \text{ mol/liter}$$

$$[Mn^{2+}] = \frac{1}{5}\left(\frac{10}{200.1} - x\right) \cong \frac{10}{5 \times 200.1} \text{ mol/liter}$$

$$[MnO_4^-] = \frac{1}{5}\left(\frac{100.1 \times 0.1 - 100.0 \times 0.1}{200.1} + x\right)$$

$$\cong \frac{0.01}{5 \times 200.1} \text{ mol/liter}$$

We are now in a position to calculate the electrode potential from the standard potential of the manganese system; that is,

$$E = +1.51 - \frac{0.059}{5} \log \frac{[\text{Mn}^{2+}]}{[\text{MnO}_4^-][\text{H}^+]^8}$$

$$= +1.51 - \frac{0.059}{5} \log \frac{(10/200.1 \times 5)}{(0.01/200.1 \times 5)(1)^8}$$

$$= +1.47 \text{ volts}$$

Additional values to establish this part of the titration curve can be arrived at in an analogous fashion. Table 17-1 contains such data.

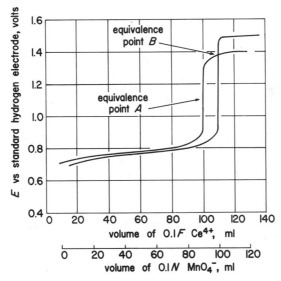

Fig. 17.1 Curves Depicting the Titration of 100 ml of 0.100 F Iron(II) Solution with (A) Quadrivalent Cerium and (B) with Permanganate. Note that the horizontal axes have been displaced to permit comparison of the curves.

Figure 17.1 illustrates titration curves for iron (II) with both permanganate and cerium (IV). Comparing the two, we see first that the plots are alike to within 99.9 percent of the equivalence point; however, the potentials at the equivalence points are quite different. Further, the permanganate curve is markedly asymmetric, the potential increasing only slightly beyond the equivalence point. Finally, the total change in potential associated with equivalence is somewhat greater with the permanganate titration; this is due to the more favorable equilibrium constant for this reaction.

17.2   Oxidation-reduction Indicators

We have seen that the equivalence point in an oxidation-reduction titration is characterized by a marked change in the reduction potential of the system. Several methods are available for detecting such a change, and these can serve to signal the end point in the titration. We shall now consider one of these methods—namely, that based upon the use of oxidation-reduction indicators.

TYPES OF CHEMICAL INDICATORS

Two types of indicators are encountered in oxidation-reduction titrations.

Specific Indicators. Specific indicators are substances that react in a specific manner with one of the participants in the titration to produce a change in color. Perhaps the best known of such indicators is starch, which forms a dark-blue complex with triiodide ion. This complex often serves to signal the end point in titrations in which iodine is either produced or consumed. Another example of such an indicator is potassium thiocyanate, which may be employed in the titration of iron (III) with solutions of titanium (II) sulfate. The end point involves decolorization of the iron (III) thiocyanate complex due to a marked decrease in the iron (III) concentration at the equivalence point.

True Oxidation-reduction Indicators. The behavior of some substances as indicators depends only upon the change in potential of the system and not specifically upon the change in concentration of one of the reactants. These are true oxidation-reduction indicators; they have a much wider scope of application than do the specific indicators.

As pointed out by Kolthoff and Stenger[1], a solution of starch containing a little iodine or iodide ion can function in this manner. In the presence of a strong oxidizing agent, the iodine-iodide ratio is high and the blue color of the iodine-starch complex is seen. With a strong reducing agent, on the other hand, iodide ion predominates and the blue color is not seen. Thus, the indicator system changes from colorless to blue in the titration of many strong reducing agents with various oxidizing agents. This color change is quite independent of the chemical composition of the reactants, and depends only upon the alteration of the oxidation potential at the equivalence point.

---

[1] I. M. Kolthoff and V. A. Stenger, *Volumetric Analysis*, 2d ed. **1**, 105. New York: Interscience Publishers, 1942.

TRANSITION RANGE OF INDICATOR

We may write a half reaction for the process leading to a color change for a true oxidation-reduction indicator as follows:

$$In_{oxid} + nH^+ + ne \rightleftharpoons In_{red}$$

With a few indicators no hydrogen ions are involved in the reduction.

TABLE 17-2

A Selected List of Oxidation-Reduction Indicators[2]

Indicators	Color		Transition Potential, volts	Conditions
	Oxidized	Reduced		
5-nitro-1,10-phenan- throline iron (II) complex	pale blue	red violet	+1.25	1 F H_2SO_4
2,3′-diphenylamine dicarboxylic acid	blue violet	colorless	+1.12	7–10 F H_2SO_4
1,10-phenanthroline iron (II) complex	pale blue	red	+1.11	1 F H_2SO_4
erioglaucin A	bluish red	yellow green	+0.98	0.5 F H_2SO_4
diphenylamine sulfonic acid	red violet	colorless	+0.85	dilute acid
diphenylamine	violet	colorless	+0.76	dilute acid
p-ethoxychrysoidine	yellow	red	+0.76	dilute acid
methylene blue	blue	colorless	+0.53	1 F acid
indigo tetrasulfonate	blue	colorless	+0.36	1 F acid
phenosafranine	red	colorless	+0.28	1 F acid

[2] Data taken in part from I. M. Kolthoff and V. A. Stenger, *Volumetric Analysis*, 2d ed. **1**, 140. New York: Interscience Publishers, 1942.

If the foregoing is a reversible process, we may write

$$E = E° - \frac{0.059}{n} \log \frac{[In_{red}]}{[In_{oxid}][H^+]^n}$$

Typically a color change can be seen when the ratio of reactants shifts by a factor of about 100; that is, when

$$\frac{[In_{red}]}{[In_{oxid}]} \geqq 10$$

changes to

$$\frac{[In_{red}]}{[In_{oxid}]} \leqq \frac{1}{10}$$

By substituting these values into the Nernst equation, we find the conditions for color change for a typical indicator.

$$E = E° \pm \frac{0.059}{n} - 0.059 \log \frac{1}{[H^+]} \tag{17-1}$$

For simplicity, we have assumed that the indicator reaction does not alter the pH of the solution; this is reasonable since the concentration of the indicator substance is ordinarily quite small.

Equation (17-1) suggests that a typical indicator will exhibit a detectable color change when the volumetric reagent causes a shift in potential of the system of about $0.118/n$ volt. With many indicators, $n = 2$, and a change of 0.059 volt is sufficient.

The potential at which a color transition will occur depends upon $E°$— the standard potential for the particular indicator system. From Table 17-2 we see that indicators are available which function in any desired potential range up to about $+ 1.25$ volts.

As shown by equation (17-1), the potential range for many indicators is pH dependent, shifting 0.059 volt for each unit change in pH.

SOME TYPICAL REDOX INDICATORS

Iron (II) Complexes of the Orthophenanthrolines. A class of organic compounds known as 1, 10-phenanthrolines (or orthophenanthrolines) forms stable complexes with iron (II) and certain other ions. The parent compound has the structure

1,10-phenanthroline

Each nitrogen atom has a pair of unshared electrons that can coordinate with certain metallic ions to give complexes. In the case of iron (II) ion the orthophenanthroline complex is quite stable and is intensely red in color; its structure may be written

The complex is sometimes called ferroin; for convenience we will write its formula as $(Ph)_3Fe^{2+}$.

Ferroin undergoes a reversible oxidation-reduction reaction that may be written

$$(Ph)_3Fe^{3+} + e \rightleftharpoons (Ph)_3Fe^{2+} \qquad E° = +1.06 \text{ volts}$$

pale bluered

The iron (III) complex is a pale blue; in practice the color change associated with the oxidation is actually from nearly colorless to red. Because of the difference in color intensity, the end point is usually taken when only about 10 percent of the indicator is in the iron (II) form. This leads to a transition potential of approximately +1.11 volts in 1 F sulfuric acid.

Of all of the oxidation-reduction indicators, ferroin approaches most closely the ideal substance. The color change is very sharp, and its solutions are readily prepared and stable. In contrast to many indicators, the oxidized form is remarkably inert towards strong oxidizing agents. The indicator reaction is rapid and reversible.

A number of substituted phenanthrolines have been investigated for their indicator properties, and some of these have proven to be as useful as the parent compound. Among these the 5-nitro and the 5-methyl derivatives are noteworthy, having transition potentials of +1.25 volts and +1.02 volts, respectively.

Diphenylamine and its Derivatives. One of the first redox indicators to be proposed was diphenylamine.

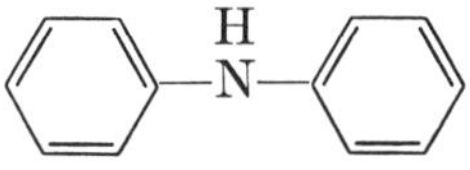

diphenylamine

This was recommended by Knop in 1924 for the titration of iron (II) with potassium dichromate.

In the presence of a strong oxidizing agent diphenylamine is believed to undergo the following reactions:

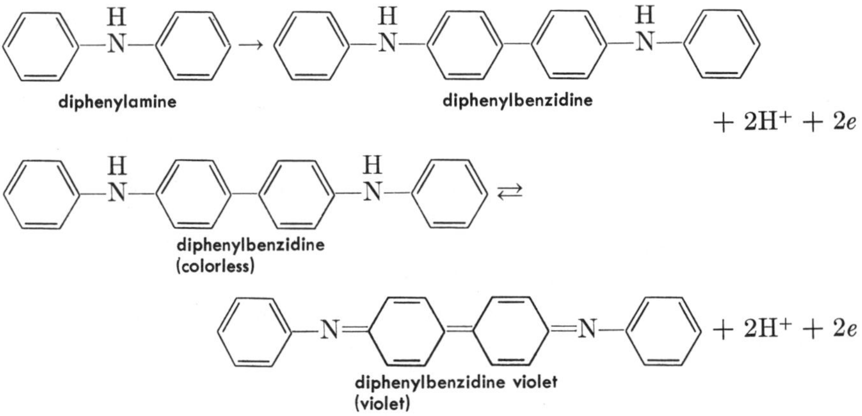

diphenylamine   diphenylbenzidine

$$+ 2H^+ + 2e$$

diphenylbenzidine
(colorless)

$$\rightleftharpoons$$

$$+ 2H^+ + 2e$$

diphenylbenzidine violet
(violet)

The first reaction, involving the formation of the colorless diphenyl-benzidine, is nonreversible; the second, however, giving a violet product can be reversed and constitutes the actual indicator reaction.

The reduction potential for the second reaction is about +0.76 volt, and despite the fact that hydrogen ions appear to be involved, variations in acidity have little effect upon the magnitude of this potential. This may be due to association of hydrogen ions with the colored product.

There are drawbacks in the application of diphenylamine as an indicator. Because of its low solubility in water, for example, the reagent must be prepared in rather concentrated sulfuric acid solutions. Further, the oxidation product forms an insoluble precipitate with tungstate ion, which renders its use in the presence of this element quite unsatisfactory. Finally, the indicator reaction is slowed by mercury (II) ions.

The sulfonic acid derivative of diphenylamine does not suffer from these disadvantages.

diphenylamine sulfonic acid

The barium or sodium salt of this acid may be used to prepare aqueous indicator solutions; these behave in essentially the same manner as the parent substance. The color change is somewhat sharper, passing from colorless through green to a deep violet. The transition potential is about +0.8 volt and again is independent of acid concentration. The sulfonic acid derivative is now widely used in redox titrations.

It might be surmised from the two equations for the indicator reaction of diphenylamine that diphenylbenzidine should behave in an identical fashion and consume less oxidizing agent in its reaction. This is the case; however, the compound has not been widely used because of its very low solubility in water and sulfuric acid. As might be expected, the sulfonic acid derivative of diphenylbenzidine has proved to be a satisfactory indicator.

SELECTION OF OXIDATION-REDUCTION INDICATORS

Theoretically deduced titration curves such as those given in Figure 17.1 suggest the necessary transition range of an indicator for a given titration. For example, in the determination of iron (II) with cerium (IV), an indicator having a transition potential from about +0.95 volt to +1.25 volts should be satisfactory; the orthophenanthroline-iron (II) complex would therefore suffice.

SUMMARY

Conclusions based on the theoretical calculations in this chapter are extremely helpful to the analytical chemist as a guide to the choice of proper conditions and indicators for oxidation-reduction titrations; at the same time, however, it is well to emphasize the theoretical nature of such computations and to point out that these do not necessarily take into account all of the factors that determine the applicability and feasibility of a volumetric method. Also to be considered are the rates at which the principal and the indicator reactions occur; the effects of electrolyte concentration, pH, and complexing agents; the presence of colored components other than the indicator in the solution; and the variation among individuals in color perception. The state of the science of chemistry has not advanced to the point where the effects of all of these variables can be determined by computation. Theoretical calculations can and will eliminate useless experiments and act as a guide to the ones most likely to be profitable. The final test must always come in the laboratory.

Problems

1. Calculate the reduction potential at the equivalence point for each of the following reactions. Where necessary, assume the reactant solutions are initially 0.1 N and that the $[H^+]$ at the equivalence point is unity.
   (a) $2Fe^{3+} + Sn^{2+} \rightleftharpoons 2Fe^{2+} + Sn^{4+}$ ans. $+0.36$ volt
   (b) $2Ce^{4+} + H_3AsO_3 + H_2O \rightleftharpoons 2Ce^{3+} + H_3AsO_4 + 2H^+$
   (c) $2V^{3+} + Zn \rightleftharpoons 2V^{2+} + Zn^{2+}$
   (d) $V(OH)_4^+ + Fe^{2+} + 2H^+ \rightleftharpoons VO^{2+} + Fe^{3+} + 3H_2O$ ans. $+0.88$ volt
   (e) Example (d) when $[H^+] = 0.01$ at the equivalence point

                                                     ans. $+0.76$ volt

   (f) $2Ce^{4+} + U^{4+} + 2H_2O \rightleftharpoons 2Ce^{3+} + UO_2^{2+} + 4H^+$
   (g) $Sn^{4+} + Cd \rightleftharpoons Sn^{2+} + Cd^{2+}$
   (h) $5NO_2^- + 2MnO_4^- + 6H^+ \rightleftharpoons 5NO_3^- + 2Mn^{2+} + 3H_2O$
   (i) $Br_2 + H_3AsO_3 + H_2O \rightleftharpoons 2Br^- + H_3AsO_4 + 2H^+$
   (j) $V(OH)_4^+ + V^{3+} \rightleftharpoons 2VO^{2+} + 2H_2O$

2. Calculate the equivalence-point equilibrium concentration of the first-mentioned species in each of the equations in Problem 1.

3. Calculate the equivalence-point reduction potential in the titration of 50 ml of 0.1 N Cr^{2+} with 0.1 N I_3^-.

   $$I_3^- + 2Cr^{2+} \rightleftharpoons 3I^- + 2Cr^{3+}$$ ans. $E = +0.24$ volt

4. Calculate the reduction potential at the equivalence point in the titration of 50.0 ml of 0.1 F I^- with 0.1 N $K_2Cr_2O_7$. Assume $[H^+] = 1$.

$$Cr_2O_7^{2-} + 6I^- + 14H^+ \rightleftharpoons 2Cr^{3+} + 3I_2 + 7H_2O$$

5. Choose the indicator from the list in Table 17-2 that would be best suited for each of the titrations in Problem 1.

6. Construct titration curves for each of the following, calculating points at 10, 25, 49, 49.9, 50.0, 50.1, 51, and 60 ml of reagent. Assume $[H^+] = 1$ at all points.
   (a) 50 ml of 0.1 N Sn^{2+} with 0.1 N Fe^{3+}
   (b) 50 ml of 0.1 N Cr^{2+} with 0.1 N Fe^{3+}
   (c) 50 ml of 0.1 N Ti^{3+} with 0.1 N Fe^{3+}

7. Propose an indicator for each of the titrations in Problem 6.

8. Calculate the equilibrium concentrations of the various species (including H^+) in a solution prepared by mixing 50 ml of a solution that is 0.1 N in Fe^{2+} and 0.2 N in acid with 30 ml of a neutral 0.1 N solution of MnO_4^-.

9. Derive a titration curve for 50 ml of 0.1 N Sn^{2+} with 0.1 N I_3^-. Calculate points at 25, 49, 49.9, 50.0, 50.1, 51, and 60 ml of reagent.

10. Derive a titration curve for the titration of 50 ml of 0.1 F V^{3+} with 0.1 F Ce^{4+}. Assume that $[H^+] = 1$ at all times. Reactions:

$$Ce^{4+} + V^{3+} + H_2O \rightleftharpoons Ce^{3+} + VO^{2+} + 2H^+$$
$$Ce^{4+} + VO^{2+} + 3H_2O \rightleftharpoons Ce^{3+} + V(OH)_4^+ + 2H^+$$

Calculate potentials for the following additions of the reagent: 10, 25, 49, 50, 51, 60, 75, 99, 100, 101, and 110 ml.

(18)

Applications of Oxidation-reduction Titrations

Although a complete catalog of substances that have been proposed as reagents for quantitative oxidations or reductions would be imposing, most redox reactions of analytical importance are accomplished with a relatively small number of reagents; we shall consider only those that have found wide application. We shall also consider an important group of reagents that are used in the pretreatment of solutions prior to their titration with a standard oxidizing or reducing agent.

18.1   Standard Solutions and Primary Standards

OXIDIZING AGENTS

Most of the common oxidizing agents used in the preparation of standard solutions are listed in Table 18-1. From the table we see that their reduction potentials vary from about $+0.5$ volt up to $+1.7$ volts. The stronger oxidizing agents have a considerably wider applicability. They tend to be less stable, however, decomposing water to give oxygen; in addition, they are particularly lacking in selectivity.

REDUCING AGENTS

In general, standard solutions of reducing agents are used much less frequently than oxidizing agents. This is due, in part, to their lower

TABLE 18-1

Some Common Oxidizing Agents Used for the Preparation of Standard Solutions

Reagent	Usual Conditions for Use	Half Reaction	Standard Potential, volts	Stability of Solution
Potassium permanganate ($KMnO_4$)	Strong acid	$MnO_4^- + 8H^+ + 5e \rightleftharpoons Mn^{2+} + 4H_2O$	1.51	Solutions require occasional standardization
	Weakly acid or neutral	$MnO_4^- + 4H^+ + 3e \rightleftharpoons MnO_2 + 2H_2O$	1.69	
	Strongly basic	$MnO_4^- + e \rightleftharpoons MnO_4^{2-}$	0.56	
Quadrivalent cerium (Ce^{4+})	H_2SO_4 solution	$Ce^{4+} + e \rightleftharpoons Ce^{3+}$	1.44	Indefinitely stable
Periodic acid (H_5IO_6)	Weakly acid solution	$H_5IO_6 + H^+ + 2e \rightleftharpoons IO_3^- + 3H_2O$	1.6	Occasional standardization necessary
Potassium dichromate ($K_2Cr_2O_7$)	Acid solution	$Cr_2O_7^{2-} + 14H^+ + 6e \rightleftharpoons 2Cr^{3+} + 7H_2O$	1.33	Indefinitely stable
Potassium iodate (KIO_3)	Strong HCl solution	$IO_3^- + 2Cl^- + 6H^+ + 4e \rightleftharpoons ICl_2^- + 3H_2O$	1.23	Stable
Potassium bromate ($KBrO_3 + KBr$)	Dilute acid solution	$BrO_3^- + 5Br^- + 6H^+ \rightleftharpoons 3Br_2 + 3H_2O$ $Br_2 + 2e \rightleftharpoons 2Br^-$	1.05	Indefinitely stable
Ammonium metavanadate (NH_4VO_3)	Strongly acid solution	$V(OH)_4^+ + 2H^+ + e \rightleftharpoons VO^{2+} + 3H_2O$	1.0	Stable
Calcium hypochlorite ($Ca(ClO)_2$)	Neutral or slightly alkaline solution	$OCl^- + H_2O + 2e \rightleftharpoons Cl^- + 2OH^-$	0.89	Restandardization necessary
Iodine (I_3^-)	Neutral, dilute acid or base solution	$I_3^- + 2e \rightleftharpoons 3I^-$	0.54	Restandardization necessary

stability. All are subject to air oxidation to some degree and must be protected from oxygen of the atmosphere or be standardized at frequent intervals. In addition, the more potent reagents reduce hydrogen ions; for this reason also their solutions will change in concentration.

Because of this inherent instability, reducing agents are often used in conjunction with a standard solution of stable oxidizing agent, an excess of the former being added to a solution containing the sample; after the reaction is complete the excess is determined by titration with the standard oxidant. A blank titration of the reductant then gives its concentration at the time of the analysis.

Table 18-2 lists common reducing agents used for preparing standard solutions.

PRIMARY STANDARDS

In Chapter 9 we noted the desirable properties of a primary standard substance. Table 18-3 lists a large number of oxidizing and reducing agents that meet these requirements.

18.2 Auxiliary Reagents

An obvious requirement for a successful redox titration is that the component being determined exist at the outset in a single oxidation state. Since the steps preliminary to the titration frequently result in a mixture of states, a reagent must be introduced to convert the component to a single form. For example, an iron alloy dissolved in acid almost always results in a mixture of iron (II) and iron (III) ions. Before the iron can be titrated, therefore, a reagent must be added that will convert the element quantitatively either to the divalent state for titration with a standard oxidizing agent or to the trivalent state for titration with a reducing reagent. Such a substance must possess certain unique properties. It must be a sufficiently strong oxidizing or reducing agent to convert the substance to be titrated quantitatively to the desired oxidation state. Nevertheless, it should not be so strong as to convert other components of the solution into states in which they will also react with the volumetric reagent. Yet another requirement is that the unused portion of the reagent be easily removed from the solution, for it will almost inevitably interfere with the titration by reacting with the standard solution. Thus, a reagent that would convert iron quantitatively to the divalent state for titration with a standard solution of permanganate would be a good reducing agent; any excess remaining after the reduction would surely consume permanganate unless removed from the solution.

TABLE 18-2

Common Reducing Agents Used for the Preparation of Standard Solutions

Reagent	Half Reaction	Standard Oxidation Potential, volts	Stability
Iron (II) (Fe^{2+})	$Fe^{2+} \rightleftharpoons Fe^{3+} + e$	-0.77	Not stable unless protected from oxygen
Arsenic (III) (H_3AsO_3)	$H_3AsO_3 + H_2O \rightleftharpoons H_3AsO_4 + 2H^+ + 2e$	-0.56	Acid solution stable
Titanium (III) (Ti^{3+})	$Ti^{3+} + H_2O \rightleftharpoons TiO^{2+} + 2H^+ + e$	-0.1	Not stable unless protected from oxygen
Sodium thiosulfate ($Na_2S_2O_3$)	$2S_2O_3^{2-} \rightleftharpoons S_4O_6^{2-} + 2e$	-0.08	Frequent restandardization necessary
Chromium (II) (Cr^{2+})	$Cr^{2+} \rightleftharpoons Cr^{3+} + e$	$+0.41$	Not stable

TABLE 18-3

**Common Primary-Standard Substances Used in
Oxidation-Reduction Reactions**

Substance	Formula	Uses
Arsenic (III) oxide	As_2O_3	Preparation of H_3AsO_3 solutions Standardization of MnO_4^-, Ce^{4+}, I_3^-, H_5IO_6, OCl^- solutions
Sodium oxalate	$Na_2C_2O_4$	Standardization of MnO_4^-, Ce^{4+}, $V(OH)_4^+$ solutions
Mohr's salt	$FeSO_4 \cdot (NH_4)_2SO_4 \cdot 6H_2O$	Preparation of Fe^{2+} solutions Standardization of MnO_4^-, Ce^{4+}, $V(OH)_4^+$ solutions
Iron wire	Fe	Standardization of MnO_4^-, Ce^{4+} solutions
Potassium iodide	KI	Standardization of MnO_4^-, Ce^{4+} solutions
Potassium ferrocyanide	$K_4Fe(CN)_6$	Standardization of MnO_4^-, Ce^{4+}, $S_2O_3^{2-}$ solutions
Sodium thiosulfate	$Na_2S_2O_3 \cdot 5H_2O$	Preparation of $S_2O_3^{2-}$ solutions Standardization of I_3^- solutions
Cerium (IV) ammonium nitrate	$(NH_4)_2Ce(NO_3)_6$	Preparation of Ce^{4+} solutions
Potassium dichromate	$K_2Cr_2O_7$	Preparation of $Cr_2O_7^{2-}$ solutions Standardization of $S_2O_3^{2-}$, Fe^{2+}, Ti^{3+} solutions
Iodine	I_2	Preparation of I_3^- solutions Standardization of $S_2O_3^{2-}$ solutions
Potassium iodate	KIO_3	Preparation of IO_3^- solutions Standardization of $S_2O_3^{2-}$ solutions
Potassium bromate	$KBrO_3$	Preparation of BrO_3^- solutions Standardization of $S_2O_3^{2-}$ solutions

Reagents that find fairly general application to the pretreatment of samples are described in the following paragraphs.

OXIDIZING AGENTS

Sodium Bismuthate. Sodium bismuthate is an extremely powerful oxidizing agent capable, for example, of converting manganese (II) quantitatively to the permanganate state. It exists as an insoluble solid of rather uncertain composition. The formula for the substance is usually written as $NaBiO_3$; upon reaction the bismuth (V) is converted to the more common bismuth (III) state. Ordinarily the solution to be oxidized is boiled in contact with an excess of the solid; the unused reagent is then removed by filtration.

Ammonium Persulfate. In acid solutions, ammonium persulfate, $(NH_4)_2S_2O_8$, is a potent oxidizing agent that will convert chromium to dichromate, cerium (III) to the quadrivalent state, and manganese (II) ion to permanganate. The oxidations are catalyzed by the presence of a small amount of silver ion. The half reaction is

$$S_2O_8^{2-} + 2e \rightleftharpoons 2SO_4^{2-} \qquad E^\circ = 2.01 \text{ volts}$$

The excess reagent is readily removed by boiling the solution for a few minutes

$$2S_2O_8^{2-} + 2H_2O \rightleftharpoons 4SO_4^{2-} + O_2 + 4H^+$$

Sodium and Hydrogen Peroxide. Peroxide is a convenient oxidizing agent. It can be obtained in the form of the solid sodium salt or as dilute solutions of the acid. Its half reaction in acid solution is written

$$H_2O_2 + 2H^+ + 2e \rightleftharpoons 2H_2O \qquad E^\circ = 1.77 \text{ volts}$$

Any excess peroxide is readily removed from solution by boiling for a short period.

$$2H_2O_2 \rightleftharpoons 2H_2O + O_2$$

REDUCING REAGENTS

Metals. An examination of a table of standard electrode potentials reveals a number of good reducing agents among the pure metals[1]; such elements as zinc, cadmium, aluminum, lead, nickel, copper, mercury, and silver have proved useful for prereduction purposes. The removal of

---

[1] For a discussion of metal reductants the reader should see I. M. Kolthoff and R. Belcher, *Volumetric Analysis*, **3**, 11–23. New York: Interscience Publishers, Inc., 1957; W. I. Stephen, *Ind. Chemist*, **28**, 13, 55, 107 (1952).

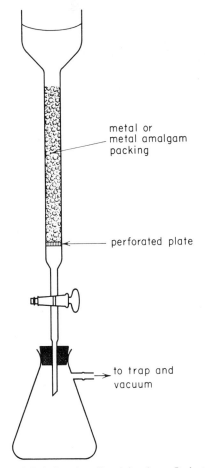

metal or
metal amalgam
packing

perforated plate

to trap and
vacuum

Fig. 18.1 A Metal or Metal Amalgam Reductor.

excess reagent is not a difficult problem. Where sticks or coils of the metal
are used, the excess reductant is simply lifted from the solution and washed
thoroughly. If granular or powdered forms of the metal are employed,
filtration will be required. An alternative method involves the use of a
reductor, an example of which is illustrated in Figure 18.1. Here the solution
is passed through a column packed with granules of the metallic reducing
agent.

The reducing strength of the various metals mentioned above varies
considerably. Thus, zinc and cadmium are rather powerful reagents compared with silver or mercury. The latter two are usually used in conjunction

with hydrochloric acid solutions; since both form insoluble chlorides, they are particularly effective reducing agents in the presence of that acid.

Of the several simple metallic reductors, that containing silver is perhaps the most widely used because of the somewhat selective nature of its reducing properties. Some applications of this reductor are given in Table 18-4. The silver reductor is nearly always used with hydrochloric acid solutions.

TABLE 18-4

Uses of the Silver Reductor and the Jones Reductor[2]

Silver Reductor	Jones Reductor
$e + Fe^{3+} \rightarrow Fe^{2+}$	$e + Fe^{3+} \rightarrow Fe^{2+}$
$e + Cu^{2+} \rightarrow Cu^+$	Cu^{2+} reduced to metallic Cu
$e + H_2MoO_4 + 2H^+ \rightarrow MoO_2^+ + 2H_2O$	$3e + H_2MoO_4 + 6H^+ \rightarrow Mo^{3+} + 4H_2O$
$2e + UO_2^{2+} + 4H^+ \rightarrow U^{4+} + 2H_2O$	$2e + UO_2^{2+} + 4H^+ \rightarrow U^{4+} + 2H_2O$
	$3e + UO_2^{2+} + 4H^+ \rightarrow U^{3+} + 2H_2O$ [3]
$e + V(OH)_4^+ + 2H^+ \rightarrow VO^{2+} + 3H_2O$	$3e + V(OH)_4^+ + 4H^+ \rightarrow V^{2+} + 4H_2O$
TiO^{2+} not reduced	$e + TiO^{2+} + 2H^+ \rightarrow Ti^{3+} + H_2O$
Cr^{3+} not reduced	$e + Cr^{3+} \rightarrow Cr^{2+}$

[2] Taken from I. M. Kolthoff and R. Belcher, *Volumetric Analysis*, **3**, 12. New York: Interscience Publishers, Inc., 1957.

[3] A mixture of oxidation states is obtained; this does not, however, preclude the use of the Jones reductor for the analysis of uranium since any U^{3+} formed can be converted to U^{4+} by shaking the solution with air for a few minutes.

One disadvantage of the very reactive reductants such as cadmium and zinc arises from their tendency to evolve hydrogen when in contact with acids. This parasitic reaction not only consumes reductant but also introduces large quantities of the metallic ion into the solution. The problem of hydrogen evolution can be largely overcome by amalgamation of the reducing metal with mercury. The presence of the mercury so inhibits the formation of hydrogen that strong reductants such as zinc and cadmium can be used even in quite acid solutions.

An amalgam is ordinarily a somewhat poorer reducing agent than the pure metal itself. For example, the potential for the oxidation of a zinc amalgam

$$Zn(Hg) \rightleftharpoons Zn^{2+} + Hg + 2e$$

is less than that for pure zinc since the activity of the element is less in the amalgam than in the pure metal. In general, the magnitude of the change in reducing power is not very great, amounting to 0.05 to 0.1 volt or less.

The most widely used amalgam reductor—commonly called a Jones reductor—employs zinc as the reducing agent. Figure 18.1 illustrates a typical Jones reductor. The column is packed with granular zinc that has been amalgamated by treatment with a solution of mercury (II) nitrate or chloride; metallic mercury forms as a surface deposit as a consequence of the reaction.

$$Zn + Hg^{2+} \rightleftharpoons Zn^{2+} + Hg$$

A column so prepared can be used for many hundreds of reductions. When not in service, it is filled with water to prevent contact of the packing with air and the resultant formation of basic salts—these tend to clog the column.

When a column is put in use, it is first activated by passage of a dilute acid solution. The solution to be reduced is then pulled through at a rate of about 75 to 100 ml per minute. Finally, the column is washed with more acid. Throughout these operations care is taken to avoid exposure of the packing to the atmosphere.

Table 18-4 lists the principal uses to which the Jones reductor has been put.

★THE JONES REDUCTOR

Preparation of a Jones Reductor. The reductor (Figure 18.1) should be about 40 to 50 cm in length and 2 cm in diameter. It should be thoroughly cleaned and ﬁtted with a porcelain disk supporting a mat of glass wool or asbestos in the lower end. This mat must be sufficiently thick to prevent passage of zinc granules when the reductor is in use.

The zinc should be 20 to 30 mesh and free of impurities such as iron. Cover a suitable quantity of the metal with 1 N HCl and let stand for about 1 minute. Decant the liquid and cover the zinc with a 0.25 F solution of $Hg(NO_3)_2$ or $HgCl_2$. Stir the mixture vigorously for 3 minutes, decant and wash 2 or 3 times with distilled water. Fill the reductor tube with water and slowly add the amalgam until a column of about 30 cm is achieved. Wash with 500 ml of water, being sure that the packing is never uncovered by liquid. Keep the reductor filled with water during storage.

Use of the Jones Reductor. Solutions containing 3 to 15 volume percent of HCl or 1 to 10 volume percent of H_2SO_4 may be used in the reductor. Warm solutions may be passed through the column without harm. Wash the column by drawing through it several 20- to 30-ml portions of an acid solution of about the same composition as the sample. After each addition of wash liquid, drain the column to about 1 cm above the zinc; then add the next portion. Leave the last washing on the column.

Attach a receiver to the column and add the sample to the reservoir at the top. The sample can be pulled through the column at a rate of 75 to 100 ml per minute. When the sample solution has been drawn to within a centimeter of the top of the packing, add 25 ml of a dilute acid as a wash. Follow this with two additional acid washes and then with 100 to 200 ml of water. Leave the column covered with water and place a beaker over its top during storage.

Interferences. Nitrates interfere because they are partially reduced by zinc amalgam to various compounds that subsequently react with the volumetric oxidant. In addition, arsenic, antimony, tin, organic, and polythionic compounds must be absent as they also are reduced to substances that may consume the reagent. Ammoniacal solutions should be avoided because they react with the mercury and very shortly render the packing worthless.

Gaseous Reductants. Both hydrogen sulfide and sulfur dioxide are fairly good reducing reagents and have been applied to the problem of prereduction. With these, the excess reagent can be readily removed by boiling the acidified solution.

The reactions of these reagents are often slow, half an hour or more being required to complete the reduction and rid the solution of excess reagent. In addition to this time disadvantage, the noxious and toxic nature of these gases complicate their use. The employment of other reductants is much preferred.

Sulfur dioxide is used for the reduction of iron (III) to iron (II). Trivalent chromium and titanium are not affected by the reagent and therefore do not interfere. Vanadium (V) is reduced to the quadrivalent state. Pentavalent arsenic and antimony are reduced quantitatively to the trivalent state by sulfur dioxide.

The principal application of hydrogen sulfide has been in the reduction of iron (III) to the divalent state.

18.3   Volumetric Oxidizing Agents—Potassium Permanganate

Potassium permanganate is probably the most widely used of all volumetric oxidizing agents. It is a powerful oxidizer and readily available at modest cost. The intense color of the permanganate ion is sufficient to signal the end point in most titrations; this eliminates the need for an indicator. Several disadvantages attend the use of the reagent. Thus, the tendency of permanganate to oxidize chloride ion represents a serious limitation since hydrochloric acid is often a desirable solvent. The multiplicity of possible reaction products can, at times, result in uncertainty regarding its stoichiometry. Finally, solutions of permanganate have limited stability.

REACTIONS OF PERMANGANATE ION

In solutions that are 0.1 N or greater in mineral acid, the common reduction product is manganese (II) ion

$$MnO_4^- + 8H^+ + 5e \rightleftharpoons Mn^{2+} + 4H_2O \qquad E^\circ = 1.51 \text{ volts}$$

This is the most widely used of the permanganate reactions. Although the mechanisms involved in the formation of manganese (II) ion are frequently complicated, the oxidation of most substances proceeds rapidly in acid solution. Notable exceptions include the reaction with oxalic acid, for which elevated temperatures are required, and with arsenic (III) oxide, for which a catalyst is needed.

In solutions that are weakly acid (above pH 4), neutral, or weakly alkaline, manganese dioxide is the most common reduction product. Titrations of certain species with permanganate can be carried out to advantage under these conditions. For example, cyanide is oxidized to cyanate; sulfide, sulfite, and thiosulfate are converted to sulfate; manganese (II) is oxidized to manganese dioxide; and hydrazine is oxidized to nitrogen.

In solutions that are greater than 1 N in sodium hydroxide, permanganate ion undergoes a 1-electron reduction to give manganate ion, MnO_4^{2-}. Alkaline oxidations with permanganate have proved useful for the determination of a number of organic compounds.

END POINT

One of the most obvious of the properties of potassium permanganate is its intense purple color; this commonly serves as the indicator for titrations. As little as 0.1 to 0.2 ml of a 0.01 N solution is enough to impart a perceptible color to 100 ml of water. With solutions more concentrated than 0.01 N, then, the titration error is negligible. For very dilute permanganate solutions, diphenylamine sulfonic acid or orthophenanthroline-iron (II) complex will give a sharper end point.

The permanganate end point is not permanent, and gradually fades to give a colorless solution. The decolorization results from the reaction of the excess permanganate ion with the relatively large concentration of manganese (II) ion formed during the titration

$$2MnO_4^- + 3Mn^{2+} + 2H_2O \rightleftharpoons 5MnO_2 + 4H^+$$

The equilibrium constant for this reaction is readily calculated from the standard potentials for the two half reactions and has a numerical value of about 10^{47}. Thus, even in highly acidic solution, the concentration of permanganate in equilibrium with manganese (II) ion is very small. Fortunately, the rate at which this equilibrium is attained is quite slow, with the result that the end point fades only gradually.

Measurement of the volume of a permanganate solution in a buret is complicated by the intense color of the reagent. The surface of the liquid, rather than the meniscus, is often taken as the point of reference.

STABILITY OF PERMANGANATE SOLUTIONS

Aqueous solutions of permanganate are not completely stable because of the tendency of that ion to oxidize water. The over-all process may be depicted in terms of the half reactions

$$4MnO_4^- + 16H^+ + 12e \rightleftharpoons 4MnO_2 + 8H_2O \qquad E° = \quad 1.70 \text{ volts}$$

$$\frac{6H_2O \rightleftharpoons 3O_2 + 12H^+ + 12e \qquad\qquad\qquad E° = -1.23 \text{ volts}}{4MnO_4^- + 4H^+ \rightleftharpoons 4MnO_2 + 2H_2O + 3O_2}$$

From the magnitude of the standard potentials we see that the equilibrium for the over-all reaction should lie to the right even in neutral solutions; it is only by virtue of the very low rate of the reaction that permanganate solutions are stable at all. Experiments show that this decomposition is catalyzed by light, heat, acids, bases, manganese (II) ion, and manganese dioxide. In order to obtain a stable reagent for analysis it is necessary to minimize the influence of these effects.

Solid manganese dioxide greatly accelerates decomposition. Since this is a potential decomposition product we might expect the reaction rate to increase with time as a result of the build-up in amount of the solid; this is indeed observed. It is an example of an *autocatalytic* process, since the reaction product serves to catalyze its own formation.

The photochemical catalysis of the decomposition is often observed when a permanganate solution is allowed to stand in a buret for any extended period; manganese dioxide forms as a brown stain and serves to show that the concentration of the reagent has been altered.

In general, the heating of acidic solutions containing an excess of permanganate should be avoided because of the decomposition error that cannot adequately be compensated for with a blank. At the same time it is perfectly acceptable to titrate hot, acidic solutions of reductants directly with the reagent since at no time during the titration is the oxidant concentration large enough to cause a measurable uncertainty.

PREPARATION, STANDARDIZATION, AND STORAGE
OF PERMANGANATE SOLUTIONS

Preparation. Permanganate solutions are prepared from the potassium salt. This compound is seldom, if ever, of sufficient purity to allow the direct preparation of a standard solution. Furthermore, the water used in preparation of the reagent is frequently contaminated with small amounts of dust, organic compounds, and other oxidizable substances; these alter the concentration by reacting with the permanganate to give manganese dioxide.

Certain precautions must be taken to obtain a permanganate solution of reasonable stability. Perhaps the most important variable affecting stability is the catalytic effect of manganese dioxide. As initially prepared, the solution will always contain some of this compound as a contaminant in the starting material and from the oxidation of organic matter in the water. Removal of manganese dioxide by filtration markedly enhances the life of the standard reagent. Enough time should be allowed for complete oxidation of contaminants in the water before filtration. Boiling the solution may hasten this process. Paper cannot be used for the filtration since it reacts with the permanganate to form the undesirable dioxide.

Standardized solutions should be stored in the dark. If any solid is detected in the solution, filtration and restandardization is necessary. In any case restandardization every few weeks is a good precautionary measure.

> ★METHOD OF PREPARATION. To prepare a 0.1 N solution dissolve 3.2 grams of $KMnO_4$ in about 1 liter of distilled water. Heat to boiling and keep hot for about 1 hour. Cover and let stand overnight. Filter the solution through a fine-porosity sintered glass crucible or through a Gooch crucible with an asbestos mat. Store the solution in a clean, glass-stoppered bottle and keep in the dark when not in use.

Standardization against Sodium Oxalate. In acid solution, permanganate oxidizes oxalic acid to carbon dioxide and water

$$2MnO_4^- + 5H_2C_2O_4 + 6H^+ \rightleftharpoons 2Mn^{2+} + 10CO_2 + 8H_2O$$

This is a complex reaction that proceeds only slowly at room temperature. Even at elevated temperatures the reaction is not rapid unless catalyzed by manganese (II) ion. Thus, several seconds are required to decolorize a hot oxalic acid solution at the outset of a permanganate titration. Later, when the concentration of manganese (II) ion has become appreciable, the decolorization becomes very rapid. This is yet another example of autocatalysis.

Even though the mechanism by which oxalic acid reduces permanganate ion has been the subject of extensive studies,[4] some details about the reaction remain obscure. It seems clear, however, that an important step in the reaction is the formation of oxalate complexes of +3 and +4 manganese as a result of oxidation of manganese (II) ion by permanganate. These complex ions then react rapidly with oxalate to give carbon dioxide and manganese (II) ion again. Thus, until a reasonable concentration of manganese (II) ions has been built up in the solution, the formation of these intermediates is inhibited and the reaction remains slow.

The stoichiometry of the reaction has been investigated in great detail by McBride[5] and more recently by Fowler and Bright.[6] The former devised a procedure in which the oxalic acid is titrated slowly at a temperature between 60° and 90° C until the faint pink color of the permanganate persists. Fowler and Bright have demonstrated that this titration consumes 0.1 to 0.4 percent too little permanganate, due perhaps to air oxidation of a small part of the oxalic acid.

$$H_2C_2O_4 + O_2 \rightleftharpoons H_2O_2 + 2CO_2$$

In the hot solution, the peroxide is postulated to decompose spontaneously to oxygen and water.

Fowler and Bright devised a scheme for standardization in which 90 to 95 percent of the required permanganate is added rapidly to the cool oxalic acid solution. After all of this reagent has reacted, the solution is heated to 55° to 60° C and titrated as before. While this procedure minimizes the air oxidation of oxalic acid and gives data that appear to be in exact accord with the theoretical stoichiometry, it suffers from the disadvantage of requiring a knowledge of the approximate normality of the permanganate solution in order to make the proper initial addition of the reagent. In this respect the Fowler-Bright procedure is not as convenient as the McBride method.

For many purposes the method of McBride will give perfectly adequate data (usually 0.2 to 0.3 percent too high). If a more accurate standardization is required, it is convenient to run one titration by this procedure to obtain the approximate normality of the solution; then a pair of titrations employing the Fowler and Bright method can be made. Directions for both procedures follow.

★METHOD OF FOWLER AND BRIGHT. Dry primary-standard grade $Na_2C_2O_4$ for 1 hour at 110° to 200° C. Cool in a desiccator and accurately weigh suitable portions (0.2 to 0.3 gram for 0.1 N

[4] H. F. Launer, *J. Am. Chem. Soc.*, **54**, 2597 (1932); H. F. Launer and D. M. Yost, *ibid*, **56**, 2571 (1934); and J. M. Malcolm and R. M. Noyes, *ibid*, **74**, 2769 (1952).

[5] R. S. McBride, *J. Am. Chem. Soc.*, **34**, 393 (1912).

[6] R. M. Fowler and H. A. Bright, *J. Research Nat. Bur. Standards*, **15**, 493 (1935).

$KMnO_4$) into 500-ml beakers. Add 250 ml of 1:19 sulfuric acid that has been boiled for 10 to 15 minutes and cooled to room temperature; stir until dissolved. A thermometer is convenient for this purpose since the temperature must be measured later. Introduce from a buret sufficient permanganate to consume 90 to 95 percent of the oxalate (about 40 ml for a 0.1 N solution and a 0.3-gram sample). A preliminary titration by the McBride method will provide the approximate volume required. Let stand until the solution is decolorized; then warm to 55° to 60° C and complete the titration, taking the first pale pink color that persists for 30 seconds as the end point. Determine an end-point correction by titrating 250 ml of 1:19 sulfuric acid at this same temperature. Correct for the blank and calculate the normality.

★METHOD OF McBRIDE. Dissolve weighed samples of dried $Na_2C_2O_4$ in a solution prepared by diluting 30 ml of 6 N H_2SO_4 to about 250 ml. Heat to 80° to 90° C and titrate with the $KMnO_4$, stirring vigorously with a thermometer. The first addition of reagent should be made slowly enough so that the pink color is discharged before further additions are made. If the solution drops below 60° C, heat. The end point is the first persistent pink color. Correct the titration for an end-point blank determined by titrating an equal volume of the water and acid.

NOTES:

1. To measure the volume of $KMnO_4$, take the surface of the liquid as a point of reference. Alternatively, use a flashlight or match to provide sufficient back lighting for reading of the meniscus in the conventional manner.

2. Solutions of permanganate should not be allowed to stand in burets any longer than necessary, as decomposition to MnO_2 may occur. Freshly formed MnO_2 can be removed from burets and glassware by rinsing with a warm solution prepared by dissolving 1 to 2 grams of $Na_2C_2O_4$ in 6 N H_2SO_4 or with hot, concentrated HCl.

3. Any $KMnO_4$ spattered on the sides of the titration vessel should be washed down immediately with a stream of water.

4. If the addition of $KMnO_4$ is too rapid, some MnO_2 will be produced in addition to Mn^{2+}. Evidence for this is a faint brown discoloration of the solution. This is not a serious problem as long as sufficient oxalate remains to reduce the MnO_2 to Mn^{2+}; the titration is temporarily discontinued until the solution clears. The solution must be free of MnO_2 at the equivalence point.

Other Primary Standards. Several other primary standards can be employed to give the normality of permanganate solutions. These include arsenic (III) oxide, Mohr's salt ($FeSO_4 \cdot (NH_4)_2SO_4 \cdot 6H_2O$), potassium iodide, and metallic iron.

TABLE 18-5

Applications of Potassium Permanganate in Acid Solution

Substance Sought	Half Reaction	Condition
·I	$I^- + HCN \rightleftharpoons ICN + H^+ + 2e$	In 0.1 F HCN with ferroin indicator
·Br	$2Br^- \rightleftharpoons Br_2 + 2e$	Boiling H_2SO_4 solution
As	$H_3AsO_3 + H_2O \rightleftharpoons H_3AsO_4 + 2H^+ + 2e$	KIO_3 or ICl catalyst in HCl solution
Sb	$H_3SbO_3 + H_2O \rightleftharpoons H_3SbO_4 + 2H^+ + 2e$	IICl solution
Sn	$Sn^{2+} \rightleftharpoons Sn^{4+} + 2e$	Prereduction with Zn
H_2O_2	$H_2O_2 \rightleftharpoons O_2 + 2H^+ + 2e$	
Fe	$Fe^{2+} \rightleftharpoons Fe^{3+} + e$	Prereduction with Jones reductor, SO_2, etc.
$Fe(CN)_6^{4-}$	$Fe(CN)_6^{4-} \rightleftharpoons Fe(CN)_6^{3-} + e$	
V	$VO^{2+} + 3H_2O \rightleftharpoons V(OH)_4^+ + 2H^+ + e$	Prereduction with Bi amalgam or SO_2
Mo	$Mo^{3+} + 4H_2O \rightleftharpoons MoO_4^{2-} + 8H^+ + 3e$	Prereduction with Jones reductor
W	$W^{3+} + 4H_2O \rightleftharpoons WO_4^{2-} + 8H^+ + 3e$	Prereduction with Zn or Cd
U	$U^{4+} + 2H_2O \rightleftharpoons UO_2^{2+} + 4H^+ + 2e$	Prereduction with Jones reductor
Ti	$Ti^{3+} + H_2O \rightleftharpoons TiO^{2+} + 2H^+ + e$	Prereduction with Jones reductor
Nb	$Nb^{3+} + H_2O \rightleftharpoons NbO^{3+} + 2H^+ + 2e$	Prereduction with Zn amalgam
$H_2C_2O_4$	$H_2C_2O_4 \rightleftharpoons 2CO_2 + 2H^+ + 2e$	
Mg, Ca, Zn, Co, La, Th, Ba, Sr, Ce, Ag, Pb	$H_2C_2O_4 \rightleftharpoons 2CO_2 + 2H^+ + 2e$	Insoluble metal oxalates filtered, washed, and dissolved in acid. Liberated oxalic acid titrated.
HNO_2	$HNO_2 + H_2O \rightleftharpoons NO_3^- + 3H^+ + 2e$	15 minute reaction time. Excess $KMnO_4$ determined.

TABLE 18-5   (Continued)

Applications of Potassium Permanganate in Acid Solution

Substance Sought	Half Reaction	Condition
K	$K_2NaCo(NO_2)_6 + 6H_2O \rightleftharpoons$ $Co^{2+} + 6NO_3^- + 12H^+ + 2K^+ + Na^+ + 11e$	Precipitated as $K_2NaCo(NO_2)_6$. Filtered and dissolved in $KMnO_4$. Excess $KMnO_4$ determined.
Na	$U^{4+} + 2H_2O \rightleftharpoons UO_2^{2+} + 4H^+ + 2e$	Precipitated as $NaZn(UO_2)_3 \cdot (OAc)_9 \cdot 6H_2O$. Filtered, washed, dissolved, and U determined as above.

APPLICATIONS OF PERMANGANATE TITRATIONS TO ACID SOLUTIONS

Table 18-5 indicates the multiplicity of analyses that make use of standard permanganate solutions in acidic media. Most of these reactions are rapid enough for direct titrations. Manganese (II) ion is the product in each case. Specific directions follow for the determination of iron and for calcium.

Determination of Iron in an Ore. The main iron ores are hematite (Fe_2O_3), magnetite (Fe_3O_4), and limonite ($3Fe_2O_3 \cdot 3H_2O$). Volumetric methods for iron analysis of samples containing these substances can be broken down into three steps: (1) solution of the sample, (2) reduction of the iron to the divalent state, and (3) titration with a standard oxidant. In most cases elements tending to interfere with step (3) are either absent or their effects can be avoided without preliminary separations.

Iron ores are often completely decomposed in concentrated hydrochloric acid. The rate of attack by this reagent is increased by the presence of a small amount of tin (II) chloride, which probably acts by reducing the rather insoluble iron (III) oxides on the surface of the particles. Hydrochloric acid is a much more efficient solvent than either sulfuric or nitric acids; this is explained, in part, by the tendency of iron (III) to form chloride complexes.

Most iron ores contain silicates that may or may not be decomposed by treatment with hydrochloric acid. Where decomposition is complete, the white residue of hydrated silica that remains behind in no way interferes with the analysis. Incomplete decomposition is indicated by a dark residue remaining after prolonged treatment with the acid. Since this solid residue may contain iron, it must be broken down by more rigorous treatment. The usual procedure entails filtration and ignition of the solid followed by fusion with sodium carbonate. This process converts the metallic components of the residue into carbonates, which can then be dissolved in acid and combined with the solution containing the bulk of the sample.

The dissolution step in an iron analysis will almost inevitably result in part or all of the iron being converted to the trivalent state; prereduction of the sample must, therefore, precede final titration with the oxidant. Any of the methods described earlier may be used—the Jones reductor, for example. Zinc amalgam, however, will also reduce other elements commonly associated with iron, including titanium, niobium, vanadium, chromium, uranium, tungsten, molybdenum, and arsenic. In their lower oxidation states these, too, react with permanganate; their presence, if undetected, will lead to high results.

A silver reductor has the advantage of being inert with respect to titanium and trivalent chromium, both of which are likely to be present in high concentration. Vanadium continues to interfere.

Perhaps the most satisfactory of all prereductants for iron is tin (II) chloride. The only other common elements reduced by this reagent are vanadium, copper, molybdenum, tungsten, and arsenic. The excess reducing agent is removed from solution by the addition of mercury (II) chloride

$$Sn^{2+} + 2HgCl_2 \rightleftharpoons Hg_2Cl_2 + Sn^{4+} + 2Cl^-$$

The insoluble mercury (I) chloride produced will not consume permanganate nor will the excess mercury (II) chloride reoxidize divalent iron. Care must be exerted, however, to prevent occurrence of the alternate reaction

$$Sn^{2+} + HgCl_2 \rightleftharpoons Hg + Sn^{4+} + 2Cl^-$$

Metallic mercury reacts with permanganate to cause a high result. This reaction is favored by appreciable excesses of tin (II); it is prevented by careful control of this excess and by the prompt addition of a sufficient quantity of mercury (II) chloride; a proper reduction is indicated by the appearance of a small amount of white precipitate after addition of this reagent. A gray precipitate indicates the presence of mercury; the sample must then be discarded. The total absence of precipitate indicates that an insufficient amount of tin (II) chloride was added; again, the sample must be discarded.

The reaction of iron (II) with permanganate proceeds smoothly and rapidly to completion. In the presence of hydrochloric acid, however, high results are obtained due to oxidation of the chloride ion by the permanganate. This reaction, which normally does not occur rapidly enough to cause serious errors, is induced by the presence of divalent iron. Its effects are avoided by preliminary removal of chloride by evaporation with sulfuric acid or by use of the Zimmermann-Reinhardt reagent. The latter consists of a solution of manganese (II) ions in fairly concentrated sulfuric and phosphoric acids. The manganese (II) ions inhibit the oxidation of chloride ion while the phosphoric acid complexes the iron (III) ions produced in the titration and prevents the intense yellow color of the iron (III) chloride complexes from interfering with the end point.

The detailed procedure that follows provides a choice between two methods. The first consists of a tin (II) chloride reduction followed by titration in the presence of Zimmermann-Reinhardt reagent. In the second, chloride ion is distilled from a sulfuric acid solution before passing the sample through a Jones reductor.

★ANALYSIS OF IRON IN AN ORE BY PREREDUCTION WITH TIN (II) CHLORIDE

1. Special Solutions.

(a) Tin (II) chloride. In 1 liter of 1:2 HCl dissolve 150 grams of iron-free $SnCl_2 \cdot 2H_2O$. The solution should be freshly prepared.

(b) Mercury (II) chloride. Dissolve 5 grams of $HgCl_2$ in 100 ml of water.

(c) Zimmermann-Reinhardt reagent. Dissolve 70 grams of $MnSO_4 \cdot 4H_2O$ in 500 ml of water; cautiously add 125 ml of concentrated H_2SO_4 and 125 ml of 85-percent phosphoric acid. Dilute to about 1 liter.

2. Sample Treatment. Dry the ore at 105° to 110° C and weigh individual samples into 250-ml beakers; a sample of optimum size will require 25 to 40 ml of the standard $KMnO_4$. Add 10 ml of concentrated HCl, 3 ml of $SnCl_2$ solution, and heat at just below boiling until the sample is decomposed; this is indicated by the disappearance of all of the dark particles. A pure white residue may remain. A blank consisting of 10 ml of HCl and 3 ml of $SnCl_2$ should be heated for the same length of time. If the solutions become yellow during the heating, add another milliliter or two of $SnCl_2$. After the decomposition is complete, add approximately $0.2\ F\ KMnO_4$ dropwise until the solution is just yellow. Dilute the solution to about 15 ml. In the case of the blank, add $KMnO_4$ until the solution just turns pink; then decolorize with $SnCl_2$ and add 1 drop in excess. *Carry samples individually through subsequent steps.*

3. Reduction of Iron. Heat the solution containing the sample nearly to boiling and add $SnCl_2$ drop by drop until the yellow color disappears. Add 1 *drop* in excess (Note 1). Cool to room temperature and add *rapidly* 10 ml of the $HgCl_2$ solution. A small quantity of white precipitate should appear. If no precipitate forms or if the precipitate is gray, the sample should be discarded. The blank solution should also be treated with 10 ml of the $HgCl_2$ solution.

4. Titration. After 2 to 3 minutes—not much more—transfer the reduced solution quantitatively to a 600-ml beaker containing 25 ml of the Zimmermann-Reinhardt reagent and 300 ml of water. Titrate *immediately* with the $KMnO_4$ to the first faint pink that persists for 15 to 20 seconds. Do not titrate rapidly at any time. Correct the volume of $KMnO_4$ for the blank titration.

NOTES:

1. The solution may not become entirely colorless but instead acquire a pale yellow-green hue. This color will not decrease with additional $SnCl_2$. If too much $SnCl_2$ is inadvertently introduced, add $0.2\ F$ $KMnO_4$ until the yellow color is restored and repeat the reduction.

2. If all dark particles cannot be decomposed, filter the solution through ashless paper, wash with 5 to 10 ml of 6 N HCl and retain the filtrate and washings. Place the paper in a small platinum crucible and ignite. Mix 0.5 to 0.7 gram of finely ground anhydrous Na_2CO_3 with the residue and heat until a liquid melt is obtained. Cool, add 5 ml of water, followed by the cautious addition of an equal volume of 6 N HCl. Warm the crucible and wash the contents into the original filtrate. Evaporate the combined solutions to about 15 ml and proceed with the reduction step.

3. These directions are satisfactory for prereduction of electrolytic iron wire samples used for standardization purposes.

★ANALYSIS OF IRON IN AN ORE BY PREREDUCTION WITH A JONES REDUCTOR

1. Sample Treatment. Dry the sample and weigh portions of suitable size into 250-ml beakers. Add 10.0 ml of concentrated HCl and heat until the sample is decomposed. Also heat a blank of 10.0 ml of HCl for the same length of time. If solution of the sample is incomplete, filtration and fusion of the dark residue with Na_2CO_3, as described in Note 2 above may be necessary.

Add 15.0 ml of 1:1 H_2SO_4 to the solution and heat until fumes of SO_3 are observed. Swirl the solution to dissolve any iron salts that may form on the sides of the beaker. Cool and slowly add 100 ml of water. The first few milliliters should be added a drop at a time down the sides of the beaker.

2. Reduction of Iron. Drain the solution from the Jones reductor to within 1 inch of the top of the packing (Note). Pass 200 ml of 2 N H_2SO_4 through the tube, again draining to about 1 inch from the top of the zinc. Disconnect the receiver, discard the contents, and rinse with distilled water. Again attach the receiver, pass 50 ml of 2 N H_2SO_4 followed by the sample through the reductor at a rate of about 50 to 100 ml per minute. Wash the beaker with five 10-ml portions of 2 N H_2SO_4 passing each through the reductor. Finally pass 100 ml of water through the tube. Leave the reductor filled with water. *Throughout the entire process the amalgam should be covered with liquid and never exposed to the atmosphere.*

3. Titration. Disconnect the receiver at once, rinse the tip of the reductor into the flask and add 5 ml of 85-percent H_3PO_4. Titrate. The blank should be treated in the same way as the sample, the volume of $KMnO_4$ consumed being subtracted from that required for the sample.

NOTE:

If the reductor has not been in constant use, it may be partially clogged with various oxides; the first acid passed through may consume some oxidant. Therefore, test the apparatus before use by passage of about 200 ml of 2 N H_2SO_4 and 100 ml of water. The resulting solution should require no more than 0.06 ml of 0.1 N $KMnO_4$; if it does require more, repeat the operation until a blank of the required size is obtained.

Determination of Calcium. Calcium is conveniently determined by an indirect volumetric method. The element is first precipitated as calcium oxalate. This is filtered, washed, and then redissolved in dilute acid. The liberated oxalic acid is titrated with a standard solution of permanganate or some other oxidizing agent. This method is applicable to samples that contain magnesium and the alkali metals. Most other cations must be absent, however, as they either precipitate or coprecipitate as oxalates and lead to positive errors in the analysis.

In order to obtain satisfactory results from this procedure, the mol ratio of calcium to oxalate must be exactly one in the solution at the time of titration; to assure this, several precautions are necessary. For example, calcium oxalate formed in neutral or ammoniacal solutions is likely to be contaminated with calcium hydroxide or a basic calcium oxalate. The presence of either leads to low results that can be avoided by adding the oxalate to an acid solution of the sample and slowly forming the precipitate by the dropwise addition of ammonia. Losses due to the solubility of calcium oxalate are negligible at a pH of about 4 provided washing is restricted to freeing the precipitate of excess oxalic acid. A precipitate formed in this way is coarsely crystalline and readily filtered.

Another potential source of positive error in the analysis arises from coprecipitation of sodium oxalate. This occurs when sodium is present in concentrations greater than the calcium. The error from this source can be eliminated by double precipitation; that is, by solution of the precipitate in acid and reprecipitating it as before.

Magnesium, if present in high concentrations, may also contaminate the calcium oxalate precipitate. This interference is minimized if the excess of oxalate is sufficient to allow formation of a soluble complex with the magnesium, and if filtration is made shortly after the completion of precipitation. When the magnesium content exceeds that of calcium in the sample, a double precipitation may be required.

The instructions that follow are applicable to samples containing calcium carbonate and moderate amounts of magnesium and the alkali metals. An alternate procedure for the analysis of limestones is also given. This will give satisfactory results in the presence of moderate amounts of iron and aluminum as well as small amounts of manganese and titanium.

★METHOD FOR THE ANALYSIS OF CALCIUM IN SAMPLES OF CALCIUM CARBONATE. Dry the sample at 110° C. Weigh, into 600-ml beakers, samples large enough to contain about 100 mg of calcium. Cover with a watch glass and add 10 ml of 6 N HCl from a pipet. To avoid losses by spattering, the acid should be added slowly. Heat the solution to drive off the CO_2. Wash the watch glass and sides of the beaker with water and dilute to about 150 ml. Heat to 60° to 80° C and add 50 ml of a warm solution containing about 3 grams of $(NH_4)_2C_2O_4 \cdot H_2O$ (if the $(NH_4)_2C_2O_4$ solution is not clear, filter before use). Add 3 to 4 drops of methyl orange; then introduce 1:1 NH_3 dropwise from a pipet until the color changes from red to yellow. Allow the solution to stand for about 30 minutes (but no longer than 1 hour if magnesium is present) without further heating.

Filter the solution through a glass crucible or a Gooch crucible fitted with an asbestos mat (page 98). Wash the beaker and precipitate with 10- to 20-ml portions of chilled distilled water until the washings show only a faint cloudiness when tested with an acidified $AgNO_3$ solution (Note). A quantitative transfer of the precipitate is unnecessary.

Rinse the outside of the crucible with water and place it in the beaker in which the precipitate was formed. Add 150 ml of water and 50 ml of 6 N H_2SO_4; heat to 80° to 90° C to dissolve the precipitate. Titrate with 0.1 N $KMnO_4$ with the crucible still in the beaker. The temperature of the solution should not be allowed to drop below 60° C; take as an end point the first pink color that persists for 15 to 20 seconds.

NOTE:

If the sample contains very large concentrations of sodium or magnesium ions, more accurate results can be obtained by reprecipitation of the calcium oxalate. To do this, filter the precipitate through paper and wash 4 or 5 times with 0.1-percent $(NH_4)_2C_2O_4$ solution. Pour 50 ml of hot 1:4 HCl through the paper, collecting the washings in the beaker in which the precipitation was made. Wash the paper several times with hot 1:100 HCl and dilute all of the washings to about 200 ml. Proceed with the precipitation as before, this time collecting the precipitate in a Gooch or glass crucible and washing with cold water. Proceed with the analysis, as before.

Determination of Calcium in a Limestone. Limestones are composed principally of calcium carbonate. Dolomitic limestones contain large concentrations of magnesium carbonate in addition. Also present in smaller amounts are calcium and magnesium silicates as well as carbonates and silicates of iron, aluminum, manganese, titanium, the alkalies, and other metals.

Hydrochloric acid will often decompose limestones completely; only silica remains undissolved. Some limestones are more readily decomposed if first ignited; a few will yield only to a carbonate fusion.

The following method is remarkably effective for the analysis of calcium in most limestones. Iron and aluminum, in amounts equivalent to the calcium, do not interfere; small amounts of titanium and manganese can be tolerated.[7]

> ★METHOD FOR CALCIUM IN LIMESTONES. Dry the sample for 1 to 2 hours at 110° C. Weigh out 0.25- to 0.3-gram samples. If the material can be readily decomposed with acid, weigh into a 250-ml beaker and cover with a watch glass. Add 5 ml of water and 10 ml of concentrated HCl, taking care to avoid loss by spattering. Proceed with the analysis as given in the next paragraph. If the limestone is not completely decomposed by acid, weigh the sample into a small porcelain crucible and ignite. Heat slowly to 800° to 900° C and maintain this temperature for 30 minutes. After cooling, place the crucible in a 250-ml beaker, add 5 ml of water, and cover with a watch glass. Carefully add 10 ml of concentrated HCl and heat to boiling. Remove the crucible with a stirring rod, rinsing thoroughly with water.
>
> Add 5 drops of saturated bromine water to oxidize any iron present and boil for 5 minutes to remove the excess bromine. Dilute to 50 ml, heat to boiling and add 100 ml of hot, filtered 5-percent $(NH_4)_2C_2O_4$ solution. Add 3 to 4 drops of methyl orange and precipitate the calcium oxalate by the dropwise addition of 1:1 NH_3. The rate of addition should be 1 drop every 3 or 4 seconds until the solution turns to the intermediate orange-yellow color of the indicator (pH 3.5 to 4.5). Allow the solution to stand for 30 minutes and filter. A Gooch crucible or a filtering crucible is satisfactory. Wash the precipitate with several 10-ml portions of cold water. Rinse the outside of the crucible and place it in the beaker in which the original precipitation was made. Add 50 ml of water containing 5 to 6 ml of concentrated H_2SO_4.
>
> Heat the solution to 80° to 90° C. If a Gooch crucible was used, stir to break up the asbestos pad. Then titrate with 0.1 N KMnO$_4$. The solution should be kept above 60° C throughout the titration.

---

[7] For further details of the method see J. J. Lingane, *Ind. Eng. Chem., Anal. Ed.*, **17,** 39 (1945).

18.4   Quadrivalent Cerium

A solution of +4 cerium in sulfuric acid is very nearly as potent an oxidizing reagent as permanganate; it, therefore, can be substituted for the latter in most of the applications described in the previous section. The reagent is indefinitely stable and does not oxidize chloride ion at a detectable rate; in these respects, it offers considerable advantage over permanganate. Further, only a single reduction product, trivalent cerium, is formed; thus, the stoichiometry of the reaction is less subject to uncertainty. On the other hand, the color of cerium (IV) solutions is not sufficiently intense to serve as an indicator. In addition, the reagent cannot be used in neutral or basic solutions. A final disadvantage is the relatively high cost of cerium compounds. The price differential is quite great because of the large equivalent weight of cerium salts. For example, the cost of the potassium permanganate in 1 liter of 0.1 N solution is about 1 cent; the cost for a similar solution of quadrivalent cerium is about 50 cents. The greater number of man hours required to prepare a permanganate solution may, of course, more than compensate for the difference in cost of the starting materials.

PROPERTIES OF QUADRIVALENT CERIUM

Solutions of quadrivalent cerium can be readily prepared from any of several commercially available sulfate or nitrate salts. These have a strong tendency to hydrolyze, even in acid solutions, with production of slightly soluble basic salts. To avoid this the acidity must be 0.1 N or greater. The hydrolytic reaction precludes titration of neutral or basic solutions with the reagent.

The reduction potential of cerium (IV) is dependent upon the kind of acid employed in preparing solutions of the reagent. Sulfuric acid solutions are comparable in oxidizing power to those of permanganate whereas nitric and perchloric acid solutions are appreciably more potent. To a lesser degree, the reduction potential is also influenced by the concentration of the acid.

Stability of Cerium (IV) Solutions. Sulfuric acid solutions of quadrivalent cerium are remarkably stable, remaining constant in titer for years. Even solutions heated to 100° C for considerable periods of time do not change appreciably. The same, however, cannot be said for perchloric and nitric acid solutions of the reagent. These decompose water and decrease in normality by 0.3 to 1 percent during storage over the period of one month. The decomposition reaction is catalyzed by light.

The oxidation of chloride is so slow that other reducing agents can be titrated without error in the presence of high concentrations of this ion. Hydrochloric acid solutions of cerium (IV), however, are not stable enough to be used as standard reagents.

Indicators for Cerium (IV) Titrations. Several of the redox indicators discussed in Chapter 16 are suitable for use in titrations with cerium (IV) solutions. The various phenanthrolines deserve particular mention because their transition potentials frequently correspond to the equivalence-point potentials in these reactions.

PREPARATION AND STANDARDIZATION OF CERIUM (IV) SOLUTIONS

Preparation of Solutions. Several cerium (IV) salts are commercially available.[8] The most common of these are listed below.

Name	Formula	Equivalent Weight
Cerium (IV) ammonium nitrate	$(NH_4)_2Ce(NO_3)_6$	548.3
Cerium (IV) ammonium sulfate	$(NH_4)_4Ce(SO_4)_4 \cdot 2H_2O$	632.6
Cerium (IV) hydroxide	$Ce(OH)_4$	208.2
Cerium (IV) hydrogen sulfate	$Ce(HSO_4)_4$	528.4

Cerium (IV) ammonium nitrate of primary-standard quality can be purchased; from this, standard solutions can be prepared directly by weight. More frequently, solutions of approximately the desired normality are prepared from one of the less expensive reagent-grade salts and then standardized. A stable and entirely satisfactory sulfuric acid solution of quadrivalent cerium is obtained from cerium (IV) ammonium nitrate without removal of the ammonium or nitrate ions.

★PREPARATION OF APPROXIMATELY 0.1 N CERIUM (IV) SOLUTION IN H_2SO_4. Carefully add 30 ml of concentrated H_2SO_4 to 500 ml of water, and then add 63 grams of $Ce(SO_4)_2 \cdot 2(NH_4)_2$-$SO_4 \cdot 2H_2O$ with continual stirring. Cool, filter if the solution is not clear, and dilute to about 1 liter.

If $(NH_4)_2Ce(NO_3)_6$ is used, weigh about 55 grams into a 1-liter beaker. Add about 60 ml of 95-percent H_2SO_4 and stir for 2 minutes.

---

[8] For further information regarding the preparation, standardization, and use of cerium (IV) solutions see: G. Frederick Smith, *Cerate Oxidimetry*. Columbus, Ohio: The G. Frederick Smith Chemical Co., 1942; I. M. Kolthoff and R. Belcher, *Volumetric Analysis*, **3,** 121–167. New York: Interscience Publishers, Inc., 1957.

Cautiously introduce 100 ml of water and again stir for 2 minutes. Repeat the operations of adding water and stirring until all of the salt has dissolved; then dilute to about 1 liter.

Standardization against Arsenic (III) Oxide. Arsenic (III) oxide is perhaps the most satisfactory primary standard for solutions of quadrivalent cerium. In the absence of a catalyst the reaction is so slow that iron (II) can be titrated without interference in the presence of trivalent arsenic. Fortunately good catalysts are available that permit standardization with this useful reagent. The best of these is osmium tetroxide which needs to be present only in very low concentrations (10^{-5} F). Iodine monochloride also catalyzes the reaction.

The orthophenanthroline-iron (II) complex is an excellent indicator for sulfuric acid solutions of cerium.

★METHOD. Dry the primary standard As_2O_3 for 1 hour at 110° C and weigh about 0.2-gram portions (to the nearest 0.1 mg) into 250-ml flasks. Dissolve in 15 ml of 2 N NaOH, warming to hasten the process. After solution is complete, cool and add 25 ml of 1:5 H_2SO_4. Dilute to about 100 ml, add 3 drops of 0.01 M osmium tetroxide (Note 1), and 1 drop of iron (II) orthophenanthroline (Note 2). Titrate to a color change from red to very pale blue or colorless.

NOTES:

1. The catalyst solution may be purchased from the G. Frederick Smith Chemical Co., Columbus, Ohio. It should contain about 0.025 gram of OsO_4 in 100 ml of 0.1 N H_2SO_4.

2. The orthophenanthroline indicator is prepared by dissolving 1.485 grams of orthophenanthroline in 100 ml of water containing 0.695 gram of $FeSO_4 \cdot 7H_2O$.

Standardization against Sodium Oxalate. Several methods are available for the standardization of sulfuric acid solutions of cerium (IV) against sodium oxalate.[9] The directions that follow call for titration at 50° C in hydrochloric acid solution. Iodine monochloride is used as a catalyst and orthophenanthroline as the indicator.

★METHOD. Weigh out 0.3-gram portions of dried sodium oxalate (to the nearest 0.1 mg) into 250-ml beakers and dissolve in 75 ml of water. Add 20 ml of concentrated HCl and 1.5 ml of 0.017 F ICl (Note). Heat to 50° C and add 2 to 3 drops of iron (II) orthophenanthroline indicator (Note 2, above). Titrate with cerium (IV) until the solution turns pale blue or colorless and the pink does not

[9] I. M. Kolthoff and R. Belcher, *Volumetric Analysis*, **3**, 132–134. New York: Interscience Publishers, Inc., 1957.

return within 1 minute. The temperature should be between 45° and 50° C throughout.

NOTE:

Iodine monochloride catalyst can be prepared by mixing 25 ml of 0.04 F KI, 40 ml of concentrated HCl, and 20 ml of 0.025 F KIO$_3$. Add 5 to 10 ml of CCl$_4$ and shake thoroughly. Titrate with the KI or KIO$_3$ until the CCl$_4$ layer is barely pink after shaking. The KI should be added if the CCl$_4$ is colorless and the KIO$_3$ if it is too pink.

APPLICATIONS OF QUADRIVALENT CERIUM SOLUTIONS

Many applications of cerium (IV) solutions are found in the literature. Generally these parallel the uses of permanganate given in Table 18-5.[10] A detailed procedure for one such application follows.

Determination of Iron in an Ore. Quadrivalent cerium oxidizes iron (II) smoothly and rapidly at room temperature; orthophenanthroline is an excellent indicator for the titration. In contrast to the analysis based upon oxidation with permanganate, consumption of the reagent by chloride ion is of no concern.

The problems associated with solution of the sample and prereduction of the iron are the same as in the permanganate method (page 377), the only major difference being that here there is no need for the Zimmermann-Reinhardt solution.

★METHOD FOR THE ANALYSIS OF IRON IN AN ORE

1. Special Solutions. (a) Tin (II) chloride (p. 379). (b) Mercury (II) chloride (p. 379). (c) Orthophenanthroline indicator (0.025 F) (Note 2, p. 386). (d) Standard quadrivalent cerium solution.

2. Preparation of the sample. Use the directions on page 380 if a Jones reductor is to be used; see page 379 if tin (II) chloride reduction is to be employed.

3. Titration. If the tin (II) chloride is used, allow about 2 to 3 minutes after addition of the HgCl$_2$; then add 300 ml of 1 F HCl, a drop of orthophenanthroline, and titrate to the disappearance of the pink color of the indicator. For accurate work a blank should be carried through the entire procedure.

If the Jones reductor is used for prereduction, complete the analysis by titration with the cerium (IV) solution using 1 drop of orthophenanthroline indicator.

---

[10] Information about these methods can be found in I. M. Kolthoff and R. Belcher, *Volumetric Analysis*, **3**, 136–158. New York: Interscience Publishers, Inc., 1957.

18.5   Potassium Dichromate

Potassium dichromate is more limited in application than either potassium permanganate or quadrivalent cerium owing to its lower oxidation potential and the slowness of some of its reactions. Despite these handicaps, the reagent has nonetheless proved useful for those analyses where it can be applied. Among the virtues of the reagent are the stability of its solutions and its inertness toward hydrochloric acid. Further, the solid reagent can be obtained in high purity and at modest cost; standard solutions may be prepared directly by weight.

PREPARATION AND PROPERTIES OF DICHROMATE SOLUTIONS

For most purposes commercially available reagent-grade or primary-standard grade potassium dichromate can be used to prepare standard solutions with no treatment other than drying at 150° to 200° C. If desired, two or three recrystallizations of the solid from water will assure a high quality primary-standard substance.

Solutions of dichromate are orange in hue; the color is not sufficiently intense for end-point determination, however, and an oxidation-reduction indicator is ordinarily used. Diphenylamine sulfonic acid (page 358) is most commonly employed. The color change is from the green of the chromium (III) ion to the violet color of the oxidized form of the indicator. An indicator blank is not readily obtained because dichromate oxidizes the indicator only slowly in the absence of other oxidation-reduction systems. Ordinarily, however, this leads to a negligible error. The indicator reaction is reversible and back titration of small excesses of dichromate with iron (II) is possible. In the presence of a large concentration of the oxidant and at low acidities (above pH 2), diphenylamine is irreversibly oxidized to yellow or red compounds.

In its analytical applications, dichromate ion is reduced to the trivalent state

$$Cr_2O_7^{2-} + 14H^+ + 6e \rightleftharpoons 2Cr^{3+} + 7H_2O \qquad E° = 1.33 \text{ volts}$$

Standard solutions of potassium dichromate are stable indefinitely and may be boiled for long periods without decomposition.

★PREPARATION OF A 0.1 N $K_2Cr_2O_7$ SOLUTION. Dry primary-standard $K_2Cr_2O_7$ for 2 hours at 150° to 200° C. After cooling, weigh 4.903 grams of the solid, dissolve this in distilled water, transfer quantitatively to a 1-liter volumetric flask, and dilute to the mark.

If the purity of the salt is suspect, recrystallize 3 times from water before drying. Alternatively, prepare a solution of approximate normality by dissolving about 5 grams of the salt in a liter of water, and standardize this against weighed samples of electrolytic iron wire.

APPLICATIONS OF DICHROMATE

Determination of Iron. The principal use of dichromate involves titration of iron (II)

$$6Fe^{2+} + 2Cr_2O_7^{2-} + 14H^+ \rightleftharpoons 6Fe^{3+} + 2Cr^{3+} + 7H_2O$$

Moderate amounts of hydrochloric acid do not affect the accuracy of the titration. The procedure given below may be readily applied to the analysis of iron after prereduction by tin (II) chloride or with a Jones reductor (pages 377–380).

★METHOD FOR THE ANALYSIS OF IRON. To the prereduced solution (page 380) add 10 ml of concentrated H_2SO_4 and 15 ml of syrupy H_3PO_4. Add water, if necessary, to bring the volume to about 250 ml. Cool, add 8 drops of diphenylamine sulfonate indicator (Note), and titrate with dichromate to the violet-blue end point.

NOTE:

The indicator solution should contain 0.2 gram of sodium diphenylamine sulfonate in 100 ml of water.

Other Applications. Uranium can be oxidized from the $+4$ to the $+6$ state by a direct titration with dichromate. Since the color change of diphenylamine is not rapid in the presence of this system, it is a preferable procedure to titrate the iron (II) produced when an excess of iron (III) chloride is added to the quadrivalent uranium

$$UO^{2+} + 2Fe^{3+} + H_2O \rightleftharpoons UO_2^{2+} + 2Fe^{2+} + 2H^+$$

Dichromate solutions are also used for the volumetric determination of sodium ion. The sodium is first precipitated as sodium zinc uranyl acetate

$$(UO_2)_3NaZn(C_2H_3O_2)_9 \cdot 6H_2O$$

The solid is filtered, washed, and then redissolved in sulfuric acid. The uranium is reduced to the $+4$ state in a Jones reductor and titrated as before.

A common method for the determination of oxidizing agents calls for treatment of the sample with a known excess of iron (II), followed by titration of the excess with standard dichromate. This technique has been successfully applied to the determination of nitrate, chlorate, permanganate, dichromate, and organic peroxides, among others.

18.6   Iodine — Direct Iodimetric Methods

A large number of volumetric analyses are based on the half reaction

$$I_3^- + 2e \rightleftharpoons 3I^- \qquad E° = 0.536 \text{ volt}$$

These analyses fall into two categories. The first comprises procedures that use a standard solution of iodine to titrate easily oxidized substances. These are termed *direct* or *iodimetric methods* and have rather limited applicability since iodine is a relatively weak oxidizing agent. The second class of procedures, called *indirect* or *iodometric methods*, involve the analysis of oxidizing agents. Here the substance to be determined is brought into contact with an excess of iodide ion; a quantity of iodine, chemically equivalent to the amount of the oxidizing agent, is liberated. This is determined by titration with a standard solution of sodium thiosulfate. The quantity of iodide added is not measured; it is only important that enough be present to cause the reaction with the oxidizing agent to proceed to completion.

We shall confine this discussion to direct methods involving a standard iodine solution. In the next section the indirect iodometric method will be considered in some detail.

Iodine, as a standard oxidant, has some attractive features. Among these is the selectivity of its behavior resulting from its low oxidizing power; only easily oxidized substances react with the reagent. Another factor contributing to the popularity of iodine solutions is the sensitive and reversible indicator available for end-point detection.

The lack of stability of iodine solutions is a distinct disadvantage; frequent restandardizations are necessary. Also, the low reduction potential of the reagent, while important from the standpoint of selectivity, severely limits the number of analyses to which it can be applied.

PREPARATION AND PROPERTIES OF IODINE SOLUTIONS

Solubility of Iodine. Iodine is not very soluble in water, a saturated solution at room temperature being only somewhat greater than 0.001 F. In aqueous solutions of potassium iodide, however, the element dissolves readily as a result of formation of the soluble triiodide complex

$$I_2 + I^- \rightleftharpoons I_3^- \qquad K = 7.1 \times 10^2$$

Advantage is taken of this in preparing solutions for analysis. The concentration of the species I_2 is low in these solutions; from a chemical standpoint, therefore, it would be more proper to refer to them as *triiodide solutions*. As a practical matter, however, they are called *iodine solutions* because of the convenience this affords in writing equations and describing stoichiometric behavior.

Preparation of Solutions. Standard iodine solutions can be directly prepared from commercial reagent grades of the element. Where necessary, the solid is readily purified by sublimation. It is usually more convenient, however, to prepare an iodine solution in approximately the desired concentration, and to standardize it against a primary-standard material.

The rate at which iodine dissolves in potassium iodide solution is slow, particularly where the iodide concentration is low. Because of this, it is common practice to dissolve the solid completely in a few milliliters of a very concentrated iodide solution before diluting to the desired volume. All of the element must be dissolved before dilution; otherwise the normality of the resulting reagent will increase continuously as the remaining iodine slowly passes into solution.

> ★PREPARATION OF AN APPROXIMATELY 0.1 N I_2 SOLUTION. Weigh about 40 grams of pure KI into a small beaker and dissolve in 10 ml of water. Add 12.7 grams of pure I_2 and stir occasionally until solution is complete. After filtering through an asbestos mat, dilute to about 1 liter. If possible, let the solution stand for 2 to 3 days before standardizing.

Stability. Iodine solutions require restandardization every few days. The instability arises from several sources, one being the volatility of the iodine; even in the presence of a considerable amount of iodide, measurable losses from open containers occur in a relatively short period.

Iodine will slowly attack rubber or cork stoppers as well as other organic materials. Reasonable precautions must therefore be taken to protect standard solutions of the reagent from contact with these materials. Contact with organic dust and fumes must also be avoided.

Finally, changes in iodine normality result from air oxidation of the iodide present in the solution

$$4I^- + O_2 + 4H^+ \rightleftharpoons 2I_2 + 2H_2O$$

This reaction is catalyzed by light, heat, and acids. Consequently, it is good practice to store the reagent in a dark, cool place. In contrast to the other effects, air oxidation results in an increase in normality.

Completeness of Iodine Oxidations. Because iodine is such a weak oxidizing agent, the chemist must often take full advantage of those experimental variables that favor its reduction to iodide by the substance being analyzed. Two effects, pH and the presence of complexing agents, are of particular importance.

In acid solutions, the pH has little influence upon the oxidation potential of the iodine-iodide couple since hydrogen ions do not participate in the half reaction. Many of the substances that react with iodine, however, evolve hydrogen ions in their oxidation; the position of equilibrium may therefore be markedly influenced by pH. An interesting example arises in the case of the arsenic (III)-arsenic (V) system, which has a standard potential differing by only 0.02 volt from that for the iodide-iodine half reaction,

$$H_3AsO_4 + 2H^+ + 2e \rightleftharpoons H_3AsO_3 + H_2O \qquad E^\circ = 0.559 \text{ volt}$$

In 1 F acid, the oxidation of arsenious acid by iodine is quite incomplete; as a matter of fact, in very strong acids, the reverse reaction can be made quantitative. On the other hand, in a nearly neutral medium the titration of arsenious acid with iodine is quite feasible. Although iodine oxidations often become more complete with lowered acidity, care must be taken to avoid hydrolysis of the iodine that tends to occur in alkaline solutions.

$$I_2 + OH^- \rightleftharpoons HOI + I^-$$

The hypoiodite that first forms may disproportionate in part to iodate and iodide as shown by the equation

$$3HOI + 3OH^- \rightleftharpoons IO_3^- + 2I^- + 3H_2O$$

The occurrence of these reactions may lead to serious errors in iodine titrations. In some instances the reaction of iodate and hypoiodite with the reducing reagent is so slow that overconsumption of iodine is observed. In other cases, the presence of these two species may alter the reaction products; the oxidation of thiosulfate is an important example of such behavior. In general, then, solutions to be titrated with iodine cannot have pH values much higher than 9; in a few cases a pH greater than 7 is detrimental.

Complexing reagents are also used to force certain iodine oxidations to the point where they are complete enough for analytical purposes. For example, it is readily seen that the reduction potential of iodine is too low to permit oxidation of iron (II) quantitatively to the trivalent state. In the presence of reagents that strongly complex iron (III), however, complete conversion is achieved. Pyrophosphate ion and ethylenediaminetetraacetate are useful for this purpose.

The reduction potential of iodine is markedly increased in the presence of ions that form complexes with iodide. Thus in the presence of mercury

(II), which forms stable iodide complexes, iodine will oxidize arsenious acid quantitatively even in strongly acid solutions; this is in distinct contrast to its behavior in the absence of mercury (II) ion.

End Points for Iodine Titrations. Several sensitive methods are available for determining the end point in an iodine titration. For one, the color of the triiodide ion itself is sufficiently intense to serve where colorless solutions are being titrated. Ordinarily, a concentration of about $5 \times 10^{-6} F$ triiodide can just be detected by the eye; this corresponds to an overtitration of less than one drop of 0.1 N iodine solution in the typical case.

A greater sensitivity can be obtained, at the sacrifice of convenience, by adding a few milliliters of an immiscible organic solvent such as chloroform or carbon tetrachloride to the solution. The bulk of any iodine present is transferred to the organic layer by shaking, and imparts an intense violet color to it. When this end point is used, the titration is carried out in a glass-stoppered flask; after each addition of reagent, the flask is shaken vigorously and then upended so that the organic layer collects in the narrow neck for examination.

The most widely used indicator in iodimetry is an aqueous suspension of starch; this imparts an intense blue color to a solution containing a trace of triiodide ion. The nature of the colored species has been the subject of much speculation and controversy.[11] It is now believed that the iodine is held as an adsorption complex within the helical chain of the macromolecule, β-amylose, one of the components of most starches. Another component, α-amylose, is undesirable because it produces a red coloration with iodine that is not readily reversible in behavior. Interference from α-amylose is seldom serious, however, because the substance tends to settle rapidly from aqueous suspension. Other starch fractions do not appear to form colored complexes with iodine. Potato, arrowroot, and rice starches contain large proportions of α- and β-amylose and can be employed as indicators. Corn starch is not suitable because of its high content of the former. The so-called *soluble starch* that is commercially available consists principally of β-amylose, the α-fraction having been removed. Indicator solutions are readily prepared from this product.

Aqueous-starch suspensions decompose within a few days, primarily because of bacterial action. The decomposition products may consume iodine as well as interfere with the indicator properties of the preparation. The rate of decomposition can be greatly reduced by preparing and storing the indicator under sterile conditions or by the addition of mercury (II) iodide which inhibits the growth of bacteria. Alternatively, a

---

[11] See R. E. Rundle, J. F. Foster, and R. R. Baldwin, *J. Am. Chem. Soc.*, **66,** 2116 (1944).

fresh indicator solution can be prepared each day an iodine titration is to be carried out.

Starch added to a solution containing a high concentration of iodine is decomposed to products whose indicator properties are not entirely reversible. Thus, when an excess of iodine is present, addition of the indicator must be postponed until most of the iodine has been titrated, as indicated by the color of the solution.

> ★PREPARATION OF STARCH INDICATOR. Make a paste by rubbing about 2 grams of soluble starch and 10 mg of HgI_2 in about 30 ml of water. Pour this into 1 liter of boiling water and heat until a clear solution results. Cool and store in stoppered bottles. For most titrations, about 5 ml of this solution should be used.

STANDARDIZATION OF IODINE SOLUTIONS

Iodine solutions are most commonly standardized against arsenious oxide although sodium thiosulfate, potassium antimony (III) tartrate, and other materials have also been recommended.

The equilibrium constant for the reaction

$$H_3AsO_3 + I_2 + H_2O \rightleftharpoons H_3AsO_4 + 2I^- + 2H^+$$

has been found experimentally[12] to be 1.6×10^{-1}. From the magnitude of this constant it is clear that a quantitative oxidation of arsenious acid can be expected only if steps are taken to keep the concentration of the products small; from a practical standpoint, the hydrogen ion and the iodide ion concentrations are most readily controlled. Kolthoff[13] has shown that a quantitative reaction occurs even at a pH of 3.5; however, the approach to equilibrium is prohibitively slow and, in practice, it is advisable to maintain the pH at values in excess of 5. The pH of the medium may be as high as 11 without adverse effect on the results if the arsenic (III) is titrated with iodine. The reverse titration, however, requires a pH less than 9 in order to avoid hydrolysis of the iodine; the iodate and hypoiodite formed react only slowly with the trivalent arsenic.

The iodimetric titration of arsenious acid must be carried out in a buffered system to use up the hydrogen ions formed in the reaction; otherwise the pH may decrease below the tolerable limit. Buffering is conveniently accomplished by acidifying the sample slightly and then saturating with sodium hydrogen carbonate. The carbonic acid-hydrogen carbonate buffer so established will hold the pH in a range between 7 and 8.

---

[12] H. A. Liebhafsky, *J. Phys. Chem.*, **35**, 1648 (1931).
[13] I. M. Kolthoff and R. Belcher, *Volumetric Analysis*, **3**, 217. New York: Interscience Publishers, Inc., 1957.

★STANDARDIZATION AGAINST SOLID As_2O_3. Dry a quantity of primary-standard grade As_2O_3 for about 1 hour at 110° C. For standardization of 0.1-N I_2 solutions weigh out 0.2-gram samples (to the nearest 0.1 mg). Dissolve in 10 ml of 1 N NaOH; if necessary, warm the solution. Cool, dilute with about 75 ml of water, and add 2 drops of phenolphthalein. Introduce 6 N HCl carefully until the red color disappears; then add about 1 ml of acid in excess. Carefully add 3 to 4 grams of solid $NaHCO_3$, in small portions at first to avoid losses of solution due to effervescence of the CO_2. Add 5 ml of starch indicator and titrate to the first faint purple or blue color that persists for at least 30 seconds.

APPLICATIONS OF STANDARD IODINE

Table 18-6 lists the more common analyses that make use of iodine as an oxidizing reagent.

TABLE 18-6

Analysis with Standard Iodine Solutions

Substance Analyzed	Half Reaction
As	$H_3AsO_3 + H_2O \rightleftharpoons H_3AsO_4 + 2H^+ + 2e$
Sb	$H_3SbO_3 + H_2O \rightleftharpoons H_3SbO_4 + 2H^+ + 2e$
Sn	$Sn^{2+} \rightleftharpoons Sn^{4+} + 2e$
H_2S	$H_2S \rightleftharpoons S + 2H^+ + 2e$
SO_2	$SO_3^{2-} + H_2O \rightleftharpoons SO_4^{2-} + 2H^+ + 2e$
$S_2O_3^{2-}$	$2S_2O_3^{2-} \rightleftharpoons S_4O_6^{2-} + 2e$
N_2H_4	$N_2H_4 \rightleftharpoons N_2 + 4H^+ + 4e$
Te	$Te + 3H_2O \rightleftharpoons H_2TeO_3 + 4H^+ + 4e$
Cd^{2+}, Zn^{2+}, Hg^{2+}, Pb^{2+}, etc.	$M^{2+} + H_2S \rightleftharpoons 2H^+ + MS$ (filter and wash) $MS \rightleftharpoons M^{2+} + S + 2e$

Determination of Arsenic, Antimony, and Tin. Arsenic, antimony, and tin, are conveniently determined by titration with iodine. The reaction of the reagent with arsenious acid was discussed in a previous section.

In acid solutions divalent tin is rapidly oxidized to the quadrivalent state by iodine. The principal difficulty in the use of this reaction arises from the ease with which the tin (II) is oxidized by air. This is avoided by covering the solution with an inert gas during the titration and using oxygen-free solutions throughout the analysis. Prereduction of quadrivalent tin is ordinarily accomplished with metallic lead or nickel.

The reaction of trivalent antimony with iodine is quite analogous to that of trivalent arsenic. Here, however, steps are also necessary to prevent precipitation of such basic salts as antimony oxide chloride, SbOCl, from the solution as it is neutralized; these react incompletely with iodine and lead to erroneously low results. This difficulty is readily overcome by addition of tartaric acid before dilution; the tartrate complex, $SbOC_4H_4O_6^-$ that forms is rapidly and completely oxidized by iodine.

Determination of Antimony in Stibnite. The analysis of the common antimony ore, stibnite, illustrates the application of a direct iodimetric method. Stibnite is primarily antimony sulfide containing silica and other contaminants. Provided the material is free of iron and arsenic, determination of its antimony content is a straightforward process. The sample is decomposed in hot, concentrated hydrochloric acid which causes the sulfide to be evolved as hydrogen sulfide. Some care is required in this step to prevent losses of the volatile antimony trichloride; addition of potassium chloride is helpful by increasing the tendency for formation of nonvolatile chloride complexes. These probably have the formulas $SbCl_4^-$ and $SbCl_6^{3-}$.

> ★METHOD. Dry the sample in an oven. After cooling, weigh into 500-ml Erlenmeyer flasks sufficient quantities of the ore to consume 25 to 35 ml of 0.1 N I_2. Add about 0.3 gram of KCl and 10 ml of concentrated HCl. Heat the mixture to just below boiling and maintain at this temperature until only a white or slightly gray residue of silica remains.
>
> Add 3 grams of solid tartaric acid to the solution and heat for another 10 to 15 minutes. While swirling the solution, slowly add water from a pipet until the volume is about 100 ml. The addition of water should be slow enough to prevent white SbOCl from forming. If reddish Sb_2S_3 forms, stop the addition of water and heat further, adding more acid if necessary.
>
> Add 3 drops of phenolphthalein to the solution, and 6 N NaOH until the first pink color is obtained. Add 6 N HCl dropwise until the solution is decolorized, and then 1 ml in excess. Add 4 to 5 grams of NaHCO₃, taking care to avoid losses of solution during the addition. Add 5 ml of starch and titrate to the first blue color that persists for 30 seconds or longer.

18.7 Iodometric Methods

Iodide ion is a moderately good reducing agent that has been widely employed for the analysis of oxidants. A fair number of substances, in one form or another, have potentials greater than that for iodine.

$$I_2 + 2e \rightleftharpoons 2I^- \qquad E° = 0.54 \text{ volt}$$

All of these are capable of oxidizing iodide to iodine, and hence are potentially susceptible to analysis with this reagent.

The lack of a good method of end-point detection makes direct titration of oxidizing agents by solutions of iodide salts impractical. Consequently, the indirect, iodometric, procedure is always employed. This involves reduction with a moderate and unmeasured excess of potassium iodide. The iodine liberated, equivalent in quantity to the oxidant being determined, is then titrated with a standard solution of a reducing reagent. Sodium thiosulfate is nearly always employed for this purpose, although solutions of arsenious acid or other reducing reagents can be used instead.

THE REACTION OF IODINE WITH THIOSULFATE ION

Because of its widespread employment in analysis, the reaction between iodine and thiosulfate ion

$$2S_2O_3^{2-} + I_2 \rightleftharpoons S_4O_6^{2-} + 2I^-$$

warrants discussion in some detail. The production of the tetrathionate ion requires the loss of two electrons from two thiosulfate ions; the equivalent weight of thiosulfate in this reaction must therefore be equal to its gram formula weight.

The quantitative conversion of thiosulfate to tetrathionate ion is somewhat unique with iodine; other oxidizing reagents tend to carry the oxidation, wholly or in part, to sulfate ion. Hypoiodous acid provides an important example of this.

$$4HOI + S_2O_3^{2-} + H_2O \rightleftharpoons 2SO_4^{2-} + 4I^- + 6H^+$$

The pertinence of this reaction becomes apparent when we recall that hypoiodite is a hydrolysis product of iodine itself (page 392); its presence in an iodine solution, then, will seriously upset the stoichiometry of the iodine-thiosulfate reaction causing too little thiosulfate or too much iodine to be used in the titration.

The equilibrium constant for the hydrolysis reaction

$$I_2 + H_2O \rightleftharpoons HOI + I^- + H^+$$

is about 3×10^{-13}.[14] From this it can be shown that hypoiodite formation should become significant in titrations where the pH is greater than 7. Kolthoff has demonstrated this to be the case;[15] in the titration of 25 ml of 0.1 N iodine with 0.1 N thiosulfate he found an error of about 4 percent in the presence of 0.5 gram of sodium bicarbonate and of 10 percent in a solution containing about 2 grams of this salt. He recommends that the pH

---

[14] W. C. Bray and E. L. Connolly, *J. Am. Chem. Soc.*, **33**, 1485 (1911).

[15] I. M. Kolthoff and R. Belcher, *Volumetric Analysis*, **3**, 214–215. New York: Interscience Publishers, Inc., 1957.

should always be less than 7.6 for titration of 0.1 N solutions, 6.5 or less for 0.01 N solutions, and less than 5 for 0.001 N solutions.

The titration of highly acidic solutions of iodine with thiosulfate yields quantitative results provided care is taken to prevent air oxidation of iodide ion, and provided also that the thiosulfate solution is added slowly to prevent its decomposition.

The end point in the titration is readily established by means of a starch solution. The preparation and properties of this indicator have been described on page 393; it should be emphasized that starch is partially decomposed in the presence of a large excess of iodine. For this reason the indicator is never added to an iodine solution until the bulk of that substance has been reduced. The change in color of the iodine from a red to a faint yellow signals the proper time for the addition of the indicator.

PREPARATION AND PROPERTIES OF STANDARD THIOSULFATE SOLUTIONS

Purity of Compounds. A pentahydrate, $Na_2S_2O_3 \cdot 5H_2O$, of sufficient purity for the direct preparation of standard solutions can be obtained by equilibrating the recrystallized salt with an atmosphere of appropriate moisture content. Most chemists, however, consider that the effort involved does not justify this convenience and ordinarily use the commercial salt to give a solution of only approximate normality; standardization is readily accomplished.

Anhydrous sodium thiosulfate has also been recommended as a primary standard; the hygroscopic nature of the compound, however, has prevented its wide adoption.

Stability of Thiosulfate Solutions. Principal among the variables affecting the stability of thiosulfate solutions are the pH, the presence of microorganisms and other impurities, the concentration of the solution, exposure to sunlight, and the presence of atmospheric oxygen. Generally, there is a decrease in iodine titer that may amount to as much as several percent in a few weeks. Occasionally, however, increases in normality are observed. Proper attention to detail makes possible the preparation of standard thiosulfate solutions that need only occasional restandardization.

In solutions of pH much lower than about 5, the following reaction occurs at an appreciable rate:

$$S_2O_3^{2-} + H^+ \rightleftharpoons HS_2O_3^- \rightarrow HSO_3^- + S$$

The velocity of this reaction increases with the hydrogen ion concentration, and in strongly acid solution, elemental sulfur is formed very rapidly. The hydrogen sulfite ion produced is also oxidized by iodine, consuming twice the quantity of that reagent as the thiosulfate from which it was derived. Clearly, thiosulfate solutions cannot be allowed to stand in contact with acid. On the other hand, iodine solutions that are 3 to 4 N in acid may be titrated without error as long as care is taken to introduce the thiosulfate slowly and with good mixing. Under these conditions the thiosulfate is so rapidly oxidized by the iodine that the slower acid decomposition cannot occur to any measurable extent.

Experiments indicate that the stability of thiosulfate solutions is at a maximum in the pH range between 9 and 10 although, for most purposes, a pH of 7 is adequate. Addition of small amounts of bases such as sodium carbonate, borax, or disodium hydrogen phosphate is frequently recommended as a means of preserving standard solutions of the reagent. If this is done, the iodine solutions to be titrated must be made sufficiently acidic to neutralize this base; otherwise hydrolysis of the iodine may occur before the equivalence point is attained, resulting in the partial oxidation of the thiosulfate to sulfate.

The most important single cause of instability of thiosulfate can be traced to certain bacteria that are capable of metabolizing the thiosulfate ion, converting it to sulfite, sulfate, and elemental sulfur.[16] Solutions prepared free of bacteria are remarkably stable, and it is common practice to impose reasonably sterile conditions in preparation of standard solutions. Addition of such substances as chloroform, sodium benzoate, or mercury (II) iodide inhibits the growth of bacteria and is reported to have a salutary effect. Bacterial activity appears to be at a minimum at a pH between 9 and 10 which accounts, at least in part, for the maximum stability of solutions in this range.

Many other variables affect the stability of thiosulfate solutions. Decomposition is reportedly catalyzed by copper (II) ions as well as by the decomposition products themselves. As a consequence, solutions that have become turbid should be discarded. Exposure to sunlight increases the rate of decomposition as does atmospheric oxygen. Finally, the decomposition rate is greater in more dilute solutions.

★PREPARATION OF APPROXIMATELY 0.1 N SODIUM THIOSULFATE. Heat 1 liter of distilled water to boiling in a beaker covered with a watch glass. Boil for at least 5 minutes. Cool, add about 25 grams of $Na_2S_2O_3 \cdot 5H_2O$ and 0.1 gram of Na_2CO_3. Stir until solution is complete, then transfer to a clean glass-stoppered bottle. Store in the dark.

STANDARDIZATION OF THIOSULFATE SOLUTIONS

Several excellent primary standards are available for the standardization of thiosulfate solutions. In general, these are oxidizing agents that

---

[16] M. Kilpatrick, Jr., and M. L. Kilpatrick, *J. Am. Chem. Soc.*, **45**, 2132 (1923); F. O. Rice, M. Kilpatrick, Jr., and W. Lemkin, *ibid.*, 1361 (1923).

liberate an equivalent amount of iodine when treated with an excess of iodide ion; this can then be titrated with the solution to be standardized.

Potassium Iodate. Iodate ion reacts rapidly with iodide in slightly acid solution to give iodine.

$$IO_3^- + 5I^- + 6H^+ \rightleftharpoons 3I_2 + 3H_2O$$

Each formula weight of potassium iodate furnishes 3 mols of iodine for the standardization process; thus its equivalent weight is one sixth its formula weight since a six-electron change is associated with the reduction of the three iodine molecules, the species actually titrated.

The sole disadvantage of potassium iodate as a primary standard arises from its low equivalent weight (35.67). Only slightly more than 0.1 gram can be taken for standardization of a 0.1 N thiosulfate solution, and the relative error normally incurred in weighing this quantity is somewhat greater than desirable for a standardization. This problem often is circumvented by dissolving a larger quantity of the solid in a known volume and taking aliquots of this solution.

> ★PROCEDURE. Weigh (to the nearest 0.1 mg) about 0.12 gram of pure dry KIO_3 into a 250-ml Erlenmeyer flask. Dissolve in 25 ml of water, and add about 2 grams of iodate-free KI. After solution is complete, add 10 ml of 1.0 N HCl and titrate immediately with the thiosulfate solution until the color of the solution becomes pale yellow. Add 5 ml of starch (page 394) and titrate to the disappearance of the blue color.
>
> In order to minimize the weighing error, the foregoing can be modified by taking a 0.6-gram sample, dissolving in water, and diluting to exactly 250 ml in a volumetric flask. A 50-ml aliquot of this solution can then be used for each standardization.

Potassium Dichromate. Highly pure potassium dichromate is available from commercial sources. Because of its ready availability in such pure form, the stability of its solutions, and its reasonably high equivalent weight, it is an ideal primary standard.

In acidic solutions, dichromate oxidizes iodide ion slowly to iodine according to the equation

$$Cr_2O_7^{2-} + 6I^- + 14H^+ \rightleftharpoons 2Cr^{3+} + 3I_2 + 7H_2O$$

For this reaction to be quantitative, control must be maintained over the hydrogen ion concentration, the iodide concentration, and the time of reaction. At the maximum pH for complete oxidation (about 5), the reaction is prohibitively slow; fortunately the rate increases with hydrogen ion content. There is, however, a lower limit to the pH of the solution because the rate at which iodide ion is oxidized by atmospheric oxygen also increases rapidly with increases in hydrogen ion concentration. Experiments indicate that a quantitative oxidation requires 5 minutes when the hydrogen ion concentration is 0.2 molar and the initial iodide concentration is 0.1 molar. Further, for periods of 10 minutes or less, the air oxidation of iodide ion is not appreciable in solutions as acidic as 0.4 molar. Success of the titration, therefore, hinges upon control of the hydrogen ion concentration between these moderately broad limits.

> ★PROCEDURE. Dry the $K_2Cr_2O_7$ for 1 to 2 hours at 100° to 200° C and weigh (to the nearest 0.1 mg) 0.20 to 0.23-gram portions into 500-ml flasks. Dissolve in 50 ml of water. Then add a freshly prepared solution consisting of 3 grams of KI, 5 ml of 6 N HCl, and 50 ml of water. Swirl gently, cover with a watch glass, and let stand in a dark place for 5 minutes. Wash down the sides of the flask, add 200 ml of water, and titrate with the thiosulfate solution. When the yellow color of the iodine can no longer be seen, add 5 ml of starch (page 394). Continue the titration until a color change from the blue starch-iodine complex to the green color of the Cr (III) ion is observed.

Other primary standards for sodium thiosulfate include potassium bromate, potassium hydrogen iodate, [$KH(IO_3)_2$], potassium ferricyanide, and metallic copper. Details for the use of these may be found in various reference works.[17]

SUMMARY OF SOURCES OF ERRORS IN IODOMETRIC METHODS

1. Air Oxidation of Iodide Ion. Considered solely from the standpoint of equilibrium, the reaction

$$4I^- + O_2 + 4H^+ \rightleftharpoons 2I_2 + 2H_2O$$

should make necessary the exclusion of atmospheric oxygen from all iodometric titration mixtures. Fortunately, however, the rate at which this oxidation occurs is so slow that such a precaution is quite unnecessary in most instances.

Kinetic studies of the reaction have shown that the velocity of this reaction increases greatly with the hydrogen ion concentration and becomes of real concern in media greater than 0.4 to 0.5 N in acid. Light also catalyzes the process; thus, storage in a dark place is recommended if time is required for completion of the reaction between iodide ion and an oxidizing agent.

Traces of copper (II) ion and nitrogen oxides are known to catalyze the oxidation of iodide by air. These latter are potential sources of inter-

---

[17] For example, see I. M. Kolthoff and R. Belcher, *Volumetric Analysis*, **3**, 234–243. New York: Interscience Publishers, Inc., 1957.

TABLE 18-7

Some Applications of the Indirect Iodometric Method
$$2I^- \rightleftharpoons I_2 + 2e$$

Substance	Half Reaction	Special Conditions
IO_4^-	$IO_4^- + 8H^+ + 7e \rightleftharpoons \frac{1}{2}I_2 + 4H_2O$	acidic solution
	$IO_4^- + 2H^+ + 2e \rightleftharpoons IO_3^- + H_2O$	neutral solution; titration with arsenic (III)
IO_3^-	$IO_3^- + 6H^+ + 5e \rightleftharpoons \frac{1}{2}I_2 + 3H_2O$	
BrO_3^-	$BrO_3^- + 6H^+ + 6e \rightleftharpoons Br^- + 3H_2O$	
ClO_3^-	$ClO_3^- + 6H^+ + 6e \rightleftharpoons Cl^- + 3H_2O$	strong acid; slow reaction
$HClO$	$HClO + H^+ + 2e \rightleftharpoons Cl^- + H_2O$	
Cl_2	$Cl_2 + 2e \rightleftharpoons 2Cl^-$	
Br_2	$Br_2 + 2e \rightleftharpoons 2Br^-$	
I^-	$I^- + 3Cl_2 + 3H_2O \rightleftharpoons IO_3^- + 6Cl^- + 6H^+$	excess Cl_2 removed by boiling
	$IO_3^- + 6H^+ + 5e \rightleftharpoons \frac{1}{2}I_2 + 3H_2O$	
NO_2^-	$HNO_2 + H^+ + e \rightleftharpoons NO + H_2O$	
H_3AsO_4	$H_3AsO_4 + 2H^+ + 2e \rightleftharpoons H_3AsO_3 + H_2O$	strong HCl
H_3SbO_4	$H_3SbO_4 + 2H^+ + 2e \rightleftharpoons H_3SbO_3 + H_2O$	strong HCl
$Fe(CN)_6^{3-}$	$Fe(CN)_6^{3-} + e \rightleftharpoons Fe(CN)_6^{4-}$	
MnO_4^-	$MnO_4^- + 8H^+ + 5e \rightleftharpoons Mn^{2+} + 4H_2O$	
Ce^{4+}	$Ce^{4+} + e \rightleftharpoons Ce^{3+}$	
$Cr_2O_7^{2-}$	$Cr_2O_7^{2-} + 14H^+ + 6e \rightleftharpoons 2Cr^{3+} + 7H_2O$	
Pb^{2+}, Ba^{2+}, Sr^{2+}	$Pb^{2+} + CrO_4^{2-} \rightleftharpoons PbCrO_4$	filter and wash; dissolve in $HClO_4$
	$2PbCrO_4 + 2H^+ \rightleftharpoons 2Pb^{2+} + Cr_2O_7^{2-} + H_2O$	
	$Cr_2O_7^{2-} + 14H^+ + 6e \rightleftharpoons 2Cr^{3+} + 7H_2O$	
Fe^{3+}	$Fe^{3+} + e \rightleftharpoons Fe^{2+}$	strong HCl solution; slow reaction
Cu^{2+}	$Cu^{2+} + e \rightleftharpoons Cu^+$	Cu^+ precipitates as CuI
O_2	$O_2 + 4Mn(OH)_2 + 2H_2O \rightleftharpoons 4Mn(OH)_3$	basic solution + iodide; solution finally acidified
	$Mn(OH)_3 + 3H^+ + e \rightleftharpoons Mn^{2+} + 3H_2O$	
O_3	$O_3 + 2H^+ + 2e \rightleftharpoons O_2 + H_2O$	neutral solution
H_2O_2	$H_2O_2 + 2H^+ + 2e \rightleftharpoons 2H_2O$	molybdate catalyst
organic peroxides	$ROOH + 2H^+ + 2e \rightleftharpoons ROH + H_2O$	
MnO_2	$MnO_2 + 4H^+ + 2e \rightleftharpoons Mn^{2+} + 2H_2O$	

ference to any iodometric analysis that makes use of nitric acid in the preliminary steps.

Where air oxidation is believed to be a problem, recourse must be made to an inert atmosphere over the titration mixture. This is conveniently accomplished by periodically adding small portions (300 mg) of sodium bicarbonate to the acid solution as the titration progresses; alternatively, carbon dioxide can be introduced from a tank or in the form of small pieces of dry ice.

2. Volatilization of Liberated Iodine. Errors due to the volatilization of liberated iodine are avoided by using stoppered containers when solutions must stand, by maintaining a goodly excess of iodide ion, and by avoiding elevated temperatures.

3. Decomposition of Thiosulfate Solutions. The decomposition of thiosulfate solutions has been discussed in a preceding section.

4. Alteration in Stoichiometry of the Iodine-thiosulfate Reaction. As mentioned earlier, alteration in stoichiometry is encountered when basic solutions are titrated.

5. Premature Addition of Starch Indicator. See page 394 for control of the addition of starch indicator.

APPLICATIONS OF THE INDIRECT IODOMETRIC METHOD

The number of substances that can be determined by iodometry is large and varied. Some of the more common applications are found in Table 18-7. Detailed instructions follow for the iodometric determination of copper, a typical example of the indirect procedure.

Determination of Copper. A cursory examination of electrode potentials suggests that an analysis based upon reduction of copper (II) ion by iodide would not be feasible; that is,

$$Cu^{2+} + e \rightleftharpoons Cu^+ \qquad E° = 0.15 \text{ volt}$$

$$I_2 + 2e \rightleftharpoons 2I^- \qquad E° = 0.54 \text{ volt}$$

In fact, however, the reduction is quantitative in the presence of a reasonable excess of iodide by virtue of the low solubility of copper (I) iodide. Thus, when the more appropriate half reaction

$$Cu^{2+} + I^- + e \rightleftharpoons CuI \qquad E° = 0.86 \text{ volt}$$

is employed, it becomes apparent that the equilibrium

$$2Cu^{2+} + 4I^- \rightleftharpoons 2CuI + I_2$$

lies reasonably far to the right. Here, the iodide ion serves not only as a reducing agent for copper (II) ion but also as a precipitant for copper (I).

Much systematic experimentation has been devoted to establishing ideal conditions for this analysis.[18] These studies have established that sufficient potassium iodide should be added to give a solution that will be 4 percent or greater with respect to this reagent. Further, a pH less than 4 is expedient; in less acidic solutions, hydrolysis of the copper (II) ion causes a slower and less complete oxidation of iodide ion. In the presence of copper (II) ion, hydrogen ion concentrations greater than about 0.3 molar must be avoided to prevent air oxidation of iodide ion.

It has been found experimentally that the titration of iodine by thiosulfate in the presence of copper (I) iodide tends to yield slightly low results as a consequence of the physical adsorption of small but appreciable quantities of the element on the solid. The adsorbed iodine is released only slowly, even in the presence of thiosulfate ion; transient and premature end points result. This difficulty is largely overcome by the addition of thiocyanate ion, which also forms an insoluble precipitate with copper (I) ion. Conversion of a part of the copper (I) thiocyanate occurs at the surface of the solid

$$CuI + SCN^- \rightleftharpoons CuSCN + I^-$$

As a consequence of this reaction, the adsorbed iodine is released to the solution and becomes available for titration. Early addition of thiocyanate must be avoided, however, because there is a tendency for that ion to reduce iodine slowly.

Analysis of Copper in an Ore. The iodometric method is convenient for the assessment of the copper content of an ore. Ordinarily, the samples dissolve readily in hot, concentrated nitric acid. Care must be taken to volatilize any nitrogen oxides formed in the process since these catalyze the air oxidation of iodide. Some samples require the addition of hydrochloric acid during the solution step. If this becomes necessary, the chloride ion must later be removed by evaporation with sulfuric acid because iodide ion will not quantitatively reduce copper (II) from its chloride complexes.

Of the elements ordinarily associated with copper in nature, only iron, arsenic, and antimony interfere with the iodometric procedure. Fortunately, the difficulties caused by the presence of these elements are readily eliminated. Iron is rendered nonreactive by the addition of such complexing agents as fluoride or pyrophosphate; because these form more stable complexes with iron (III) than with iron (II), the potential of this system is altered to the point where oxidation of iodide cannot occur.

We have seen that the arsenite-arsenate couple behaves reversibly with

---

[18] See E. W. Hammock and E. H. Swift, *Anal. Chem.*, **21**, 975 (1949).

respect to the iodine-iodide system, the position of equilibrium being determined by the pH of the solution. Antimony is similar in deportment. By proper pH control, the two elements are converted to the $+5$ state during solution of the sample and no longer constitute a source of interference. Ordinarily the hot nitric acid will assure this although a small amount of bromine water can be added in case of doubt; any excess bromine is then expelled by boiling. The $+5$ arsenic and antimony will not interfere provided the pH of the solution is kept above 3. As was mentioned earlier, however, incomplete oxidation of iodide by copper (II) is encountered at pH values greater than 4; thus in the presence of arsenic or antimony control of the pH between 3 and 4 is essential. A convenient buffer system for this is obtained by the addition of ammonium hydrogen fluoride, NH_4HF_2, to the solution. This salt dissociates as follows:

$$HF_2^- \rightleftharpoons HF + F^- \qquad K = 0.26$$

$$HF \rightleftharpoons H^+ + F^- \qquad K = 6.7 \times 10^{-4}$$

The first reaction gives equal quantities of hydrogen fluoride and fluoride ion which then buffer the solution to a pH somewhat greater than 3. In addition to acting as a buffer, the salt also serves as a source of fluoride ions to complex any iron (III) that may be present.

The method that follows is essentially that of Park,[19] and incorporates the details discussed in the preceding paragraphs.

★PROCEDURE. Weigh appropriate-sized samples of the finely ground and dried ore (about 1 gram for a sample containing 10- to 30-percent Cu) into 150-ml beakers and add 20 ml of concentrated HNO_3. Heat until all of the Cu is in solution. If the volume becomes less than 5 ml, add more HNO_3. Continue the heating until only a white or slightly gray siliceous residue remains (Note 1). Evaporate to about 5 ml.

Add 25 ml of water and boil to bring all soluble salts into solution. Filter the solution through a small paper, collecting the filtrate in a 250-ml flask. Wash the paper with several small portions of hot 1:100 HNO_3. (If the residue is small and light in color no filtration is necessary.) Evaporate the solution to about 25 ml, cool, and slowly add 1:1 NH_3 to the first appearance of the deep blue-ammonia complex. A faint odor of NH_3 should be detectable over the solution. If it is not, add another drop of NH_3 and repeat the test. Avoid an excess (Note 2).

From this point on, treat the samples individually. Add 2.0 ± 0.1 grams NH_4HF_2 and swirl until completely dissolved. Then add 3 grams of KI and titrate immediately with 0.1 N $Na_2S_2O_3$. When the color of the iodine is nearly discharged, add 2 grams of KSCN and 3 ml of starch (page 394). Continue the titration until the blue

[19] B. Park, *Ind. Eng. Chem., Anal. Ed.*, **3**, 77 (1931).

starch-iodine color is decolorized and does not return for several minutes.

NOTES:

1. If the ore is not readily decomposed by the HNO_3, add 5 ml of concentrated HCl and heat until only a small white or grey residue remains. Do not evaporate to dryness. Cool, add 10 ml of concentrated H_2SO_4, and evaporate until copious white fumes of SO_3 are observed (hood). Cool, carefully add 15 ml of water and 10 ml of saturated bromine water. Boil the solution vigorously in a hood until all of the bromine has been removed. Cool and proceed as above, beginning with the filtration step.

2. If too much NH_3 is added, remove the excess by boiling.

Determination of Copper in a Brass. A brass is an alloy consisting principally of copper, zinc, lead, and tin. In addition, several other elements may be present in minor amounts, including iron and nickel. The iodometric method is convenient for estimating the copper content of such materials.

The method that follows is relatively simple and is applicable to the analysis of brasses containing less than 1 to 2 percent of iron. It involves solution in nitric acid, removal of nitrate by fuming with sulfuric acid, adjustment of the pH by neutralization with ammonia, acidification with a measured quantity of phosphoric acid, and finally the iodometric determination of the copper.

It is instructive to consider the fate of each of the major constituents during the course of this treatment. Tin is oxidized to the $+4$ state by the nitric acid solvent and precipitates slowly as the insoluble hydrous tin (IV) oxide, $SnO_2 \cdot 4H_2O$. This precipitate, which tends to be colloidal in nature, is sometimes called *metastannic acid.* It has a tendency to adsorb copper (II) and other cations from the solution. Lead, zinc, and copper are oxidized to soluble divalent salts by the nitric acid, and iron is converted to the trivalent state. Evaporation and fuming with sulfuric acid redissolves the metastannic acid but may cause precipitation of part of the lead as the sulfate. The copper, zinc, and iron are unaffected. Upon dilution with water, lead is nearly completely precipitated as lead sulfate while the remaining elements are left in solution. None, except copper and iron, is reduced by iodide; interference from the iron is eliminated by complexing with phosphate ion.

★PROCEDURE. Weigh (to the nearest 0.1 mg) about 0.3-gram samples of the clean, dry metal into 250-ml flasks and add 5 ml of 6 N HNO_3. Warm the solution in a hood until decomposition is complete. Then add 10 ml of H_2SO_4 and evaporate to copious white fumes of SO_3. Allow the mixture to cool; then carefully add 20 ml of H_2O. Boil for 1 to 2 minutes and cool.

With good mixing, add concentrated NH_3 dropwise until the first dark-blue color of the copper (II) ammonia complex appears. The solution should smell faintly of NH_3. Add 6 N H_2SO_4 dropwise until the dark-blue color just disappears. Then add 2.0 ml of syrupy phosphoric acid. Cool to room temperature.

From this point on treat samples individually. Dissolve 4.0 grams of KI in 10 ml of H_2O and add this to the sample. Titrate immediately with $Na_2S_2O_3$ until the iodine color is no longer distinct. Add 3 ml of starch solution (page 394) and titrate until the blue begins to fade. Add 2 grams of KSCN and complete the titration.

Problems

1. A solution of permanganate was standardized against pure As_2O_3. Exactly 0.200 gram of the standard required 38.1 ml of $KMnO_4$. What was the normality of the solution? The formality?   ans. 0.106 N; 0.0212 F

2. What is the normality of a cerium (IV) sulfate solution having a titer of 26.0 mg of Mohr's salt [$FeSO_4 \cdot (NH_4)_2SO_4 \cdot 6H_2O$] per ml?

3. A solution of $KMnO_4$ was standardized against 0.179 gram of pure KI. The titration was carried out in the presence of HCN; the reaction was

$$2MnO_4^- + 5I^- + 5HCN + 11H^+ \rightleftharpoons 2Mn^{2+} + 5ICN + 8H_2O.$$

Exactly 37.9 ml of reagent was used. What was the normality?

4. A 1.27-gram sample containing Fe_3O_4 was dissolved, the iron reduced in a Jones reductor and then titrated with 26.6 ml of 0.0584 N Ce^{4+}. Calculate the percent Fe and the percent Fe_3O_4 in the sample.

5. A 0.814-gram sample of a stibnite ore was decomposed in acid and the +3 Sb oxidized to the +5 state with 40.0 ml of 0.119 N $KMnO_4$. The excess $KMnO_4$ was back titrated with 3.82 ml of 0.0961 N Fe^{2+}. Calculate the percent Sb_2S_3 in the sample.   ans. 45.8 percent

6. A solution of KNO_2 was analyzed by treating exactly 25.0 ml with 50.0 ml of 0.0880 N $KMnO_4$. After reaction was complete the solution was heated and the excess $KMnO_4$ back titrated with 1.20 ml of 0.100 N Fe^{2+}. Calculate the formality of the KNO_2 solution. How many grams KNO_2 are in 1 liter of the solution?

7. A 2.02-gram sample of La_2O_3 (gfw = 325.8) was brought into solution and the La precipitated as $La_2(C_2O_4)_3$. The precipitate was filtered, washed, dissolved in acid, and the oxalic acid titrated with 43.2 ml of 0.120 N cerium (IV) sulfate. Calculate the percent La_2O_3 present.

8. A sample containing both iron and titanium was analyzed by solution of a 3.00-gram sample and dilution to exactly 500 ml in a volumetric flask. A 50-ml aliquot of the solution was passed through a silver reductor that reduced the iron to the divalent state but left the titanium in the plus four state;

titration with 0.0750 N Ce^{4+} required 18.2 ml. A 100-ml aliquot was passed through a Jones reductor that reduced both Fe and Ti ($Ti^{4+} \rightarrow Ti^{3+}$). The reduced solution consumed 46.3 ml of the Ce^{4+} solution. Calculate the percent Fe_2O_3 and the percent TiO_2 in the sample.

9. How would you prepare 500 ml of exactly 0.200 N Ce^{4+} in 1 F H_2SO_4 from primary-standard grade $(NH_4)_2Ce(NO_3)_6$ (gfw = 548.3)?

10. A 0.412-gram sample containing potassium azide (KN_3) was treated with 50.0 ml of 0.100 N C^{4+}. This resulted in oxidation of the azide to N_2

$$2N_3^- \rightarrow 3N_2 + 2e$$

The excess Ce^{4+} consumed 8.11 ml of 0.150 N Fe^{2+}. Calculate the percent KN_3 in the sample.

11. Exactly 5.00 ml of a hydrogen peroxide solution consumed 39.6 ml of 0.250 N Ce^{4+}. What was the weight percent H_2O_2 in the sample? Assume a density of 1.00 gram/ml for the solution.

12. The potassium in a 0.314-gram sample was precipitated as

$$K_2NaCo(NO_2)_6 \cdot H_2O$$

The precipitate was washed and dissolved in 50 ml of 0.100 N $KMnO_4$ which resulted in oxidation of the NO_2^- to NO_3^- and reduction of the Co^{3+} to Co^{2+} (see Table 18-5 for the half reaction). The excess $KMnO_4$ was titrated with 22.1 ml of 0.114 N Fe^{2+}.
(a) Write a balanced equation for the reaction between MnO_4^- and $Co(NO_2)_6^{3-}$.
(b) Calculate the percent K_2SO_4 present in the sample.

13. Describe a method for preparation of 2 liters of 0.333 N $K_2Cr_2O_7$.

14. A sample of alkali metal chlorides was analyzed for sodium by dissolving a 0.800-gram sample in water and diluting to exactly 500 ml. A 25.0-ml aliquot of this was treated in such a way as to precipitate the sodium as

$$NaZn(UO_2)_3(OAc)_9 \cdot 6H_2O$$

The precipitate was filtered, dissolved in acid and passed through a lead reductor which converted the uranium to U^{4+}. Oxidation of this to UO_2^{2+} required 19.9 ml of 0.100 N $K_2Cr_2O_7$. Calculate the percent NaCl in the sample.

15. A 0.320-gram sample was analyzed for Cr by solution and oxidation of the Cr^{3+} to $Cr_2O_7^{2-}$ with an excess of ammonium persulfate. After the excess oxidant was destroyed by boiling, exactly 1.00 gram of Mohr's salt (gfw = 392.2) was added and the excess Fe^{2+} titrated with 8.77 ml of 0.0500 N $K_2Cr_2O_7$. Calculate the percent Cr_2O_3 in the sample.

16. A 25.0-ml sample containing ClO_3^- was made strongly acid and the ClO_3^- reduced to Cl^- by the addition of 10.0 ml of 0.250 N iron (II) ammonium sulfate. After reaction was complete, the excess Fe^{2+} was titrated with 9.12 ml

of 0.100 N $K_2Cr_2O_7$. Calculate the number of milligrams of $NaClO_3$ in the solution.

17. A solution of iodine was standardized against 0.186 gram of pure As_2O_3. The volume of reagent required was 27.7 ml. What was the normality?

18. A 0.402-gram sample of cadmium containing alloy was dissolved and the cadmium precipitated as CdS. After filtration and washing, the precipitate was dissolved in an acidified solution containing 40.0 ml of 0.128 N I_2. The excess iodine remaining after oxidation of the sulfide to sulfur was titrated with 11.6 ml of 0.108 N thiosulfate. What was the percent Cd in the sample?

19. The H_2S concentration of a sample of air was obtained by bubbling 10 liters of the air through an absorption tower containing a solution of Cd^{2+}. The solution was treated with 20.0 ml of 0.0107 N I_2 and acidified, which resulted in the sulfide being oxidized to elemental sulfur. The excess iodine consumed 10.1 ml of 0.0120 N thiosulfate. Calculate the parts per million H_2S present in the air assuming a gas density of 12×10^{-4} gram/ml.

20. What is the titer of a 0.200 N I_2 solution in terms of milligrams of As_2O_3, Sb, SO_2, H_2S, As?

21. Write balanced equations for the $KMnO_4$ oxidation of the following substances; assume solutions are strongly acidic (see Table 18-5 for products).
    (a) Br^- (hot H_2SO_4 solution)
    (b) VO^{2+}
    (c) Mo^{3+}
    (d) H_2O_2
    (e) I^- (in HCN solution)
    (f) $Co(NO_2)_6^{3-}$

22. Calculate the numerical value of the equilibrium constant for the reaction

$$2MnO_4^- + 3Mn^{2+} + 2H_2O \rightleftharpoons 5MnO_2 + 4H^+$$

ans. $K = 2 \times 10^{47}$

23. Assume that the acid concentration at the end point in a $KMnO_4$ titration is 1.0 F and the Mn^{2+} concentration is about 0.010. From the value of K in Problem 22 calculate the MnO_4^- concentration in equilibrium with these species.

24. Calculate the equilibrium constant for the chemical reaction involving the decomposition of H_2O by MnO_4^- (page 372).

25. Calculate the equilibrium constant for the oxidation of Cl^- to Cl_2 by $KMnO_4$. On the basis of equilibrium considerations alone should it be possible to use $KMnO_4$ for the titration of reducing agents dissolved in HCl?

26. Calculate the equivalence-point potential for the titration of 50.0 ml of 0.1 N Sn^{2+} with (a) 0.1 N $KMnO_4$, (b) 0.1 N $K_2Cr_2O_7$. Assume $[H^+] = 1.0$ M where necessary.

27. What is the equilibrium concentration of Fe^{3+} remaining in a solution prepared by passage of a 0.010 F solution of Fe^{3+} in 0.10 F HCl through a silver reductor?

28. What is the equilibrium concentration of Fe^{3+} remaining in a solution prepared by passage of a 0.01 F solution of Fe^{3+} through a silver reductor in the absence of chloride ion?

29. Calculate the equilibrium constant for the reaction

$$BrO_3^- + 5Br^- + 6H^+ \rightleftharpoons 3Br_2 + 3H_2O$$

ans. $K = 4 \times 10^{38}$

30. What weights of the following compounds, when treated with an excess of KI, are equivalent to 10.0 ml of 0.1 N $Na_2S_2O_3$: (a) $KBrO_3$, (b) $K_2Cr_2O_7$, (c) $CuSO_4$, (d) KIO_3, (e) $(NH_4)_2Ce(NO_3)_6$?

ans. (a) 0.0278 gram; (b) 0.049 gram

31. A solution of $Na_2S_2O_3$ was standardized by treatment of 0.0600 gram of pure KIO_3 with an excess of KI. After acidification, 32.1 ml of the reagent were required to reach a starch end point. Calculate the normality.   ans. 0.0524 N

32. How many grams of $Na_2S_2O_3 \cdot 5H_2O$ are contained in 763 ml of a 0.0500 N solution of that reagent?

33. A 0.418-gram sample containing $Ba(ClO_3)_2$ was dissolved in 2 N HCl and treated with an excess of KI. After 5 minutes the liberated iodine was titrated with a 0.0810 N $Na_2S_2O_3$ solution, 19.2 ml being required. What was the percent $Ba(ClO_3)_2$ present?   ans. 9.45 percent

34. An excess of KI is added to 50.0 ml of bromine water. The liberated iodine requires 28.6 ml of a 0.0516 N $Na_2S_2O_3$ solution for titration. How many milligrams of Br_2 are contained per milliliter of solution?

35. A 0.661-gram sample containing $BaCl_2 \cdot 2H_2O$ was dissolved and the barium precipitated as $BaCrO_4$. After filtration and washing the precipitate was dissolved in acid and the $Cr_2O_7^{2-}$ formed in this process reduced by the addition of an excess of KI. The iodine liberated required 37.5 ml of 0.121 N $Na_2S_2O_3$. What was the percent $BaCl_2 \cdot 2H_2O$ in the sample?

ans. 55.9 percent

36. The lead in a 0.477-gram sample of Pb_3O_4 was precipitated as $PbCrO_4$. After filtration and washing the solid was dissolved in acid and treated with an excess of KI. The liberated iodine consumed 22.2 ml of 0.0916 N $Na_2S_2O_3$. What was the percent Pb_3O_4 in the sample?

37. A solution containing IO_3^- and IO_4^- was analyzed as follows: A 50.0-ml aliquot was buffered with a borax buffer and treated with an excess of KI; this resulted in reduction of the IO_4^- to IO_3^-. The liberated iodine consumed 18.4 ml of 0.100 N $Na_2S_2O_3$. A 10.0-ml aliquot was then acidified strongly and an excess of KI added. This required 48.7 ml of the thiosulfate. Calculate the formal concentration of IO_3^- and IO_4^- in the solution.

38. Chlorine water was added to the solution of a 1.05-gram sample containing a small amount of KI; this converted the I^- to IO_3^-. After removal of the excess Cl_2 by boiling, KI was added and the liberated iodine titrated with 11.7 ml of 0.0412 N $Na_2S_2O_3$. What was the percent KI in the sample?

39. A fresh solution of $Na_2S_2O_3$ was found to be 0.100 N against iodine. After standing for some time its normality had increased to 0.112. Assuming the only change in the solution was due to the reaction $S_2O_3^{2-} \rightleftharpoons SO_3^{2-} + S$ and that the SO_3^{2-} was oxidized to SO_4^{2-} in the second standardization, calculate the formal concentration of $Na_2S_2O_3$ and Na_2SO_3 in the 0.112 N solution.

40. A 0.284-gram sample of sodium peroxide was dissolved in an excess of KI. The liberated iodine consumed 35.4 ml of 0.0896 N thiosulfate. What percent Na_2O_2 was present?

41. A sample containing KI, KBr, and other inert substances was analyzed as follows: A 1.00-gram sample was dissolved in water and diluted to exactly 200 ml. A 25.0-ml aliquot was treated with Br_2 in neutral solution which converted the I^- to IO_3^-. The excess Br_2 was removed by boiling and KI added. After acidification, the liberated iodine was titrated with 40.8 ml of 0.0500 N thiosulfate.

A 50.0-ml aliquot was oxidized with strongly acidic $K_2Cr_2O_7$; the liberated I_2 and Br_2 were distilled and collected in a strong KI solution. The iodine present after reaction was complete required 29.8 ml of the thiosulfate. Calculate the percent KI and KBr in the sample.

42. A 0.941-gram sample containing $Ca_3(AsO_4)_2$ was dissolved in strong HCl. Excess KI was added and the liberated iodine required 27.7 ml of a $Na_2S_2O_3$ solution which had a titer of 2.47 mg of Cu. Calculate the percent $Ca_3(AsO_4)_2$.

43. The equilibrium constant for the reaction $I_3^- + H_2O \rightleftharpoons HOI + 2I^- + H^+$ is about 4×10^{-16}. What percent of the I_3^- is converted to HOI in a solution that is 0.01 F in I_3^- and 0.02 F in KI and buffered to (a) pH 8.0, (b) pH 9.0, (c) pH 10.0?

44. Calculate the solubility-product constant for CuI from the following data:

$$Cu^{2+} + e \rightleftharpoons Cu^+ \qquad E^\circ = 0.153 \text{ volt}$$

$$Cu^{2+} + I^- + e \rightleftharpoons CuI \qquad E^\circ = 0.86 \text{ volt}$$

45. Calculate the equilibrium constant for the reaction

$$O_2 + 6I^- + 4H^+ \rightleftharpoons 2H_2O + 2I_3^-$$

(19)

Potentiometric Methods

It has been shown in Chapter 16 that the potential of a metallic conductor is often sensitive to the concentration of one or more of the components of the solution in which it is immersed. Thus it is possible to employ potential measurements for the analysis of these components.

Analytical methods based on the measurement of potential are performed in either of two ways. The first involves comparing the potential of an indicator electrode in contact with the sample with the potential of the same electrode when immersed in a series of standard solutions of the component being determined. Such a procedure is termed a *direct potentiometric method*. In a second category, the progress of a titration is followed by measurement of the potential of an electrode immersed in the solution being titrated. Clearly, this electrode must be sensitive to one or more of the participants of the analytical reaction. The equivalence point can then be located by observation of the potential changes. Such a procedure is termed a *potentiometric titration*.

With one important exception, direct potentiometry is not widely employed in quantitative analysis because the technique requires highly precise potential measurements and careful control of variables. In addition, such procedures frequently lack selectivity. Potentiometric titrations, on the other hand, are less demanding insofar as control of experimental conditions and accuracy of potential measurements are concerned; they also tend to be less subject to interference by other components in the solution being analyzed.

The potentiometric end point has been applied to all types of chemical reactions. It can be used with colored or opaque solutions that mask ordinary indicator changes. It is less subjective than indicator methods and inherently more accurate. Finally, the data from a potentiometric titration may reveal the presence of hitherto unsuspected species in the solution that are competing with the unknown for the volumetric reagent. At the same time, however, a potentiometric titration is likely to be more time consuming than the typical volumetric procedure; the necessity for special equipment is another disadvantage.

In this chapter we shall be concerned primarily with potentiometric titrations. However, we must discuss in detail the determination of *p*H, which represents the one important application of direct potentiometry.

19.1 Methodology

In a potentiometric titration a galvanic cell is formed by immersion of a pair of suitable electrodes in the solution to be analyzed. The emf of this cell is then followed as a function of the volume of reagent added; rapid changes in potential occurring in the region of the equivalence point serve to indicate completion of the titration. In addition to the usual equipment needed for a volumetric analysis, a potentiometric titration requires a device for measuring potential, a reference electrode, and an indicator electrode.

19.2 Potential Measurements

For a potentiometric titration an instrument is needed that will measure potentials in the range of 0 to 1.5 volts with an accuracy of at least 0.01 volt and preferably 0.001 to 0.002 volt. An ordinary direct-current voltmeter is not satisfactory because an appreciable current is required to operate such a device. When current is drawn from the cell whose potential is being measured, a diminution in voltage occurs. This is due, in part, to changes in the concentrations of the reacting species as the cell starts to discharge. In addition, the cell has an internal resistance of its own; when current is passed, an ohmic potential drop (equal to the current times the resistance) develops; this opposes the galvanic potential between the two electrodes. A truly significant value for the output of a cell can thus be attained only if the measurement is made with a negligible passage of current. The most satisfactory method of accomplishing this is with a *potentiometer*. Of the several varieties and modifications of this device, two warrant discussion.

Principles of the Potentiometer. In Figure 19.1 is shown a simple *voltage divider*, a device consisting of a resistance AB along which a sliding contact C can be moved. If a battery is placed across this resistance, a current I will flow; from Ohm's law we may write $E_{AB} = IR_{AB}$ where R_{AB} is the ohmic resistance of the resistor. Of specific interest here is the potential drop between the contact C and one end of the resistor A—that is, E_{AC}. The current passing through the portion of the resistor AC is identical to that through the entire resistor; it follows, then, that $E_{AC} = IR_{AC}$. Dividing this by the foregoing relationship, we get

$$E_{AC} = E_{AB} \frac{R_{AC}}{R_{AB}} \qquad (19\text{-}1)$$

Thus, we have a device that will supply a continuously variable voltage from zero (when contact C is at A) to the total output E_{AB} of the power

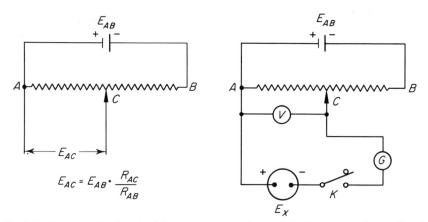

Fig. 19.1 Diagram of a Simple Voltage Divider.

Fig. 19.2 Diagram of a Simple Potentiometer.

supply (when the contact C has been moved to B). This very simple and useful contrivance is employed in a wide variety of electroanalytical instruments.

A Simple Potentiometer. A relatively simple instrument that permits the measurement of the emf of galvanic cells with passage of but negligible current is illustrated in Figure 19.2. This consists of a voltage divider powered by a battery whose emf is equal to, or greater than, the emf to be measured, E_x. The galvanic cell is placed across AC in such a way that its output *opposes* that of the working battery. In parallel with the galvanic cell is a tapping key K, which permits momentary closing of the circuit, and a galvanometer G, which serves as a current detector. The direct-current voltmeter V measures the potential drop across AC.

Now, if the potential across the voltage divider E_{AC} is greater than that of the galvanic cell E_x, electrons will be forced from right to left through the latter when K is closed. On the other hand, if E_{AC} is smaller than E_x, the electron flow will occur in the opposite direction. Finally, when E_x is equal to E_{AC}, no current will flow *in the circuit containing G, K, and the galvanic cell.*

Measurement of an unknown voltage E_x with a device such as this consists of adjusting C until the galvanometer G indicates no current flow. This is done by momentarily closing K several times and making suitable adjustments of C as indicated by the galvanometer. The entire process draws only infinitesimal currents from the galvanic cell being measured. When balance is achieved, the voltage drop across AC is read on the meter V and is equal, of course, to E_x. Thus, at balance, the voltmeter is powered by the current from the working battery and not from the unknown galvanic cell.

A potentiometer such as this is limited in accuracy by the precision of the voltmeter V; typically this ranges between about 0.005 and 0.01 volt— entirely adequate for many purposes. Where greater precision is required, recourse must be made to a potentiometer with a linear voltage divider.

Potentiometer Employing a Linear Voltage Divider. To achieve the highest precision in potential measurements an instrument such as that shown in Figure 19.3 is utilized. This differs from the previous potentiometer in several important respects. For example, the voltage divider contains an additional variable resistance R to allow adjustment of the voltage across AB. In addition, the resistance AB must now be *linear* in character. Thus the resistance between one end A and any point C is directly proportional to the length AC of that portion of the resistor; then $R_{AC} = kAC$, where AC is expressed in convenient units of length and k is a proportionality constant. Similarly, $R_{AB} = kAB$. A scale, such as that shown in the illustration, can be attached to the resistor to aid in measuring these lengths. Substituting the proportionality relationships into equation (19-1), we obtain

$$E_{AC} = E_{AB} \frac{AC}{AB} \tag{19-2}$$

The instrument in Figure 19.3 also contains a cell E_s whose potential is constant and known exactly. Most commonly, a standard Weston cell is employed. The Weston cell can be represented as

$$Cd(Hg) \mid CdSO_4 \cdot 8/3 \ H_2O(\text{sat'd}), \ Hg_2SO_4(\text{sat'd}) \mid Hg$$

The half reactions for the cell are

$$Cd(Hg) \rightleftharpoons Cd^{2+} + Hg + 2e$$

$$Hg_2SO_4 + 2e \rightleftharpoons 2Hg + SO_4^{2-}$$

The potential of this cell at 25° C is 1.0186 volts. Either the Weston cell or the unknown cell E_x can be placed in the circuit by means of the switch S. As in the earlier case, E_{AC} will equal the potential of the unknown or the standard cell when no current flow is indicated; with equation (19-2) we may write, then, that

$$E_x = E_{AC_x} = E_{AB} \frac{AC_x}{AB}$$

and

$$E_s = E_{AC_s} = E_{AB} \frac{AC_s}{AB}$$

where AC_x and AC_s represent the linear distances corresponding to balance when the unknown and standard cells are in the circuit. Dividing these equations, we obtain the relationship

$$E_x = E_s \frac{AC_x}{AC_s} \tag{19-3}$$

Thus, E_x may be obtained from the known emf of the Weston cell and the two measurable quantities AC_x and AC_s.

For convenience, the scale reading of AC_x is ordinarily made to correspond directly to the potential in volts. This is accomplished by first switching the Weston cell into the circuit and positioning the contact so that AC_s corresponds numerically to the output of this standard cell (1.0186 volts). The potential across AB is then adjusted by means of R until no current is indicated by the galvanometer. With the potentiometer adjusted thus, AC_s and E_s will be numerically equal; from equation (19-3), then, AC_x and E_x will also be identical when balance is achieved with the unknown cell in the circuit.

The necessity for a working battery P may be questioned; in principle, there is nothing to prevent a direct measurement of E_x by replacing P with the standard cell E_s. It must be remembered, however, that current is being continuously drawn from P; a standard cell could not be expected to maintain a constant potential for long under such usage.

The accuracy of a voltage measurement with an instrument such as the foregoing depends upon several factors. For one thing, it is necessary to assume that the voltage of the working battery P remains constant during the period of time required to balance the instrument against the standard cell and to measure the potential of the unknown cell. Ordinarily this does not lead to appreciable error if P consists of one or two heavy duty dry cells in good condition, or a lead storage battery. The instrument should be calibrated against the standard cell before each voltage measurement to compensate for possible changes in P, however.

The linearity of the resistance AB as well as the precision with which distances along its length can be estimated also contribute to the accuracy of the potentiometer. Ordinarily, however, the ultimate precision of a good quality instrument is determined by the sensitivity of the galvanometer relative to the resistance of the circuit. Suppose, for example, that the electrical resistance of the galvanometer plus that of the unknown cell is 1000 ohms—a typical figure. Further, if we assume that the galvanometer is just capable of detecting a current of 1 microampere (10^{-6}

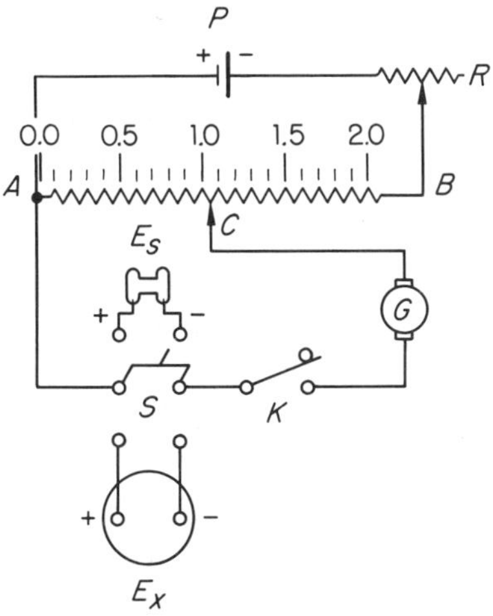

Fig. 19.3 Diagram of a Potentiometer with a Linear Voltage Divider, **AB**.

ampere), we can readily calculate from Ohm's law that the minimum distinguishable voltage difference will be $10^{-6} \times 1000 = 10^{-3}$ volt or 1 mv. By use of a galvanometer sensitive to 10^{-7} ampere, a difference of 0.1 mv will be detectable. A sensitivity of this order is found in an ordinary pointer-type galvanometer; more refined instruments with sensitivities up to 10^{-10} ampere are available.

From this discussion we see that the sensitivity of a potentiometric measurement decreases as the electrical resistance of the cell increases; as a matter of fact, potentials of cells with resistances much greater than a megohm (10^6 ohms) cannot be measured accurately with an instrument employing a galvanometer as the current-sensing device. At first glance this appears to be a very large resistance for a cell. Actually, however, one of the most important electroanalytical applications of potential measurements—that of measuring pH—requires the use of a cell with a resistance in the 1- to 100-megohm range. To detect the very small out-of-balance currents associated with such high resistances, a direct-current amplifier must be used in place of the galvanometer. This multiplies the current sufficiently to make its detection easy.

Vacuum-tube Voltmeters. Potentials of cells can be measured directly with vacuum-tube voltmeters. These instruments have a very high internal resistance; as a consequence they draw a vanishingly small current from the cell whose potential is being measured. Inherently, a vacuum-tube voltmeter is not as accurate as a good potentiometer but for many applications to potentiometric titrations, voltage measurements with this type of device are entirely satisfactory.

REFERENCE ELECTRODES

In a potentiometric titration, as with most electroanalytical methods, it is desirable to employ one electrode whose half-cell potential is constant and independent of the progress of the analysis. Such an electrode or half cell is called the *reference electrode*. With a reference electrode in the system, all changes in the cell behavior can be attributed to the other half cell or *indicator electrode*.

A good reference electrode should be easy to assemble, provide reproducible potentials, and be constant in behavior with passage of small currents. Several electrode systems meet these requirements.

Calomel Electrodes. Calomel half cells may be represented as follows:

$$\text{Hg} \mid \text{Hg}_2\text{Cl}_2(\text{sat'd}), \text{ KCl } (xF)$$

where x represents the formal concentration of potassium chloride in the solution. The electrode reaction is given by the equation

$$\text{Hg}_2\text{Cl}_2 + 2e \rightleftharpoons 2\text{Hg} + 2\text{Cl}^- \qquad E^\circ = 0.2676 \text{ volt}$$

The potential of this cell will clearly vary with the chloride concentration x, and this must be specified in describing the electrode.

The most common calomel electrode is the so-called saturated calomel electrode in which the solution is not only saturated with mercury (I) chloride but with potassium chloride as well. At room temperature, the concentration of potassium chloride in the half cell will be about 3.5 F. The potential of the saturated calomel electrode is 0.242 volt at 25° C.

Normal and decinormal calomel electrodes are also used; in these the concentration of potassium chloride is 1.0 F and 0.1 F, respectively, and the potentials are 0.280 and 0.334 volt.

A simple, easily constructed saturated calomel electrode is shown in Figure 19.4. The salt bridge is simply a tube filled with saturated potassium

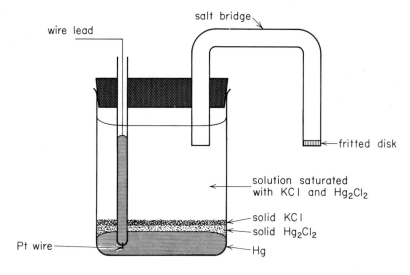

half reaction:
$$Hg_2Cl_2 + 2e \rightleftharpoons 2Hg + 2Cl^-$$

Fig. 19.4 Diagram of a Saturated Calomel Electrode.

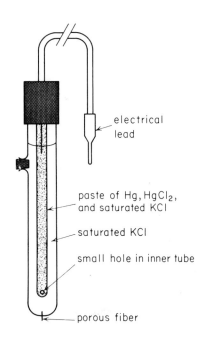

Fig. 19.5 Diagram of a Commercial Fiber-type Saturated Calomel Electrode. (By permission, Beckman Instruments, Inc., Fullerton, California.)

chloride and provides electric contact to the solution surrounding the indicator electrode. A fritted disk at one end of the salt bridge is often employed to prevent siphoning of cell liquid.

Several convenient calomel electrodes are available commercially. Typical of these is the one illustrated in Figure 19.5 which consists of a tube 5 to 15 cm in length and 0.5 to 1.0 cm in diameter. The mercury-mercury (I) chloride paste is contained in an inner tube that is connected to the saturated potassium chloride solution in the outer tube by means of a small opening. Contact with the second half cell is made by means of a porous fiber sealed in the end of the outer tubing. An electrode such as this has a relatively high resistance (2000 to 3000 ohms) and very limited current-carrying capacity.

Silver-silver Chloride Electrodes. A reference electrode system analogous to the foregoing consists of a silver electrode immersed in a solution of potassium chloride that is also saturated with silver chloride.

$$Ag \mid AgCl(sat'd), KCl \ (xF)$$

The half reaction is

$$AgCl + e \rightleftharpoons Ag + Cl^- \qquad E° = 0.222 \text{ volt}$$

Normally this electrode is prepared with a saturated potassium chloride solution, the potential at 25° C being $+0.197$ volt with respect to the standard hydrogen electrode.

INDICATOR ELECTRODES

The potential of the indicator electrode must be directly related to the concentration of one or more of the participants or products of the analytical reaction. Then, if the reference electrode output is constant, the changes in the measured emf of the galvanic cell will reflect the concentration changes taking place in the solution as the titration proceeds. Rapid response of the indicator electrode to changes in concentration is a convenience; clearly, its potential behavior should be reproducible within reasonable limits.

Many indicator electrodes are available to the chemist. Where the volumetric process involves the formation of a precipitate or a stable complex, the best electrode is often the elemental form of the cationic participant of the reaction. Thus, for example, a silver electrode can be employed in the titration of silver ion with chloride, bromide, or cyanide since its potential is sensitive to the cationic concentration. Copper, lead, cadmium, and mercury are also satisfactory indicator electrodes for their ions. Some of the harder and more brittle metals, such as iron, nickel, cobalt, tungsten, and chromium, are not; these tend to develop nonreproducible potentials that are due in part to strains or crystal deformations in their structures.

Metal electrodes can also serve as indicator electrodes for those anions that form slightly soluble precipitates with the cation of the metal. For this application it is only necessary to saturate the solution under study with the insoluble salt. For example, the potential of a silver electrode can be made to reflect the concentration of chloride ion in a solution by saturating the solution with silver chloride; under these circumstances we may describe the electrode behavior as

$$E = E°_{AgCl \to Ag+Cl^-} - 0.059 \log [Cl^-]$$

Such an electrode, then, can serve as the indicator for any volumetric reaction in which chloride ion is a participant. It is an example of an *electrode of the second order* because it measures the concentration of an ion not directly involved in the electron-transfer process. In contrast, the potential of an *electrode of the first order* is a function of the concentration of a direct participant in the electrode process.

For oxidation-reduction reactions, the indicator electrode is most commonly an inert metal such as platinum or gold. We have seen that the potential developed at such an electrode is a function of the concentration ratio between the oxidized and reduced forms of one or more of the species in the solution.

For a neutralization titration the hydrogen gas electrode may be used; other indicator electrodes for hydrogen ions are also available, and these will be discussed in detail in later sections.

Metal indicator electrodes take a variety of physical forms, often being constructed as coils of wire, as flat metal plates, or as heavy cylindrical billets. Generally, exposing a large surface area to the solution will assure rapid attainment of equilibrium. Thorough cleaning of the metal surface before use is often important; a brief dip in concentrated nitric acid followed by several rinsings with distilled water is satisfactory for many metals.

Figure 19.6 shows a typical apparatus for carrying out a potentiometric titration.

THE TITRATION

A typical potentiometric titration involves measuring and recording the cell potential after each addition of reagent. Initially the standard solution is added in large increments; as the end point is approached (as indicated by larger potential changes per addition) the increments are reduced in size. For some purposes it is convenient to make small and *equal* additions near the equivalence point. Ordinarily the titration is carried well beyond the end point.

Sufficient time must be allowed for the attainment of equilibrium after each addition of reagent; precipitation titrations may require several minutes for this, particularly in the vicinity of the equivalence point. A close approach to equilibrium is indicated when the measured potential ceases to drift by more than a few millivolts. Good stirring is frequently effective in hastening the achievement of this condition.

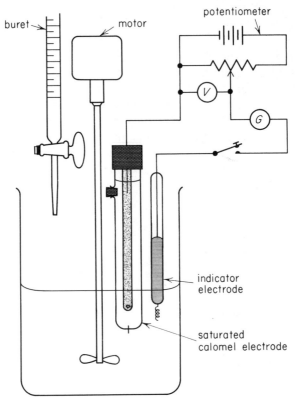

Fig. 19.6 Apparatus for a Potentiometric Titration.

The first two columns of Table 19-1 consist of a typical set of potentiometric-titration data. These have been plotted in Figure 19.7. This experimentally obtained graph closely resembles the titration curves derived from theoretical considerations. This is not surprising when we recall that the measured potential is a logarithmic function of the concentration of the ion to which the electrode responds, and that we employed an analogous function in producing the theoretical curves.

TABLE 19-1

Potentiometric Titration Data for 2.433 Milliequivalents of Chloride
with 0.1000 N Silver Nitrate

Vol AgNO$_3$, ml	E vs. S.C.E., volt	$\Delta E/\Delta V$, volt/ml
5.0	0.062	
		0.002
15.0	0.085	
		0.004
20.0	0.107	
		0.008
22.0	0.123	
		0.015
23.0	0.138	
		0.016
23.50	0.146	
		0.050
23.80	0.161	
		0.065
24.00	0.174	
		0.09
24.10	0.183	
		0.11
24.20	0.194	
		0.39
24.30	0.233	
		0.83
24.40	0.316	
		0.24
24.50	0.340	
		0.11
24.60	0.351	
		0.07
24.70	0.358	
		0.050
25.00	0.373	
		0.024
25.5	0.385	
		0.022
26.0	0.396	
		0.015
28.0	0.426	

END-POINT DETERMINATION

Graphical Methods. Determination of the end point for a potentiometric titration may be accomplished in any of several ways. The most straightforward is a graphical method which involves a visual estimation of the midpoint in the steeply rising portion of the titration curve. Various mechanical methods have been suggested for evaluation of this point; it seems doubtful, however, that the accuracy is greatly improved by these.

Another graphical approach involves a plot of the change in potential per unit change in volume of reagent ($\Delta E/\Delta$ ml) as a function of the average volume of reagent added. The data from columns 1 and 2 of Table 19-1 have been used to calculate values for $\Delta E/\Delta$ ml shown in column 3; these are plotted in Figure 19.8. The end point is taken as the maximum in the curve and is obtained by extrapolation of the experimental points. Because of the uncertainty in the extrapolation procedure, however, it is questionable whether much is gained in terms of accuracy by such an approach despite the appearance of a spectacular change in the parameter plotted; such a plot is certainly more trouble to obtain.

With both of these techniques the assumption is made that the titration curve is symmetric about the true equivalence point, and that the inflection in the curve therefore corresponds to that point. This assumption is perfectly valid provided the participants in the chemical process react with one another in a one-to-one molar ratio, and provided also that the

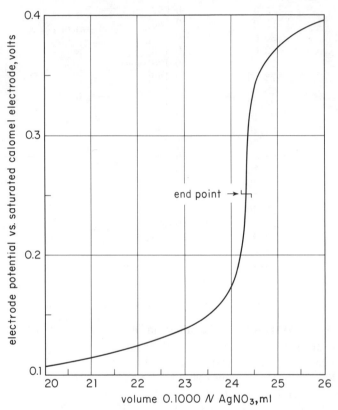

Fig. 19.7 Potentiometric Titration Curve in the Vicinity of the Equivalence Point. Titration of 2.433 milliequivalents of Cl⁻ with 0.1000 N AgNO₃ solution.

electrode process is perfectly reversible. Where these provisions are not met an asymmetric curve will result; an example is the titration curve shown in Figure 17.1 where five iron (II) ions are consumed by one permanganate ion.

Ordinarily the change in potential at the equivalence point region of these curves is large enough so that a negligible titration error is introduced by choosing the midpoint of the steeply rising portion of the curve as the end point. Only when unusual accuracy is desired, or where very small quantities are being determined, must consideration be given to the effect of this source of error upon an analysis. In such cases a correction can be applied. This can be determined empirically by titration of a standard;

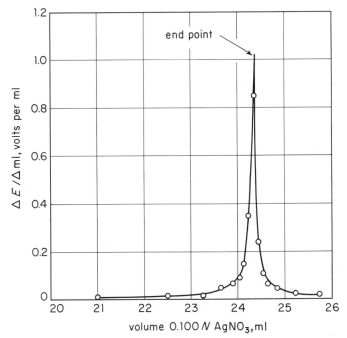

Fig. 19.8 Derivative Curve for the Titration Illustrated in Figure 19.7.

when the error is due to a nonsymmetrical reaction, it can be also calculated from theoretical considerations.[1]

19.3 Precipitation and Complex-formation Titrations

ELECTRODE SYSTEMS

For a precipitation titration the indicator electrode usually consists of the metal from which the reacting cation was derived. Occasionally, how-

[1] See I. M. Kolthoff and N. H. Furman, *Potentiometric Titrations*, 2d ed. Chaps. 2, 3. New York: John Wiley and Sons, Inc., 1931.

ever, an electrode system directly responsive to the anion is employed. Thus, for example, the titration of zinc ion with ferrocyanide may be followed with a platinum electrode, provided a quantity of ferricyanide ion is also present. The potential developed by this electrode is determined by the half reaction

$$Fe(CN)_6^{3-} + e \rightleftharpoons Fe(CN)_6^{4-}$$

With the first excess of reagent, the ferrocyanide concentration increases rapidly; this results in a corresponding alteration in the potential of the electrode.

When the anion involved in the precipitation or complex formation reaction possesses basic character, an indicator electrode sensitive to pH changes can be used (pH electrodes are considered in a later section of this chapter). An example arises in the titration of calcium with ethylenediaminetetraacetate which was discussed in Chapter 12. The analytical reaction is

$$Ca^{2+} + Y^{4-} \rightleftharpoons CaY^{2-}$$

The ethylenediaminetetraacetate ion (Y^{4-}), however, is extensively hydrolyzed

$$Y^{4-} + 2H_2O \rightleftharpoons H_2Y^{2-} + 2OH^-$$

Consequently, near the equivalence point in the titration there is a sharp rise in hydroxyl ion concentration corresponding to the first excess of Y^{4-} ions; this can easily be detected by an acid-sensitive indicator electrode.

TITRATION CURVES

Theoretical curves for a potentiometric titration are often easy to derive. For example, we can readily convert the values shown in Table 11-1 (page 207) for titration of chloride ion with silver nitrate into potentiometric data for a silver electrode. For this we need the standard potential for the half reaction

$$AgCl + e \rightleftharpoons Ag + Cl^- \qquad E° = 0.222 \text{ volt}$$

and we may describe the potential of the silver electrode during the titration as

$$E_{Ag} = +0.222 - 0.059 \log [Cl^-]$$

From the definition of pCl we may therefore write

$$E = +0.222 + 0.059 \, pCl$$

For any point in the titration, this relationship will allow us to calculate the theoretical potential of the silver electrode *against* the *standard hydrogen electrode* as reference. To obtain the *cell potential* where a saturated calomel electrode is used as a reference, we need to know the potential for that electrode

$$Hg_2Cl_2 + 2e \rightleftharpoons 2Hg + 2Cl^-(\text{sat'd KCl}) \qquad E_{\text{S.C.E.}} = +0.242 \text{ volt}$$

Reversing the sign on the potential of the calomel electrode in order to combine this with the silver electrode potential gives

$$E_{\text{cell}} = -0.242 + 0.222 + 0.059\ p\text{Cl}$$
$$= -0.020 + 0.059\ p\text{Cl}$$

With the aid of this equation a theoretical potentiometric titration curve could be computed from $p\text{Cl}$ data; its shape would be similar to that shown in Figure 19.7.

Effect of Adsorption. Experimental curves for precipitation titrations usually correspond closely to the shape predicted from theory. Such discrepancies as are observed can be traced in part to adsorption of ions by the precipitate. This effect can be seen in the titration of iodide ion with silver nitrate. Before the equivalence point, silver iodide strongly adsorbs iodide ions thus reducing their concentration in the solution. The effect of this phenomenon on the potential of a silver electrode in the solution is particularly noticeable near the end point. A similar effect is noted when the equivalence point has been passed; under these conditions adsorption of some of the excess silver ions occurs and results in a lower concentration of this species in the solution. This in turn causes the experimental potential to differ somewhat from the calculated one. Adsorption phenomena unfortunately tend to produce less sharply defined end points, as may be seen from Figure 19.9. In most instances, however, the extent of adsorption is low enough so that interference is not serious.

Titration Curves for Mixtures. Separate end points are often revealed by a potentiometric titration when more than one reacting species is present. An important application of this arises in the analysis of halide mixtures by titration with silver nitrate. To illustrate the derivation of a theoretical curve for such a system, consider the titration of 25.0 ml of a solution that is 0.100 F in both iodide and chloride ions with a standard 0.100 F silver nitrate solution. From the table of solubility products we find that

$$[Ag^+][I^-] \ = 8.3 \times 10^{-17}$$
$$[Ag^+][Cl^-] = 1.8 \times 10^{-10}$$

and conclude that the first additions of reagent will result in precipitation of silver iodide in preference to silver chloride. It is of interest to determine the extent to which this reaction occurs before appreciable chloride precipitation takes place. With the first appearance of silver chloride, both of the foregoing solubility product relations apply; thus, dividing the one by the other we get

$$\frac{[I^-]}{[Cl^-]} = \frac{8.3 \times 10^{-17}}{1.8 \times 10^{-10}} = 4.6 \times 10^{-7}$$

After the first silver chloride forms, this ratio is maintained throughout the remainder of titration. The magnitude of the ratio suggests that nearly all the iodide will have precipitated before the appearance of any silver chloride. Thus, the chloride ion concentration, because of dilution, will be very

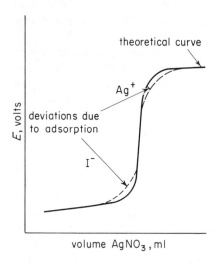

Fig. 19.9 **Effect of Adsorption upon the Curve for the Potentiometric Titration of Iodide Ion.**

close to half of its original concentration at the outset of its precipitation. With this assumption we can determine the iodide concentration when the chloride precipitate just appears; that is,

$$\frac{[I^-]}{0.1/2} \cong 4.6 \times 10^{-7}$$

$$[I^-] \cong 2.3 \times 10^{-8} \text{ mol/liter}$$

We can then calculate the percentage of iodide unprecipitated at this point in the titration.

$$\text{original no. meq } I^- = 25 \times 0.1 = 2.5$$

$$\text{no. meq } I^- \text{ at onset of } Cl^- \text{ precipitate} \cong 50 \times 2.3 \times 10^{-8} = 1.2 \times 10^{-6}$$

$$\text{percent } I^- \text{ unprecipitated} = \frac{1.2 \times 10^{-6}}{2.5} \times 100 = 0.00005$$

Thus within 0.00005 percent of the first end point, the titration curve should be that of a simple iodide solution; the necessary data for plotting the theoretical curve may be calculated on this basis.

> ★EXAMPLE. Calculate the potential of the silver electrode against a saturated calomel electrode after the addition of 5 ml of 0.100 N $AgNO_3$ to the mixture under consideration.

$$[I^-] = \frac{25.00 \times 0.1 - 5.0 \times 0.1}{30.0} = \frac{1}{15}$$

> We find in the table of standard potentials (page 507)

$$AgI + e \rightleftharpoons Ag + I^- \qquad E° = -0.151 \text{ volt}$$

> Thus

$$E = -0.151 - 0.059 \log [I^-]$$
$$= -0.151 - 0.059 \log \tfrac{1}{15}$$
$$= -0.081 \text{ volt}$$

> Combining this with the potential for the saturated calomel electrode as an anode, we obtain

$$E_{cell} = -0.081 - 0.242$$
$$= -0.323 \text{ volt}$$

The first half of the curve (solid line) shown in Figure 19.10 was obtained from data calculated in this manner. As expected, the curve rises steeply in the vicinity of the iodide equivalence point. This increase in potential, however, is terminated abruptly at a point corresponding to the first formation of silver chloride. This occurs slightly before the iodide equivalence point.

Once precipitation of chloride occurs, the potential can be most conveniently calculated by means of the standard potential for the reaction

$$AgCl + e \rightleftharpoons Ag + Cl^- \qquad E° = 0.222 \text{ volt}$$

The remainder of the titration curve is thus essentially identical to that for chloride by itself; points defining this portion are calculated as described previously.

Figure 19.10 illustrates that the theoretical titration curve for the mixture is a synthesis of the two curves for the individual ions, and that marked potential changes are associated with each equivalence point. It is to be expected that the first equivalence point in the titration of a mixture will become less well defined as the solubilities of the two precipitates approach one another. This is shown by the dotted line in Figure 19.10 which represents the theoretical curve for the titration of bromide ion in the presence of chloride. Even here an end point can be distinguished fairly readily. As a matter of fact, the solubility of the three silver halides differ sufficiently

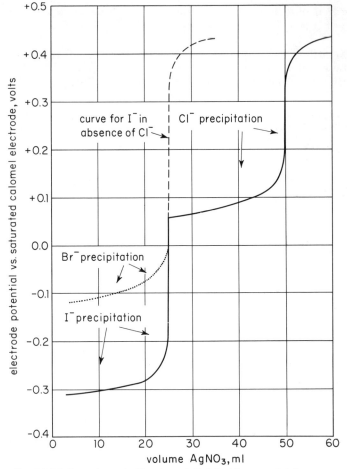

Fig. 19.10 Potentiometric Titration of Halide Mixtures. Solid curve represents titration of 25.0 ml of solution that is 0.100 *F* with respect to I⁻ and to Cl⁻. Broken curve indicates the course of the titration had sample contained no Cl⁻. Dotted curve represents titration of 25.0 ml of a solution that is 0.100 *F* with respect to Br⁻ and to Cl⁻.

for a mixture of the three to give a titration curve with three distinct end points.

The obvious conclusion from Figure 19.10 is that the potentiometric method should make possible the analysis of the individual components in halide mixtures. These curves, of course, are theoretical and subject to experimental verification. When this is done, the sharp discontinuities shown in the theoretical curves are not observed; instead, the experimental graphs are curved in these regions. More important, the volume of silver nitrate required to reach the first end point is generally somewhat greater than theoretical while that for the second tends to be low; the total volume, however, approaches the theoretical amount. These observations apply to the titration of chloride-bromide, chloride-iodide, and bromide-iodide mixtures and can be explained by assuming that coprecipitation of the more soluble silver halide occurs during formation of the less soluble compound. This would account for the overconsumption of reagent in the first part of the titration and a corresponding underconsumption during the second. The formation of a solid solution is likely.

Despite the coprecipitation error, the potentiometric method is useful for the analysis of halide mixtures. When approximately equal quantities are present, the relative errors can be kept to about 1 to 2 percent.[2]

19.4   Neutralization Titrations and the Measurement of *p*H

The hydrogen ion concentration of aqueous solutions can vary over a tremendous range; yet relatively small changes in this quantity may greatly alter the chemical behavior and properties of a solvent. For example, a tenfold change in hydrogen ion concentration may have a hundredfold or even a thousandfold effect on the solubility of a compound; indeed, there are instances where such a change brings about a millionfold alteration in the concentration of a participant in an oxidation-reduction equilibrium. As a consequence, a knowledge of hydrogen ion concentration is of vital importance to the chemist, and its measurement is one of the most important quantitative analytical processes.

There are actually two measurable quantities of interest relating to the acidity or basicity of a solution. One of these is the equilibrium hydrogen ion concentration (or hydroxyl ion concentration). The other is the total acidity or basicity—that is, the concentration of acid or base available for chemical reaction. For a weak acid or base these are quite different quantities, related to each other through the acid dissociation constant. The first, usually expressed in terms of *p*H, is most commonly determined by a direct potentiometric measurement. The second, on the other hand, is established by a neutralization titration; this may use a potentiometric determination to establish the end point. A consideration of both of these measurements is clearly important.

---

[2] For further details see I. M. Kolthoff and N. H. Furman, *Potentiometric Titrations*, 2d ed., 154–158. New York: John Wiley and Sons, Inc., 1931.

INDICATOR ELECTRODES

In principle, at least, any electrode process involving the production or consumption of hydrogen ions can be used for potentiometric pH measurements. The number of these, however, is greatly limited by practicality and convenience.

The Hydrogen Gas Electrode. An electrode similar to the standard hydrogen electrode shown on page 325 can clearly be used for the determination of pH. In this application the platinized platinum surface is immersed in the solution to be analyzed and exposed to hydrogen gas of a known partial pressure. The half reaction is

$$\tfrac{1}{2}H_2 \rightleftharpoons H^+ + e$$

and we may write for 25° C

$$E = 0 - 0.059 \log \frac{[H^+]}{(p_{H_2})^{1/2}}$$

where p_{H_2} is the partial pressure of the hydrogen gas expressed in atmospheres. The electrode must be used in conjunction with a reference electrode of known potential such as a calomel half cell; the observed cell potential may be represented as

$$E_{obs} = -0.059 \log \frac{[H^+]}{(p_{H_2})^{1/2}} + E_{Hg_2Cl_2} + E_j \qquad (19\text{-}4)$$

where the first term on the right side of the equation gives the potential for the hydrogen indicator electrode and the second is the potential for the saturated calomel reference electrode. The third term, E_j, is called the *liquid junction potential*. This potential arises at the interface between the solution whose pH is being measured and the saturated potassium chloride of the calomel half cell. The junction potential results from differences in the rates at which cations and anions diffuse across the phase boundary; this difference in migration rate leads to a charge separation and thus a potential.

The magnitude of the junction potential is dependent upon the ionic composition of the two solutions on either side of the junction; where one of these is a saturated potassium chloride solution, the junction potential is only a few thousandths of a volt because the potassium and chloride ions are present in large concentrations and the migration rate of these two ions is nearly identical. The magnitude of the junction potential will, however, be somewhat dependent upon the ionic composition of the solution in contact with the saturated potassium chloride. Thus the numerical value of E_j in equation (19-4), while small with respect to the other terms, will depend upon the ionic composition of the solution whose pH is being measured.

Equation (19-4) may be rewritten as

$$-0.059 \log [\text{H}^+] = E_{\text{obs}} - E_{\text{Hg}_2\text{Cl}_2} - E_j + 0.059 \log \frac{1}{(p_{\text{H}_2})^{1/2}}$$

or

$$pH = \frac{E_{\text{obs}} - (E_{\text{Hg}_2\text{Cl}_2} + E_j)}{0.059} + \log \frac{1}{(p_{\text{H}_2})^{1/2}}$$

A close examination of the equation in this form reveals the disconcerting fact that it contains two unknown quantities, pH and E_j. Ordinarily E_j cannot be evaluated exactly; it can only be reduced to a fairly small quantity (a few millivolts) through the use of a suitable salt bridge (page 326).

In most potentiometric pH measurements, the attempt is made to circumvent the dilemma presented by the existence of a junction potential by first measuring the cell potential with a buffer solution whose pH is reliably known. Then, from the observed potential, the sum $(E_j + E_{\text{Hg}_2\text{Cl}_2})$ is measured and employed in determining the pH of the unknown. This expedient still contains an assumption—namely, that the junction potential associated with the known buffer is identical with that of the unknown solution. This cannot be exactly true and creates a small error which, incidentally, is inherent to all potentiometric pH measurements.

Use of the hydrogen electrode is limited to solutions that contain no substances that react directly with hydrogen gas and thus alter the pH of the solvent. Examples of interferences of this kind are permanganate, iodine, iron (III), and easily reduced organic compounds. Titanium (II) and chromium (II) ions, whose oxidation by hydrogen ions is catalyzed by platinum, must also be absent. Further, a number of other substances such as proteins, hydrogen sulfide, and arsine cause the platinum electrode to behave in a sluggish and erratic manner; such interferences plus the inconvenience and hazard associated with the use of hydrogen severely restrict widespread use of the hydrogen electrode for pH determinations.

The Glass Electrode.[3] The glass electrode is unquestionably the most important indicator electrode for hydrogen ions and has almost completely displaced all other electrodes for pH measurements. It is convenient to use and subject to few of the interferences affecting other electrodes.

The phenomenon upon which the glass electrode is based, and recognition of its potentialities as a means for evaluating pH, date from the early days of this century. Measurement of the potentials developed was highly inconvenient, however, and widespread exploitation of the glass electrode was delayed until 1935 when suitable electronic voltmeters became available.

---

[3] For a complete discussion of this most useful electrode see M. Dole, *The Glass Electrode*. New York: John Wiley and Sons, Inc., 1941.

The experimental observation fundamental to the development of this electrode is that a potential difference develops across a thin, conducting glass membrane interposed between solutions of different pH. The potential can be detected by placing reference electrodes of known and constant potential in the solutions on either side of the membrane, as shown schematically in Figure 19.11. With this arrangement the potential across the reference electrodes varies as a function of the ratio between the hydrogen ion concentrations C_1 and C_2. Thus, at 25° C the following relationship is found to hold

$$E_{\text{obs}} = k - 0.059 \log \frac{C_1}{C_2}$$

where k is a constant.

To measure the pH of an unknown solution, the hydrogen ion concentration of one of the compartments (say C_2) is kept constant. The solution to be measured is placed in the other compartment; if we denote its concentration as C_1, the equation can be rewritten as

$$E_{\text{obs}} = K - 0.059 \log C_1$$

$$= K + 0.059 \, p\text{H} \qquad (19\text{-}5)$$

where K is a new constant that contains the logarithmic function of C_2. The numerical value of K is obtained by measuring E for a solution whose hydrogen ion concentration C_1 is known exactly. Equation (19-5) is identical in form to that for the hydrogen electrode.

It is important to emphasize that the potentials of the two reference electrodes E_1 and E_2 are quite independent of C_1 and C_2. Thus, any changes in potential between them must arise at some other point in the system— most logically at the glass interface. A reasonable explanation for this phenomenon involves the assumption that the glass membrane of the cell is selectively permeable to hydrogen ions and that these tend to migrate preferentially in the direction of the lesser concentration. The result is that the solution of lower hydrogen ion concentration acquires a positive charge with respect to the solution from which the migration occurred, and a junction potential then develops.

Consistent with this explanation is the experimental fact that passage of current through the glass electrode is accompanied by a transfer of hydrogen ions through the membrane, and that the transfer approaches that predicted by Faraday's law. It has also been established that the glass must contain water within its structure if it is to be effective as a pH indicator. When this water is removed by drying in air or by treatment for prolonged periods with a dehydrating agent, the pH sensitivity of the electrode is lost. The water in the glass clearly plays a fundamental part in the proton-transfer process.

Not all glasses function as pH indicators; a soda-lime variety is commonly employed. This responds well except in relatively alkaline (above pH 9 or 10) media where it becomes sensitive not only to hydrogen ions but to sodium ions as well. Other alkali metal ions also interfere, but to a lesser extent. As a consequence, a pH value calculated from theoretical-potential data is likely to be low by several tenths of a unit in solutions containing high concentrations of sodium ion. The alkaline error can be

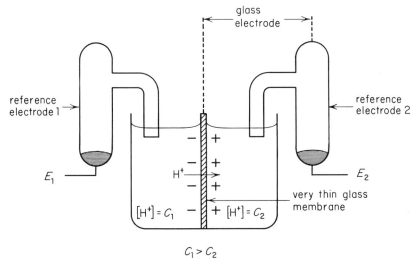

Fig. 19.11 Schematic Diagram of a Cell for pH Measurement. The glass electrode consists of reference electrode 2, the solution of known hydrogen ion concentration C_2, and the glass membrane. The pH of solution C_1 is being determined.

largely avoided by employing a glass membrane constructed of a lithium glass. These are available commercially.[4]

Turning once more to the equation (19-5)

$$E = K + 0.059\ pH$$

it is well to consider what is contained in the constant K, in addition to the logarithmic function of C_2. As might be expected, the sum of the refer-

<hr>

[4] For a systematic study on glasses for electrode construction see G. A. Perley, *Anal. Chem.*, **21**, 391, 394, 559 (1949).

ence potentials E_1 and E_2 are certainly included. Their sum will, of course, be zero if the two electrodes are identical. The constant K will also take account of the junction potentials between reference electrode 1 and the solution in which it is immersed as well as reference electrode 2 and its solution. The assumption is made that these quantities are constant and independent of the composition of the solution whose pH is being measured. In addition, there is contained in K another term called the *asymmetry potential* which is believed to arise from differences in the strains set up in the two glass surfaces during manufacture. That this exists is evident from the fact that a small potential develops across a glass membrane even when the two solutions are identical. The asymmetry potential changes slowly with time; from a practical standpoint, this means that K must be re-established at regular intervals (every few days) by measuring E_{obs} for a solution of known pH.

Potential Measurements with a Glass Electrode. Even a very thin glass membrane has an electrical resistance amounting to 100 megohms or more, and this complicates the measurement of the potential of a cell containing a glass electrode. The very high resistance precludes the use of a simple potentiometer because the out-of-balance current is reduced to such a small value (page 417) that detection of the current is impossible even by the most sensitive galvanometer. Two types of instruments overcome this problem. The first, which is entirely adequate for most purposes and convenient to use, is a vacuum-tube voltmeter accurate to about 0.005 volt (or 0.1 pH unit). For more precise measurements, the potentiometric circuit shown on page 417 can be modified by replacing the galvanometer with a direct-current amplifier. This device magnifies the very small out-of-balance currents to the point where they can easily be detected with a rugged ammeter. Several instruments of each type, calibrated directly in pH units, are available commercially. These are called pH meters.

Applications of the Glass Electrode. Glass electrodes, in a variety of shapes and sizes, are available commercially at a relatively low cost. One form is illustrated in Figure 19.12. Here, the electrode consists of a glass tube with the pH-sensitive membrane sealed in one end. Within the tube is a dilute hydrochloric acid solution; a piece of silver wire coated with silver chloride is immersed in this solution. This forms a silver-silver chloride reference electrode. As shown in the illustration, the second reference electrode is usually a commercial saturated-calomel electrode.

The glass-calomel electrode system is a remarkably versatile tool for the measurement of pH under a wide variety of conditions. In contrast to other electrode systems, strong oxidants, reductants, proteins, gases, and many other substances do not interfere; the pH of viscous or even semi-solid fluids can be determined. Electrodes for a variety of special applications are available. Included among these are microelectrodes for the measurement of a drop or less of solution; systems for insertion in a flowing stream of liquid to provide the continuous monitoring of pH; and a small glass electrode that can be swallowed to indicate the acidity of the stomach contents (the calomel electrode is kept in the mouth).

We have noted that water in the membrane of a glass electrode is essential to its proper performance as a pH indicator. As a consequence, conditions leading to the dehydration of the glass should be avoided whenever

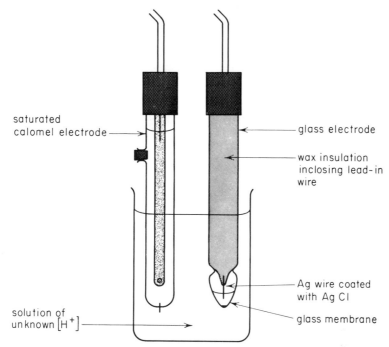

saturated
calomel electrode

glass electrode

wax insulation
inclosing lead-in
wire

Ag wire coated
with Ag Cl

solution of
unknown $[H^+]$

glass membrane

Fig. 19.12 Typical Electrode System for the Potentiometric Measurement of *p*H.

possible. Removal of water will occur upon prolonged exposure of the glass to the atmosphere or to such dehydrating solvents as alcohol or concentrated sulfuric acid. Fortunately, the water is easily restored by soaking the electrode for several hours. To avoid dehydration, glass electrodes should be stored in distilled water.

A well-soaked glass electrode does retain enough moisture to permit evaluation of "pH numbers" of nonaqueous solutions and, more important, to indicate end points for acid-base titrations carried out in such solvents.

While the theoretical interpretation of these numbers is not possible, their empirical application to analysis has proved useful.[5]

Errors in *p*H Measurements with the Glass Electrode. The ubiquity of the *p*H meter and the general applicability of the glass electrode tends to lull the chemist into the attitude that any reading obtained with such an instrument is surely correct. It is well to guard against this sense of security since there are distinct limitations to the electrode system. These are summarized below.

1. *The alkaline error.* As mentioned previously, the ordinary glass electrode becomes somewhat sensitive to the alkali metals at *p*H values greater than 10. Thus, in a solution that is 1.0 *F* in sodium ion, a negative error of nearly 1 *p*H unit is obtained at a *p*H of 12; a 0.1 *F* concentration of this same ion creates an error of about −0.4 unit at this same *p*H. Electrodes designed for high *p*H values are available; with these the alkaline error is greatly reduced.

2. *The acid error.* At a *p*H less than zero, values obtained with a glass electrode tend to be somewhat high.

3. *Dehydration.* Dehydration of the electrode may lead to unstable behavior and errors.

4. *Errors in unbuffered neutral solutions.* Equilibrium between the electrode surface layer and the solution is achieved only slowly in poorly buffered, approximately neutral, solutions. Since the measured potential is determined by the surface layer of liquid, errors will arise unless time is allowed for equilibrium to be established; this process may take several minutes. In determining the *p*H of such solutions, the glass electrode should be thoroughly rinsed with water before use. Good stirring is also helpful, and several minutes should be allowed to obtain steady readings.

5. *Variation in junction potential.* In the equation (19-5) relating potential to *p*H we saw that the constant *K* consists of a summation of the reference-electrode potentials, the asymmetry potential, and the junction potentials between the reference electrodes and their respective solutions. Normally *K* is evaluated by measuring the cell potential developed with a buffer solution of known *p*H. The assumption is then made that *K* will have the same value when the unknown solution replaces the buffer. This will not be strictly realized, however, because the junction potential will vary slightly with the composition of the solution being measured, even when a good salt bridge is used. The uncertainty introduced is small, amounting to about ±1 mv; in terms of *p*H this corresponds to an error on the order of 0.02 unit. As shown before, this error is not unique to the glass electrode, but is inherent in all hydrogen ion electrodes since all contain a

---

[5] For example see J. S. Fritz, *Acid-Base Titrations in Nonaqueous Solvents.* Columbus, Ohio: G. F. Smith Chemical Co., 1952.

liquid junction. *The student should appreciate the existence of this fundamental uncertainty in the measurement of pH for which a correction cannot
be applied.* Values more reliable than 0.01 to 0.02 pH unit are simply
unobtainable by potentiometric measurements; it is noteworthy that this
uncertainty corresponds to a relative error in hydrogen ion concentration
of about 3 percent.

6. *Error in the pH of the buffer solution.* Since the glass electrode must
be regularly calibrated, any inaccuracies in the preparation or changes in
composition of the buffer during storage will be reflected as errors in pH
measurements.

POTENTIOMETRIC ACID-BASE TITRATIONS

In Chapters 13 and 14 we considered theoretical curves for various
neutralization titrations in some detail. These curves can be closely approximated experimentally; by measurement of the potential of a pH-
sensitive electrode, end points can be determined by inspection, or with
the analytical methods described earlier in the chapter. In any case, a
study of the theoretical curves will show that the small error inherent in
the potentiometric measurement of pH is normally of no consequence insofar as locating the end point is concerned.

Potentiometric acid-base titrations are frequently employed where the
sample solutions are colored or turbid. They are particularly useful when
mixtures of acids or polyprotic acids (or bases) are to be analyzed since
discrimination between the end points can often be made. A numerical
value for the dissociation constant of the reacting species can also be estimated from potentiometric titration curves. In theory, this can be obtained
from any point along the curve; as a practical matter, it is most easily
found from the pH at the point of half neutralization. For example, in the
titration of the weak acid HA, we may ordinarily assume that at the
midpoint

$$[HA] = [A^-]$$

and therefore

$$K_a = \frac{[H^+][A^-]}{[HA]} = [H^+]$$

or

$$pK_a = pH$$

If desired, the relative concentrations of A^- and HA can be expressed more
exactly (Chapter 13) for a better estimate of K_a.

A value of the dissociation constant and the equivalent weight of a
pure sample of an unknown acid can be obtained from a single potentio-

metric titration; this information is frequently sufficient to identify the acid.

19.5   Oxidation-reduction Titrations

In Chapter 17 we developed techniques for derivation of theoretical titration curves for oxidation-reduction processes. In each example, an electrode potential related to the concentration ratio of the oxidized and reduced forms of either of the reactants was determined as a function of the volume of reagent. These curves can be duplicated experimentally provided an indicator electrode responsive to one or both of the couples involved in the reaction is available. Such electrodes exist for most, but not all, of the reagents described in Chapter 18.

Indicator electrodes for oxidation-reduction titrations are generally constructed from platinum, gold, mercury, or silver. The metal chosen must be unreactive with respect to the components of the solution—it is merely a medium for electron transfer. Without question, platinum constitutes the most widely employed indicator-electrode material for oxidation-reduction systems. Curves similar to those shown on page 353 can be obtained experimentally with a platinum-calomel electrode system. End-point detection can be accomplished from a plot of the experimental data or by the analytical methods already discussed.

19.6   Some Special Techniques

This section is devoted to a brief consideration of some special techniques designed to make potentiometric titrations less time consuming or to simplify the equipment needed for these methods.

DIFFERENTIAL TITRATION METHODS

We have already seen that a derivative titration curve can be obtained from the data of an ordinary potentiometric titration (Figure 19.8), and that such a graph exhibits a marked maximum in the vicinity of the equivalence point. It is possible to acquire titration data directly in the derivative form with rather simple equipment. To do this, the potential of a pair of identical indicator electrodes is measured throughout the titration; one of these is immersed in a portion of the solution that is kept slightly behind the rest of the solution insofar as the progress of the titration is concerned. The principle is illustrated by the original differential method developed by

Cox.[6] Here the solution to be titrated is divided into two exactly equal portions and connected by a salt bridge; identical indicator electrodes are then placed in each. Reagent is slowly added from two burets, the volume from one always being slightly less (ideally 0.1 to 0.2 ml) than that from the other. The difference in potential ΔE for the small volume difference ΔV results directly from measurement of the cell potential. Initially this differential quantity is small; it steadily increases, however, and reaches a maximum at the end point.

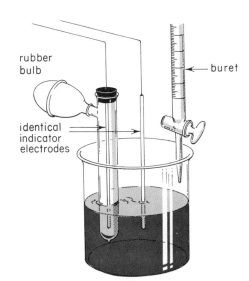

Fig. 19.13 Apparatus for Differential Potentiometric Titrations.

Cox's procedure is inconvenient, and were this the only method for performing a differential titration it would probably never be used. Actually, a number of ingenious cells have been devised that accomplish the desired purpose in a much simpler manner. Figure 19.13, illustrates such a cell. One of the indicator electrodes is partially shielded by a glass tube that is constricted at one end. As a consequence, additions of reagent to the bulk of the solution do not materially alter the composition of the small volume surrounding this electrode. When mixing is desired, the rubber bulb is squeezed. In using this cell, the reagent is added in appropriate increments and the potential difference is measured. The solution is then homogenized by squeezing the rubber bulb several times before the next addition is made. At the equivalence point, the potential measured will be at a maximum as in Cox's procedure. If the volume in the tube enclosing the electrode is kept

[6] D. C. Cox, *J. Am. Chem. Soc.*, **47**, 2138 (1925).

small (say 1 to 5 ml), the error arising from failure of the final addition of reagent to react with this portion of the solution can be shown to be negligibly small.

The main advantage of a differential method is the elimination of the reference electrode and salt bridge. The end points are ordinarily very well defined.

AUTOMATIC TITRATIONS

In recent years several automatic titrators based on the potentiometric principle have come on the market. These are useful where a large number of routine analyses are to be carried out. Such instruments cannot yield more accurate results than those obtained by manual potentiometric techniques; however, they do decrease the number of man-hours required for the performance of titrations and thus may offer some economic advantages.

Basically, two types of automatic titrators are available. With the first of these, a titration curve is plotted automatically; the end point is then determined by inspection of this curve. In the second type, the titration is stopped automatically when the indicator-reference electrode potential reaches some predetermined value; the volume of reagent consumed can then be read at the operator's convenience.

19.7 Laboratory Experiments Involving Potentiometric Titrations

This section contains several experiments suitable for demonstrating the potentiometric method. Because these experiments can be performed with any of several types of potentiometers, we have made no attempt to include specific operating instructions.

GENERAL METHOD FOR CARRYING OUT A POTENTIOMETRIC TITRATION

Although the following general instructions can be applied to most potentiometric titrations, some modification may be required in special cases.

★PROCEDURE. 1. Place the sample, dissolved in 50 to 250 ml of water, in the titration vessel. Rinse the electrodes with distilled water and then immerse them in the sample solution. Make provision for magnetic (or mechanical) stirring. Position the buret so that reagent can be delivered without splashing. See Figure 19.6 (page 422).

2. Start the stirring motor, connect the electrodes to the potentiometer, measure, and record the initial potential.

3. Measure and record the potential after each addition of reagent. Introduce fairly large volumes (1 to 5 ml) at the outset; withhold each succeeding increment until the potential remains constant within 1 to 2 mv (0.03 pH unit) for 30 sec. A stirring motor will occasionally cause erratic potential readings; it may be advisable to turn off the motor during the actual measuring process. Judge the volume of reagent to be added by calculating an approximate value of $\Delta E/\Delta$ ml for each addition. In the immediate vicinity of the equivalence point, introduce the reagent in exact 0.1-ml increments. Continue the titration 2 to 3 ml past the equivalence point; increase the volumes added as $\Delta E/\Delta$ ml once again decreases.

4. Locate the end point by one of the methods described on pages 423–425.

POTENTIOMETRIC ANALYSIS OF A CHLORIDE-IODIDE MIXTURE

★EQUIPMENT. A polished silver wire or a commercial billet-type silver electrode may be used as an indicator electrode. A commercial fiber-type calomel electrode can be employed as a reference electrode although this will lead to slightly high results as a consequence of diffusion of Cl^- from the salt bridge. An alternative is to place the calomel electrode in a saturated KNO_3 solution and connect this to the solution to be titrated with a KNO_3 bridge.

★REAGENT. Prepare a 0.1000 N $AgNO_3$ solution as instructed on page 216.

★PROCEDURE. Prepare a solution of the sample that contains a combined total of 2 to 4 meq of Cl^- and I^- in 100 ± 10 ml of water. Titrate with the silver nitrate, adding the reagent in large increments except near the two end points. Plot the data and determine the end point for each ion. Plot $\Delta E/\Delta V$ vs. V to ascertain the end point. Plot a theoretical titration curve assuming the measured concentrations of the two constituents to be correct. Report the number of milligrams of I^- and Cl^- found in the sample.

POTENTIOMETRIC NEUTRALIZATION TITRATIONS

★EQUIPMENT. Use a glass-calomel electrode system and a commercial pH meter. The electrode system should be calibrated against a buffer solution of known pH.

★REAGENTS. For the titration of weak acids, prepare and standardize a 0.1 N solution of carbonate-free sodium hydroxide according to the directions on page 301. For titration of weak bases, follow the directions on page 297 for the preparation and standardization of a 0.1 N hydrochloric acid solution.

★TITRATION OF A WEAK ACID. Prepare a solution containing between 1 and 4 meq of the acid in about 100 ml of water; a larger volume may be required to dissolve some of the less soluble organic acids. Add 2 drops of phenolphthalein to the solution.

Titrate as directed in the general instructions. Some samples will contain more than one replaceable hydrogen; be alert for more than one break in the titration curve. Note the point at which the indicator changes color.

Plot the titration data and determine the end point or points. Compare these with the phenolphthalein end point. The derivative method for end-point determination may also be used; (pages 423–425).

Calculate the number of milliequivalents of H^+ present in the sample.

ANALYSIS OF A CARBONATE–BICARBONATE MIXTURE. Dissolve the sample, which contains a total of 2 to 3 mfw of the two salts, in 200 ml of water. Add 2 drops of phenolphthalein and 2 drops of methyl orange to the solution. Then titrate as directed in the general instructions. Carry the titration 3 to 5 ml beyond the second end point. Note where the two indicators change color.

Plot the data and determine the end points. Compare the potentiometric and indicator end points. Estimate the two dissociation constants for carbonic acid from the curves and compare these with literature values.

Calculate the percent Na_2CO_3 and $NaHCO_3$ in the sample.

POTENTIOMETRIC OXIDATION-REDUCTION TITRATIONS

Titration of Iron (II) with Quadrivalent Cerium. The iron in an ore or other iron-containing compound is conveniently determined by a potentiometric titration with quadrivalent cerium. Prereduction of any iron (III) can be accomplished with a tin (II) chloride solution as described earlier. Removal of the excess tin (II) ion is not necessary in this case, however, because the potentiometric curve will show two breaks, the first corresponding to the oxidation of the tin (II) and the second to the oxidation of iron (II). The difference in volume between these then reflects the amount of iron present.

Equipment. Prepare a platinum-calomel electrode system and connect the leads to a potentiometer.

★PROCEDURE. Prepare and standardize a 0.1 N solution of quadrivalent cerium in sulfuric acid as directed on pages 385 and 386. Weigh, dissolve, and reduce the iron sample as directed on page 379. Do not, however, remove the excess tin (II) with mercury (I). Dilute the solution to about 50 ml and titrate immediately with the cerium (IV). Two end points will be observed.

Plot the voltage data against the volume of reagent and determine the two end points. Calculate the percent iron in the sample.

★PROCEDURE EMPLOYING A DIFFERENTIAL END POINT. In this experiment a pair of platinum electrodes is used; one is housed in a glass tube such as shown in Figure 19.13. An ordinary potentiometer may be employed for potential measurements.

Prepare the reagent and sample as directed in the previous section. Add about 1 ml of the reagent and measure the potential. Then homogenize the solution by squeezing the rubber bulb connected to the shielded electrode and add more reagent. Again record the potential and volume of reagent before mixing the solution around the shielded electrode with the bulk of the solution. Continue this process, reducing the volume increments to 0.1 ml in the vicinity of each end point. Carry the titration 2 to 5 ml beyond the second end point.

Plot the data and calculate the percent iron from the difference in reagent volume between the first and second end point.

Problems

1. Derive the theoretical potentiometric titration curve for 50 ml of a solution that is 0.05 F each in Br^- and Cl^- ions. The reagent is 0.1 F $AgNO_3$; a silver-saturated calomel-electrode system is used. Calculate the cell potential corresponding to the following volumes of reagent: 10, 20, 24, 24.9, 25.0, 25.1, 26.0, 35, 45, 49, 49.9, 50.0, 50.1, 51.0, and 60.0.

2. Calculate the equivalence-point potential for the titration of 0.2 N I^- with 0.2 N $AgNO_3$. The electrode system consists of a saturated-calomel electrode and a platinum wire. The solution was made 0.02 F in I_2 at the start of the titration (assume the indicator electrode half reaction is $I_2 + 2e \rightleftharpoons 2I^-$).

ans. 0.71 volt

3. What is the potential of a titration cell consisting of a saturated calomel electrode and a hydrogen gas electrode at the point in the titration of acetic acid where half of the acid has been neutralized? Assume the hydrogen gas is at a pressure of 1 atmosphere. Which electrode is the cathode?

4. What is the pH of a solution determined by an emf measurement of a cell consisting of a saturated calomel cathode and a hydrogen gas anode (p_{H_2} = 725 mm) if the measured potential is 0.98 volt?

5. What is the emf of the cell

saturated calomel electrode || 0.1 F NH_4Cl, hydrogen electrode

6. What is the dissociation constant of the acid HX if the following cell develops a potential of +0.612 volt with the calomel electrode as the cathode?

Pt | H_2(1 atm), HX(0.05 F), NaX(0.05 F) || saturated calomel electrode

7. (a) Calculate the equilibrium constant for the process

$$Tl^{3+} + 2Fe^{2+} \rightleftharpoons Tl^+ + 2Fe^{3+}$$

(b) Calculate the potential of a platinum indicator electrode at the equivalence point in the titration of 25.0 ml of 0.02 F Fe^{3+} with 0.01 F Tl^{3+}.

(c) What will be the iron (II) concentration of the solution at the equivalence point?

8. A platinum-saturated calomel electrode system is employed for the potentiometric titration of 40.0 ml of $0.050\ F$ Sn^{2+} with $0.080\ F$ $V(OH)_4^+$ in a medium maintained at a pH of 1.00.

(a) What will be the potential of the indicator electrode with respect to the reference electrode after the addition of 36.0 ml of oxidizing agent?

(b) What (if any) material-balance or charge-balance equations (or both) can be written to describe the system at this point in the titration?

9. A 40.0 ml aliquot of $0.06\ F$ VO^{2+} is diluted to 75.0 ml and titrated with $0.08\ F$ Ce^{4+}. A platinum-saturated calomel electrode system is used to follow the course of the titration; the pH is held constant at 1.00 throughout.

(a) Calculate the potential of the indicator electrode (versus S.H.E.) after the addition of 5.0, 10.0, 20.0, 29.0, 30.0, 31.0, and 40.0 ml of Ce^{4+}.

(b) Plot a curve for this titration using the potential of the indicator electrode (versus S.C.E.) for the vertical axis.

(c) Evaluate the equilibrium constant for this reaction.

(d) Calculate the concentration of Ce^{4+} in the solution at the equivalent point.

10. Consider the titration of 60.0 ml of $0.080\ F$ V^{2+} with $0.060\ F$ I_3^- in $0.20\ F$ KI:

$$I_3^- + 2V^{2+} \rightleftharpoons 3I^- + 2V^{3+}$$

(a) Calculate the potential of a platinum indicator electrode with respect to a saturated calomel reference electrode after the addition of 5.0, 15.0, 25.0, 39.0, 40.0, 41.0, and 50.0 ml of I_3^-.

(b) Calculate the concentration of each species in solution at the equivalence point in the titration.

(20)

Methods Based on Absorption
of Radiation

The selective absorption of electromagnetic radiation as it passes through a solution causes the emerging beam to differ from the incident one. In the case of visible radiation, this difference is frequently obvious to the naked eye. For example, a white light viewed through a copper (II) sulfate solution appears blue because the copper (II) ions interact with and absorb the red components of the beam while transmitting completely the blue portions of the radiation. The application of this type of absorption phenomenon to the qualitative identification of substances is undoubtedly familiar to most readers, for many of the tests in the ordinary qualitative scheme are based upon observation of the color of solutions. Of equal importance is the employment of light absorption for the quantitative measurement of chemical systems.

20.1   Fundamental Concepts, Definitions, and Laws

Electromagnetic radiation is a form of energy that can be described in terms of its wavelike properties. In contrast to sound waves, electromagnetic waves travel at extreme velocities and do not require the existence of some supporting medium for propagation.

The *wavelength* λ of a beam of electromagnetic radiation is the linear distance traversed by one complete wave cycle. The *frequency* ν is the number of cycles occurring per second; it is readily obtained by dividing the wavelength into the velocity of the radiation

$$\nu = \frac{c}{\lambda}$$

The *velocity* c varies with the medium through which the radiation is passing; it has a value of 3×10^{10} cm/sec when measured in a vacuum.

In some of its interactions with matter, radiation can be shown to behave as if it were composed of discrete packets of energy, called *photons*.

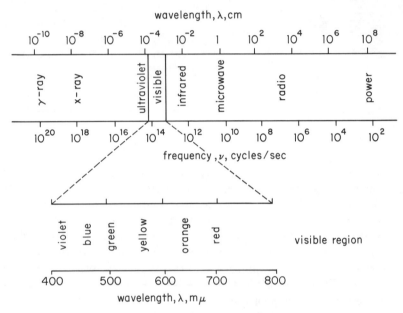

Fig. 20.1 The Electromagnetic Spectrum.

The energy of a photon is variable and depends upon the frequency or wavelength of the radiation. The relationship between the energy E of a photon and frequency is given by the relationship

$$E = h\nu$$

where h is *Planck's constant* with a numerical value of 6.62×10^{-27} erg sec. The equivalent expression involving wavelength is

$$E = \frac{hc}{\lambda}$$

Clearly short wavelengths are more energetic than long ones.

Electromagnetic radiation exhibits what appears to be a duality of properties. Thus the phenomena of refraction and diffraction are best explained by assigning it the properties of waves. On the other hand, in its interaction with matter, radiation is best described as having particulate properties, the energy of the particles being equal to $h\nu$.

The electromagnetic spectrum covers an immense range of wavelengths. Figure 20.1 depicts qualitatively the major divisions of the spectrum. A logarithmic scale has been employed in this representation; note that the portion to which the human eye is perceptive is small indeed. Such diverse radiations as gamma rays and radio waves are also electromagnetic radiations, differing from visible light only in the matter of wavelength, and hence energy.[1]

THE ABSORPTION PROCESS

We have noted that partial absorption often accompanies the passage of a beam of radiation through a transparent medium, and also that the absorption of electromagnetic radiation is tantamount to the absorption of energy. We must now examine qualitatively the processes responsible for this absorption, and the ultimate fate of the energy so absorbed.

When an atom, ion, or molecule absorbs a photon, the added energy results in an alteration of state; the species is then said to be *excited*. Excitation may involve any of the following processes:

(1) Transition of an electron to a higher energy level;
(2) A change in the mode of vibration of the molecule;
(3) Alteration of its mode of rotation.

Each of these transitions requires a definite quantity of energy; the probability of occurrence for a particular transition is greatest when the photon absorbed supplies precisely this quantity of energy.

The energy requirements for these transitions vary considerably. In general, promotion of electrons to higher levels requires greater energies than those needed to bring about vibrational changes. Alterations in rotational mode are likely to have the lowest energy requirements of all. Thus, absorptions observed in the microwave and far infrared regions will be due to shifts in rotational level since the energy of the radiation is insufficient to cause other types of transitions. Changes in vibrational levels are responsible for absorptions in the near infrared and visible regions. Because a series of rotational states exists for each vibrational level, groups of wavelengths are

---

[1] The units commonly used for describing the wavelength of radiation differ considerably in the various spectral regions. For example, the Ångstrom unit Å, 10^{-7} mm, is convenient for x-ray and ultraviolet radiation; the millimicron mμ, 10^{-6} mm, is employed with visible and ultraviolet radiation; the micron μ, 10^{-3} mm, is commonly employed for infrared radiation.

likely to be absorbed that differ only slightly in energy. Absorption due to promotion of an electron to some higher energy level takes place in the visible, ultraviolet, and x-ray regions of the spectrum. An even greater number of wavelengths is likely to be absorbed in the first two of these

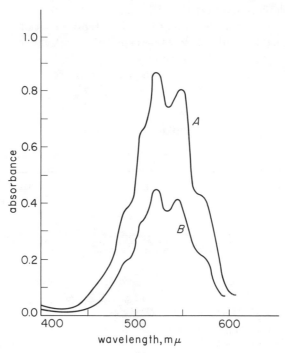

Fig. 20.2 Absorption Spectrum for Potassium Permanganate in the Visible Region. The concentration of MnO_4^- in solution *A* is twice that of solution *B*.

regions, since a series of vibrational levels and rotational sublevels exist within each electronic level.[2]

The absorption of the very energetic x-ray radiation involves electronic transitions of the innermost electrons of an atom whereas absorption of ultraviolet and visible radiation involves the outer bond-forming electrons. An interesting consequence of this is that the x-ray absorption spectra of all but the lightest elements are quite unaffected by the form in which the

---

[2] Some transitions are more probable than others and some are "forbidden"—that is, highly improbable. The reasons for this are beyond the scope of this book. Recommended for further study is E. J. Bowen, *The Chemical Aspects of Light*, 2d ed. Oxford: The Clarendon Press, 1946.

element occurs—that is, whether the element is present in the sample as a compound or in its elemental form. On the other hand, the ultraviolet and visible spectra are profoundly influenced by the manner in which the element is combined. Thus, using manganese as an example, the permanganate ion is red, manganate ion is green, and manganese (II) ion is essentially colorless.

The absorption of radiation by a system can be described by a means of a plot of the absorption as a function of wavelength; such a graph is called an *absorption spectrum* (Figure 20.2). Inasmuch as the energies required for the various processes responsible for absorption are unique for a given species, its absorption spectrum is also unique; as a consequence absorption spectra are often helpful for qualitative identification purposes. This is particularly true for the low-energy absorptions that occur in the infrared region.

Irrespective of the amount of energy absorbed, an excited species tends spontaneously to return to its unexcited, or ground, state. To accomplish this, the energy of the absorbed photon must somehow be given up, and this is ordinarily dissipated in the form of heat. In some instances, however, transition to another excited state precedes return to the ground state. Here, the energy of the absorbed photon may be dissipated partially by emission of a photon of lower energy and partially as heat. The phenomenon of fluorescence is accounted for in this fashion.

BEER'S LAW

When a beam of monochromatic radiation passes through a solution containing an absorbing species, the radiant power of the beam is progressively reduced as a consequence of absorption of part of the energy by the particles of that species. The reduction in power is dependent upon the concentration of the substance responsible for the absorption as well as upon the length of the path traversed by the beam. These relationships are expressed by *Beer's law*.

Let P_0 be the radiant power[3] of a beam incident upon a section of solution that contains c mols of an absorbing substance per liter. Further, let P be the power of the beam after it has passed through a section having a thickness of b centimeters (Figure 20.3). As a consequence of absorption, P will be smaller than P_0. Beer's law relates these quantities as follows:

$$\log \frac{P_0}{P} = \epsilon bc = A \tag{20-1}$$

In this equation, ϵ is a constant called the molar absorptivity. The logarithm (to the base 10) of the ratio of the incident power to the transmitted

---

[3] Radiant power is the radiant energy striking a unit area in unit time.

power is called the absorbance of the solution; this quantity is given the symbol A. Clearly the absorbance of the solution increases directly with the concentration of the absorbing substance and with the path length traversed by the beam.

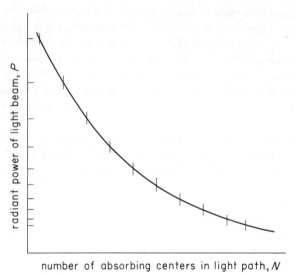

Fig. 20.3 Passage of a Beam of Monochromatic Radiation through a Solution. Vertical markings indicate attenuation suffered for a unit change in the number of absorbing centers in the light path.

MEASUREMENT OF ABSORPTION

Beer's law, as given by equation (20-1), is not directly applicable to chemical analysis because neither P nor P_0, as defined, can be measured easily in the laboratory. The main reason for this is that the solution to be studied must be held in some sort of container; thus, the beam of radiation must pass through the walls of this container before it can be measured. Interaction between the radiation and the walls is inevitable, producing a loss in power at each interface as a consequence of reflection or possibly absorption. In addition, the beam may suffer a diminution in power during its passage through the solution as a result of scattering by large molecules or inhomogeneities. Reflection losses can be quite appreciable; for example, about 4 percent of visible light is reflected upon vertical passage from air to glass.

The experimental applications of Beer's law require a correction for these effects. This is most easily done by comparing the power of the beam transmitted through the solution of interest with the power of a beam passing through an identical cell containing only the solvent for the sample. An experimental absorbance can then be evaluated which closely approximates the true absorbance of the solution; that is,

$$A \cong \log \frac{P_{solvent}}{P_{solution}} \cong \log \frac{P_0}{P}$$

The term P_0, when used henceforth, will refer to the power of a beam of radiation after it has passed through a cell containing the solvent for the component of interest.

TERMINOLOGY ASSOCIATED WITH ABSORPTION MEASUREMENTS

In recent years an attempt has been made to develop a standard nomenclature for the various quantities related to the absorption of radiation. The recommendation of the American Society for Testing Materials is given in Table 20-1 along with some of the alternate names and symbols that are frequently encountered. An important term found in this table is the transmittance T, which is defined as

$$T = \frac{P}{P_0}$$

The transmittance is the fraction of incident radiation transmitted by the solution; it is often expressed as a percent. The transmittance is clearly related to the absorbance as follows:

$$- \log T = A$$

LIMITATIONS TO THE APPLICABILITY OF BEER'S LAW

The linear relationship between absorbance and path length at a fixed concentration of absorbing substance is a generalization for which no exceptions have been found. On the other hand, deviations from the direct proportionality between absorbance and concentration at constant path length are quite frequently encountered. Some of these deviations are of such a fundamental nature that they represent a real limitation of the law; others, however, occur as a consequence of the manner in which the absorbance measurements are made or as a result of chemical changes associated with concentration changes; the latter two are sometimes known, respectively, as *instrumental* and *chemical deviations*.

TABLE 20-1

Important Terms and Symbols Employed in Absorption Measurement

Term and Symbol[4]	Definition	Alternate Name and Symbol
Radiant power, P, P_0	energy of radiation reaching a given area of a detector per second	radiant intensity, I, I_0
Absorbance, A	$\log \dfrac{P_0}{P}$	optical density, D; extinction, E
Transmittance, T	$\dfrac{P}{P_0}$	transmission, T
Path length of radiation, in cm, b		l, d
Molar absorptivity, ϵ	$\dfrac{A}{bc}$ (c = mol/liter)	molar extinction coefficient
Absorptivity, a	$\dfrac{A}{bc}$	extinction coefficient, k

[4] Taken from H. K. Hughes, *et al.*, *Anal. Chem.*, **24**, 1349 (1952).

Real Limitations to Beer's Law. Beer's law is successful in describing the absorption behavior of dilute solutions only; in this sense it is a limiting law. At high concentrations the average distance between the absorbing species is diminished to the point where each affects the charge distribution of its neighbors. This interaction, in turn, can alter their ability to absorb a given wavelength of radiation. Because the degree of interaction is dependent upon concentration, the occurrence of this phenomenon causes deviations from the linear relationship between absorbance and concentration.

Chemical Deviations. Apparent deviations from Beer's law are frequently encountered as a consequence of association, dissociation, or reaction of the absorbing species with the solvent. A classical example of this is observed with unbuffered potassium dichromate solutions, in which the following equilibria exist:

$$Cr_2O_7^{2-} + H_2O \rightleftharpoons 2HCrO_4^- \rightleftharpoons 2H^+ + 2CrO_4^{2-}$$

At most wavelengths, the molar absorptivities of dichromate ion and the two chromate species are quite different. Thus the total absorbance of the solution at any point is dependent upon the ratio of concentrations between the dimeric and monomeric forms. This ratio, however, changes markedly with dilution and causes a pronounced deviation from linearity between the absorbance and the total concentration of chromium. Nevertheless, the absorbance due to the dichromate ion is directly proportional to its molar concentration; the same is true for that of the chromate ion. This is easily demonstrated by making measurements in strongly acidic or strongly basic solution where one or the other of these species will predominate. Thus, deviations in the absorbance of this system from Beer's law are more apparent than real, because they result from shifts in chemical equilibria. These deviations can, in fact, be readily predicted from the equilibrium

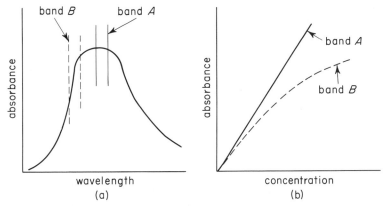

Fig. 20.4 Effect of Polychromatic Radiation upon the Beer's Law Relationship. Band *A* shows little deviation since ϵ does not change greatly throughout the band. Band *B* shows marked deviation since ϵ undergoes significant changes in this region.

constant for the reaction and the molar absorptivities of the dichromate and chromate ions.

Instrumental Deviation. Strict adherence of an absorbing system to Beer's law is observed only when monochromatic radiation is employed. This is another manifestation of the limiting character of the relationship. Use of a monochromatic beam for absorbance measurements is seldom practical, however, and polychromatic radiation may lead to departures from Beer's law.

Experiments show that deviations from Beer's law due to the use of a polychromatic beam are not appreciable provided the radiation used does not encompass a spectral region in which the absorber exhibits large changes in absorbance as a function of wavelength. This is illustrated in Figure 20.4.

20.2   Instruments for the Measurement of Absorption of Radiation

Having seen that the amount of radiation absorbed by a solution is related to the concentration of the absorbing species, we may now consider some of the ways and means by which the chemist makes use of this relationship for analysis.

The apparatus needed to perform an absorption analysis contains four basic components: (1) a stable source of radiant energy, (2) a device for restricting the band width of radiation employed, (3) transparent containers for the sample and the solvent, and (4) a radiation detector. The nature of these components varies considerably depending upon the region of the spectrum used; the degree of sophistication and refinement in their design also varies tremendously. Their functions, nevertheless, remain unchanged.

RADIATION SOURCES

In order to be suitable for absorption measurements, the source of radiation must meet certain requirements. First, it must generate a beam with sufficient power to make detection and measurement easy. Second, the radiation should be continuous; that is, its spectrum should contain all wavelengths over the region in which it is to be used. Finally, the source should be stable; to meet this requirement, the power of the radiant beam must remain constant for a period long enough to measure both P and P_0. Only then will the absorbance measurements be reproducible. Some instruments are designed so that P and P_0 are measured simultaneously; with these, fluctuations in the power output of the source are not a problem.

Sources of Ultraviolet Radiation. The common source of ultraviolet radiation is a hydrogen discharge tube; this consists of a pair of electrodes housed in a glass envelope with a quartz window. The tube contains hydrogen gas at a reduced pressure. Application of a direct-current or an alternating-current voltage to the electrodes causes excitation of the hydrogen molecules and production of continuous radiation in the region between 180 and 350 millimicrons.

Visible Radiation. In the simplest types of absorption analysis, ordinary daylight is employed as a source. More commonly, however, a tungsten filament bulb is used. If this is operated by a 110-volt source, a constant-voltage transformer is generally needed to stabilize the radiant-power output. An alternative is to operate the lamp from an ordinary storage battery; this produces a beam that is constant in power for relatively long periods. The tungsten lamp produces continuous radiation in the region between 350 and 2500 millimicrons.

Infrared Sources. Continuous infrared radiation is produced by electric heating of an inert solid. A silicon carbide rod, called a *Globar*, is often employed. It is heated to perhaps 1500° C by clamping it between a pair of electrodes. Radiant energy in the region of 1 to 40 microns results. A *Nernst glower* produces radiation in the region between 0.4 and 20 microns. This consists of a rod of zirconium and yttrium oxides that is heated to about 1500° C by passage of current.

DEVICES WHICH ISOLATE A LIMITED REGION OF THE SPECTRUM

There are several advantages to be gained from employment of radiation with a limited band width. We have seen that one of these is a greater probability of adherence to Beer's law. In addition, greater specificity of measurement is assured since substances absorbing in other regions of the spectrum will not interfere. Finally, by restricting the radiation to that portion of the spectrum that is most strongly absorbed by the substance being analyzed, a greater change in absorbance per increment of concentration is observed. This results in increased sensitivity of measurement.

The devices employed for restricting radiation fall into two categories. *Filters* function by absorbing large portions of the spectrum and transmitting relatively limited wavelength regions; these are employed primarily in the visible region of the spectrum. *Monochromators* are more sophisticated devices that isolate a beam of high spectral purity. In contrast to filters, the wavelengths employed can be varied continuously. Monochromators are used for ultraviolet, visible, and infrared radiation.

Filters. It is useful to compare filters in terms of the range of wavelengths over which the transmittance decreases to one half of its maximum value; this is sometimes called the *effective band width* and is illustrated in Figure 20.5.

Colored-glass filters are widely used in absorption analysis. The effective band width will vary from filter to filter, but typically will embrace from 20 to 50mμ. Glass filters with transmission maxima throughout the visible spectrum are readily available.

An *interference filter* consists of two extremely thin semitransparent metallic films separated by a very thin transparent material. When a nearly perpendicular beam of light strikes this array, a portion passes through the first metallic layer while a portion is reflected; see Figure 20.6. The portion that is passed undergoes a similar partition upon striking the second layer. If the reflected portion from this interaction is of the proper wavelength, it will be partially reflected from the inner side of the first

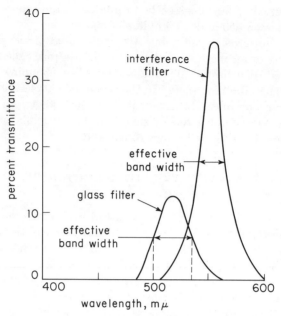

Fig. 20.5 Comparison of the Transmittance Characteristics of Typical Glass and Interference Filters.

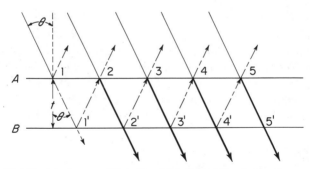

Fig. 20.6 The Interference Filter. At point 1, light strikes the semitransparent film at an angle θ from the perpendicular, is partially reflected, partially passed. The same process occurs at 1', 2, 2', etc. For reinforcement to occur at point 2, the distance traveled by the reflected beam must be some multiple of its wavelength, λ. Since the path length between surfaces can be expressed as $t \cos \theta$, the condition for reinforcement is that

$$n\lambda = 2t \cos \theta$$

where n is a small whole number. In practice, θ is made to approach $0°$; under these conditions

$$n\lambda \cong 2t$$

surface in phase with light of the same wavelength that is passing through at this point. The result is that the wavelength is reinforced while all others, being out of phase, suffer destructive interference.

Interference filters provide a degree of spectral purity that is seldom attained in their glass counterparts, effective band widths on the order of 10 mμ being readily achieved. Furthermore, a greater amount of light of the desired wave is transmitted. This is shown in Figure 20.5.

Monochromators. A monochromator serves to resolve the radiation from the source into its component wavelengths and to provide for the isolation of these in very narrow band widths. Light admitted through an entrance slit is collimated with a lens or mirror. It is then dispersed by means of a prism or grating. Any portion of the resulting spectrum can then be focused upon an exit slit, again with a lens or mirror.

The effective band width of radiation emerging from a monochromator is dependent upon a variety of structural features of the device and upon the wavelength. Typically band widths of a few tenths of a millimicron to perhaps 10 millimicrons are obtainable in the ultraviolet and visible region.

Dispersion in a prism arises from the phenomenon of *refraction*. Because its velocity depends upon the medium through which it travels, light is frequently refracted, or bent, as it passes from one medium to another. The extent of this effect depends upon the angle of the oncoming beam with respect to the interface, the wavelength of radiation, and the refractive indices of the two media. Dispersion occurs because the refractive index of the prism material is dependent upon the wavelength. Because this variation in refractive index is most pronounced at short wavelengths, passage through a prism results in the spreading of a polychromatic beam into its components, with the short wavelengths being dispersed to a greater extent than the longer ones. Figure 20.7 illustrates this schematically.

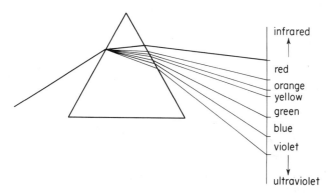

Fig. 20.7 **Dispersion of Polychromatic Light with a Prism.**

The material used to construct a prism will depend upon the portion of the spectrum to be studied. For the region between 350 and 2000 mμ, glass is often employed; quartz has a greater range of usefulness, extending from about 180 to 4000 mμ. In the infrared region where glass and quartz are not transparent, materials such as sodium chloride, lithium fluoride, calcium fluoride, or potassium bromide must be employed. Unfortunately these substances are susceptible to mechanical abrasion and attack by water vapor; consequently special precautions are required for their use.

Polychromatic light can also be dispersed with a *diffraction grating*. The reflection grating, shown schematically in Figure 20.8, is widely employed in spectrophotometry; it consists of a highly polished surface upon which

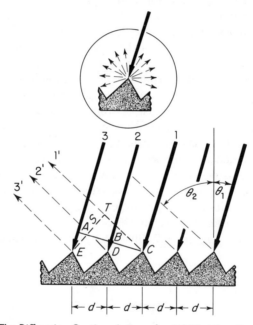

Fig. 20.8 The Diffraction Grating. A wave front ABC strikes the grating at an angle θ_1 and is diffracted (inset). In order for reinforcement with the next wave front, distances CT and (BD + DS) must be integer multiples of the wavelength that is,

$$CT = n\lambda$$

$$(BD + DS) = n'\lambda$$

In terms of the diffraction angle θ_2 and the spacing of the grating, d, the condition for reinforcement is that

$$CT = 2d \sin \theta_2 = n\lambda$$

or, more generally

$$(BD + DS) = d(\sin \theta_1 + \sin \theta_2) = n'\lambda$$

are scribed a large number of equally spaced, parallel grooves. A typical grating will have between 1000 and 2000 of these lines per millimeter, or 25,000 to 50,000 lines to the inch.

When illuminated, a grating partitions the radiation into as many small beams as there are lines; each of these, in effect, behaves as if it were a miniscule light source, sending out radiation in all directions. This accounts for the diffraction, or bending, of light as it strikes a sharp edge or traverses a narrow opening. With many thousands of sources, the possibilities are enormous for interference and for reinforcement of the diffracted radiation from a grating.

Now consider the diffraction of a collimated beam of *monochromatic radiation*. Although it will be diffracted through various angles, reinforcement will occur only where successive light paths differ from each other by integer multiples of the wavelength. For a given line spacing this condition will be satisfied at definite angles (Figure 20.8). Radiation diffracted at other angles will suffer destructive interference. A focusing lens placed between the grating and a viewing plate would cause the reinforced beams to appear as a series of bright lines on the latter—each line corresponding to a different value of n. The line corresponding to $n = 1$ is said to be *first order*, that for $n = 2$ is *second order*, and so forth.

Since reinforcement occurs at different diffraction angles for each wavelength, illumination of a grating with *polychromatic radiation* will result in the formation of a series of spectra, each corresponding to a different *order*, or value of n (Figure 20.8). In contrast to that produced by a prism, spectra produced by gratings are uniformly dispersed. Overlap of spectra of different orders can, however, lead to difficulties. Fortunately, the intensity of the high-order spectra is much less than that of the first order and generally can be removed with suitable filters.

SAMPLE CONTAINERS

In common with monochromators, the cells or *cuvettes* that hold the samples must be made from materials that pass radiation in the spectral region of interest. Thus quartz or fused silica is required for work in the ultraviolet region. These materials, as well as glass, can be employed for visible radiation; the infrared region requires windows of such substances as sodium chloride or calcium fluoride. In general, the windows should be perfectly normal to the direction of the beam of radiation in order to minimize losses by reflection. For reasons of economy, however, the simpler instruments employ cells that are cylindrical and thus present a curved surface to the incident beam. With such cells, particular care is needed to reproduce the position of the cell with respect to the beam if reproducible results are to be achieved; it is good practice to mark cylindrical cells so that the same surface is always presented to the radiation front. Variations in the path length will otherwise occur since these cells are seldom perfectly circular in cross section.

RADIATION DETECTORS

To determine the absorbance of a solution it is necessary to have a means for comparing the power of the radiation passing through the sample with that traversing the solvent. Most devices used for this purpose convert the radiant energy into electric energy, which can then be measured by conventional equipment.

The device chosen should be responsive over a wide wavelength range. Furthermore it is essential that the signal produced by the detector be directly proportional to the power of the beam impinging upon it. When this condition is satisfied, we may write

$$P = kG$$

and

$$P_0 = kG_0$$

where G and G_0 represent the electrical response of the detector when placed in the path of the radiation passing through the solution and the solvent, respectively. Thus, the absorbance is given by

$$\log \frac{P_0}{P} = \log \frac{kG_0}{kG} = \log \frac{G_0}{G}$$

Detectors for Ultraviolet and Visible Radiation. The *barrier layer* or *photovoltaic* cell is a photoelectric device that is used primarily for the detection and measurement of visible radiation. It consists of a flat copper or iron electrode upon which is deposited a layer of semiconducting material, such as selenium or copper (I) oxide. A transparent metallic film of gold, silver, or lead covers this and serves as the second or collector electrode; the entire array is protected by a transparent envelope. The interface between the selenium and the metal film serves as a barrier to the passage of electrons. Irradiation with light, however, provides some electrons with sufficient energy to overcome this barrier, and electrons flow from the semiconductor to the metal film. If the metal film is connected via an external circuit to the plate on the other side of the semiconducting layer, a flow of electrons through this circuit will occur provided its resistance is not too great. Ordinarily this current is large enough to be measured with a galvanometer or microammeter; under proper conditions its magnitude will be directly proportional to the power of the radiation striking the cell. Currents on the order of 10 to 100 microamperes are typical.

The barrier layer cell constitutes a rugged, low-cost means for measuring radiant power. No external source of electric energy is required. On the other hand, its output cannot be readily amplified owing to its low internal resistance. Thus, although the barrier cell layer delivers a readily measured response at high levels of illumination, it suffers from lack of sensitivity at low levels when compared with other detectors. Finally, a barrier layer cell exhibits fatigue, its response falling off with time upon prolonged illumination; proper circuit design and choice of experimental conditions largely eliminate this source of difficulty.

A second type of photoelectric device, which may be used in both the ultraviolet and visible regions, is the *phototube*. This consists of a semi-cylindrical cathode and a wire anode sealed inside an evacuated glass envelope. The concave surface of the cathode supports a layer of photo-emissive material, often an alkali-metal or alkaline-earth oxide. The composition of this layer determines the spectral region to which the tube is responsive. A potential is impressed between anode and cathode, the former being positive with respect to the latter.

Electrons emitted from the cathode surface upon illumination are accelerated toward the anode by the applied potential; their number is proportional to the radiant power of the light. The fraction of these electrons collected by the anode becomes greater as the applied potential increases. At so-called saturation, essentially all are collected and further increases in potential have no effect. The current passing through a phototube operated at potentials in excess of that required for saturation will be linear with respect to the radiant power of the light striking it.

Instruments employing phototubes are somewhat more complicated than their counterparts equipped with photovoltaic cells. This results from the need for an external source of electric energy. In addition, the output currents are generally so small that amplification is necessary before they can be measured accurately. Finally, it is necessary to compensate for the small currents, called *dark currents*, that flow even in total darkness owing to the thermal emission of electrons from the cathode. Notwithstanding these drawbacks, however, important advantages accrue from the use of a phototube. Because its output is readily amplified, the phototube is potentially a more sensitive radiation detector than the photocell. Moreover, phototubes can be constructed that respond to ultraviolet radiation; this property renders absorption measurements feasible in this region.

Figure 20.9 is a schematic diagram of a typical phototube arrangement.

The *photomultiplier tube* is a type of phototube in which the primary signal resulting from photoemission is amplified internally by factors as great as 10^8. In addition to a photosensitive cathode and an anode, this tube contains a number of other electrodes, called dynodes. Each dynode is focused upon the next succeeding one, and each is maintained at a higher

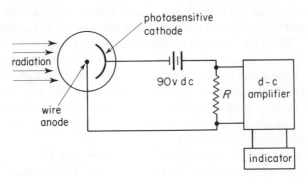

Fig. 20.9 Schematic Diagram of a Phototube and its Accessory Circuit. The current induced by the radiation causes a potential drop across the resistor *R*; this is amplified and measured by the indicator.

positive potential than the preceding one. As a result, any given dynode serves as anode for the one that precedes it and as cathode for the one that follows.

Every electron striking a dynode surface causes the emission of several electrons. These, in turn, are accelerated toward the next dynode where the same process takes place. After this has occurred at six or seven dynodes, each photoelectron emitted by the cathode will have indirectly caused a cascade of 10^6 or more electrons to be collected at the anode. This yields an extremely sensitive photoelectric device.

Detectors for Infrared Radiation. Generally, infrared radiation is detected by measuring the temperature rise of a blackened material placed in the beam of radiation. The temperature changes resulting from absorption of the radiant energy are minute indeed; thus the ambient temperature must be carefully controlled to avoid large errors in the measurements.

One method of determining the temperature change involves use of a tiny thermocouple or a group of thermocouples called a *thermopile*. With this device the electromotive force developed across a dissimilar metal junction is measured.

A *bolometer* is a second type of temperature detector and consists of a resistance wire or a thermistor whose resistance varies as a function of temperature. Here, it is the change in electrical resistance of the detector that is measured.

SOME TYPICAL INSTRUMENTS AND TECHNIQUES

Having considered the four basic components required for measuring the absorbance of a solution, we can now consider how they are combined to give a finished instrument. Inasmuch as each of these components may take a variety of forms, a considerable variation in the design of instruments is to be expected; we shall limit this discussion to a few typical examples.

Absorption methods are commonly classified on the basis of the instruments and techniques employed in the measurements. Thus, a *spectrophotometric method* employs a *spectrophotometer* consisting, in essence, of a light source, a prism or grating monochromator, a photoelectric detector of radiation, and other suitable accessories. Ultraviolet, visible, and infrared spectrophotometers are commonly employed in analytical work.

A *photometer* is a simpler instrument consisting of a photoelectric detector, a light source, and cells. Filters are employed to restrict the radiation from the source. Generally, *photometric* methods are restricted to the visible region of the spectrum; the instruments have also been called *photoelectric colorimeters* or *colorimeters.*

We shall limit use of the term *colorimeter* to those instruments that employ the human eye as the detector for radiation. Colorimetric methods represent the simplest form of absorption analysis.

Colorimetry. In its simplest form, colorimetry consists of visual matching of the color of the solutions of the substance with a set of standards. For this purpose flat-bottomed *Nessler tubes* are frequently employed. These are calibrated so that a uniform light path is achieved. Daylight, reflected through the bottoms of the tubes, commonly serves as a radiation source. Ordinarily, no attempt is made to restrict the portion of the spectrum employed.

A somewhat more refined colorimetric procedure involves the comparison of the unknown with a single standard solution. Here, the two solutions are contained in flat-bottomed tubes; the path lengths are varied by means of adjustable transparent plungers that can be moved up and down in the solutions. After balance has been achieved visually, the path lengths are measured; assuming that Beer's law is applicable, the concentration of the unknown may then be calculated

$$A_x = A_s$$
$$\epsilon b_x c_x = \epsilon b_s c_s$$

or

$$c_x = c_s \frac{b_s}{b_x}$$

where x refers to the unknown and s to the standard. A *Duboscq* colorimeter embodies these principles and is equipped with an optical system that permits the ready comparison of the beams passing through an eyepiece with a split field.

Visual colorimetric methods suffer from several disadvantages. A standard or series of standards must always be available. Furthermore, the eye may not be capable of matching colors if a second colored substance is present in the solution. Finally, the eye is not as sensitive to small differences in absorbance as a photoelectric device; as a consequence, concentration differences smaller than about 5 percent relative cannot be detected.

Photometric Methods and Instruments. A considerable increase in sensitivity results from the substitution of a photoelectric detector in place of the eye, and from limiting the range of radiation to those wavelengths that are most strongly absorbed by the sample. Figure 20.10 presents schematic diagrams for two instruments that accomplish this.

The first of these is a simple single-beam photometer, consisting of a tungsten filament bulb, a lens to provide a parallel beam of light, a filter, and photovoltaic cell. The current produced in the last is measured with a microammeter. In most single-beam instruments provision is made for the scale of the meter to read directly in terms of percent transmittance. The face of the meter is scribed with a linear scale from 0 to 100. A cell containing only the solvent is first placed in the light path and the power of the beam adjusted until the meter needle indicates 100. This is accomplished either by varying the voltage applied to the lamp or, as in the diagram, by varying the opening of a diaphragm interposed in the light path. The sample is then placed in the beam; since the signal from the photovoltaic cell is linear, the resultant scale reading will be the percent transmittance (that is, the percent of full scale). Clearly, a logarithmic scale would give the absorbance of the solution directly.

A disadvantage of a single-beam photometer lies in the uncertainty in the measurements resulting from fluctuations in light intensity during the measurement of transmittance. The magnitude of this uncertainty can be minimized by employing a double-beam instrument such as that shown in Figure 20.10. Here, the light beam is split by some means. A portion passes through the sample or solvent and thence to a detector. The other portion is directed to a second reference detector that continuously monitors the output of the lamp. The output of the working photocell is then compared with that of the reference by a suitable circuit design. In the instrument shown, the currents from the two photovoltaic cells are passed through variable resistances; one of these is calibrated as a transmittance scale in linear units from 0 to 100. A sensitive galvanometer, which serves as a null indicator, is connected across the two resistances. When the potential drop across AB is equal to that across CD, no current will pass through the galvanometer; under all other circumstances a current flow will be indicated. At the outset, the solvent is introduced into the cell and contact A is set at 100; contact C is then adjusted until no current is indicated. Introduction of the sample into the cell results in a reduction of the power and therefore a reduction in the potential drop across CD; this

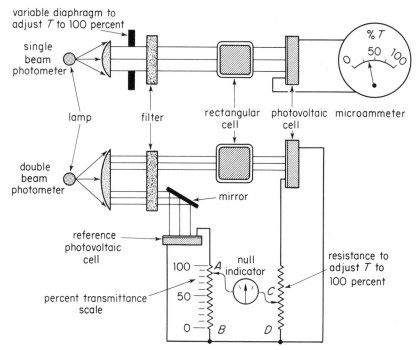

Fig. 20.10 Schematic Diagrams for a Single-beam Photometer (top) and a Double-beam Photometer (bottom).

is compensated for by moving A to a lower value. At balance, the percent transmittance is given on the scale.

Filter Selection for a Photometric Analysis. Photometers are generally supplied with an array of filters, each of which transmits a different portion of the spectrum. Selection of the proper one for a given application is important inasmuch as the sensitivity of the measurement is directly dependent upon the filter. Empirically, the choice of the most suitable filter from a group is relatively simple; it should preferably be the color complement of the sample. If several filters possessing the same general hue are available, the one that causes the sample to exhibit the greatest absorbance (or least transmittance) should be used.

Spectrophotometric Instruments Employing Ultraviolet and Visible Radiation. Several excellent spectrophotometers are available commercially that operate in the visible region of the spectrum; some of these can be used in the ultraviolet region as well, being equipped with quartz optics and phototubes sensitive to this radiation. Less expensive glass optics are employed in those instruments that are useful for visible

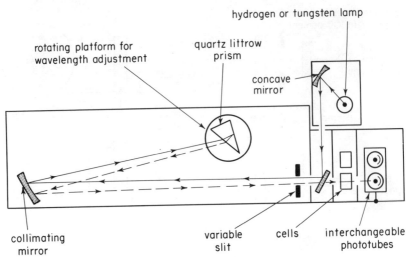

hydrogen or tungsten lamp

rotating platform for wavelength adjustment

quartz littrow prism

concave mirror

collimating mirror

variable slit

cells

interchangeable phototubes

Fig. 20.11 Schematic Diagram of the Beckman DU ® Spectrophotometer. (By permission, Beckman Instruments, Inc., Fullerton, California.)

radiation only. Among the available instruments, there is a great range not only in wavelength region covered but also in the design, quality of components, performance characteristics, and cost. The highest quality spectrophotometers make possible the use of effective band widths of the order of a few tenths of a millimicron while some of the less refined instruments operate at 10 to 20 mμ band widths. These latter instruments are considerably less expensive and are entirely adequate for many applications. Recording instruments that give a plot of transmittance or absorbance as a function of wavelength are also available. Instruments of this sort are naturally more expensive than manual ones; they greatly reduce the time required to obtain a complete absorption spectrum of a solution. On the other hand, they save little time in a quantitative analysis where the measurement consists of determining the absorbance at a single predetermined wavelength.

Figures 20.11 and 20.12 illustrate the components of two spectrophotometers that are widely employed by chemists. The first of these is the Beckman DU spectrophotometer which has quartz optics and can be operated in both the ultraviolet and visible regions of the spectrum. The instrument is provided with interchangeable radiation sources, including a hydrogen discharge tube for the lower wavelengths and a battery-operated tungsten filament lamp for the visible region. A pair of mirrors reflect radiation through an adjustable slit into the monochromator compart-

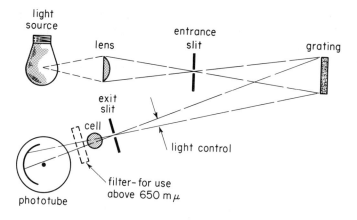

Fig. 20.12 Schematic Diagram of the Bausch and Lomb Spectronic 20 Spectrophotometer. (By permission, Bausch and Lomb, Inc., Rochester, New York.)

ment. After traversing the length of the instrument, the radiation is reflected into a Littrow prism; by adjusting the position of the prism, light of the desired wavelength can be focused on the slit. The optics are so arranged that the entrance and exit beams are displaced from one another on the vertical axis; thus, the exit beam passes beneath the entrance mirror as it enters the cell compartment. After passing through the cell containing sample or solvent, the light passes into the phototube compartment where its power is measured with the more appropriate of a pair of interchangeable phototubes. One of these is sensitive to radiation above 625 mμ and the other to shorter wavelengths. The photoelectric current is passed through a fixed resistance, and the potential drop across this resistance is measured by means of a potentiometer circuit. Amplification of the out-of-balance currents in the potentiometer circuit is necessary since these are very small.

The Beckman instrument is an example of a high-quality manual spectrophotometer that is capable of operating at narrow band widths. Under optimum conditions, uncertainties in transmittance readings with this instrument can be reduced to a few tenths of a percent.

The Bausch and Lomb Spectronic 20, shown schematically in Figure 20.12, may be considered as representative of instruments in which a degree of photometric accuracy is sacrificed in return for simplicity of operation and low cost. Its normal range is 350 to 650 mμ although this can be extended to 900 mμ by the use of a red-sensitive phototube. The monochromator system consists of a reflection grating, lenses, and a pair of fixed slits. Because the grating produces a dispersion that is independent of wavelength, a constant band width of 20 mμ is obtained throughout the entire operating region. The instrument employs a single phototube. Its output is amplified and used to actuate the pointer of a meter calibrated in terms of both transmittance and absorbance. Instruments of this type find extremely wide application for routine analytical work.

Infrared Spectrophotometers. In principle, an infrared spectrophotometer does not differ greatly from instruments for measuring absorption of shorter wavelengths. In detail, however, spectrophotometers for this region are quite dissimilar from those considered in the previous sections. As we have already noted, heated solids are used as sources, and detection of the radiation is accomplished by means of heat-sensitive devices. Both prisms and gratings are employed for dispersion of the radiation; the former are constructed of such infrared-transparent materials as sodium chloride, lithium fluoride, or calcium fluoride; the first of these is by far the most common. Because most of these materials are attacked by water vapor, great care must be exercised to avoid damage from this source.

Concave mirrors, rather than lenses, are used to focus infrared radiation in order to reduce power losses and also because good achromatic lenses are not available for this type of radiation.

The infrared spectrum of most substances is generally complex when compared with that of the ultraviolet and visible regions; the manual collection of data for such a spectrum is a long and tedious process. Consequently, infrared spectrophotometers are designed as recording instruments that automatically produce a plot of transmittance as a function of wavelength. There are no infrared spectrophotometers commercially available comparable to the simple and inexpensive instrument described in the previous section.

20.3   Photometric and Spectrophotometric Measurement

Methods based upon the absorption of radiation represent powerful and useful tools for the analytical chemist. The ultraviolet region is particularly important for the quantitative determination of a variety of organic compounds. Absorption measurements in the visible region provide the means for quantitative determination of trace amounts of most inorganic elements. Spectrophotometric measurement in the infrared is perhaps the most important single tool for the qualitative identification of organic compounds and for elucidation of the structure of such compounds.

SOME GENERAL REMARKS ON QUANTITATIVE
ABSORPTION SPECTROSCOPY

Several important steps precede a quantitative analysis based upon the absorption of radiation; these determine, in no small degree, the ultimate accuracy of the method.

Selection of Wavelength Region. In a spectrophotometric analysis, absorbance measurements are ordinarily made at a wavelength corresponding to an absorption peak. At this wavelength the change in absorbance per unit of concentration is greatest and thus the maximum sensitivity is realized. In addition, the absorption curve is often flat in this region; thus good adherence to Beer's law is to be expected (page 455) and the measurements will be less sensitive to uncertainties arising from failure to reproduce the wavelength setting of the instrument.

The absorption spectrum, if available, will aid in choosing the most suitable filter for a photometric analysis; if this is lacking, the alternate method for selection given on page 467 may be used.

In order to avoid interference from other absorbing substances, a wavelength other than a peak may be appropriate for analysis. If this is necessary, the region selected should be one in which the change in absorbance with wavelength is not too great.

Variables that Influence the Absorbance. A number of common variables often influence the absorption spectrum of a substance. The nature of the solvent, the pH of the solution, the temperature, the presence of high electrolyte concentrations, and the presence of certain other substances may be cited as common examples. The effects of these variables must be known and a set of analytical conditions chosen such that the absorbance will not be materially influenced by their uncontrolled variation.

Determination of the Relationship between Absorbance and Concentration. Having decided upon a set of conditions for the analysis, it is necessary to prepare a calibration curve from a series of standard solutions. These standards should approximate the over-all composition of the actual samples and should cover a reasonable range of concentrations with respect to the species being determined. Seldom, if ever, is it safe to assume adherence to Beer's law and use only a single standard to determine the molar absorptivity. It is even more foolhardy to make use of a literature value for the molar absorptivity to calculate the results of an analysis.

Accuracy. The accuracy obtainable by spectrophotometric or photometric procedures varies considerably depending upon the type of instrument employed, the chemistry of the system being studied, and the care taken. In general, it is not difficult to reduce the relative error to 1 or 2

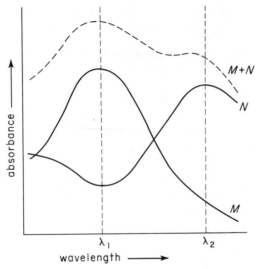

Fig. 20.13 Absorption Spectrum of a Two-component Mixture.

percent. By taking special precautions this figure can often be reduced to
0.2 percent.[5]

Quantitative Analysis of Mixtures of Absorbing Substances. The
total absorbance of a solution at a given wavelength is equal to the sum of
the absorbances of the individual components present. This relationship
makes possible the analysis of the individual components of a mixture even
when an overlap in their spectra occurs. Consider, for example, the spectra
of M and N, shown in Figure 20.13. There is obviously no wavelength at
which the absorbance of this mixture is due simply to one of the components; thus an analysis for either M or N is impossible by a single measurement. However, the absorbances of the mixture at the two wavelengths λ_1
and λ_2 may be expressed as follows:

for λ_1

$$A' = \epsilon'_M bc_M + \epsilon'_N bc_N$$

and for wavelength λ_2

$$A'' = \epsilon''_M bc_M + \epsilon''_N bc_N$$

The four molar absorptivities ϵ'_M, ϵ'_N, ϵ''_M, and ϵ''_N can be evaluated from

[5] See C. F. Hiskey, *Anal. Chem.*, **21**, 1440 (1949); C. N. Reilley and C. M. Crawford,
ibid., **27**, 716 (1955).

individual standard solutions of M and of N. The absorbances of the mixture, A' and A'', are experimentally determinable as is b, the cell thickness. Thus, from these two equations, the concentration of the individual components in the mixture, c_M and c_N, can be readily calculated. These relationships obviously are valid only if Beer's law is followed. The best accuracy in an analysis of this sort is attained by choosing wavelengths at which the differences in molar absorptivities are large.

Mixtures containing more than two absorbing species can be analyzed, in theory at least, if an additional absorbance measurement is made for each added component. The uncertainties in the resulting data become greater, however, as equations are added. This technique is particularly important when infrared radiation is employed for quantitative analysis; in this region, the spectrum for most compounds is complex and the probability of overlap is great when mixtures are analyzed.

SPECTROPHOTOMETRY IN THE ULTRAVIOLET REGION

The most important application of absorption in the ultraviolet region lies in the quantitative determination of organic compounds containing certain functional groups. In addition, a number of inorganic species, particularly among the rare-earth metals, absorb ultraviolet radiation and are thus susceptible to analysis by this method. Ultraviolet absorption spectra can also be employed at times for qualitative identification; applications for this purpose are limited, however, because of the rather broad and nonspecific nature of the absorption peaks.

Organic Functional Groups that Absorb in the Ultraviolet Region. Excitation of a molecule by ultraviolet radiation involves electronic transitions and these processes are affected by the electron distribution within the entire molecule. Thus, the position of an absorption band associated with a given functional group is determined, at least to some degree, by the over-all structure of the molecule. This is in contrast to absorption peaks in certain portions of the infrared where the position of a maximum associated with a certain functional group is only slightly affected by the composition of the molecule as a whole.

Absorption in the ultraviolet region above 200 mμ occurs whenever any of a number of functional groups is present. Some of the more important of these are given in Table 20-2.

Conjugation among the groups shown in Table 20-2 (or with olefinic or aromatic double bonds) leads to marked alterations in the spectra, generally causing a shift in the peaks to longer wavelengths. The aromatic hydrocarbons in particular show well-defined absorption peaks in the region of

TABLE 20-2

Some Functional Groups which Absorb in the Ultraviolet Region

Functional Group		Approximate Wavelength of Maximum, millimicrons
Carbonyl	$\diagdown C{=}O$	280
Nitro	$-NO_2$	370
Nitrate	$-NO_3$	300
Mercapto	$-SH$	230
Alkyl iodide	$R-I$	250
Alkyl bromide	$R-Br$	200
Acid chlorides	$-\overset{\overset{\displaystyle O}{\|\|}}{C}-Cl$	240
Thiocarbonyl	$\diagdown C{=}S$	330
Azo	$-N{=}N-$	370

270 mμ that are associated with the conjugated nature of their double bonds.[6]

Quantitative Analyses Based upon Ultraviolet Absorption. A principal concern in developing a method employing ultraviolet radiation is the choice of a solvent. Clearly this must be a substance that not only dissolves the sample but also is transparent in the region of interest. Water, transmitting radiation as low as 200 mμ, is excellent from the latter standpoint but is seldom a satisfactory solvent for organic compounds. Aliphatic hydrocarbons, methyl and ethyl alcohol, and diethyl ether are transparent to ultraviolet radiation and are often employed. Since the solvent may affect the position of a given absorption maximum, the same solvent should be used for calibration and analysis.

Most analyses employing ultraviolet radiation require the use of quartz or fused silica cells.

---

[6] For a more extensive discussion of the relation between structure and absorption spectra, see W. West in A. Weissberger, Ed., *Physical Methods of Organic Chemistry*, 3d ed., **1**, part 3, 1939–1955. New York: Interscience Publishers, Inc., 1960; W. R. Brode, *Chemical Spectroscopy*, 2d ed. New York: John Wiley and Sons, Inc., 1943. Extensive catalogues of ultraviolet spectra can be found in the following: R. A. Friedel and M. Orchin, *Ultraviolet Spectra of Aromatic Compounds*. New York: John Wiley and Sons, Inc., 1951; American Petroleum Institute, *Ultraviolet Spectral Data*, API Research Project 44. Pittsburgh: Carnegie Institute of Technology.

The reader can obtain an idea of the numerous applications of quantitative ultraviolet spectrophotometry by consulting the series of review articles by Rosenbaum and Hirt.[7]

APPLICATION OF ABSORPTION SPECTROSCOPY IN THE VISIBLE REGION

The most important applications of photometry and spectrophotometry in the visible region are for the determination of traces of inorganic ions.[8] Although a few of these ions are sufficiently colored to allow their direct determination, the majority do not strongly absorb ultraviolet or visible radiation. Most inorganic ions, however, form intensely colored solutions with various complexing reagents and can thus be analyzed.

Colorimetric and spectrophotometric methods are among the most sensitive of all analytical procedures. Thus, determination of metal ions in the concentration range from 10^{-4} to 10^{-5} percent is often feasible by these techniques. Furthermore, many of the chelating agents employed for colorimetric work exhibit a remarkable degree of selectivity; as a result, the analysis for a given ion can frequently be carried out in the presence of overwhelming concentrations of others.

APPLICATION OF INFRARED SPECTROPHOTOMETRY[9]

Infrared spectrophotometry is one of the chemist's most powerful tools for the qualitative identification of organic compounds. It also has some important applications in quantitative analysis but these are overshadowed by its qualitative uses.

Solvents; Preparation of Samples. No single solvent is transparent throughout the infrared region of the spectrum, nor are there any rugged transparent solids, similar to quartz or glass, that can be employed for cells. As a result, the techniques employed in handling samples differ considerably from those used for ultraviolet or visible work.

---

[7] E. J. Rosenbaum, *Anal. Chem.*, **21**, 16 (1949); **22**, 14 (1950); **23**, 12 (1951); **24**, 14 (1952); **26**, 20 (1954); R. C. Hirt, *ibid.*, **28**, 579 (1956); **30**, 589 (1958); **32**, 225R (1960); **34**, 276 R (1962); **36**, 308 R (1964).

[8] The following references describe methods for the majority of the inorganic ions: E. B. Sandell, *Colorimetric Determination of Traces of Metals*, 3d ed. New York: Interscience Publishers, Inc., 1959; D. F. Boltz, Ed., *Colorimetric Determination of Nonmetals*. New York: Interscience Publishers, Inc., 1958; F. D. Snell and C. T. Snell, *Colorimetric Methods of Analysis*, 3d ed., 4 vols. New York: D. Van Nostrand Co., Inc., 1948, 1959.

[9] For a more detailed discussion, see D. H. Anderson, N. B. Woodall, and W. West in A. Weissberger, Ed., *Physical Methods of Organic Chemistry*, 3d ed., **1**, part 3, 1959–2020. New York: Interscience Publishers, Inc., 1960; L. J. Bellamy, *The Infra-Red Spectra of Complex Molecules*, 2d ed. New York: John Wiley and Sons, Inc., 1958.

Generally, water must be avoided in infrared work; not only does it absorb broad regions of radiation, but it also attacks many of the materials used for constructing cells. From the standpoint of transparency, carbon tetrachloride and carbon disulfide are the two most satisfactory solvents; the former is useful in the region up to about 7.6 microns and the latter from that point to 15 microns. Unfortunately, not all samples will dissolve in these liquids, and solvents with more restricted ranges must be employed if a solution technique is to be used. In general, rather concentrated solutions are employed to minimize absorption due to the solvent; this requires narrow cells, thicknesses between 0.01 and 1 mm being common.

Because of the difficulty of finding suitable solvents, liquid samples are frequently studied without dilution. This requires that the thickness of the liquid be kept to a minimum. For qualitative work a very thin film of the liquid placed between rock salt plates will often suffice.

Another technique widely employed for solids is to disperse the finely ground sample in a liquid or solid diluent to form what is called a *mull*. Liquid mulls are prepared by grinding the sample in a viscous hydrocarbon having a high refractive index (to reduce scattering of the radiation); the mineral oil Nujol is widely used for this purpose. The slurry is then examined in a cell for liquids. Absorption by the mineral oil does occur in certain spectral regions. A second dispersing medium that is highly transparent to infrared radiation is solid potassium bromide. The finely ground sample is mixed with this compound and a solid pellet is formed by compressing the mixture in a hydraulic press at pressures of 10,000 to 20,000 lb/in^2. The resulting thin disks are held in the beam for study.

Qualitative Analysis. The general appearance of an infrared absorption spectrum is quite different from that of the ultraviolet and visible regions. Even for relatively simple compounds there is a bewildering array of sharp peaks and minima. It is this multiplicity of peaks, however, that imparts specificity to the spectrum; no two compounds give identical spectrograms. Thus, identity of spectra between an unknown and a known is widely accepted as proof of identity of composition.

In the shorter wavelength region of the infrared (below about 7.5 microns) are found peaks useful for the identification of certain functional groups; the positions of the maxima in this region are only slightly affected by the carbon skeleton to which the groups are attached. Investigation of this portion of the spectrum then gives considerable information regarding the over-all constitution of the molecule under investigation. Table 20-3 gives the positions of characteristic maxima for some common functional groups.[10]

---

[10] For more detailed information, see N. B. Colthup, *J. Opt. Soc. Amer.*, **40**, 397 (1950).

TABLE 20-3

Some Characteristic Infrared Absorption Peaks

Functional Group		Wavelength of Absorption Peak, microns
O—H	(alcohol)	2.8—3.3
—NH$_2$	(primary amine)	2.9—3.0
C—H	(aromatic)	3.2—3.3
C—H	(aliphatic)	3.3—3.7
C≡N		4.2—4.6
C=O	(ester)	5.7—5.8
C=O	(acid)	5.8—6.0
C=O	(aldehyde and ketone)	5.8—6.0
C=C		6.0—6.2

In most instances identification of the functional groups in a molecule is not sufficient to permit positive identification of the compound and the entire spectrum must be compared with that of known compounds. Collections of spectra are available for this purpose.[11]

Quantitative Analysis. Quantitative measurements in the infrared region are not different in principle from similar measurements in the ultraviolet and visible region. Several practical problems, however, make the attainment of comparable accuracies difficult. Among these is the necessity of using very narrow cell widths that are difficult to reproduce, the complexity of the spectra that leads to a high probability of overlap in absorption among the components in the sample, and the narrowness of the peaks that often leads to deviations from Beer's law.

20.4 Experiments

DETERMINATION OF IRON IN WATER

An excellent and sensitive method for the determination of iron is based upon the formation of the orange-red iron (II)-orthophenanthroline complex, the structure of which is shown on page 356. Orthophenanthroline is a weak base, and in acidic solution the principal species present is the phenan-

---

[11] American Petroleum Institute, *Infrared Spectral Data*, A.P.I. Research Project 44, Carnegie Institute of Technology, Pittsburgh, Penn.; *Sadtler Standard Spectra*, Sadtler Research Laboratories, Philadelphia, Penn.

throlium ion PhH^+. Thus, the complex-formation reaction is best described by the following equation:

$$Fe^{2+} + 3PhH^+ \rightleftharpoons Fe(Ph)_3^{2+} + 3H^+$$

The equilibrium constant for this reaction is 2.5×10^6 at 25° C. Clearly, the position of equilibrium is dependent upon the pH; at values lower than 2, incomplete reaction is encountered at the usual reagent concentration. Ordinarily a pH of about 3.5 is recommended for the analysis, but careful control of this variable is not required.

In using this reagent for the analysis of iron, an excess of reducing agent is added to the solution to keep the iron in the reduced state; hydroquinone or hydroxylamine hydrochloride are convenient for this purpose. Once formed, the color of the complex is stable for long periods of time.

Certain ions interfere with the analysis for iron and must therefore be absent. These include colored ions in general; silver and bismuth which form precipitates with the reagent; and cadmium, mercury, and zinc which form colorless soluble complexes with the reagent thus reducing the intensity of the color. Under certain conditions molybdenum, tungsten, copper, cobalt, nickel, and tin may also interfere.[12]

★REAGENTS. *Hydroquinone solution,* 1 percent in water.

Sodium citrate solution, 250 grams/liter of solution.

o-Phenanthroline, 0.5 percent of the monohydrate in water. Warm to effect solution and store in a dark place. Discard the reagent when it becomes colored.

Standard iron solution, 0.1 mg Fe/ml. Dissolve 0.702 gram of analytical reagent grade $FeSO_4 \cdot (NH_4)_2SO_4 \cdot 6H_2O$ in 50 ml of water containing 1 ml of concentrated H_2SO_4. Transfer to a volumetric flask and dilute to exactly 1 liter.

★APPARATUS. This experiment can be carried out with a spectrophotometer at 508 mμ or with a photometer equipped with a green filter. Consult the manufacturer's instructions for operating details of the instrument to be used.

★PREPARATION OF CALIBRATION CURVE. Measure a 5-ml aliquot of the iron solution into a beaker, add a drop of bromthymol-blue indicator and add the sodium citrate solution from a pipet until the intermediate color of the indicator is achieved. Note the volume of citrate required and discard the solution. Now measure a second 5-ml aliquot of the iron standard into a 100-ml volumetric flask, and add 1 ml each of the hydroquinone and orthophenanthroline solutions. Introduce the same quantity of citrate solution as was required for the preliminary titration, and allow the mixture to stand 1 hour. Dilute to the mark.

---

[12] See E. B. Sandell, *Colorimetric Determination of Traces of Metals,* 3d ed., 537. New York: Interscience Publishers, Inc., 1959.

Clean the cells for the instrument, rinse one of these with the standard solution and then fill. Rinse and fill the second cell with a blank containing all of the reagents except the iron solution. Carefully wipe the windows of the cells with tissue and place them in the instrument. Measure the absorbance of the standard against the blank.

Prepare at least three other standards so that a range of absorbances of about 0.1 to 1.0 will be covered. Construct a calibration curve for the instrument.

★ANALYSIS OF SAMPLE. Measure 5 ml of the sample into a beaker and adjust the acidity with the sodium citrate solution as before. If the original sample is basic to the indicator, add measured quantities of 0.1 N H_2SO_4 until the color just changes; then proceed as before. Discard the aliquot and transfer 5 ml of the sample to a 100-ml volumetric flask. Add 1 ml of orthophenanthroline, 1 ml of hydroquinone, and the amounts of citrate (and H_2SO_4) required to adjust the pH. After 1 hour, dilute to the mark and measure the absorbance. Repeat the analysis using quantities of sample that will give an absorbance in the range of the calibration curve.

Calculate the milligrams of iron per liter of sample solution.

DETERMINATION OF MANGANESE IN STEEL

Small quantities of manganese are readily determined colorimetrically by oxidation to the highly colored permanganate ion. Potassium periodate is effective for this purpose.

$$5IO_4^- + 2Mn^{2+} + 3H_2O \rightarrow 2MnO_4^- + 5IO_3^- + 6H^+$$

Permanganate solutions containing an excess of periodate are relatively stable.

Interferences to this procedure are few. The presence of colored ions can be compensated for by employing as a blank an aliquot of the sample that has not been oxidized by the periodate. This method of correction is not effective in the presence of appreciable quantities of cerium (III) or chromium (III) ions, for both of these are oxidized by the periodate to a greater or lesser extent and their reaction products absorb in the region commonly employed for the permanganate.

The accompanying method is applicable to most steels except those containing large amounts of chromium. The sample is dissolved in nitric acid; any carbon present is removed by oxidation with peroxydisulfate. Phosphoric acid is added to complex the iron (III) and prevent the color of this species from interfering with the analysis. One aliquot of the sample is carried through the entire procedure except that no periodate is added. This serves as a blank to correct for the presence of colored foreign ions.

★APPARATUS. A spectrophotometer set at 525 mμ or a photometer with a green filter may be used for absorbance measurements. Consult the manual of the instrument for operating instructions.

★PREPARATION OF CALIBRATION CURVE. Prepare a solution of $KMnO_4$ that contains the equivalent of 0.100 gram Mn/liter by dilution of a standardized solution of $KMnO_4$. Alternatively, exactly 0.100 gram of pure manganese metal can be dissolved in 10 ml of HNO_3. The solution is boiled to remove oxides of nitrogen and diluted to exactly 1 liter. In this case, aliquots of the sample are oxidized with KIO_4 in the same way as the sample; proceed as in the second paragraph for the analysis of steel below.

Transfer 5.00 ml of the permanganate solution to a 50-ml volumetric flask and dilute to the mark with water. Rinse and fill one of the absorption cells of the instrument with this solution; fill a second cell with water and dry the windows of both with a clean tissue. Determine the absorbance of the solution.

Now prepare a series of standards (at least three more) in the same way to cover an absorbance range between 0.1 and 1.0; plot a calibration curve.

★ANALYSIS OF STEEL. Weigh out duplicate 0.8-gram samples of the steel and dissolve in 50 ml of 1 : 3 HNO_3 with boiling. Heating for 5 minutes should suffice. Cautiously add about 1 gram of ammonium peroxydisulfate and boil gently for 10 to 15 minutes. If the solution is pink or contains a brown oxide of manganese, add approximately 0.1 gram of sodium hydrogen sulfite or ammonium hydrogen sulfite and heat for another 5 minutes. Cool and dilute the solution to exactly 100 ml in a volumetric flask.

Pipet two 25-ml aliquots of the sample into small beakers and add 3 to 5 ml of H_3PO_4. To *one* of the two aliquots add 0.4 gram of KIO_4 and boil the solution for 5 minutes. The second aliquot serves as a blank and is *not treated with periodate*. Cool and dilute both aliquots to exactly 50 ml in volumetric flasks. Determine the absorbance of the periodate-treated sample against the blank that contains no periodate and obtain the milligrams of manganese present from the calibration curve.

Report the percent manganese in the steel.

SPECTROPHOTOMETRIC ANALYSIS OF A
PERMANGANATE—DICHROMATE MIXTURE

Both potassium dichromate and potassium permanganate absorb strongly in the visible and ultraviolet regions; their spectra overlap sufficiently so that the presence of one interferes with the quantitative analysis of the other. By employing the techniques described on page 472, however, accurate analysis of a mixture of these compounds is possible.

★REAGENTS. *Standard potassium dichromate solution.* This solution should be about $4 \times 10^{-3} F$; it can be prepared from pure $K_2Cr_2O_7$

by suitable dilution of a weighed quantity of the reagent grade substance. Its concentration should be known to within 1 percent.

Standard potassium permanganate solution. This solution should be about 4×10^{-3} F. It can be prepared by suitable dilution of a more concentrated solution which has been standardized in the usual way (page 373).

★APPARATUS. A spectrophotometer is needed for this experiment.

★ABSORPTION SPECTRA. Transfer 10.0 ml of standard $K_2Cr_2O_7$ solution to a 100-ml volumetric flask and dilute to the mark with approximately 0.5 N H_2SO_4. Prepare a solution of $KMnO_4$ in the same way.

Rinse and fill one of the cells of the spectrophotometer with the $K_2Cr_2O_7$ solution, one with the $KMnO_4$, and a third with a 0.5 N solution of H_2SO_4. Measure the absorbance of the $K_2Cr_2O_7$ and the $KMnO_4$ against the H_2SO_4 solution at intervals throughout the wavelength region between 350 and 650 mμ. Sufficient data should be collected to define clearly the maxima in the curves.

Plot absorption curves for the two ions.

★CALIBRATION CURVES. Prepare additional standard solutions of the $KMnO_4$ and $K_2Cr_2O_7$ in 0.5 N H_2SO_4 and determine the absorbance of each at two wavelengths chosen as suitable for the analysis of a mixture of the two substances (see the absorption spectrum for each).

Plot absorbance versus concentration for each species at the two wavelengths and calculate the best values of ϵb at these.

★ANALYSIS OF A MIXTURE. The unknown will consist of an aqueous solution of $K_2Cr_2O_7$ and $KMnO_4$.

Transfer the sample quantitatively to a 100-ml volumetric flask and dilute to the mark with 0.5 N H_2SO_4. Measure the absorbance at the wavelengths at which calibration data were obtained. Calculate the concentration of $KMnO_4$ and $K_2Cr_2O_7$ in the solution.

Report the number of millimols of $KMnO_4$ and the number of millimols of $K_2Cr_2O_7$ in the sample.

Problems

1. What would be the color of
   (a) a solution that absorbs strongly all radiation above 500 mμ
   (b) a solution with a transmission peak at 575 mμ
   (c) a filter suitable for a photometric analysis based upon the blue copper-ammonia complex
   (d) a filter for a solution that has an absorption peak at 500 mμ

2. A photometer consisting of a photovoltaic cell and a microammeter was employed for measurements of light absorption. When a beam of radiation that had passed through the colored solution was caused to fall on the photocell, a current of 16.1 microamperes was observed; the same beam caused a current of 47.1 microamperes when it had passed through the solvent.

(a) What was the percent transmittance of the solution?   ans. 34.2 percent

(b) What was the absorbance of the solution?   ans. 0.466

(c) What would be the microammeter reading if a solution containing twice the concentration of colored substance was placed in the same beam?

ans. 5.51 microamperes

(d) What would be the percent transmittance of the solution if a layer of solution half the width of the above were measured?   ans. 58.5 percent

3. A photometer with a linear response to radiation gave a reading of 237 mv when a colored solution was placed in the light path. A reading of 412 mv was obtained when the solvent was interposed in the same beam.

(a) Calculate the absorbance and percent transmittance of the solution.

(b) What would be the transmittance and absorbance of a solution that contained three fourths the above concentration?

(c) What would be the photometer response in millivolts if the layer of the original solution were increased in thickness by 50 percent?

4. The colored substance M was found to have an absorption peak at 405 mμ. A solution containing 3.00 mg M/liter was found to have an absorbance of 0.842 when examined in a 2.50-cm cell. The formula weight of M is 150.

(a) Calculate the absorptivity of M at 405 mμ.

ans. $1.12 \times 10^2 \text{cm}^{-1}\text{gram}^{-1}$ liter

(b) What is the molar absorptivity of M at 405 mμ?

ans. $1.68 \times 10^4 \text{cm}^{-1}\text{mol}^{-1}$ liter

(c) What weight of M is contained in 100 ml of a solution that has an absorbance of 0.760 at 405 mμ when measured with a 1.00-cm cell?

ans. 0.678 mg

5. A 4.00×10^{-4} M solution of X (gfw = 125) was found to have an absorbance of 0.636 at 500 mμ when examined with a 1.50-cm cell.

(a) What is the molar absorptivity of X at 500 mμ?

(b) Calculate the absorptivity of X at 500 mμ.

(c) What weight of X is contained in 400 ml of a solution having a percent transmittance of 34.8 when a 2.00-cm cell is employed?

(d) A 0.2-gram sample containing approximately 0.05 percent of X was dissolved and diluted to exactly 100 ml. What dilution of this solution should be made so that an absorbance of about 0.5 will be obtained with a 1.00-cm cell?

6. The substance Y has a molar absorptivity of 4,300 at 360 mμ. What is the concentration of Y in a solution having an absorbance of 0.830 at 360 mμ when measured in a 2.50-cm cell?

7. A 0.400-gram sample containing manganese was dissolved, oxidized with periodate, and diluted to 500 ml. The resulting solution was compared with a 2.07×10^{-3} F solution of $KMnO_4$. A visual color match was obtained when the path length for the standard was 5.35 cm and that for the unknown was 4.00 cm. Calculate the percent manganese in the sample.

8. The anion X^{2-} reacts with the metal ion M^{2+} to form the colored complex MX_2^{2-}. In the presence of a hundredfold or greater excess of X^{2-}, the color is found to obey Beer's law. With smaller amounts of reagent, however, deviations are found as a consequence of incompleteness of the reaction.

A $1.00 \times 10^{-3} F$ solution of M^{2+} was made $0.1 F$ in X^{2-} and the absorbance was found to be 0.850 with a 1.00-cm cell. A $1.00 \times 10^{-3} F$ solution that was $10 \times 10^{-3} F$ in X^{2-} had an absorbance of 0.612. Calculate the instability constant for the complex. ans. $K = 2.85 \times 10^{-5}$

9. A colored complex ion AB_2^{2-} is formed when A^{2+} is mixed with B^{2-}. Various quantities of Na_2B were added to a $2.00 \times 10^{-3} F$ solution of A^{2+}; it was found that the absorbance became independent of the quantity of this salt at formal concentrations greater than about 0.2. This was taken to mean that the complex-formation reaction was essentially complete under these conditions. The absorbance in the level region was 0.982.

When the formal concentration of Na_2B was 9.00×10^{-3}, the absorbance was 0.670. Calculate the instability constant for the complex.

(21)

The Analysis of Real Substances

Thus far we have concentrated mainly upon the measurement of the concentration of the constituent of interest in a solution uncluttered by interfering components. Frequently this final analytical step is a relatively simple process, because the number of variables to be controlled is small, and the tools available are numerous and refined. Further, we usually have sufficient theoretical knowledge of simple systems to allow definition and solution of problems arising in the final phase of an analysis. Indeed, if every chemical analysis consisted of determining the concentration of a single element or compound in a simple and readily soluble homogeneous mixture, analytical chemistry could profitably be entrusted to the hands of a skilled mechanic; certainly a well-trained chemist could find more useful and challenging work for his mind and his hands.

In fact, the materials with which the chemist works are generally not simple, chemically speaking, regardless of whether his talents are employed in academic research or in the laboratories of industry. Rather, most substances that require analysis are complex, consisting of several, or indeed several tens, of elements or compounds. Frequently these materials fall short of the ideal in matters of solubility, volatility, stability, and homogeneity. With such substances, several steps must precede the final one of measurement. As a matter of fact the final measurement is often anticlimactic in a sense, being by far the easiest to perform.

By way of illustration, let us consider the analysis of calcium, an element that occurs widely in nature and is important in many manufacturing processes. Several excellent methods are available for determining the calcium ion concentration of a simple aqueous solution; among these may be cited precipitation as the oxalate, a compound that can be either titrated with a standard solution of permanganate or ignited to the carbonate for a gravimetric measurement. In addition, calcium ion can also be titrated directly with ethylenediaminetetraacetic acid, or its concentration determined by flame-photometric measurement. All of these methods afford an accurate measure of the calcium content of a simple salt such as the carbonate. The chemist, however, is seldom interested in the calcium content of calcium carbonate. Rather he needs to know the percentage of this element in a sample of animal tissue, in a silicate rock, or in a piece of glass. The analysis thus acquires new complexities. For example, none of these materials is soluble in water or in any of the common aqueous reagents; strenuous treatment of the sample may be needed in order to obtain the solution required for the final step. Unless precautions are observed such measures may cause losses of the element of interest, or perhaps its introduction from the reagents and vessels employed.

Even after the sample has been decomposed and the calcium put into solution, the excellent procedures mentioned above cannot ordinarily be applied immediately to finish the analysis, for they are all based upon reactions or properties shared by elements in addition to calcium. Thus a sample of animal tissue, a silicate rock, or a glass would almost surely contain one or more components that would precipitate with oxalate, react with ethylenediaminetetraacetic acid, or affect the intensity of emitted light in a flame-photometric measurement. As a consequence, steps to free the calcium from potential interferences must usually precede the final measurement; these could well involve several operations.

We have chosen to call substances such as those described in the preceding illustration "real" substances. In contrast, most of the samples encountered in the laboratory of an elementary quantitative analysis course definitely are not real, for they are generally homogeneous, usually stable even toward rough handling, readily soluble, and above all chemically simple. Moreover, well-established and thoroughly tested directions exist for their analysis. From the pedagogical viewpoint there is value in introducing the student to analytical techniques via such substances, for they do allow him to concentrate his attention on the mechanical aspects of an analysis. Once these mechanics have been mastered, however, there is little point in the continued analysis of unreal substances; to do so creates the impression that a chemical analysis involves nothing more than the slavish adherence to a well-defined and narrow path, at the end of which is obtained a number accurate to one or two parts in a thousand. All too many chemists retain this view far into their professional lives.

In truth, the pathway leading to the composition of real substances is often a trying one in which intellectual skills and chemical intuition are more important than mechanical aptitude. Furthermore, the chemist often finds it necessary to draw a compromise between the time he can afford to expend in performing the analysis and the accuracy he thinks he needs. If he is realistic, more often than not he is happy to settle for a part or two in one hundred rather than a part or two in a thousand; with very complex materials even the former accuracy will be obtainable only with an expenditure of a great deal of time and effort.

The difficulties encountered in the analysis of real substances arise, of course, from the complexity and variability of their composition. Particularly because of the latter property, the chemist is frequently unable to find in the literature a clearly defined and well-tested route to follow; he is thus forced to modify existing procedures to account for the composition of his material, or he must blaze a new pathway. In either case, each new component creates several new variables. Using again the analysis for calcium in a sample of calcium carbonate as an example, the number of components is small and the variables likely to affect the results are reasonable in number. Principal among these are the solubility of the sample in acid, the solubility of calcium oxalate as a function of pH, and the effect of the precipitation rate upon the purity and filterability of calcium oxalate. Contrast this with the analysis for calcium in a real sample such as a silicate rock containing a dozen or more other elements. Here the analyst has to consider not only the solubility of the calcium oxalate, but the oxalates of all of the cations present as well; coprecipitation of each with the calcium oxalate also becomes a concern. Furthermore, a more drastic treatment is required to dissolve the sample, and additional steps are necessary to separate the interfering ions. With each new step, additional variables arise; and with this increase, a theoretical treatment of the problem becomes difficult or practically impossible.

The analysis of a real substance can thus be a challenging problem requiring knowledge, intuition, and experience. The development of a procedure for such materials is not something to be taken lightly even by the experienced chemist.

21.1   Choosing a Method for the Analysis of Complex Substances

The choice of method for the analysis of a complex substance requires good judgment and a sound knowledge of the advantages and limitations of the various tools of analytical chemistry; a familiarity with the literature on the subject is also essential. We cannot be too explicit concerning this choice because there is no single best way that will apply under all circumstances.

We can, however, suggest a somewhat systematic approach to the problem and present some generalities that will aid in making an intelligent decision.

DEFINITION OF THE PROBLEM

A first step, which should precede any choice of an analytical method, is that of clearly defining the problem at hand. To do this, the chemist should seek answers to certain questions: What is the concentration range of the species to be determined? What accuracy is demanded by the use to which the data are to be put? What other elements or compounds are present in the substance? What are the physical and chemical properties of the sample as a whole? and, finally, How many samples are to be analyzed?

The answer to the question regarding the concentration range of the element or compound of interest is very pertinent, for this may well limit the choice of feasible methods. If, for example, the analyst is interested in an element present in a concentration of a few parts per million, he can generally eliminate gravimetric or volumetric methods and turn his mind to spectrophotometric, spectrographic, and other more sensitive procedures. He knows, furthermore, that in this concentration range he will have to guard against even small losses of an element by coprecipitation and volatility or slight contaminations of samples from reagents. On the other hand, if the substance in which he is interested occurs in large concentrations, these considerations become less important, and he may well want to consider the classical analytical methods.

The answer to the question regarding the accuracy demanded is of vital importance in the choice of an analytical method and the way the procedure is carried out. It is the height of folly to perform physical or chemical measurements with an accuracy significantly greater than that demanded by the use to which the data are to be put. As we have mentioned earlier, the relationship between time expended and accuracy achieved in an analysis ordinarily is not linear; as a result, a tenfold improvement in the latter often requires a twentyfold, a fiftyfold, or an even greater increase in the hours required for the measurement. As a consequence, a few minutes spent at the outset of an analysis in careful consideration of what sort of accuracy is really needed represents an investment that a chemist can well afford to make.

The demands of accuracy will frequently dictate the procedure chosen for an analysis. For example, if the allowable error in an aluminum analysis is only a few parts in a thousand, a gravimetric procedure will probably be required. On the other hand if an error of, say, fifty parts per thousand can be tolerated, spectrographic or electroanalytical procedures should be considered as well. The experimental details of the method are also affected by accuracy requirements. Thus, if precipitation with ammonia were chosen for the analysis of a sample containing 20 percent of aluminum, the presence of 0.2 percent of iron would be of serious concern where an accuracy of a few parts in a thousand was demanded; here, a preliminary separation of the two elements would be necessary. On the other hand, with a limit of error of fifty parts in a thousand, a chemist might well dispense with the separation of iron and thus shorten the analysis considerably. Further, this tolerance would govern his performance in other aspects of the analysis. He would weigh out a 1-gram sample to perhaps the nearest 10 mg and certainly no closer than 1 mg. In addition, he might well be less meticulous in transferring and washing his precipitate and in the other time-consuming operations of the gravimetric procedure. If this is done intelligently, he is not being careless, but rather, realistic in terms of economy of time. The question of accuracy then must be settled in clear terms at the very outset.

The third question to be resolved early in the planning stage of an analysis is concerned with the chemical composition of the sample. An answer can frequently be reached from a consideration of the origin of the material; in other cases a partial or complete qualitative analysis must be undertaken. Regardless of source, however, this information is necessary before an intelligent choice of procedure can be made, because methods for completion of the analysis are based on group reactions or group properties —that is, on reactions or properties shared by several elements or compounds. Thus, a procedure for measuring the concentration of a given element that is simple and straightforward in the presence of one group of elements or compounds may require many tedious and time-consuming separations before it can be used in the presence of others. A solvent that is suitable for one combination of compounds may be totally unsatisfactory when applied to another. Clearly, a qualitative knowledge of the chemical composition of the sample is a prerequisite for its quantitative analysis.

The chemist must consider the physical and chemical properties of the substance closely before attempting to derive a method for its analysis. Obviously he should know whether it is a solid, liquid, or gas under ordinary conditions and whether losses by volatility are likely to be a problem. He should also try to determine whether the sample is homogeneous and, if not, what steps can be employed to bring it to this state. It is also important to know whether or not the sample is hygroscopic or deliquescent. It is essential to know what sort of treatment is sufficient to decompose or dissolve the sample without loss. Preliminary tests of one sort or another may be needed to provide this information.

Finally, the number of samples to be analyzed is an important consideration in the choice of method. If there are many, considerable time can be expended calibrating instruments, preparing reagents, assembling equipment, and investigating short cuts since the cost of these operations can be spread over the large number of analyses. On the other hand if at most a few samples are to be analyzed, a longer and more tedious procedure involving none of these operations may prove to be the wiser choice from the economic standpoint.

Having answered the questions enumerated above, the chemist is now in a position to consider possible methods for the attack of his problem. At this point he may have a fairly clear idea, based on his past experience, of how he wishes to proceed. He may also find it prudent to speculate on the problems likely to be encountered in the analysis and how they can be solved. He will probably have eliminated some methods from consideration and put others on the doubtful list. Ordinarily, however, he will wish to turn to the analytical literature in order to profit from the experience of others. This, then, is the next logical step in choosing an analytical procedure.

INVESTIGATION OF THE LITERATURE

The literature dealing with chemical analysis is extensive. For the chemist who will take advantage of it, much of value is to be found here. A list of the reference books and journals that deal with various aspects of analytical chemistry appears on page 493. It is not intended to be exhaustive, but rather one that should be adequate for most work. The list is divided into several categories. In many instances the division is arbitrary since some of the works could be logically placed in more than one category.

In the first section are the general reference works into which the most important knowledge in the field has been distilled. Next come the books devoted to the analysis of specific types of substances such as petroleum, ferrous alloys, paints, and agricultural products. This portion of the list is quite incomplete. Following this are those publications devoted primarily to specific methods for completing the analysis; included are monographs on such diverse subjects as polarography, spectroscopy, gas chromatography, chelating agents, and volumetric methods. A portion of many of these is devoted to detailed instructions for the application of the particular technique to commonly encountered substances. Finally, there is included a list of the journals in which most space is devoted to articles concerned with analytical chemistry.

Often the chemist will begin his search of the literature by going to one or more of the general books on analytical chemistry or to those devoted to the analysis of specific types of materials. In addition, he may find it helpful to consult a general reference work relating to the compound or element in which he is interested. From this study he may get a clear picture of the problem at hand—what steps are likely to be difficult, what separations must be made, what pitfalls must be avoided. In some instances he may find all the answers he needs or even a set of specific instructions for the substance he wishes to analyze. Short of this he may find journal references that will lead directly to this information. In other cases, however, he will come away with only a general notion of how to proceed; he will perhaps have several alternative methods in mind and he may also have some clear ideas of how *not* to proceed. He may then wish to consult the works on specific substances, on specific techniques or go directly to the analytical journals. The monographs on methods for completing the analysis are valuable in deciding among several possible techniques.

One of the main problems in using the analytical journals is that of finding the articles that are pertinent to the problem at hand. The various reference books are useful since most are liberally annotated with references to the original journals. The key to a thorough search of the literature, however, is *Chemical Abstracts*. This journal contains short abstracts of all of the papers found in the major chemical publications of the world. Both yearly and decennial indexes are provided to aid in the search; by looking under the element or compound to be determined and the type of substances to be analyzed, a thorough survey of the methods available can be made. Completion of such a survey involves the expenditure of a good deal of time, however, and is often made unnecessary by consulting reliable reference works.

CHOOSING OR DERIVING A PROCEDURE

Having defined the problem and investigated the literature for possible solutions, the chemist must next decide upon the route he will follow in the laboratory. In some instances, the choice is simple and obvious, and he can proceed directly to his analysis. In others, however, the decision requires the exercise of considerable judgment and ingenuity; here, experience, an understanding of chemical principles and, perhaps, intuition are helpful.

If the substance to be analyzed is one that occurs widely, the literature survey will probably have yielded several alternative methods for the analysis. In this case economic considerations may well dictate employment of that method which will yield the desired reliability with least expenditure of effort. As mentioned earlier the number of samples to be analyzed will often be a determining factor in this choice.

Investigation of the literature will not invariably produce a method designed specifically for the type of sample in which the chemist is interested. Ordinarily, however, he will have encountered procedures for materials that are at least analogous in composition to his; he will then need to decide whether the variables introduced by differences in composition are likely to have any effect on the results. This is often difficult and fraught with uncertainty; recourse to the laboratory may be the only way of obtaining an unequivocal answer.

If it is decided that existing procedures are not applicable, the chemist must then consider whether modifications of these will overcome the problems imposed by the variation in composition. Again he may find that his knowledge of the behavior of complex systems is so limited he can propose only tentative alterations; he must go to the laboratory to establish whether these modifications will accomplish their purpose without introducing new difficulties.

After giving due consideration to existing methods and their modifications, the chemist may decide that none of these will fit his problem and he must improvise his own procedure. To do this he will need to marshal all of the facts he has gathered with respect to the chemical and physical properties of the element or compound to be determined and the state in which it occurs. From these he may be able to arrive at several possible ways of performing the desired measurement. Each of the possibilities must then be examined critically, taking into account the behavior of the other components in the sample as well as the reagents that must be used for solution or decomposition. At this point he must try to anticipate various sources of error and possible interferences arising from interactions among the components and reagents; he may well have to devise methods by which problems of this sort can be circumvented. In the end, it is to be hoped that there will be one or more tentative methods worthy of test. In all probability, the feasibility of one or more of the steps in the procedure cannot be determined on the basis of theoretical considerations alone, and recourse must be had to preliminary laboratory testing of these individual steps. Certainly, critical evaluation of the entire procedure can only come from careful laboratory work.

TESTING THE METHOD

Once a procedure for an analysis has been selected, the question usually arises as to whether the method can be employed directly, without testing, to the problem at hand.

The answer to this is not simple and depends upon a number of considerations. If the procedure chosen is one that has not been widely employed, or one to which a single, or at most a few, literature references are to be found, there may be a real point to preliminary laboratory evaluation. With experience the chemist becomes more and more cautious about accepting all of the claims regarding the virtues of a new method. It is not uncommon to find somewhat exaggerated statements regarding the accuracy and general applicability of a new method. As a consequence, a few hours spent in the laboratory testing such a procedure may be enlightening.

Whenever a major modification of a standard procedure is undertaken or an attempt is made to apply it to a type of sample different from that for which it was designed, a preliminary laboratory test is called for. The effects of such alterations simply cannot be predicted with certainty and the chemist is sanguine indeed who dispenses with such precautions.

Finally, of course, a newly devised procedure must be extensively tested before it is adapted for general use. We must now consider methods by which this can be done.

Analysis of Standard Samples. Unquestionably the best technique for evaluating an analytical method is to employ the procedure for the analysis of one or more standard samples whose composition with respect to the element or compound of interest is known exactly. For this technique to be of value, however, it is essential that the composition of the standard approximate that of the samples to be analyzed both as to the concentration range of the species of interest and the over-all makeup. In some happy instances standards of this sort can readily be synthesized from weighed quantities of pure compounds. Others may be purchased from sources such as the National Bureau of Standards; these, however, are confined largely to common materials of commerce or widely distributed natural products.

As often as not, the chemist finds himself in the position of being unable to acquire a standard sample that matches closely the substance he wishes to analyze. This is particularly true of complex materials in which the form of the species of interest is unknown or variable and quite impossible to reproduce. In these circumstances the best that can be done is to prepare a solution of known concentration whose composition approximates that of the sample after it has been decomposed and placed in solution. Obviously, such a standard gives no information at all concerning the fate of the substance being determined during the important decomposition and solution steps.

Analysis by Other Methods. An analytical method can sometimes be evaluated by comparison of one or more of the results of the procedure with some entirely different method. Clearly, a second method must exist and to be useful should differ considerably from the one under examination. Comparable results from the two serve as presumptive evidence that both are yielding satisfactory results inasmuch as it is unlikely that the same determinate error would affect each. Such a conclusion will not apply to those aspects of the two methods that are similar.

Standard Addition to the Sample. When the foregoing tests are inapplicable, there is yet another method of evaluation. This consists of carrying out the analysis by the proposed procedure; then a known quantity of the species of interest is mixed with a second portion of the sample, this being, wherever possible, in the form in which it occurs in the original sample. The mixture is then analyzed again and the recovery of the added substance determined from the difference in the two results. Such a test may reveal errors arising from the method of treating the sample or from the presence of the other elements or compounds.

21.2 The Literature of Analytical Chemistry

The literature of analytical chemistry can be divided into two broad categories: reference works and papers. The latter may be theoretical or applied in nature and are generally restricted to some specific aspect of analysis. The former are more general in scope and attempt to summarize the current knowledge in the field or in some broad portion of the field. The references and journals in the accompanying list will serve as a point of departure in a search for specific information concerned with analytical chemistry. The classification of reference works employed is certainly imperfect but may be helpful.

REFERENCE WORKS OF A GENERAL NATURE

American Society for Testing Materials, *ASTM Book of Standards*, 7 vols. Philadelphia: American Society for Testing Materials, 1952.

A. A. Benedetti-Pichler, *Essentials of Quantitative Analysis*. New York: The Ronald Press Co., 1956.

N. H. Furman, Ed., *Scott's Standard Methods of Chemical Analysis*, 6th ed. New York: D. Nostrand Co., Inc., 1962. Applied in nature.

R. C. Griffin, *Technical Methods of Analysis*, 2d ed. New York: McGraw-Hill Book Co., Inc., 1927. Applied in nature.

W. F. Hillebrand, G. E. F. Lundell, H. A. Bright, and J. I. Hoffman, *Applied Inorganic Analysis*, 2d ed. New York: John Wiley and Sons, Inc., 1953.

I. M. Kolthoff and P. J. Elving, *Treatise on Analytical Chemistry*. New York: The Interscience Encyclopedia, Inc., 1959. A multivolume reference work.

I. M. Kolthoff and E. B. Sandell, *Textbook of Quantitative Inorganic Analysis*, 3d ed. New York: The Macmillan Co., 1952.

H. A. Laitinen, *Chemical Analysis*. New York: McGraw-Hill Book Co., Inc., 1960. Devoted primarily to theory.

B. M. Margosches and W. Böttger, Eds., *Die Chemische Analyse*. Stuttgart: Ferdinand Enke, 1907– .

Louis Meites, *Handbook of Analytical Chemistry*. New York: McGraw-Hill Book Co., 1963.

C. N. Reilley, Ed., *Advances in Analytical Chemistry and Instrumentation*. New York: Interscience Publishers, Inc., 1960.

T. B. Smith, *Analytical Processes*, 2d ed. London: Edward Arnold (Publishers) Ltd., 1940.

C. R. N. Strouts, J. H. Gilfillan, and H. N. Wilson, Eds., *Analytical Chemistry*, 2 vols. Oxford: The Clarendon Press, 1955.

F. P. Treadwell and W. T. Hall, *Analytical Chemistry*, 9th ed., 2 vols. New York: John Wiley and Sons, Inc., 1942.

H. F. Walton, *Chemical Analysis*. New York: Prentice-Hall, Inc., 1952. Devoted primarily to theory.

H. H. Willard and H. Diehl, *Advanced Quantitative Analysis*. New York: D. Van Nostrand Company, Inc., 1943.

C. L. Wilson, Ed., *Comprehensive Analytical Chemistry*, several vols. Amsterdam: Elsevier Publishing Co., 1959.

REFERENCE WORKS DEVOTED LARGELY TO THE
ANALYSIS OF SPECIFIC TYPES OF SUBSTANCES

Inorganic Substances

American Society for Testing Materials, *ASTM Methods for Chemical Analysis of Metals*. Philadelphia: American Society for Testing Materials, 1956.

G. E. F. Lundell and J. I. Hoffman, *Outlines of Methods of Chemical Analysis*. New York: John Wiley and Sons, Inc., 1938.

J. W. Mellor and H. V. Thompson, *A Treatise on Quantitative Inorganic Analysis*. London: C. Griffin and Co., 1938.

E. C. Pigott, *Ferrous Analysis*, 2d ed. New York: John Wiley and Sons, Inc., 1953.

C. J. Rodden, Ed., *Analytical Chemistry of the Manhattan Project*. New York: McGraw-Hill Book Co., Inc., 1950.

W. R. Schoeller and A. R. Powell, *The Analysis of Minerals and Ores of the Rarer Elements*. London: C. Griffin and Co., 1955.

H. S. Washington, *Chemical Analysis of Rocks*. New York: John Wiley and Sons, Inc., 1930.

R. S. Young, *Industrial Inorganic Analysis*. New York: John Wiley and Sons, Inc., 1953.

Organic Substances

J. S. Fritz and G. S. Hammond, *Quantitative Organic Analysis*. New York: John Wiley and Sons, Inc., 1957.

J. Grant, Ed., *Quantitative Organic Microanalysis*, 5th ed. London: J. and A. Churchill, 1951.

J. Mitchell, Jr., I. M. Kolthoff, E. S. Proskauer, and A. Weissberger, Eds., *Organic Analysis*, 4 vols. New York: Interscience Publishers, Inc., 1956–60.

S. Siggia, *Quantitative Organic Analysis via Functional Groups*. New York: John Wiley and Sons, Inc., 1949.

S. Siggia and H. J. Stolten, *An Introduction to Modern Organic Analysis*. New York: Interscience Publishers, Inc., 1956.

A. Steyermark, *Quantitative Organic Microanalysis*, 2d ed. New York: Academic Press, Inc., 1961.

K. G. Stone, *Determination of Organic Compounds*. New York: McGraw-Hill Book Company, Inc., 1956.

A. Weissberger, *Techniques of Organic Chemistry*, 3d ed., 1, parts III and IV. New York: Interscience Publishers, Inc., 1960.

Biological Substances

D. Glick, Ed., *Methods of Biochemical Analysis*, several vols. New York: Interscience Publishers, Inc., 1954–

Gases

P. W. Mullen, *Modern Gas Analysis*. New York: Interscience Publishers, Inc., 1955.

Agricultural and Food Products

Association of Official Agricultural Chemists, *Methods of Analysis*, 9th ed. Washington, D. C.: Association of Official Agricultural Chemists, 1960.

M. B. Jacobs, *The Chemical Analysis of Foods and Food Products*. New York: D. Van Nostrand Co., Inc., 1938.

Poisons and Pollutants

M. B. Jacobs, *The Analytical Chemistry of Industrial Poisons, Hazards and Solvents*. New York: Interscience Publishers, Inc., 1941.

M. B. Jacobs, *The Chemical Analysis of Air Pollutants*. New York: Interscience Publishers, Inc., 1960.

Water

American Public Health Association, *Standard Methods of Water and Sewage Analysis*. New York: American Public Health Association, 1955.

REFERENCE WORKS DEVOTED TO METHODS FOR COMPLETION OF THE ANALYSIS

Volumetric Methods

W. Böttger, Ed., *Newer Methods of Volumetric Chemical Analysis*, trans. by R. E. Oesper. New York: D. Van Nostrand Co., Inc., 1938.

I. M. Kolthoff and N. H. Furman, *Potentiometric Titrations*, 2d ed. New York: John Wiley and Sons, Inc., 1931.

I. M. Kolthoff, V. A. Stenger, and R. Belcher, *Volumetric Analysis*, 3 vols. New York: Interscience Publishers, Inc., 1942–57.

J. Mitchell and D. M. Smith, *Aquametry*. New York: Interscience Publishers, Inc., 1948.

G. Schwarzenbach, *Complexometric Titrations*. New York: Interscience Publishers, Inc., 1957.

Organic Reagents

J. F. Flagg, *Organic Reagents*. New York: Interscience Publishers, Inc., 1948.

J. H. Yoe and L. A. Sarver, *Organic Analytical Reagents*. New York: John Wiley and Sons, Inc., 1941.

Thermogravimetric Methods

C. Duval, *Inorganic Thermogravimetric Analysis*. New York: Elsevier Publishing Co., 1953.

Micro and Ultramicro Methods

A. A. Benedetti-Pichler, *Microtechnique of Inorganic Analysis*. New York: John Wiley and Sons, Inc., 1942.

P. L. Kirk, *Quantitative Ultramicroanalysis*. New York: John Wiley and Sons, Inc., 1950.

J. B. Niederl and V. Niederl, *Micromethods of Quantitative Organic Analysis*, 2d ed. New York: John Wiley and Sons, Inc., 1942.

Instrumental Methods

W. G. Berl, Ed., *Physical Methods in Chemical Analysis*, 2d ed. New York: Academic Press, Inc., 1960.

A. G. Jones, *Analytical Chemistry, Some New Techniques*. London: Butterworths Scientific Publications, 1959.

J. H. Yoe and H. J. Koch, Jr., Eds., *Trace Analysis*. New York: John Wiley and Sons, Inc., 1957.

Electroanalytical Methods

P. Delahay, *New Instrumental Methods in Electrochemistry*. New York: Interscience Publishers, Inc., 1954.

J. J. Lingane, *Electroanalytical Chemistry*, 2d ed. New York: Interscience Publishers, Inc., 1958.

H. J. S. Sand, *Electrochemistry and Electrochemical Analysis*, 3 vols. London: Blackie & Son, Ltd., 1946.

Polarography

I. M. Kolthoff and J. J. Lingane, *Polarography*, 2d ed., 2 vols. New York: Interscience Publishers, Inc., 1952.

L. Meites, *Polarographic Techniques*. New York: Interscience Publishers, Inc., 1955.

Colorimetry and Absorption Spectroscopy

R. B. Barnes, R. C. Gore, U. Liddel, and V. Z. Williams, *Infrared Spectroscopy*. New York: Reinhold Publishing Corp., 1944.

D. E. Boltz, Ed., *Colorimetric Determination of Nonmetals*. New York: Interscience Publishers, Inc., 1958.

M. G. Mellon, Ed., *Analytical Absorption Spectroscopy*. New York: John Wiley and Sons, Inc., 1950.

E. B. Sandell, *Colorimetric Determination of Traces of Metals*, 3d ed. New York: Interscience Publishers, Inc., 1959.

F. D. Snell and C. T. Snell, *Colorimetric Methods of Analysis*, 3d ed., 4 vols. New York: D. Van Nostrand Co., Inc., 1954.

W. West, Ed., *Chemical Applications of Spectroscopy*. New York: Interscience Publishers, Inc., 1956.

Emission Spectroscopy and Flame Photometry

American Society for Testing Materials Committee E-2, *Methods for Emission Spectrochemical Analysis*. Philadelphia: American Society for Testing Materials, 1957.

J. A. Dean, *Flame Photometry*. New York: McGraw-Hill Book Co., Inc., 1960.

N. H. Nachtrieb, *Principles and Practice of Spectrochemical Analysis*. New York: McGraw-Hill Book Co., Inc., 1950.

X-Ray Spectroscopy

L. S. Birks, *X-Ray Spectrochemical Analysis*. New York: Interscience Publishers, Inc., 1959.

Chromatography

H. G. Cassidy, *Fundamentals of Chromatography*. New York: Interscience Publishers, Inc., 1957.

V. J. Coates, H. J. Noebels, and I. S. Fagerson, Eds., *Gas Chromatography*. New York: Academic Press Inc., 1958.

A. I. M. Keulemans, *Gas Chromatography*. New York: Reinhold Publishing Corp., 1957.

R. L. Pecsok, *Principles and Practice of Gas Chromatography*. New York: John Wiley and Sons, Inc., 1959.

H. H. Strain, *Chromatographic Adsorption Analysis*. New York: Interscience Publishers, Inc., 1945.

Journals

Analytica Chimica Acta
Analytical Abstracts
Analytical Chemistry
Analyst
Chimie analitique
Collection of Czechoslovak Chemical Communications
Current Chemical Papers
Journal of the Association of Official Agricultural Chemists
Microchemical Journal
Mikrochimica Acta
Talanta
Zeitschrift für analytische Chemie

21.3   Accuracy Obtainable in the Analysis of Complex Materials

To provide a clear idea of the accuracy that can be expected when the analysis of a complex material is carried out with a reasonable amount of effort and care, data on the determination of four elements in a variety of materials are presented in the tables that follow. The information in these tables was taken from a much larger set of results collected by W. F. Hillebrand and G. E. F. Lundell of the National Bureau of Standards and published in the first edition of their excellent book on inorganic analysis.[1]

The materials analyzed were of naturally occurring substances and items of commerce; these had been especially prepared to give uniform and homogeneous samples and were then distributed among analysts who were, for the most part, actively engaged in the analysis of similar materials. The analysts were allowed to use the methods they considered most accurate and best for the problem at hand. In most instances, special precautions were taken so that the results generally are better than can be expected from the average routine analysis; on the other hand they probably do not represent the ultimate in analytical perfection.

The value in column 2 of each table is a best value for the measured quantity obtained by the most painstaking analysis. It is considered to be the "true value" for calculations of the absolute and relative errors shown in columns 4 and 5. Column 4 was obtained by discarding results that were

---

[1] W. F. Hillebrand and G. E. F. Lundell, *Applied Inorganic Analysis*, 874–887. New York: John Wiley and Sons, Inc., 1929.

extremely divergent, determining the deviation of the remaining individual data from the quantity present (column 2), and averaging these deviations. Column 5, the percent relative error, was obtained by dividing the data in column 4 by the best value found in column 2 and multiplying by 100.

The results for the four elements shown in these tables are typical of the data for 26 elements reported in the original publication. It is to be concluded that analyses as good as a few tenths of a percent relative are the exception when complex mixtures are analyzed by ordinary methods, and that unless he is willing to invest an inordinate amount of time to the analysis, the chemist must accept errors on the order of 1 or 2 percent. If the sample contains less than 1 percent of the element of interest, errors greater than this figure are to be expected.

Finally, it is clear from these data that the accuracy obtainable in the determination of an element is greatly dependent upon the nature and complexity of the substrate. Thus the relative error for the determination of phosphorus in two phosphate rocks was 1.1 percent; in a synthetic mixture it was only 0.27 percent. The error in an iron determination in a refractory was 7.8 percent; in a manganese bronze, having about the same iron content, it was only 1.8 percent. Here, the limiting factor in the accuracy is not the errors in the completion step, but rather those residing in the separation of interferences and solution of the samples.

From these data it is clear that the chemist is well advised to adopt a pessimistic viewpoint regarding the accuracy of an analysis, be it his own or one performed by someone else.

TABLE 21-1

Analysis of Iron in Various Materials[2]

Material	Iron Present, percent	Number of Analysts	Average Error, absolute	Average Error, relative percent
Soda-lime glass	0.064 (Fe_2O_3)	13	0.01	15.6
Cast bronze	0.12	14	0.02	16.7
Chromel	0.45	6	0.03	6.7
Refractory	0.90 (Fe_2O_3)	7	0.07	7.8
Manganese bronze	1.13	12	0.02	1.8
Refractory	2.38 (Fe_2O_3)	7	0.07	2.9
Bauxite	5.66	5	0.06	1.1
Chromel	22.8	5	0.17	0.74
Iron ore	68.57	19	0.05	0.07

TABLE 21-2

Analysis of Manganese in Various Materials[2]

Material	Manganese Present, percent	Number of Analysts	Average Error, absolute	Average Error, relative percent
Ferro-chromium	0.225	4	0.013	5.8
Cast iron	0.478	8	0.006	1.3
	0.897	10	0.005	0.56
Manganese bronze	1.59	12	0.02	1.3
Ferro-vanadium	3.57	12	0.06	1.7
Spiegeleisen	19.93	11	0.06	0.30
Manganese ore	58.35	3	0.06	0.10
Ferro-manganese	80.67	11	0.11	0.14

TABLE 21-3

Analysis of Phosphorus in Various Materials[2]

Material	Phosphorus Present, percent	Number of Analysts	Average Error, absolute	Average Error, relative percent
Ferro-tungsten	0.015	9	0.003	20.
Iron ore	0.040	31	0.001	2.5
Refractory	0.069 (P_2O_5)	5	0.011	16.
Ferro-vanadium	0.243	11	0.013	5.4
Refractory	0.45	4	0.10	22.
Cast iron	0.88	7	0.01	1.1
Phosphate rock	43.77 (P_2O_5)	11	0.5	1.1
Synthetic mixtures	52.18 (P_2O_5)	11	0.14	0.27
Phosphate rock	77.56 ($Ca_3(PO_4)_2$)	30	0.85	1.1

TABLE 21-4

Analysis of Potassium in Various Materials[2]

Material	Potassium Oxide Present, percent	Number of Analysts	Average Error, absolute	Average Error, relative percent
Soda-lime glass	0.04	8	0.02	50.
Limestone	1.15	15	0.11	9.6
Refractory	1.37	6	0.09	6.6
	2.11	6	0.04	1.9
	2.83	6	0.10	3.5
Lead-barium glass	8.38	6	0.16	1.9

[2] The data in these tables were taken from W. F. Hillebrand and G. E. F. Lundell, *Applied Inorganic Analysis*, 874–887. New York: John Wiley and Sons, Inc., 1929. With permission.

$\left(\textbf{A-1}\right)$

The Quadratic Equation

Problems dealing with chemical equilibrium frequently require solution of a quadratic equation. The expression in question is first written in the form $ax^2 + bx + c = 0$, where a, b, and c are numerical constants. These are then substituted into the equation

$$x = \frac{-b \pm \sqrt{b^2 - 4ac}}{2a} \tag{1}$$

★EXAMPLE. The hydronium-ion concentration in a system is given by the equation

$$2 \times 10^{-2} = \frac{4 \times 10^{-3}}{2[H_3O^+]} - [H_3O^+]$$

To solve for $[H_3O^+]$ this is rearranged to

$$2[H_3O^+]^2 + 4 \times 10^{-2}[H_3O^+] - 4 \times 10^{-3} = 0$$

Substituting into equation (1)

$$[H_3O^+] = \frac{-4 \times 10^{-2} \pm \sqrt{(4 \times 10^{-2})^2 - (-4 \times 2 \times 4 \times 10^{-3})}}{2 \times 2}$$

$$= \frac{-4 \times 10^{-2} \pm \sqrt{16 \times 10^{-4} + 3.2 \times 10^{-2}}}{4}$$

$$= \frac{-4 \times 10^{-2} \pm 1.83 \times 10^{-1}}{4}$$

Of the two solutions to this equation only the positive value possesses significance in the present context; we therefore conclude that

$$[H_3O^+] = 3.6 \times 10^{-2}$$

$\left(\text{A-2}\right)$

Logarithms

A *logarithm* is the power to which some base number must be raised in order to express the number in question. Tables of logarithms are thus compilations of these exponents; for ordinary computations the base 10 is selected. Logarithmic notation greatly simplifies and speeds many common arithmetic operations. The quantities in the computation are expressed in logarthmic form, and the desired operations are performed (see below); the result is then converted from logarithmic to numerical form (this is frequently known as taking the *antilogarithm*).

Numerical Operation	Corresponding Manipulation with Logarithms
Multiplication	Add logarithms
Division	Subtract logarithms
Raise to a power	Multiply logarithm by desired power
Extract a root	Divide logarithm by desired root

The logarithm of a number is the sum of two parts, the *characteristic* and the *mantissa*. The former reflects the integer power of 10 involved, and must be supplied by the user; the latter is obtained from tables. The characteristic of numbers from 1.00 $\cdots$ to 9.99 $\cdots$ is 0; of numbers from 10.0 $\cdots$ to 99.9 $\cdots$ it is 1; of numbers from 100.0 $\cdots$ to 999.9 $\cdots$ it is 2; and so on. Numbers smaller than unity have negative characteristics. Thus numbers lying between 0.10 $\cdots$ and 0.999 $\cdots$ have a characteristic of -1; those between 0.010 $\cdots$ and 0.099 $\cdots$ have a characteristic of -2; and so on.

Thus the numbers 0.04, 4, and 4000 differ only in order of magnitude; as a consequence their logarithms will have the same mantissa (0.6021) but different characteristics (-2, 0, and 3).

The characteristic for a number smaller than 1 will carry a minus sign. Thus, the logarithm of 0.04 will be ($-2 + 0.6021$) -1.3979. This can also be expressed in an alternate form by adding 10 to, and then subtracting 10 from, the logarithm—that is,

$$\log 0.04 = -1.3979 = 8.6021 - 10$$

Through this device it is possible to extract the mantissas of numbers smaller than 1 directly from tables and eliminate the subtraction needed for the other notation. The characteristics associated with these numbers now become

9 −10 for numbers smaller than 0.999 · · · and larger than 0.0999 · · ·

8 −10 for numbers smaller than 0.0999 · · · and larger than 0.00999 · · · and so on.

A table of logarithms typically contains ten columns of mantissas; the numbers corresponding to these mantissas are found in a column to the left as well as in a row across the top.

Thus, to find the logarithm of 54.6 look down the left (n) column to 54, then move across to the column headed by 6, and read out 7372; supply the characteristic, 1, and record log 54.6 as 1.7372.

The logarithm of a number with one more significant figure than that for which the table was designed can be obtained by interpolation. To find the logarithm of 54.63, for example, proceed as before, then add $\frac{3}{10}$ of the difference (8) between 7372 and 7380 to the former number. The desired logarithm is thus 1.7374.

Conversion of a logarithm to the corresponding number is simply the reverse of this process.

★EXAMPLE. Find the antilogarithm of 1.6924. A search of the table reveals that 6924 is the mantissa of a number that lies exactly between 492 (6920) and 493 (6928). Note that at this stage no attempt is made to locate the decimal. We conclude that this number contains the figures 4925; the characteristic places the decimal between the 9 and the 2, and we write 49.25.

★EXAMPLE. Evaluate

$$x = \frac{38.26 \times 0.1020 \times 0.0864 \times 100}{1.675}$$

The several multiplications are accomplished in a single step by addition of the logarithms

log 38.26	1.5828
log 0.1020	9.0086 − 10
log 0.0864	8.9365 − 10
log 100	2.0000
	21.5279 − 20

After eliminating 20 from characteristic and remainder, we subtract log 1.675

	1.5279
log 1.675	−0.2240
log x	1.3039

Thus,

$$x = 20.14$$

FOUR-PLACE LOGARITHMS OF NUMBERS

n	0	1	2	3	4	5	6	7	8	9
10	0000	0043	0086	0128	0170	0212	0253	0294	0334	0374
11	0414	0453	0492	0531	0569	0607	0645	0682	0719	0755
12	0792	0828	0864	0899	0934	0969	1004	1038	1072	1106
13	1139	1173	1206	1239	1271	1303	1335	1367	1399	1430
14	1461	1492	1523	1553	1584	1614	1644	1673	1703	1732
15	1761	1790	1818	1847	1875	1903	1931	1959	1987	2014
16	2041	2068	2095	2122	2148	2175	2201	2227	2253	2279
17	2304	2330	2355	2380	2405	2430	2455	2480	2504	2529
18	2553	2577	2601	2625	2648	2672	2695	2718	2742	2765
19	2788	2810	2833	2856	2878	2900	2923	2945	2967	2989
20	3010	3032	3054	3075	3096	3118	3139	3160	3181	3201
21	3222	3243	3263	3284	3304	3324	3345	3365	3385	3404
22	3424	3444	3464	3483	3502	3522	3541	3560	3579	3598
23	3617	3636	3655	3674	3692	3711	3729	3747	3766	3784
24	3802	3820	3838	3856	3874	3892	3909	3927	3945	3962
25	3979	3997	4014	4031	4048	4065	4082	4099	4116	4133
26	4150	4166	4183	4200	4216	4232	4249	4265	4281	4298
27	4314	4330	4346	4362	4378	4393	4409	4425	4440	4456
28	4472	4487	4502	4518	4533	4548	4564	4579	4594	4609
29	4624	4639	4654	4669	4683	4698	4713	4728	4742	4757
30	4771	4786	4800	4814	4829	4843	4857	4871	4886	4900
31	4914	4928	4942	4955	4969	4983	4997	5011	5024	5038
32	5051	5065	5079	5092	5105	5119	5132	5145	5159	5172
33	5185	5198	5211	5224	5237	5250	5263	5276	5289	5302
34	5315	5328	5340	5353	5366	5378	5391	5403	5416	5428
35	5441	5453	5465	5478	5490	5502	5514	5527	5539	5551
36	5563	5575	5587	5599	5611	5623	5635	5647	5658	5670
37	5682	5694	5705	5717	5729	5740	5752	5763	5775	5786
38	5798	5809	5821	5832	5843	5855	5866	5877	5888	5899
39	5911	5922	5933	5944	5955	5966	5977	5988	5999	6010
40	6021	6031	6042	6053	6064	6075	6085	6096	6107	6117
41	6128	6138	6149	6160	6170	6180	6191	6201	6212	6222
42	6232	6243	6253	6263	6274	6284	6294	6304	6314	6325
43	6335	6345	6355	6365	6375	6385	6395	6405	6415	6425
44	6435	6444	6454	6464	6474	6484	6493	6503	6513	6522
45	6532	6542	6551	6561	6571	6580	6590	6599	6609	6618
46	6628	6637	6646	6656	6665	6675	6684	6693	6702	6712
47	6721	6730	6739	6749	6758	6767	6776	6785	6794	6803
48	6812	6821	6830	6839	6848	6857	6866	6875	6884	6893
49	6902	6911	6920	6928	6937	6946	6955	6964	6972	6981
50	6990	6998	7007	7016	7024	7033	7042	7050	7059	7067
51	7076	7084	7093	7101	7110	7118	7126	7135	7143	7152
52	7160	7168	7177	7185	7193	7202	7210	7218	7226	7235
53	7243	7251	7259	7267	7275	7284	7292	7300	7308	7316
54	7324	7332	7340	7348	7356	7364	7372	7380	7388	7396

FOUR-PLACE LOGARITHMS OF NUMBERS

n	0	1	2	3	4	5	6	7	8	9
55	7404	7412	7419	7427	7435	7443	7451	7459	7466	7474
56	7482	7490	7497	7505	7513	7520	7528	7536	7543	7551
57	7559	7566	7574	7582	7589	7597	7604	7612	7619	7627
58	7634	7642	7649	7657	7664	7672	7679	7686	7694	7701
59	7709	7716	7723	7731	7738	7745	7752	7760	7767	7774
60	7782	7789	7796	7803	7810	7818	7825	7832	7839	7846
61	7853	7860	7868	7875	7882	7889	7896	7903	7910	7917
62	7924	7931	7938	7945	7952	7959	7966	7973	7980	7987
63	7993	8000	8007	8014	8021	8028	8035	8041	8048	8055
64	8062	8069	8075	8082	8089	8096	8102	8109	8116	8122
65	8129	8136	8142	8149	8156	8162	8169	8176	8182	8189
66	8195	8202	8209	8215	8222	8228	8235	8241	8248	8254
67	8261	8267	8274	8280	8287	8293	8299	8306	8312	8319
68	8325	8331	8338	8344	8351	8357	8363	8370	8376	8382
69	8388	8395	8401	8407	8414	8420	8426	8432	8439	8445
70	8451	8457	8463	8470	8476	8482	8488	8494	8500	8506
71	8513	8519	8525	8531	8537	8543	8549	8555	8561	8567
72	8573	8579	8585	8591	8597	8603	8609	8615	8621	8627
73	8633	8639	8645	8651	8657	8663	8669	8675	8681	8686
74	8692	8698	8704	8710	8716	8722	8727	8733	8739	8745
75	8751	8756	8762	8768	8774	8779	8785	8791	8797	8802
76	8808	8814	8820	8825	8831	8837	8842	8848	8854	8859
77	8865	8871	8876	8882	8887	8893	8899	8904	8910	8915
78	8921	8927	8932	8938	8943	8949	8954	8960	8965	8971
79	8976	8982	8987	8993	8998	9004	9009	9015	9020	9025
80	9031	9036	9042	9047	9053	9058	9063	9069	9074	9079
81	9085	9090	9096	9101	9106	9112	9117	9122	9128	9133
82	9138	9143	9149	9154	9159	9165	9170	9175	9180	9186
83	9191	9196	9201	9206	9212	9217	9222	9227	9232	9238
84	9243	9248	9253	9258	9263	9269	9274	9279	9284	9289
85	9294	9299	9304	9309	9315	9320	9325	9330	9335	9340
86	9345	9350	9355	9360	9365	9370	9375	9380	9385	9390
87	9395	9400	9405	9410	9415	9420	9425	9430	9435	9440
88	9445	9450	9455	9460	9465	9469	9474	9479	9484	9489
89	9494	9499	9504	9509	9513	9518	9523	9528	9533	9538
90	9542	9547	9552	9557	9562	9566	9571	9576	9581	9586
91	9590	9595	9600	9605	9609	9614	9619	9624	9628	9633
92	9638	9643	9647	9652	9657	9661	9666	9671	9675	9680
93	9685	9689	9694	9699	9703	9708	9713	9717	9722	9727
94	9731	9736	9741	9745	9750	9754	9759	9763	9768	9773
95	9777	9782	9786	9791	9795	9800	9805	9809	9814	9818
96	9823	9827	9832	9836	9841	9845	9850	9854	9859	9863
97	9868	9872	9877	9881	9886	9890	9894	9899	9903	9908
98	9912	9917	9921	9926	9930	9934	9939	9943	9948	9952
99	9956	9961	9965	9969	9974	9978	9983	9987	9991	9996

(A-3)

Manipulations Involving Exponential Numbers

Arithmetic Process	Operation	Example
Addition (or Subtraction)	Express each quantity in terms of a common power of 10. Add (or subtract) numerical portions; supply the same power of 10 to the sum (or difference)	$5.0 \times 10^{-2} + 4.2 \times 10^{-3} = 50 \times 10^{-3} + 4.2 \times 10^{-3}$ $= 54.2 \times 10^{-3}$ $= 5.42 \times 10^{-2}$
Multiplication	Multiply numerical portions, add exponents	$(5.0 \times 10^{-2})(4.2 \times 10^{-3}) = 21.0 \times 10^{-5}$ $= 2.1 \times 10^{-4}$
Division	Divide numerical portions, subtract exponents	$\dfrac{5.0 \times 10^{-2}}{4.2 \times 10^{-3}} = 1.19 \times 10^{-2-(-3)}$ $= 1.19 \times 10^{1} = 11.9$
Raising to a power	Raise numerical portion to the indicated power, multiply exponent by the desired power	$(5.0 \times 10^{-2})^3 = (5)^3 \times (10^{-2})^3$ $= 125 \times 10^{-6}$ $= 1.25 \times 10^{-4}$
Extraction of a root	Express quantity to a power that is an integer multiple of desired root. Extract root of numerical portion, divide exponent by desired root	$\sqrt[3]{8.1 \times 10^{-7}} = \sqrt[3]{810 \times 10^{-9}}$ $= 9.3 \times 10^{-3}$

Standard Reduction Potentials

Half Reaction	$E°$, volts
$F_2 + 2H^+ + 2e \rightleftharpoons 2HF$	3.06
$O_3 + 2H^+ + 2e \rightleftharpoons O_2 + H_2O$	2.07
$S_2O_8^{2-} + 2e \rightleftharpoons 2SO_4^{2-}$	2.01
$Co^{3+} + e \rightleftharpoons Co^{2+}$	1.82
$H_2O_2 + 2H^+ + 2e \rightleftharpoons 2H_2O$	1.77
$MnO_4^- + 4H^+ + 3e \rightleftharpoons MnO_2 + 2H_2O$	1.695
$Ce^{4+} + e \rightleftharpoons Ce^{3+}$	1.70
$H_5IO_6 + H^+ + 2e \rightleftharpoons IO_3^- + 3H_2O$	1.6
$BrO_3^- + 6H^+ + 5e \rightleftharpoons \frac{1}{2}Br_2 + 3H_2O$	1.52
$MnO_4^- + 8H^+ + 5e \rightleftharpoons Mn^{2+} + 4H_2O$	1.51
$Mn^{3+} + e \rightleftharpoons Mn^{2+}$	1.51
$PbO_2 + 4H^+ + 2e \rightleftharpoons Pb^{2+} + 2H_2O$	1.455
$Cl_2 + 2e \rightleftharpoons 2Cl^-$	1.359
$Cr_2O_7^{2-} + 14H^+ + 6e \rightleftharpoons 2Cr^{3+} + 7H_2O$	1.33
$Tl^{3+} + 2e \rightleftharpoons Tl^+$	1.25
$MnO_2 + 4H^+ + 2e \rightleftharpoons Mn^{2+} + 2H_2O$	1.23
$O_2 + 4H^+ + 4e \rightleftharpoons 2H_2O$	1.229
$IO_3^- + 6H^+ + 5e \rightleftharpoons \frac{1}{2}I_2 + 3H_2O$	1.195
$Br_2 + 2e \rightleftharpoons 2Br^-$	1.065
$ICl_2^- + e \rightleftharpoons \frac{1}{2}I_2 + 2Cl^-$	1.06
$V(OH)_4^+ + 2H^+ + e \rightleftharpoons VO^{2+} + 3H_2O$	1.00
$HNO_2 + H^+ + e \rightleftharpoons NO + H_2O$	1.00
$NO_3^- + 3H^+ + 2e \rightleftharpoons HNO_2 + H_2O$	0.94
$2Hg^{2+} + 2e \rightleftharpoons Hg_2^{2+}$	0.920
$Cu^{2+} + I^- + e \rightleftharpoons CuI$	0.86
$Ag^+ + e \rightleftharpoons Ag$	0.799
$Hg_2^{2+} + 2e \rightleftharpoons 2Hg$	0.789

The majority of $E°$ values are taken from Wendell M. Latimer, *The Oxidation States of the Elements and Their Potentials in Aqueous Solutions*, 2d ed., ©, 1952, by permission of Prentice-Hall, Inc., Englewood Cliffs, N. J.

A-4 (Continued)

Half Reaction	$E°$, volts
$Fe^{3+} + e \rightleftharpoons Fe^{2+}$	0.771
$PtCl_4^{2-} + 2e \rightleftharpoons Pt + 4Cl^-$	0.73
$C_6H_4O_2$ (quinone) $+ 2H^+ + 2e \rightleftharpoons C_6H_4(OH)_2$	0.699
$O_2 + 2H^+ + 2e \rightleftharpoons H_2O_2$	0.682
$PtCl_6^{2-} + 2e \rightleftharpoons PtCl_4^{2-} + 2Cl^-$	0.68
$MnO_4^- + e \rightleftharpoons MnO_4^{2-}$	0.564
$H_3AsO_4 + 2H^+ + 2e \rightleftharpoons H_3AsO_3 + H_2O$	0.559
$I_3^- + 2e \rightleftharpoons 3I^-$	0.536
$I_2 + 2e \rightleftharpoons 2I^-$	0.5355
$Cu^+ + e \rightleftharpoons Cu$	0.521
$H_2SO_3 + 4H^+ + 4e \rightleftharpoons S + 3H_2O$	0.45
$Ag_2CrO_4 + 2e \rightleftharpoons 2Ag + CrO_4^{2-}$	0.446
$VO^{2+} + 2H^+ + e \rightleftharpoons V^{3+} + H_2O$	0.361
$Fe(CN)_6^{3-} + e \rightleftharpoons Fe(CN)_6^{4-}$	0.36
$Cu^{2+} + 2e \rightleftharpoons Cu$	0.337
$UO_2^{2+} + 4H^+ + 2e \rightleftharpoons U^{4+} + 2H_2O$	0.334
$BiO^+ + 2H^+ + 3e = Bi + H_2O$	0.32
$Hg_2Cl_2 + 2e \rightleftharpoons 2Hg + 2Cl^-$	0.268
$AgCl + e \rightleftharpoons Ag + Cl^-$	0.222
$SO_4^{2-} + 4H^+ + 2e \rightleftharpoons H_2SO_3 + H_2O$	0.17
$Cu^{2+} + e \rightleftharpoons Cu^+$	0.153
$Sn^{4+} + 2e \rightleftharpoons Sn^{2+}$	0.15
$S + 2H^+ + 2e \rightleftharpoons H_2S$	0.141
$TiO^{2+} + 2H^+ + e \rightleftharpoons Ti^{3+} + H_2O$	0.1
$AgBr + e \rightleftharpoons Ag + Br^-$	0.095
$S_4O_6^{2-} + 2e \rightleftharpoons 2S_2O_3^{2-}$	0.08
$Ag(S_2O_3)_2^{3-} + e \rightleftharpoons Ag + 2S_2O_3^{2-}$	0.01
$2H^+ + 2e \rightleftharpoons H_2$	0.000
$Pb^{2+} + 2e \rightleftharpoons Pb$	-0.126
$Sn^{2+} + 2e \rightleftharpoons Sn$	-0.136
$AgI + e \rightleftharpoons Ag + I^-$	-0.151
$CuI + e \rightleftharpoons Cu + I^-$	-0.185
$N_2 + 5H^+ + 4e \rightleftharpoons N_2H_5^+$	-0.23
$Ni^{2+} + 2e \rightleftharpoons Ni$	-0.250
$V^{3+} + e \rightleftharpoons V^{2+}$	-0.255
$Co^{2+} + 2e \rightleftharpoons Co$	-0.277
$Ag(CN)_2^- + e \rightleftharpoons Ag + 2CN^-$	-0.31
$Tl^+ + e \rightleftharpoons Tl$	-0.336

A-4 (Continued)

Half Reaction	$E°$, volts
$Ti^{3+} + e \rightleftharpoons Ti^{2+}$	$- 0.37$
$Cd^{2+} + 2e \rightleftharpoons Cd$	$- 0.403$
$Cr^{3+} + e \rightleftharpoons Cr^{2+}$	$- 0.41$
$Fe^{2+} + 2e \rightleftharpoons Fe$	$- 0.440$
$2CO_2(g) + 2H^+ + 2e \rightleftharpoons H_2C_2O_4$	$- 0.49$
$Cr^{3+} + 3e \rightleftharpoons Cr$	$- 0.74$
$Zn^{2+} + 2e \rightleftharpoons Zn$	$- 0.763$
$Mn^{2+} + 2e \rightleftharpoons Mn$	$- 1.18$
$Al^{3+} + 3e \rightleftharpoons Al$	$- 1.66$
$Mg^{2+} + 2e \rightleftharpoons Mg$	$- 2.37$
$Na^+ + e \rightleftharpoons Na$	$- 2.71$
$Ca^{2+} + 2e \rightleftharpoons Ca$	$- 2.87$
$Ba^{2+} + 2e \rightleftharpoons Ba$	$- 2.90$
$K^+ + e \rightleftharpoons K$	$- 2.92$
$Li^+ + e \rightleftharpoons Li$	$- 3.04$

Solubility Product Constants

Substance	Formula	K_{sp}
Aluminum hydroxide	$Al(OH)_3$	5×10^{-33}
Barium carbonate	$BaCO_3$	4.9×10^{-9}
Barium iodate	$Ba(IO_3)_2$	1.57×10^{-9}
Barium oxalate	BaC_2O_4	1.6×10^{-7}
Barium sulfate	$BaSO_4$	1.0×10^{-10}
Cadmium carbonate	$CdCO_3$	2.5×10^{-14}
Cadmium sulfide	CdS	1×10^{-28}
Calcium carbonate	$CaCO_3$	4.8×10^{-9}
Calcium oxalate	CaC_2O_4	1.9×10^{-9}
Calcium sulfate	$CaSO_4$	6.1×10^{-5}
Copper (II) hydroxide	$Cu(OH)_2$	1.6×10^{-19}
Copper (II) sulfide	CuS	8.5×10^{-45}
Copper (I) bromide	$CuBr$	5.9×10^{-9}
Copper (I) chloride	$CuCl$	3.2×10^{-7}
Copper (I) iodide	CuI	1.1×10^{-12}
Copper (I) thiocyanate	$CuSCN$	4×10^{-14}
Iron (III) hydroxide	$Fe(OH)_3$	1.5×10^{-36}
Lanthanum iodate	$La(IO_3)_3$	6×10^{-10}
Lead carbonate	$PbCO_3$	1.6×10^{-13}
Lead chloride	$PbCl_2$	1×10^{-4}
Lead chromate	$PbCrO_4$	1.8×10^{-14}
Lead hydroxide	$Pb(OH)_2$	2.5×10^{-16}
Lead oxalate	PbC_2O_4	3.0×10^{-11}
Lead sulfate	$PbSO_4$	1.9×10^{-8}
Lead sulfide	PbS	7×10^{-28}
Magnesium ammonium phosphate	$MgNH_4PO_4$	2.5×10^{-13}
Magnesium carbonate	$MgCO_3$	1×10^{-5}
Magnesium hydroxide	$Mg(OH)_2$	5.9×10^{-12}
Magnesium oxalate	MgC_2O_4	8.6×10^{-5}
Manganese (II) hydroxide	$Mn(OH)_2$	4×10^{-14}
Manganese (II) sulfide	MnS	1.4×10^{-15}
Silver arsenate	Ag_3AsO_4	1.0×10^{-22}
Silver bromide	$AgBr$	7.7×10^{-13}
Silver carbonate	Ag_2CO_3	8.2×10^{-12}
Silver chloride	$AgCl$	1.82×10^{-10}
Silver chromate	Ag_2CrO_4	1.1×10^{-12}
Silver cyanide	$AgCN$	2×10^{-12}
Silver iodate	$AgIO_3$	3.1×10^{-8}
Silver iodide	AgI	8.3×10^{-17}
Silver oxalate	$Ag_2C_2O_4$	1.1×10^{-11}
Silver sulfide	Ag_2S	1.6×10^{-49}
Silver thiocyanate	$AgSCN$	1.1×10^{-12}
Strontium oxalate	SrC_2O_4	5.6×10^{-8}
Strontium sulfate	$SrSO_4$	2.8×10^{-7}

A-5 (Continued)

Substance	Formula	K_{sp}
Thallium (I) chloride	TlCl	2×10^{-4}
Thallium (I) sulfide	Tl_2S	1×10^{-22}
Zinc hydroxide	$Zn(OH)_2$	2×10^{-14}
Zinc oxalate	ZnC_2O_4	7.5×10^{-9}
Zinc sulfide	ZnS	4.5×10^{-24}

$\left(\textbf{A-6}\right)$

Acid Dissociation Constants

Name	Formula	Dissociation Constant, 25° C		
		K_1	K_2	K_3
Acetic	CH_3COOH	1.75×10^{-5}		
Arsenic	H_3AsO_4	6.0×10^{-3}	1.05×10^{-7}	3.0×10^{-12}
Arsenious	H_3AsO_3	6.0×10^{-10}	3.0×10^{-14}	
Benzoic	C_6H_5COOH	6.3×10^{-5}		
Boric	H_3BO_3	5.8×10^{-10}		
1-Butanoic	$CH_3CH_2CH_2COOH$	1.51×10^{-5}		
Carbonic	H_2CO_3	4.6×10^{-7}	4.4×10^{-11}	
Chloroacetic	$ClCH_2COOH$	1.51×10^{-3}		
Citric	$HOOC(OH)C(CH_2COOH)_2$	7.4×10^{-4}	1.74×10^{-5}	4.0×10^{-7}
Formic	HCOOH	1.74×10^{-4}		
Fumaric	*trans*-HOOCCH:CHCOOH	9.6×10^{-4}	4.1×10^{-5}	
Glycine	H_2NCH_2COOH	4.5×10^{-3}		
Glycolic	$HOCH_2COOH$	1.32×10^{-4}		
Hydrazoic	HN_3	1.9×10^{-5}		
Hydrogen cyanide	HCN	2.1×10^{-9}		
Hydrogen fluoride	H_2F_2	7.2×10^{-4}		
Hydrogen peroxide	H_2O_2	2.7×10^{-12}		
Hydrogen sulfide	H_2S	5.7×10^{-8}	1.2×10^{-15}	
Hypochlorous	HOCl	3.0×10^{-8}		
Iodic	HIO_3	1.58×10^{-1}		
Lactic	$CH_3CHOHCOOH$	1.38×10^{-4}		
Maleic	*cis*-HOOCCH:CHCOOH	1.5×10^{-2}	2.6×10^{-7}	
Malic	$HOOCCHOHCH_2COOH$	4.0×10^{-4}	8.9×10^{-6}	
Malonic	$HOOCCH_2COOH$	1.58×10^{-3}	8.0×10^{-7}	
Mandelic	$C_6H_5CHOHCOOH$	4.3×10^{-4}		
Nitrous	HNO_2	5.1×10^{-4}		
Oxalic	HOOCCOOH	6.2×10^{-2}	6.1×10^{-5}	
Periodic	H_5IO_6	2.4×10^{-2}	5.0×10^{-9}	

A-6 (Continued)

Name	Formula	Dissociation Constant, 25° C		
		K_1	K_2	K_3
Phenol	C_6H_5OH	1.05×10^{-10}		
Phosphoric	H_3PO_4	7.5×10^{-3}	6.2×10^{-8}	4.8×10^{-13}
Phosphorous	H_3PO_3	1.00×10^{-2}	2.6×10^{-7}	
o-Phthalic	$C_6H_4(COOH)_2$	1.3×10^{-3}	3.9×10^{-6}	
Picric	$(NO_2)_3C_6H_2OH$	4.2×10^{-1}		
Propanoic	$CH_3CH_2COOH \cdot$	1.32×10^{-5}		
Salicylic	$C_6H_4(OH)COOH$	1.05×10^{-3}		
Sulfuric	H_2SO_4	strong	1.2×10^{-2}	
Sulfurous	H_2SO_3	1.74×10^{-2}	6.2×10^{-8}	
Tartaric	$HOOC(CHOH)_2COOH$	9.4×10^{-4}	2.9×10^{-5}	
Trichloroacetic	Cl_3CCOOH	1.29×10^{-1}		

Taken in part from I. M. Kolthoff and P. J. Elving, *Treatise on Analytical Chemistry*, part 1, 1, 432. New York: Interscience Publishers, Inc., 1959; and in part from I. M. Kolthoff and V. A. Stenger, *Volumetric Analysis*, 1, 282. New York: Interscience Publishers, Inc., 1942.

$\left(\textbf{A-7} \right)$

Ionization Constants for Bases

Name	Formula	Dissociation Constant, K, 25° C
Ammonia	NH_3	1.86×10^{-5}
Aniline	$C_6H_5NH_2$	3.8×10^{-10}
1-Butylamine	$CH_3(CH_2)_2CH_2NH_2$	4.1×10^{-4}
Ethylamine	$CH_3CH_2NH_2$	5.6×10^{-4}
Glycine	$HOOCCH_2NH_2$	2.3×10^{-12}
Hydrazine	H_2NNH_2	3.0×10^{-6}
Hydroxylamine	$HONH_2$	1.07×10^{-8}
Methylamine	CH_3NH_2	4.4×10^{-4}
Piperidine	$C_5H_{11}N$	1.6×10^{-3}
Pyridine	C_5H_5N	1.4×10^{-9}
Zinc hydroxide	$Zn(OH)_2$	$K_2 = 4.4 \times 10^{-5}$

Taken in part from I. M. Kolthoff and V. A. Stenger, *Volumetric Analysis*, 1, 284. New York: Interscience Publishers, Inc., 1942.

Element	Symbol	Atomic number	Atomic weight	Element	Symbol	Atomic number	Atomic weight
Actinium	Ac	89	(227)	Mercury	Hg	80	200.59
Aluminum	Al	13	26.9815	Molybdenum	Mo	42	95.94
Americium	Am	95	(243)	Neodymium	Nd	60	144.24
Antimony	Sb	51	121.75	Neon	Ne	10	20.183
Argon	Ar	18	39.948	Neptunium	Np	93	(237)
Arsenic	As	33	74.9216	Nickel	Ni	28	58.71
Astatine	At	85	(210)	Niobium	Nb	41	92.906
Barium	Ba	56	137.34	Nitrogen	N	7	14.0067
Berkelium	Bk	97	(247)	Nobelium	No	102	(254)
Beryllium	Be	4	9.0122	Osmium	Os	76	190.2
Bismuth	Bi	83	208.980	Oxygen	O	8	15.9994
Boron	B	5	10.811	Palladium	Pd	46	106.4
Bromine	Br	35	79.909	Phosphorus	P	15	30.9738
Cadmium	Cd	48	112.40	Platinum	Pt	78	195.09
Calcium	Ca	20	40.08	Plutonium	Pu	94	(244)
Californium	Cf	98	(249)	Polonium	Po	84	(210)
Carbon	C	6	12.01115	Potassium	K	19	39.102
Cerium	Ce	58	140.12	Praseodymium	Pr	59	140.907
Cesium	Cs	55	132.905	Promethium	Pm	61	(145)
Chlorine	Cl	17	35.453	Protactinium	Pa	91	(231)
Chromium	Cr	24	51.996	Radium	Ra	88	(226)
Cobalt	Co	27	58.9332	Radon	Rn	86	(222)
Copper	Cu	29	63.54	Rhenium	Re	75	186.2
Curium	Cm	96	(245)	Rhodium	Rh	45	102.905
Dysprosium	Dy	66	162.50	Rubidium	Rb	37	85.47
Einsteinium	Es	99	(254)	Ruthenium	Ru	44	101.07
Erbium	Er	68	167.26	Samarium	Sm	62	150.35
Europium	Eu	63	151.96	Scandium	Sc	21	44.956
Fermium	Fm	100	(252)	Selenium	Se	34	78.96
Fluorine	F	9	18.9984	Silicon	Si	14	28.086
Francium	Fr	87	(223)	Silver	Ag	47	107.870
Gadolinium	Gd	64	157.25	Sodium	Na	11	22.9898
Gallium	Ga	31	69.72	Strontium	Sr	38	87.62
Germanium	Ge	32	72.59	Sulfur	S	16	32.064
Gold	Au	79	196.967	Tantalum	Ta	73	180.948
Hafnium	Hf	72	178.49	Technetium	Tc	43	(99)
Helium	He	2	4.0026	Tellurium	Te	52	127.60
Holmium	Ho	67	164.930	Terbium	Tb	65	158.924
Hydrogen	H	1	1.00797	Thallium	Tl	81	204.37
Indium	In	49	114.82	Thorium	Th	90	232.038
Iodine	I	53	126.9044	Thulium	Tm	69	168.934
Iridium	Ir	77	192.2	Tin	Sn	50	118.69
Iron	Fe	26	55.847	Titanium	Ti	22	47.90
Krypton	Kr	36	83.80	Tungsten	W	74	183.85
Lanthanum	La	57	138.91	Uranium	U	92	238.03
Lawrencium	Lw	103	(257)	Vanadium	V	23	50.942
Lead	Pb	82	207.19	Xenon	Xe	54	131.30
Lithium	Li	3	6.939	Ytterbium	Yb	70	173.04
Lutetium	Lu	71	174.97	Yttrium	Y	39	88.905
Magnesium	Mg	12	24.312	Zinc	Zn	30	65.37
Manganese	Mn	25	54.9380	Zirconium	Zr	40	91.22
Mendelevium	Mv	101	(256)				

Numbers in parenthesis indicate mass number of most stable known isotope.

$AgBr$	187.78	K_2CrO_4	194.20
$AgCl$	143.32	$K_2Cr_2O_7$	294.19
Ag_2CrO_4	331.73	$K_3Fe(CN)_6$	329.26
AgI	234.77	$K_4Fe(CN)_6$	368.38
$AgNO_3$	169.87	$KHC_8H_4O_4$ (phthalate)	204.23
$AgSCN$	165.95	$KH(IO_3)_2$	389.92
Al_2O_3	101.96	K_2HPO_4	174.18
$Al_2(SO_4)_3$	342.14	KH_2PO_4	136.09
As_2O_3	197.85	$KHSO_4$	136.17
B_2O_3	69.62	KI	166.01
$BaCO_3$	197.35	KIO_3	214.00
$BaCl_2$	208.25	KIO_4	230.00
$BaCrO_4$	253.33	$KMnO_4$	158.04
$Ba(OH)_2$	171.36	KNO_3	101.11
$BaSO_4$	233.40	KOH	56.11
Bi_2O_3	466.0	$KSCN$	97.18
CO_2	44.01	K_2SO_4	174.27
$CaCO_3$	100.09	$La(IO_3)_3$	663.62
CaC_2O_4	128.10	$Mg(C_9H_6ON)_2$	312.59
CaF_2	78.08	$MgNH_4PO_4$	137.35
CaO	56.08	MgO	40.31
$CaSO_4$	136.14	$Mg_2P_2O_7$	222.57
$Ce(HSO_4)_4$	528.4	$MgSO_4$	120.37
CeO_2	172.12	MnO_2	86.94
$Ce(SO_4)_2$	332.25	Mn_2O_3	157.88
$(NH_4)_2Ce(NO_3)_6$	548.23	Mn_3O_4	228.81
$(NH_4)_4Ce(SO_4)_4 \cdot 2H_2O$	632.6	$Na_2B_4O_7 \cdot 10H_2O$	381.37
Cr_2O_3	151.99	$NaBr$	102.90
CuO	79.54	$NaC_2H_3O_2$	82.03
Cu_2O	143.08	$Na_2C_2O_4$	134.00
$CuSO_4$	159.60	$NaCl$	58.44
$Fe(NH_4)_2(SO_4)_2 \cdot 6H_2O$	392.14	$NaCN$	49.01
FeO	71.85	Na_2CO_3	105.99
Fe_2O_3	159.69	$Na_2H_2EDTA \cdot 2H_2O$	372.2
Fe_3O_4	231.54	Na_2O_2	77.98
HBr	80.92	$NaOH$	40.00
$HC_2H_3O_2$ (acetic)	60.05	$NaSCN$	81.07
$HC_7H_5O_2$ (benzoic)	122.12	Na_2SO_4	142.04
HCl	36.46	$Na_2S_2O_3 \cdot 5H_2O$	248.18
$HClO_4$	100.46	NH_3	17.03
$H_2C_2O_4 \cdot 2H_2O$	126.07	NH_4Cl	53.49
H_5IO_6	227.94	$(NH_4)_2C_2O_4 \cdot H_2O$	142.11
HNO_3	63.01	NH_4NO_3	80.04
H_2O	18.015	$(NH_4)_2SO_4$	132.14
H_2O_2	34.01	$(NH_4)_2S_2O_8$	228.18
H_3PO_4	98.00	NH_4VO_3	116.98
H_2S	34.08	$PbCrO_4$	323.18
H_2SO_3	82.08	PbO	223.19
H_2SO_4	98.08	PbO_2	239.19
HgO	216.59	$PbSO_4$	303.25
Hg_2Cl_2	472.09	P_2O_5	141.94
$HgCl_2$	271.50	Sb_2S_3	339.69
KBr	119.01	SiO_2	60.08
$KBrO_3$	167.01	$SnCl_2$	189.60
KCl	74.56	SnO_2	150.69
$KClO_3$	122.55	SO_2	64.06
KCN	65.12	SO_3	80.06
		$Zn_2P_2O_7$	304.68

Index

Boldface entries refer to specific laboratory instructions.

Absorbance, 452, 454*t*; chemical factors affecting, 471; and concentration, 451, *see also* Beer's law
Absorption of radiation, for analysis, 447–481; errors affecting, 453–455; instruments for, 451–465, *see also* specific listings; terminology associated with, 453, 454*t*
Absorption spectrum, 451
Accuracy, in analysis of complex substances, 497–500; of analytical data, 37; as factor in selection of method, 487–488
Acetic acid, apparent dissociation constant, 24; determination of, in vinegar, **304**
Acid(s), definition of, 8–10, 240; dissociation constants for, 22*t*, 511*t*; preparation and standardization of reagent solutions, 296, **297**, **298**
Acid-base concepts, 8–10
Acid-base indicators, 258–264; applications, in complex-formation titrations, 229, in volumetric precipitation analysis, 214; preparation of solutions, **296**; selection, for strong acid-strong base titrations, 267, for titrations of weak acids, 272, for titrations of weak bases, 274; theory of behavior, 258–260; types, 260–264; variables influencing behavior of, 264
Acid-base ratio, **303**
Acid dissociation constant, 22*t*, 511*t*; calculations involving, 241–244; evaluation from titration curves, 268; potentiometric estimation of, 439
Acid error, glass electrode, 438
Acid mixtures, titration curves for, 290–291

Acid salts, *p*H of solutions containing, 280–283
Acid strength, 10
Activity, 25
Activity coefficient, 25
Adsorption, 131–133, 139–143; errors arising from, 141; effect on precipitation titration curves, 427
Adsorption indicators, dichlorofluorescein, **222**; for precipitation titrations, 215–216
Adsorption isotherm, 141
Aliquot, measurement of, **196**
Alizarin yellow, 261*t*
Alkaline error, glass electrode, 438
Aluminum, use in prereduction of samples, 366
Aluminum oxide, as filtering medium, 85
Amalgams, for prereduction, 368
Ammonia, species in aqueous solution, 245; distillation of, 309; titration of, 309
Ammonium metavanadate, as oxidizing agent, 362*t*
Ammonium persulfate, as preoxidizer, 366
Ammonium salts, analysis of, 308–310, **311**
Amphiprotic solvent behavior, 10
Analysis, gravimetric, 61–66, 149–163; of real substances, 484–500, *see also* Complex substances; photometric, 466–467; spectrophotometric, 470–481; volumetric, 165–182, *see also* specific listings
Analytical balance, construction, 70–73; damped, 72, operation of, **79**; deflection scale, 76; equal-arm, 70–72, operation of, **77–79**; keyboard, 73; rules for use, 81–82; unequal-arm, 74, operation of, **79**

Analytical chemistry, literature of, 493–497; scope of, 1–6

Antimony, iodimetric determination of, **396**

Anode, definition of, 322

Anodic reactions, typical, 323

Argentometry, 216*t*, 215–221

Arithmetic mean, 35

Arndt's alloy, 311

Arrhenius concept, of acids and bases, 9

Arsenic, iodimetric determination of, 395

Arsenic (III), as reducing agent, 364*t*

Arsenic (III) oxide, as primary standard, 365*t*, for cerium (IV) solutions, **386**, for iodine solutions, 394, **395**, for permanganate, 375

Arsonic acids, as precipitating agents, 154

Asbestos, as filtering medium, 85, 98–99

Ashless paper, as filtering medium, 85; ashing of, 96–98

Asymmetry potential, 436

Autocatalysis, in decomposition of permanganate solutions, 372

Average, 35

Azo indicators, 261*t*, 263

Back-titration, 165

Barium chloride dihydrate, determina- of water in, **155**

Barium hydroxide, as volumetric reagent, 299

Barrier-layer cell, 462

Base(s), definition of, 8–10, 240; ionization constants for, 22*t*, 511*t*; preparation and standardization of solutions, 299–302, **301**, **302**

Base strength, 10

Basic ionization constant, 22*t*, 512*t*; calculations involving, 244

Bausch and Lomb Spectronic 20 spectrophotometer, 469

Beckman DU spectrophotometer, 468

Beer's law, 451–453; deviations from, 453–455; establishment of adherence to, 471

Benzidine, as precipitating agent, 154

Benzoic acid, as primary standard for bases, 302

Bicarbonate-carbonate mixtures, analysis of, 304–308; potentiometric titration of, **444**; titration of, **307**

Blank determination, 39

Bolometer, 464

Boric acid, for collection of ammonia, **309–311**

Brass, iodometric determination of copper in, **406**

Bromcresol green, 261*t*; preparation of solution, **296**

Bromphenol blue, preparation of solution, **296**

Bromthymol blue, 261*t*; preparation of solution, **296**

Brønsted-Lowry concept, acids and bases, 9

Buffer capacity, 257

Buffer solutions, 255–258

Bunsen valve, 193

Buoyancy, correction in calibration work, 200; effect upon weighing data, 80–81

Buret, 193; calibration of, **202**; directions for use of, **196–198**

Cadmium, use in prereduction of samples, 366–367

Calcium chloride, as desiccant, 83

Calcium determination, with EDTA, **236**; in limestone, **383**; with permanganate, 381, **382–383**

Calcium hypochlorite, as oxidizing agent, 362*t*

Calcium sulfate, as desiccant, 83

Caldwell-Moyer modification, Volhard method, 213, **219**

Calibration, of buret, **202**; relative, **203**; of volumetric flask, **202–203**; of volumetric pipet, **202**; of volumetric ware, 199–202

Calomel electrode, 418–420

Carbon dioxide, absorption by base solutions, 299–300

Carbonate-bicarbonate mixtures, analysis of, 304–308; determination of, **307**; potentiometric titration of, **444**

Carbonate errors, 299–300

Carbonate-hydroxide mixtures, analysis of, 304–308, **308**

Carbonate mixtures, analysis of, 304–307

Cathode, definition of, 322

Cathodic reactions, typical, 322

Cell, 321, *see also* Electrochemical cell; barrier layer, 462; Weston, 415–416

Cerium (IV) ammonium nitrate, as primary standard, 365*t*, 385

Cerium (IV) ion, as oxidizing agent, 362*t*, 384–387; properties of, 384–385

Cerium (IV) solutions, preparation of, **385**; stability of, 384–385; standardization against arsenic (III) oxide, **386**, against sodium oxalate, **386–387**

Cerium (IV) titrations, 384–387; applications, 387; determination of iron in an ore, **387**; indicators for, 385

Charge-balance equation, 110, 242

Chelates, 223

Chemical Abstracts, 490

Chemical analysis, development of a new method, 4–6, 490–491; evaluation of new method, 491–493; factors governing choice of method, 486–489; preliminary steps in, 486–490; of real substances, 484–500, *see also* Complex substances

Chemical equilibrium, 18–26, *see also* specific listings; calculation of constants from electrode-potential data, 338–340

Chemical factor, 63

Chemical literature, 493–497

Chemically pure grade reagents, 86

Chloride determination, Fajans method, 213–214, 216*t*, 217*t*, **220–221**; gravimetric, **156**; Mohr method, 210–211, 216*t*, **218**; Volhard method, 211–213, 216*t*, **218–220**

Chlorophenol red, 261*t*

Chromium (II), as reducing agent, 364*t*

Clark and Lubs, buffer solutions, 258

Cleaning solution, **88**

Clear point, 215; applications, 216*t*

Colloidal precipitates, 133–136, 139; peptization of, 135–136; surface adsorption upon, 131–133, 139–143

Colloidal suspensions, 124, 129–136

Colloids, coagulation of, 133–135; stability of, 134–135; surface adsorption upon, 131–133, 139–143

Colorimeter, 465

Colorimetry, 465–466

Common ion effect, and solubility, 105–108

Complex formation, effect upon electrode potential, 334–335; effect upon solubility, 113–117

Complex-formation titrations, 223–237; applications, 230–234, **234–237**; definition of equivalent weight for, 174–176; end-point detection for, 228–230; potentiometric end points for, 425–426; titration curves for, 224–228

Complex ions, instability constants for, 22*t*, 224

Complex substances, accuracies attainable in analysis of, 497–500; analysis of, 484–500; selection of analytical methods for, 486–491

Concentration range, as factor in selection of analytical method, 487

Concentration of solutions, methods of expressing, 13–15, 16*t*, 177

Confidence limits, 48–49

Conjugate acids and bases, 9–10, 22*t*; equilibrium relationship between, 247–249

Coordination compounds, applications in gravimetric analysis, 151–153, in volumetric analysis, 223–237, *see also* Complex-formation titrations

Coordination number, 223

Copper, iodometric determination of, 403–407, in brass, **406**, in an ore, **404**; as primary standard for thiosulfate solutions, 401; use in prereduction of samples, 366

Coprecipitation, by colloidal precipitates, 139–143; by crystalline precipitates, 143–146; definition, 139; effect on potentiometric titration curves, 427; effect on gravimetric analysis, 146; types of, 139

Counter-ion layer, 133

Cox method, for differential titration, 440–442, 444

Cresol purple, 261*t*
Cresol red, preparation of solution, **296**
Crucibles, 83; filtering, 84, directions for use of, **98–99**; preparation for service, **92**
Crystalline precipitates, 136–138; co-precipitation by, 143–146
Cubic centimeter, definition of, 190
Cuvette, 461

Dark currents, 463
Data, statistical evaluation of, 46–52
Decantation, 92
Dehydration, effect upon glass electrode, 434, 438
Desiccants, 83
Desiccator, 82; preparation for service, **89**; use of, **89**
Detectors, for electromagnetic radiation, 462–464
Determinate error, 38; detection of, 39–40
Devarda's alloy, 311
Deviation, from mean or median, 36; standard, 44, *see also* Standard deviation
Dichlorofluorescein, as indicator, **222**
Dichromate ion, properties, 388–390; spectrophotometric determination of, **480–481**
Dichromate solutions, preparation, **388**
Dichromate titrations, applications, 389; analysis of iron, **389**
Differential titration, 440–442, **444**
Diffraction grating, 460–461
Digestion, of precipitates, 137, 145
Dimethylglyoxime, 152–153; determination of nickel with, **162–163**
Diphenylamine, as oxidation-reduction indicator, 355*t*, 357–358
2,3′-Diphenylaminedicarboxylic acid, as oxidation-reduction indicator, 355*t*
Diphenylaminesulfonic acid, as oxidation-reduction indicator, 355*t*, 358; for dichromate titrations, 388; preparation of solutions, **389**
Diphenylbenzidine, as intermediate in oxidation of diphenylamine, 357
Displacement titrations, with EDTA, 233, **236**

Dissociation constant, 22*t*, 511*t*, 512*t*, *see also* Equilibrium constants, Acid dissociation constant, Basic ionization constant
Duboscq colorimeter, 465
Dumas method, for determination of organic nitrogen, 311
Dynode, 463

EDTA, 230, *see also* Ethylenediamine-tetraacetic acid
Effective band width, of filters, 457
Electrochemical cell, 321; behavior during passage of current, 321–322; calculation of potential for, 337; schematic representation of, 335–336
Electrode, glass, 433–439; indicator, 420–421; reference, 418–420; saturated calomel, 418–420; silver-silver chloride, 420; standard hydrogen, 324–326
Electrode potential(s), calculation of equilibrium constant(s) from, 338–340; effect of complexing reagents upon, 334–335; effect of concentration upon, 329, *see also* Nernst equation; measurement of, 326–328; sign conventions, 328–329; standard, 331, 332*t*, 507*t*
Electrode processes, 322–323
Electrolyte concentration, effect on solubility, 119–120
Electrolytes, classification of, 7
Electrolytic cell, 321
Electromagnetic radiation, absorption of, 449–451, *see also* Beer's law; detectors for, 462–464; energy of, 448; frequency of, 447; wavelength of, 447
Electromagnetic spectrum, 448–449
End point, definition, 166
End-point detection, complex-formation reactions, 228–230; differential, 440–442; neutralization titrations, 258–264; potentiometric, 423–425; precipitation titrations, 209–215; in volumetric analysis, 166, 167

Equilibrium, in acid-base systems, 239–292; for complex-formation reactions, 224–230; and electrode potentials, 338–340, *see also* Nernst equation; for oxidation-reduction systems, 318–359; with slightly soluble substances, 103–118, 204–209; in stepwise processes, 21, 224–228, 283–292, 427–431

Equilibrium constants, 19–23, 22*t*, 510*t*, 511*t*, 512*t*; effect of temperature upon, 20; role of water in, 21

Equilibrium law, 18–20; limitations to, 23–26

Equipment, marking of, 88

Equivalence point, definition, 166

Equivalence-point potential, oxidation-reduction titrations, 346–349

Equivalent, 16

Equivalent weight, complex-formation reactions, 174, *see also* Complex-formation titrations; definition of, 172–177; determination, for a weak acid, **305**; neutralization reactions, 172; oxidation-reduction reactions, 173; volumetric precipitation reactions, 174

Eriochrome black T, 233; preparation of solutions, **235**

Erioglaucin A, as oxidation-reduction indicator, 355*t*

Error, 37; determinate, 38–40; indeterminate, 40–44; sources in analysis, 38, 40; titration, 166

p-Ethoxychrysoidine, as oxidation-reduction indicator, 355*t*

Ethylenediaminetetraacetic acid, 230–233; preparation of solutions, **234–235**; titrations with, **235–237**

Evaporation, technique for, 92

Exponential numbers, manipulation of, 506

Extinction, 454*t*

Extinction coefficient, 454*t*

Fajans method, 213–214; applications, 216*t*, 217*t*; determination of chloride by, **220–221**

Ferroin, oxidation-reduction indicator, 356–357, *see also* 1,10-Phenanthroline-iron (II) complex

Filter paper, ashless, directions for use, **94–98**

Filter-paper pulp, as filtering aid, 86

Filtering characteristics, of gravimetric precipitates, 62, 124–138

Filtering crucibles, 84; directions for use, **98–99**

Filtering media, 85–86

Filters, for electromagnetic radiation, 457–459; selection of, 467

Filtration, of precipitates, **92–94**

Flasks, volumetric, 193, *see also* Volumetric flasks

Fluorescein, as adsorption indicator, 213

Formality, 13, 16*t*

Formation constant, 224, *see also* Instability constant

Formula weight, 11, 16*t*

Fowler and Bright, method for standardization of permanganate, **374**

Frequency, of electromagnetic radiation, 447

Galvanic cell, 321

Gamma, 11

Gases, for prereduction of samples, 370

Gay-Lussac method, for analysis of chloride, 215

Glass, as filtering medium, 85

Glass electrode, 433–439; applications to *p*H measurement, 436–438; construction, 434–435; errors in measurement of *p*H with, 438–439; instrument for measurement of *p*H with, 436; measurements with, in nonaqueous media, 437; role of water in functioning of, 434; potential of, 434

Globar, 457

Gooch crucible, 84; directions for use, **98–99**

Gram-equivalent weight, 172–177, *see also* Equivalent weight

Gram-formula weight, 11, 16*t*

Gram-molecular weight, 12, 16*t*

Grating, as a monochromator, 460–461

Gravimetric analysis, 61–66; applications, 149–163, 150*t*, 151*t*; calculations of, 63–66; volatilization methods of, 62

Gravimetric determination, of chloride, **156**; of hydrate water, **155**; of iron, **159–162**; of nickel, **163**; of sulfate, 157, **158–159**

Gravimetric factor, 63

Gravimetric precipitates, desirable characteristics, of, 61–62

Gunning modification, Kjeldahl method, 312, **313**

Half cell(s), 322; potentials, 324; calculation of, **333**, *see also* Nernst equation

Half reaction, 318

Halide mixtures, potentiometric titration of, 427–431, **443**

Hardness, of water, complexometric titration of, **236**

Heated objects, manipulation of, **99**

Homogeneous generation of precipitating agents, 146–148, **161**

Hydrate water, determination of, **155**

Hydrochloric acid, constant boiling, 296; preparation of standard solutions, **297**

Hydrogen discharge tube, 456

Hydrogen electrode, 324–326, *see also* Standard hydrogen electrode

Hydrogen ion, indicator electrodes for, 432–439

Hydrogen peroxide, as preoxidizer, 366

Hydrogen sulfide, use in prereduction of samples, 370

Hydronium ion, 8–10

Hydroxide-carbonate mixtures, analysis of, 304–308, **308**

Hydroxyl ion, homogeneous generation of, 147

8-Hydroxyquinoline, 152

Hygroscopic substances, weighing of, 90

Hypoiodite ion, formation in iodine solutions, 392; interference by, in titration of thiosulfate, 397

Ignition, of precipitates, 96–99

Indeterminate error, 40–41

Indicator electrode(s), 418, 420–421; for complex-formation titrations, 425–426; for neutralization reactions, 432–439; for oxidation-reduction titrations, 440; for volumetric precipitation titrations, 425–426

Indicators, 166, 209; acid-base, 258–264, 261*t*; for cerium (IV) titrations, 385; for complex-formation titrations, 228–230; for dichromate titrations, 388; for oxidation-reduction titrations, 354–358, 355*t*; for precipitation titrations, 209–215, *see also* specific listings

Indigo tetrasulfonate, as oxidation-reduction indicator, 355*t*

Infrared radiation, detectors for, 464; instruments for measurement of, 470; sources for, 457; spectrophotometric analysis employing, 475–477

Instability constant, 22*t*, 224, 334–335

Interference filter, 457–459

Iodide ion, air oxidation of, 401; as reducing agent, 396–407, 402*t*

Iodimetric methods of analysis, 390–396, 395*t*

Iodine, as primary standard, 365*t*; as volumetric oxidizing agent, 362*t*, 390–396

Iodine monochloride, as catalyst for cerium (IV) titrations, 386; preparation of, **387**

Iodine solutions, preparation of, 390, **391**; stability of, 391; standardization of, 394, **395**

Iodine titrations, applications, 395*t*; completeness of reaction, 391–393; end-point detection for, 393–394

Iodometric methods of analysis, 390, 396–407; applications, 402*t*; determination of copper, 403–405, **405–407**; sources of error in, 401

Ionic strength, 25

Ionization constant, 242, *see also* Equilibrium constant; for acids, 511*t*; for bases, 512*t*

Iron, analysis of, in ores, 377–379, **379–381**, with cerium (IV), **387**, gravimetric, **159–162**; photometric, **477–479**; precipitation from homogeneous solution, **161–162**; prereduction, with metallic reductors, 378, with Jones reductor, **380–381**,

with tin (II) chloride, 378, **379–380**; as primary standard, 365*t*, 375, **380**
Iron (II) ammonium sulfate, as primary standard for permanganate solutions, 375
Iron (II), as reducing agent, 364*t*
Iron (III), as indicator in Volhard titrations, 211–213; preparation of solution, **219**
Isomorphic inclusion, 139, 143–144

Jones reductor, 367–369; applications, 368*t*; preparation, **369–370**; use in iron analysis, **380–381**
Junction potential, 432–433, *see also* Liquid-junction potential

Kjeldahl method, of nitrogen analysis, 311–313, **313**

Laboratory notebook, suggestions for keeping, **99–101**
Law of mass action, 20
Lead, use in prereduction, 366
LeChatelier principle, 19
Lewis concept, of acids and bases, 10
Liebig determination, of cyanide, 228
Ligand, 223
Limestone, analysis of calcium in, **383**
Liquid-junction potential, 432–433; effect on measurement of *p*H, 438
Liquids, weighing of, 91
Liter, definition of, 190
Literature of analytical chemistry, 493–497; search of, 489–490
Logarithms, use of, 502
Long swings method, of weighing, **77–78**

Magnesium, complexometric determination of, **235**
Magnesium ion, coprecipitation with calcium oxalate, 381
Magnesium perchlorate, as desiccant, 83
Manganese, photometric determination of, 479, **480**

Masking agents, in complex-formation titrations, 234
Mass, distinction from weight, 69; measurement of, 69–82
Mass-balance equation, 110, 242
Mass law, 20
McBride method, for standardization of permanganate, 374, **375**
McIlvaine buffer solutions, 258
Mean, 35
Median, 35
Meniscus, 194
Mercury, use in prereduction of samples, 367–368
Metal-indicator systems, 229–230
Metals, uses in prereduction of samples, 366–370
Methylene blue, as oxidation-reduction indicator, 355*t*
Methyl orange, 261*t*, 263; preparation of solution, **296**
Methyl red, 261*t*, 263; preparation of solution, **296**
Methyl violet, 261*t*
Methyl yellow, 261*t*
Microbalance, 75
Micron, definition, 129
Milliequivalent, 16*t*
Milliequivalent weight, 172
Milliformula weight, 12, 16*t*
Milliliter, definition of, 190
Millimol, 16
Millimolecular weight, 12
Mixed crystal formation, 139, 143
Mohr method, 210–211; applications, 216*t*; determination of chloride, **218**
Mohr's salt, as primary standard, 365*t*, *see also* Iron (II) ammonium sulfate
Mol, definition, 12, 16*t*
Molar absorptivity, 454*t*
Molar extinction coefficient, 454*t*
Molarity, 13, 16*t*
Monochromator, 459–461
Mulder modification, Gay-Lussac method, 215
Mull, 476
Multiple equilibria, calculations involving, 109–117

National Bureau of Standards samples, 492

Nernst equation, 329–330; applications, 333–335; and chemical equilibrium, 338–340, 345–354

Nernst glower, 457

Nessler tubes, 465

Neutral red, 261t

Neutralization titrations, applications, 295–313, see also specific topics; curves for, 264–277, 287–292, see also Titration curves; definition of equivalent weight for, 172–177; indicator electrodes for, 432–439; indicators for, 258–264, 261t, see also Acid-base indicators; potentiometric, **443–444**; potentiometric end points for, 439; reagents for, 295–303; theory of, 239–292

Nickel, gravimetric determination of, 162, **163**; use in prereduction, 366; titration with cyanide, 229

Nitrates, analysis of, 311

Nitrilotriacetic acid, 231

Nitrobenzene, use in Volhard titrations, 213

Nitrogen analysis, Dumas method, 311; Kjeldahl method, 311–313, **313**

5-Nitro-1, 10-phenanthroline-iron (II) complex, as oxidation-reduction indicator, 355t

Nonisomorphic inclusion, 139, 144

Normal error curve, 41–44

Normality, 16t; definition of, 177; calculation of, 180

Notebook, laboratory, **99–101**

Nucleation, 126

Occlusion, 139, 144

Optical density, 454t

Organic functional groups, absorption of infrared radiation by, 476–477, 477t; absorption of ultraviolet radiation by, 473–474, 474t

Orthophenanthroline-iron (II) complex, 355t, 356–357, see also 1,10-Phenanthroline-iron (II) complex; photometric analysis of iron via, 477, **478–479**

Osmium tetroxide, as catalyst for cerium (IV) oxidations, 386

Oxalic acid, as primary standard for bases, 302

Oxidation, definition of, 318

Oxidation potentials, 328

Oxidation-reduction indicators, 354–358, 355t

Oxidation-reduction reactions, analytical applications, 361–407, see also specific listings; equilibrium in, 318–340; equilibrium constants for, 22t, 338–340

Oxidation-reduction titrations, 345–359; curves for, 345–354; definition of equivalent weight for, 173–174; equivalence-point potential, 346–349; indicators for, 354–358, 355t; potentiometric, **444–445**; potentiometric end points for, 440; primary standards for, 365t, see also specific listings; selection of indicators for, 358

Oxidizing agent(s), 362t; definition of, 319; for pretreatment of samples, 363, 366; see also specific listings

Oxine, 152

Paper, as filtering medium, 85

Parallax, 194

Particle growth, 125, 127

Particle size, of crystalline precipitates, 137; effect of relative supersaturation upon, 125–126; of precipitates, 124–138

Peptization, 135–136

Percentage concentration, 14

Periodic acid, as oxidizing agent, 362t

Permanganate ion, spectrophotometric analysis of, **479–481**; reactions of, 174, 371

Permanganate solutions, analysis with, of calcium in calcium carbonate, 381, **382**, in limestone, **383**, of iron, 377–379, **379–381**; applications, 376t; preparation of, **373**; stability of, 372, standardization against sodium oxalate, 373, **374–375**

Peroxides, as preoxidizers, 366

*p*H, control in iodimetry, 392; effect on solubility, 108, 111–113; effect on stability of thiosulfate solutions, 398; measurement, with glass electrode, 433–439, with hydrogen electrode, 432–433

*p*H, of solutions containing acid salts, 280–283; polyprotic acids, 284–287; salt of weak acid and strong base, 247–250; salt of weak acid and weak base, 251; salt of weak base and strong acid, 250–251; strong acid or strong base, 240–241; weak acid, 241–244, 246–247; weak base, 244–249; weak acid and its salt, 252–254; weak base and its salt, 254, 255; *see also* Buffer solutions

1,10-Phenanthroline-iron (II) complex, as oxidation-reduction indicator, 355*t*, 356–357, for cerium (IV) titrations, 385; preparation of solutions, **386**

Phenol red, 261*t*, 263; preparation of solution, **296**

Phenolphthalein, 261*t*, 262; preparation of solution, **296**

Phenolsulfonphthalein, 263, *see also* Phenol red

Phenosafranine, as oxidation-reduction indicator, 355*t*

Phosphorous pentoxide, as desiccant, 83

Photodecomposition, of silver chloride, 156

Photoelectric colorimeter, 465

Photometer, 466–467

Photometric analysis, 466–467; accuracy of, 471; factors affecting, 470–472; of iron in water, 477–479; of manganese in steel, 479, **480**; selection of filter for, 467; visible region, 475

Photomultiplier tube, 463

Photon, 448

Phototube, 463

Photovoltaic cell, 462–463

Phthalein indicators, 261–262

Pipet(s), calibration of, **205**; directions for use, **199**; types, 197

Platinum electrode, 421; for potentiometric titrations, 440

Polyprotic acids, calculation of *p*H for solutions of, 284–287; titration curves for, 287–290; titration curves for salts of, 291–292

Porcelain, as filtering medium, 85

Potassium antimony (III) tartrate, as primary standard for iodine solutions, 394

Potassium bromate, as primary standard; 365*t*; as oxidizing agent, 362*t*

Potassium dichromate, 362*t*, 388, *see also* Dichromate ion; as primary standard, 365*t*, 388, for thiosulfate solutions, 400, **401**

Potassium ferricyanide, as primary standard for thiosulfate solutions, 401

Potassium ferrocyanide, as primary standard, 365*t*

Potassium hydrogen iodate, as primary standard, for bases, 302, for thiosulfate solutions, 401

Potassium hydrogen phthalate, determination of, **304**; as primary standard for bases, **302**

Potassium hydroxide, as volumetric reagent, 299–300, **301**

Potassium iodate, as oxidizing agent, 362*t*; as primary standard, 365*t*, for thiosulfate solutions, **400**

Potassium iodide, as primary standard, 365*t*, for permanganate, 375

Potassium permanganate, 362*t*, 370–384, *see also* Permanganate ion

Potassium thiocyanate, as oxidation-reduction indicator, 354; as precipitating agent, 211; preparation of standard solution, **218–219**

Potential, *see also* Half-cell potential; asymmetry, 436; calculation for electrochemical cell, 336–337; equivalence-point, 346–349; measurement of, 413–418; sign convention for, 328–329

Potentiometer, 413–417; accuracy of measurement with, 417

Potentiometric titration(s), 412–445; apparatus for, 413–421; application, to complex-formation titrations, 425–426, to neutralization titrations, 431–440, **443–444**; to oxidation-reduction titrations, 440, **444–445**, to volumetric precipitation analysis, 425–430; automatic, 442; of carbonate-bicarbonate mixtures, **444**; differential method, 440–442, **444–445**; evaluation of end points for, 423–425; general directions for, **442–443**; of halide mixtures, **443**; of iron (II), **444–445**; of a weak acid, **443–444**

Precipitate formation, steps in, 126–129

Precipitates, contamination of, 138–146, *see also* Coprecipitation; manipulation of, **92–96**; mechanism of formation, 128–129, *see also* Precipitate formation; particle size and purity, 124–148; solubility of, 103–120

Precipitating agents, arsonic acids, 154–155; benzidine, 155, dimethylglyoxime, 152–153, **162–163**; effect on electrode potentials, 334–335; for gravimetric analysis, 150t, 151t, 149–155; 8-hydroxyquinoline, 152; inorganic, 150t; sodium tetraphenylboron, 154

Precipitation, from homogeneous solution, 146–148, determination of iron, **161–162**

Precipitation titrations, 204–221, *see also* Volumetric precipitation analysis; definition of equivalent weight for, 174–176

Precision, of data, 35–36

Primary standard, definition, 166; reagent chemical grade, 87

Primary standards, for acids, 297–298; for bases, 302; for oxidizing and reducing agents, 361–363, 365t; requirements for, 167, *see also* specific reagents

Prism, as monochromator, 459–460

Probability, and indeterminate error, 41–44

Purity, of gravimetric precipitates, 62, 138–146

p Values, definition, 170

Q test, 51

Quadratic equation, 501

Quadrivalent cerium, 362t, 384, *see also* Cerium (IV)

Qualitative organic analysis, application of infrared spectrophotometry to, 476–477, 477t

Radiant intensity, 454t

Radiant power, 451, 454t

Radiation sources, requirements for, 456–457

Range, of analytical results, 36

Reagent chemicals, purity of, 86–87; rules for handling, 87–88

Reagent-grade chemicals, 86

Real substances, analysis of, 484–500

Redox reactions, *see* Oxidation-reduction reactions

Reducing agent(s), 319, 361, 364t, *see also* specific listings; for pretreatment of samples, 366–370, *see also* specific listings

Reduction, definition, 318

Reduction potentials, 328, 332t, 507t

Reductors, 367–370, **369**; prereduction of iron with, 378, **380–381**

Reference electrode, 418–421, *see also* specific listings; standard hydrogen electrode, 324–326

Reflection, as source of radiation loss, 452

Refraction, of light, 459

Rejection criteria, for outlying result, 50–52

Relative calibration, pipet to volumetric flask, **203**

Relative deviation, 36

Relative error, 37

Relative supersaturation, 125

Reprecipitation, in iron analysis, **159–160**; minimization of coprecipitation by, 143, 146

Rest point, analytical balance, 76

Rubber policeman, 94

Salt bridge, 326

Salts of weak acids and bases, calculation of *p*H for, 247–251; titration curves for, 274–277, 291–292

Sample composition, as factor in selection of analytical method, 488

Sample containers, for absorption analysis, 461

Sample preparation, infrared spectrophotometry, 475–476

Saturated calomel electrode, 418–420

Semimicrobalance, 75

Sensitivity, of analytical balance, 72; calculation of, 78–79

Separations, based on solubility differences, 117–118

Short swings method, for weighing, **79**

Significant figures, 52–57

Silver, use in prereduction of samples, 366, 368

Silver chloride, photodecomposition of, 156

Silver nitrate, preparation of standard solutions, **216**; as reagent in precipitation titrations, 216*t*, **218–221**

Silver reductor, applications, 368*t*

Silver-silver chloride electrode, 420

Single-beam photometer, 466

Single-pan balance, operation of, **79–80**

Sodium bismuthate, as preoxidizer, 366

Sodium carbonate, determination of, 297–298, **307**, potentiometric, **440**; indicator selection for titration of, 292; standardization of acids with, 297, **298**; titration curve for, 291–292

Sodium hydroxide, as volumetric reagent, 299–302, **301**

Sodium oxalate, coprecipitation with calcium oxalate, 381; as primary standard, 298, 365*t*, for cerium (IV) solutions, **386–387**, for permanganate solutions, 373, **374–375**

Sodium peroxide, as preoxidizer, 366

Sodium tetraborate, as primary standard for acids, 298

Sodium tetraphenylboron, as precipitating agent, 154

Sodium thiosulfate, 397–401, *see also* Thiosulfate solutions; as primary standard, 365*t*, for iodine solutions, 394

Solubility, factors affecting: common ion, 105–108; complex formation, 113–117; electrolyte concentration, 119–120; *p*H, 108–113; solvent composition, 120; temperature, 118–119

Solubility of precipitates, 61, 103–120

Solubility-product constant, 22*t*, 204, 510*t*; applications, 103–118; prediction of feasibility of separations with, 117–118

Solvent(s), classification of, 9–10

Solvent composition, effect on solubility, 120

Sources, of electromagnetic radiation, 456–457

Specific surface, definition, 130–131

Spectronic 20, spectrophotometer, 469

Spectrophotometer, 460; Beckman DU, 468; Spectronic 20, 469

Spectrophotometric analysis, 470–477; accuracy of, 471; infrared region, 470–472; instruments for, 463–465; of iron in water, **477–479**; of manganese in steel, **479–480**; of multicomponent mixtures, 472–473, **480–481**; ultraviolet region, 473–475; visible region, 475

Spread, 36

Standard deviation, 44, 47

Standard electrode potential, 331–333, 332*t*, 507*t*; applications, 333–340, *see also* Nernst equation

Standard hydrogen electrode, 324–326, 432–433; limitations to application of, 433; measurement of *p*H with, 432–433; potential of, 326

Standard samples, detection of errors with, 39; for evaluation of an analysis, 492

Standard solutions, characteristics for, 167–168; definition, 165; for complex-formation titrations, 230–231, 234–235; for neutralization titrations, 296–302; for oxidation-reduction titrations, 362*t*, 364*t*, 370–372, 384–391; for volumetric precipitation analysis, 215

Standardization, definition, 166

Starch, as indicator, 393–394; preparation, **394**

Starch-triiodide complex, as oxidation-reduction indicator, 354

Statistical evaluation of data, 46–52

Steel, gravimetric determination of nickel in, 162, **163**; photometric analysis of manganese in, **479–480**

Stepwise equilibria, 21

Stibnite, determination of antimony in, **396**

Strong acid, weak acid mixtures, titration curves for, 290

Strong acids and bases, calculation of *p*H for, 240–241; indicator selection for titrations with, 267; titration curves for, 264–267

Sulfate, gravimetric determination of, 157, **158–159**; errors in, 158*t*

Sulfonphthalein indicators, 262–263

Sulfur dioxide, use in prereduction of samples, 370

Supersaturation, 125–127

Surface adsorption, 131–133, *see also* Adsorption

Tared watch glasses, 90

Technical grade chemicals, 86

Temperature, effect on solubility, 118–119; effect upon volume measurements, 191, 199–201

Thermopile, 464

Thiosulfate ion, reaction with iodine, 397–398

Thiosulfate solutions, preparation, 396, **399**; stability of, 398; standardization of, 399–400, **400**

Thymolphthalein, 261*t*, 262; preparation of solution, **296**

Tin, iodimetric determination of, 395–396

Tin (II) chloride, preparation of solution, **379**; prereduction of iron with, 378–379, **379**

Titanium (III), as reducing agent, 364*t*

Titer, 177

Titration, **196–198**; definition, 165

Titration curve(s), 168–172; for complex acid-base systems, 283–292; for complex-formation reactions, 224–228; for mixtures of acids, 290–291; for mixtures of weak acids, 290; for neutralization reactions, 264–277, 283–292; for oxidation-reduction reactions, 345–354; for polyprotic acid systems, 287–289; for salts of polyprotic acids, 291–292; for precipitation reactions, 204–209, 426–431; for salts of weak acids or bases, 271–274;

for strong acid, strong base systems, 264–267; for weak acid, strong base systems, 268–274; for weak base, strong acid systems, 274

Titration error, definition, 166

Transition range, acid-base indicators, 258–260, 261*t*; oxidation-reduction indicators, 355*t*, 355–356

Transitions, accompanying absorption of radiation, 449–451

Transmission, 454*t*

Transmittance, 448, 454*t*

Triiodide ion, 391

Tyndall effect, 130

U.S.P. grade reagents, 86

Ultraviolet radiation, absorption by organic functional groups, 473–474, 474*t*; detectors for, 462–464; sources for, 456

Urea, as source of hydroxyl ion, 147

Versenes, 230, *see also* Ethylenediaminetetraacetic acid

Vibrational level, transitions involving, 449

Vinegar, determination of acidity in, **304**

Visible radiation, detectors for, 462–464; photometric analysis employing, 475; sources, 456

Volatilization methods, gravimetric analysis, 62

Volhard method, 213–215; applications, 217*t*, 221; determination of chloride, **220–221**

Voltage divider, 414

Voltaic cell, 321

Voltmeter, vacuum-tube, 418

Volume, effect of temperature upon, 191, 199–201; measurement of, 190–203

Volume ratio, acid-base, **303**

Volumetric analysis, 165–182, *see also* specific topics; calculations of, 172–182; end-point detection in, 168; reaction types, 167, requirements for, 167–168; weight-volume relationships, 177–179

Volumetric flask(s), 193; calibration of, **202–203**; directions for use of, **198**

Volumetric pipet(s), 192; calibration of, **202**; directions for use of, **194–196**

Volumetric precipitation analysis, 204–221; acid-base indicators for, 214; adsorption indicators for, 213–214; applications, 216*t*, 217*t*; definition of equivalent weight for, 174–176; effect, of completeness of reaction upon, 208, of reagent concentration upon, 207; end-point detection in, 209–215; Mohr method, 210–211, 216*t*, **218**; potentiometric, 425–426, **443**; titration curves for, 204–209, 426–431; Volhard method, 211–213

Washing, of precipitates, 94

Watch glasses, tared, 90

Water, determination of hardness in, **236**; determination by weight loss, 62, **155**; dissociation of, 7–8; ion-product constant for, 22*t*, 239–240; role in equilibrium-constant expressions, 21

Water of hydration, determination, **155**

Wavelength, of electromagnetic radiation, 447

Wavelength selection, photometric analysis, 471

Weak acid(s), calculation of *p*H for solutions of, 241–247; evaluation of dissociation constant for, 439; feasibility of titration, 272–274; indicator selection for titrations with, 272–274; potentiometric titration of, **439**; titration of, **304**; titration curves for, 268–274

Weak acid mixtures, titration curves for, 290

Weak acid (or base) salts, calculation of *p*H for solutions of, 247–251

Weak acid, strong acid mixtures, titration curves for, 290

Weak base(s), calculation of *p*H for solutions of, 244–246; titration curves for, 274

Weighing, with damped balance, 79; error due to buoyancy, 80–81; of hygroscopic substances, 90; of liquids, 91; method of long swings, **77–78**; method of short swings, **79**; with single-pan balance, **79–80**

Weighing bottle(s), 82, **89–90**

Weight, distinction from mass, 69–70; expression in chemical units, 16*t*

Weights, for analytical balance, 75

Weston cell, 415–416

Winkler method, for carbonate-hydroxide mixtures, 306, **307–308**

Zero point, analytical balance, 76

Zimmermann-Reinhardt reagent, 379, **379–380**

Zinc, use in prereduction of samples, 366–369, *see also* Jones reductor

Michael Timmons